MANAGEMENT OF FRESHWATER FISHERIES

Management of Freshwater Fisheries

Jacques ARRIGNON
Member of the French Academy of Overseas' Sciences
Member of the Academy of Agriculture of France
Honarary Chief Engineer (Fisheries and Forestry) Rural Institute

OXFORD & IBH PUBLISHING CO. PVT. LTD.
New Delhi Calcutta

Published by arrangement with Technique et Documentation, Lavoisier, Paris

Published with the assistance of the Counsellor for Cultural, Scientific and Technical Cooperation, Embassy of France, New Delhi.

Translation of : *Amengament piscicole des eaux douces*, 4[e], 1991. Technique at Documentation, Lavoisier. ISBN 2-85206-766-8. **Updated by the author for he English edition in 1997.**

ISBN 81-204-1324-5

Translator : Colonel R. K. Kaula
Technical Editor : Dr. M. N. Fotedar
General Editor : Latha Anantharaman

Published by Raju Primlani for Oxford & IBH Publishing Co. Pvt. Ltd., 66 Janpath, New Delhi-110 001. Typeset by S.J.I. Services, New Delhi and printed at Baba Barkha Nath Priters, 26/7, Najafgarh Road Industrial Area, New Delhi-110015.

1-F9-05-PM

FOREWORD

The life in an aquatic medium, in a general sense, must be protected because in quantity and quality it is closely linked with the state of humans on the planet. Common disruptions are manifested in catastrophic forms like floods, drought, and other disturbances. These directly and drastically affect the health and even the lives of human beings. They also have less well-known and long-term effects in that they disturb, albeit subtly, human equilibrium and behaviour. Aquatic mediums are part of the natural environment and we cannot isolate ourselves from them without fairly long-term damage because we ourselves are a part of the natural environment.

Water is not just an element; it is a medium that supports life, a productive medium closely linked with its terrestrial environment. The quality of catchment areas has an effect on the quantity and quality of water and, eventually, on the animals that live in it. This work has been entitled MANAGEMENT OF FRESHWATER FISHERIES because it deals with a class of aquatic animals, fish, and, especially, with a human activity, fishing, which can be a means of livelihood as well as a hobby.

A source of inexpensive animal protein in southern regions, fishing is also an inexpensive pastime in northern regions and the relaxation found in fishing is as necessary for our contemporaries in relieving stress as is the food value of the fish for those who are hungry. It is, therefore, high time that we thought of managing our natural environment carefully so that there is no irreversible reduction of a popular and valuable natural resource for which we are accountable to future generations. Hence, we have not confined ourselves to aquatic mediums and fishing and found it necessary to widen the scope of this work.

In this edition we have stressed, even more than in earlier ones, the guidelines given in our first book, *Aménagement piscicole des eaux intérieures* (Management of Inland Fisheries), bearing in mind that those who are involved in the improvement of the aquatic medium are also those who are responsible for it, who own it, or who benefit from it and that confirmed and practical data, expressed in appropriate terms, will be more useful and effective than a scientific discussion, howsoever enlightening it may be. In the book, the ecological context has also been stressed, which helps clarify and justify the reasons for the suggested practical solutions.

Many fishermen, biologists, technicians, and specialists have assisted in this work. Their contribution, at all levels, has added to the combined observations made during the course of forty years of experimentation in regions that vary considerably in geography and hydrography as well as in the fisheries problems encountered in them.

We wish to record our grateful thanks to all those who have assisted us in various ways.

TABLE OF CONTENTS

Part 1
Ecological Fundamentals

Part 2
Fish Breeding

Part 3
Management of Aquatic Mediums

Part 4
Appendices

INTRODUCTION

At the beginning of the 20th century Professor Leger, a pioneer of hydrobiology in France, wrote: "There is no suitable water body, howsoever small, that cannot be used for fish production."

In view of the extremely poor conditions under which tropical fish culture is practised and also the extremely unhealthy conditions under which fish live in polluted waters of the North, there can be no doubt that the terms "small body" and "suitable water" have a wide range of meanings.

Progress, with its new demands and contributions, gives these terms an ever-increasing importance that eventually affects fishing and fish farming, not only in the economic sector of developing countries having considerable demand for food, but also with regard to fishing as a sport in the tertiary hobbies and leisure sector that is constantly growing in rich countries of the Northern Hemisphere.

Fishing involves extraction of aquatic animals from the aquatic medium for food. It must be in keeping with the capacity of this medium. Presently, the number of enthusiasts, improved methods and practices in fishing, attempts to increase the quantity of catch, or lack of restraint has resulted in not merely simple but uncontrolled fishing in an aquatic medium for which there is an increasing demand for other uses and which is progressively and increasingly degraded by many harmful activities and effects.

Fish culture involves raising and increasing the product called "fish". Like any other type of animal raising, it depends upon certain factors related to the hardiness of the raised species. The demand for fish is inversely or directly related to the consumers' standard of living, depending on whether it emanates from developing or rich countries. In the latter case, it is also directly dependent on catches by fishermen; the higher the standard of living, the greater the degradation of the medium and the greater the demand for farmed fish to restock a medium that is only a support, often very temporary, of all fish life.

As a result, fisheries management in fresh waters has become necessary and urgent at various levels of decision and intervention. It is even obligatory, in France, for all those who have fishing rights in running waters since promulgation of the 1984 Act on fishing in fresh waters and the management of fisheries resources.

Fisheries management involves ensuring in the aquatic medium and its surroundings the qualities relative to their best and most opportune use with regard to fishing and fisheries, bearing in mind the pressure exerted on the medium by direct and indirect users, professionals and amateurs, fishermen and others, while taking into account the fragility of the medium and the need to safeguard it as far as possible.

PART ONE

Ecological Fundamentals

1 AQUATIC ECOSYSTEMS

A. ECOLOGICAL APPROACH

The idea of ecological improvements in fresh waters involves a choice between two types of approaches, one connected with a knowledge of the dynamics of aquatic species in a given area and the other relating to a knowledge of the water body both in individual terms and in terms of an ecological system.

No matter how likely to be harshly judged and how imperfect an ecological classification may be, a classification is necessary when we proceed from a theoretical concept to actually implementing an improvement in a medium. From this point of view we should not compare classifications of **biotopes** and **biocoenoses** with **zonings** but, like WURTZ (1961), DUSSART (1966) with reference to stagnant waters, and VERNEAUX (1973) with regard to running waters, establish a type of "ecological spectrum" of the aquatic medium under consideration.

The aquatic **ecosystem** of a lake is less difficult to determine than the **lotic medium** of a water course. More than a pond, a lake has a particular set of characteristics and all its components, living or otherwise, and inseparably linked, are sources of interactions. Exchanges ensure that a lake remains in a relatively stable state even though, in some cases, there may be a more rapid, uncontrolled growth of components that were fewer during an earlier period (VIBERT and LAGLER, 1961).

A pond with fewer morphodynamic characteristics is more sensitive than a lake to variations in certain parameters. The same applies to minor feeders of a network of running water: streams and small rivers are more fragile than large water courses. Their typology is more delicate, and the risk of error is greater. Moreover, adoption of certain types of improvements necessitates a comparison of various attitudes regarding the ecological classification of running waters and stretches of water; one station where there has been an improvement must be compared with a zone, a type, when we are dealing with a length of a river, or even an entire stretch.

A "follow-up" of the improvement also implies a periodic comparison of the data that describe the ecosystem, especially the **parametric data**, if we are able to determine them.

The cycle of an aquatic ecosystem, whether of a lake or a river, can be described scientifically by highlighting the relatively stable elements, others that are relatively unstable, and those that, by their limited or strict demands, qualify the medium. These are mainly communities that exist in a given environment.

This is how, on a water surface, energy provided by the sun is used by the producers: phytoplankton, higher aquatic plants, and some bacteria. Using soluble

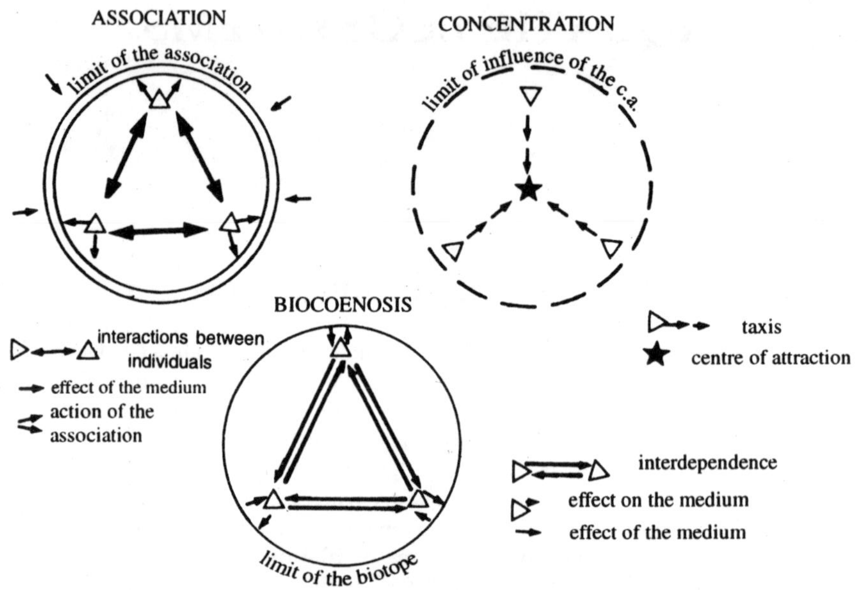

Fig. 1. Diagrams representing various groups (copied from ROUX and DAJOZ)
– interspecific piscicultural association
– type of concentration (of fish towards lighting when light fishing)
– pond = biotope + biocoenosis
biotope = area + resources
biocoenosis = group of aquatic living creatures

salts, in addition, these producers by photosynthesis produce living plant material. This plant material is consumed and transformed by zooplankton and microphytophagous and macrophytophagous fishes. These fishes, in turn, are eaten by carnivorous fish and other predators; we may consider this to be a rising predatory chain. The descending parasitic or saprophytic chain is composed, as reported by VIBERT and LAGLER (1961), of parasites, cadavericoles, and saprophytic fungi. The latter are decomposed or transformed by bacteria and fungi to organic matter and soluble salts assimilable by plants and are again incorporated by photosynthesis in a predatory food chain.

In fact, each link represents hardly one tenth of the energy units of the previous one because of the energy expended in vital catabolic activity and a coefficient of assimilation that is less than unity.

This aspect is of considerable importance when making a choice of improvements. In a region where the requirement for food is paramount, we must attempt, while making improvements, to produce species with the shortest possible food chain, such as phytophagous and herbivorous fish. When, however, an economy of leisure is predominant, effects are directed to produce carnivorous fish with a long food chain, greatly appreciated by those for whom fishing is a sport.

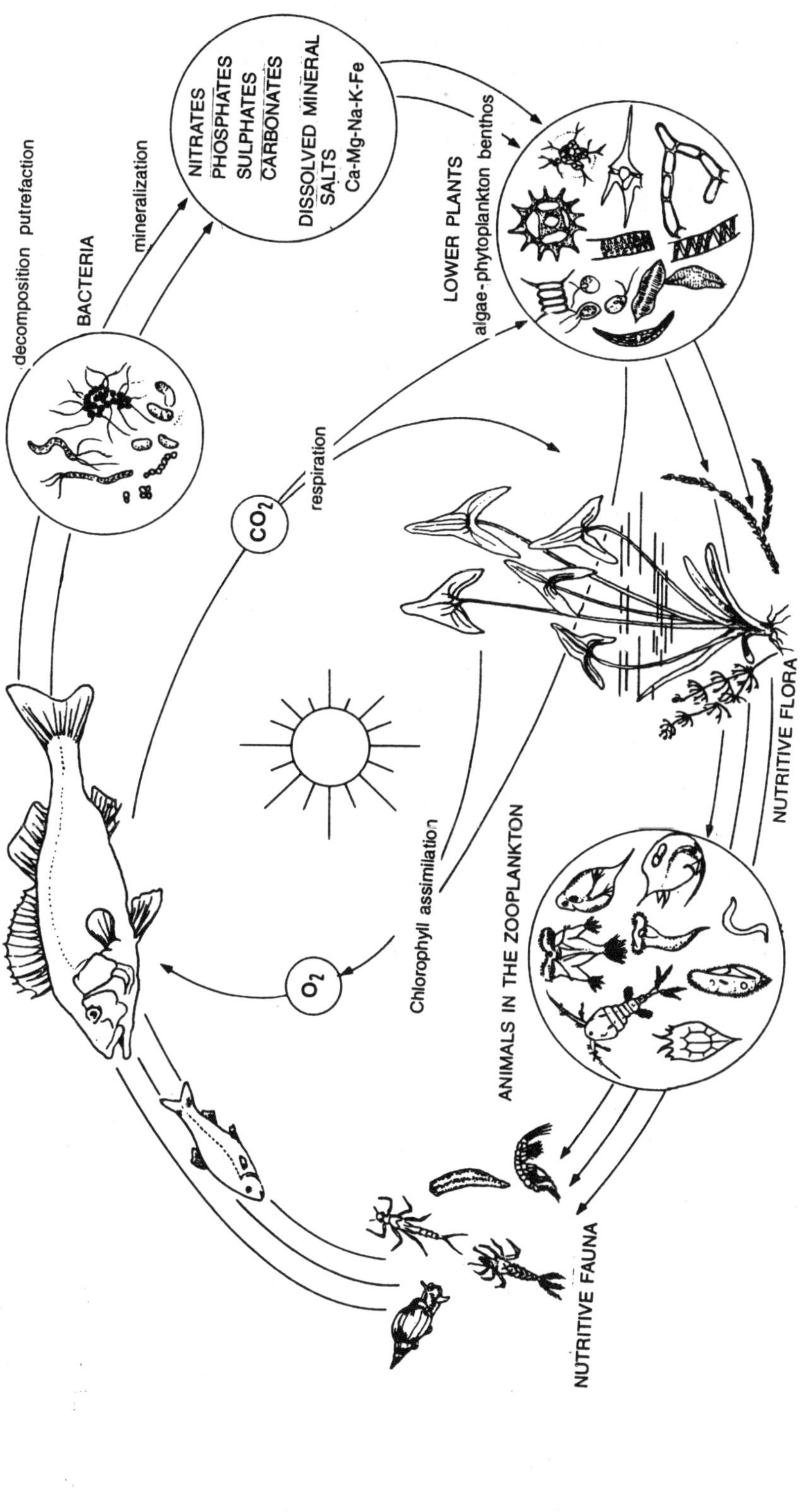

Fig. 2. Diagram of an aquatic ecosystem

B. AQUATIC ECOSYSTEMS

WURTZ (1961) identified twelve types of ecosystems in temperate regions, which are briefly described here. They constitute a useful framework in which we can more precisely identify a limited number of types.

• **Type 1** includes highly oxygenated running waters.

Group 1/A comprises high mountain torrents and waterfalls. The plant components include the algae Chrysophyceae (*Chlorotylium cataractarum*). The animal components include the stoneflies, Plecoptera; the mayflies, Ephemeroptera (*Epeorus*); blepharocerids, Diptera; and some molluscs (*Ancylus* and *Neritina*). The **biogenetic capacity** is low (I to III) and the fish productivity often nil.

Group 1/B comprises mainly mountain torrents. Richer than the previous one, this group is always in the **catharobic** zone: its biogenetic capacity can be from IV to X.

Group 1/C includes rivers and streams that are fairly wide and not very deep in which are found the grayling (*Thymallus thymallus*). There is no higher phanerogamic plant life but algae are in abundance. Aquatic insects, adult and in larval form, are also observed in very large numbers. The fish fauna comprise the grayling, the trout (*Salmo trutta fario*), the burbot (*Lota lota*), and the minnow (*Phoxinus phoxinus*). The biogenetic capacity (VIII to X) and fish productivity (250 kg/ha/yr) are high.

• **Type 2** covers waters in plains in lotic facies, clean and oxygenated; salmons thrive in these catharobic waters. The plant components include the Rhodophyceae, incrustating blue-green algae—Cyanophyceae, filamentous Chlorophyceae (*Chaetophora, Vaucheria, Ulothrix*), Bryophytes (*Brachythecium, Fissidens*), phanerogams such as *Moutia rivularis* (brookweed), *Veronica beccabunga* (brooklime), and Callitrichinae (starworts).

The fauna here includes Plecoptera—stoneflies (*Isoperla, Nemura*), Ephemeroptera—mayflies in large numbers (*Ecdyonurus, Cleon*), gammarids also in large numbers, molluscs (*Neritina, Physa, Bithynia, Ancylus*), planarians of the black group (*Pl. alpina, Pl. lugubris, Pl. gonocephala*), and fish such as the burbot, the eel (*Anguilla anguilla*), the common loach (*Cobitis barbatula*), the spined loach (*Acanthopsis taenia*), the minnow (*Phoxinus phoxinus*), the bullhead (*Cottus gobio*), and the trout.

The biogenetic capacity is extremely variable (II to X), as is also the productivity of fish (20 to 250 kg/ha/yr), depending on the geological nature of the soil (calciferous or otherwise) and that of the impluvium (forest type, agricultural farm or grassland).

• **Type 3** comprises waters on plains in **lentic facies**, adequately oxygenated; cyprinids and escolids thrive in these **oligosaprobic** waters.

Group 3/A covers what is called the "barbel zone", which also includes the salmonids (Eure river, upper reaches of the Meuse, middle region of the Marne). The fauna, different from that in the following group, comprises Trichoptera such as *Hydropsyche, Rhyacophyla*, planarians (*Dendrocoelum lacteum*), gammarids, molluscs such as *Neritina, Radix limosa, Planorbis;* mayflies are less frequently observed.

Group 3/B covers the fish zone called the "bream zone" of major water courses in their middle regions and lower reaches (Saone, Marne, Meuse, Garonne) and of water courses in general in their lower reaches, especially those south of the Loire.

The fauna includes caddis flies such as *Limnophilus* and *Anabolia*, the planarian *Polycelis nigra* and common molluscs, principally lymnaeids.

In these two groups the **potamoplankton** comprises mainly diatoms and chlorococcales.

The plant components represented here are green filamentous algae (*Cladophora*), phanerogams such as *Ranunculus fluitans, Helosciadium, Glyceria fluitans, Sagittaria, Potamogeton natans, P. densus, P. perfoliatus*, and *Callitriche* sp. The biogenetic capacity (IV to X) and fish productivity are of a high order.

- **Type 4** covers the large oligotrophic alpine lakes oxygenated to their depths and with no organic slime on their beds.

The plant components are represented by abundant phytoplankton with diatoms and a covering of green algae on the pebbles along the bank. A belt of phanerogams is almost non-existent.

The fauna is represented by abundant zooplankton and fish such as the char (*Salvelinus alpinus*), the coregonids (*Coregonus* sp.), the brook or brown trout (*Salmo trutta fario*), the perch (*Perca fluviatilis*), and the roach (*Rutilus rutilus*).

The limited productivity of fish ranges between 5 and 25 kg/ha/yr.

- **Type 5** covers the major lakes on the plains, moderately mineralized, often **eutrophic** (Lake Nantua, Lake Zurich). The bottoms of these lakes are covered with organic slime resulting in the disappearance of oxygen from the depths.

The highly abundant phytoplankton is composed mainly of diatoms in winter and blue-green algae (Cyanophyceae) in the summer. There is a wide belt of phanerogams.

Higher animals are roach, carp (*Cyprinus carpio*), perch, and pike (*Esox lucius*).

The productivity of fish, of a high order, is between 100 and 200 kg/ha/yr.

- **Type 6** covers stagnant and clean waters such as those of sources and springs.

The plant components include red algae (Rhodophyceae), tetrasporals and diatoms, mosses such as *Philonotis*, and phanerogams such as *Lemna trisulca, Nasturtium officinale, Veronica beccabunga*, and *Callitriche* sp.

The fauna includes Bryozoans, molluscs such as *Dressenia* sp., and fish such as the trout (*Salmo trutta fario*), the dace, and the brook trout (*Salvelinus fontinalis*).

The biogenetic capacity (0 to IV) and productivity of fish (0 to 40 kg/ha/yr) are very low.

- **Type 7** covers natural ponds in forests that have not been maintained by man (peat bogs with mosses and sedges—Cyperaceae).

The flora is represented by phytoplankton identical to that of ecosystem type 6. The phanerogams include *Myriophylla* sp., *Ceratophylla* sp., *Hippuris, Trapa natans, Potamogeton natans, P. crispus, Nymphea alba, Nuphar luteum, Ranunculus* sp., *Hottonia, Chara, Phragmites* sp., *Typha* sp., *Juncus* sp., and *Carex* sp.

The fauna comprises zooplankton with a predominance of Copepods, water mites, molluscs such as *Lymnaea* sp., *Planorbis, Anodonta* sp., dragonflies, and common fish, mainly cyprinids.

The fish productivity is about 50 kg/ha/yr.

- **Type 8** covers ponds created or transformed by man.

The phytoplankton is composed of seasonal algae. The water surface has no higher plants but is surrounded by higher plants that have emerged and whose growth has been restricted to some extent: *Phragmites* sp., *Typha* sp., *Juncus* sp., *Myriophyllum* sp., *Limnanthemum nymphaeoides*.

The zooplankton comprises an abundance of rotifers, and an equal abundance of copepods, cladocerans such as *Daphnia* sp., and *Bosmina* sp. The microbiocoenoses are transient, seasonal, and even of a day-to-day type. Human intervention is important in order to help planktonic and fish associations to achieve an abundant and constant fish productivity of 100 to 1000 kg/ha/yr after carrying out improvements.

- **Type 9** relates to lentic β **mesosaprobic** facies: ponds covered with silt and slow-flowing rivers at the end of the pollution stage.

If there is self-purification, the algae reappear, and diatoms indicate developments in the water course. *Elodea canadensis* is one of the first plants to reappear.

The number of bacteria is from 1000 to 10,000 per cubic cm.

The fauna includes Odonates, neuropterans (*Sialis*), hemipterans (*Nepa, Ranatra*), isopods (*Asella*), molluscs (*Sphaerium*), and fish such as the tench (*Tinca tinca*) and the eel.

The biogenetic capacity (III to V) and the fish productivity can change considerably.

- **Type 10** relates to waters that have been highly silted in an α **mesosaprobic** pollution zone.

There are no higher plants but there are algae (*Euglena* and *Volvox* sp.) as well as fungi (*Leptomitus*).

There are large numbers of bacteria (at least 100,000 per cubic cm).

The fauna includes cladocerans (*Daphnia pulex* and *D. magna*), rotifers, oscillairs, many infusorians, chironomids, leeches (*Herpobdella*), tubifexes, a very few isopods, and some molluscs (*Lymnaea stagnalis*).

The biogenetic capacity is I (maximum).

- **Type 11** includes highly polluted waters containing a number of predominant indicative bacteria of the order of 1 million per cubic cm (drains, effluents from factories).

Group 11/A covers the **polysaprobic** zones.

The fauna includes bacteria (*Oscillatoria, Sphaerotilus*), infusorians (*Carchesium, Vorticella*), oligochaetes (*Tubifex*), chironomids, and tabanids including *Eristalis*.

The biogenetic capacity is nil.

Group 11/B covers the **hypersaprobic** and **thiosaprobic** zone (characterized by the emission of hydrogen sulphide).

These waters are unsuitable for life forms; there is hardly anything other than sulphurated crimson bacteria in them.

- **Type 12** includes acid peat bogs (that can be compared with **dystrophic** lakes).

The algal flora comprises many desmids. Bryophytes are also well represented, as are peat mosses, and *Drosera*. Also present are *Equisetum* sp., *Carex* sp., *Juncus, Pinguicula, Cosmarium, Menyanthes,* and *Molinia*.

The rare fish fauna comprises mainly the cyprinids. The fish productivity is low (about 10 kg/ha/yr). A blockage of the mineralization on the bed results in a pH between 5 and 6.5.

C. ECOLOGICAL ZONING

The biocoenoses that are part of aquatic ecosystems are distributed geographically and, especially, topographically in zones with identical characteristics both in respect of water courses and plain stretches of water.

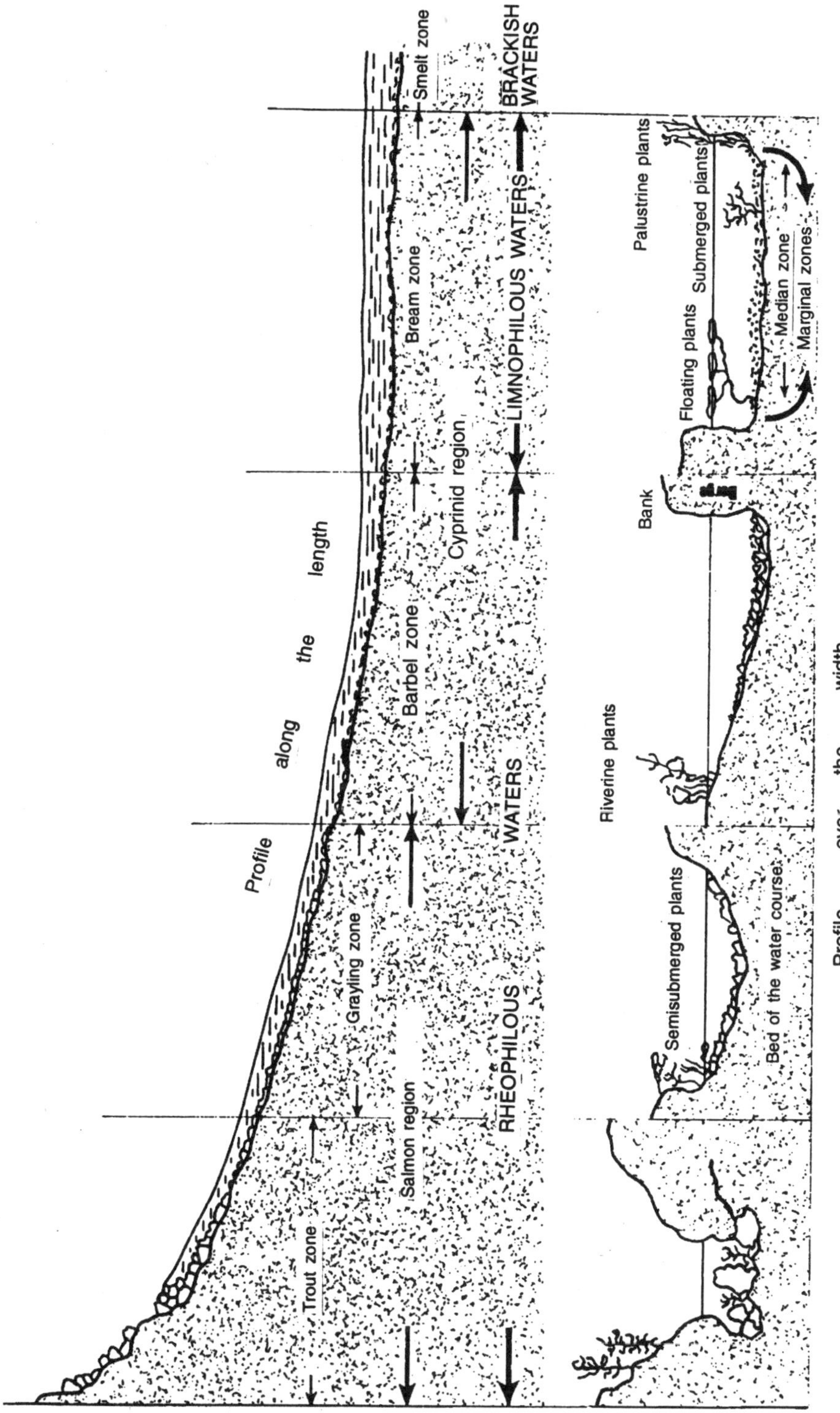

Fig. 3. Profile of a water course (after HUET, 1949)

Examination of a section of a water course will reveal two types of zones. *Marginal zones* near the banks can be colonized by marsh and partly submerged plants that provide shelter to particularly useful associations from a piscicultural viewpoint. The *median zone*, between the marginal zones, is traversed generally by a current that impedes or prevents the growth of aquatic plants. This zone is much less productive than the marginal zones.

A section of the water plane reveals a *littoral zone* between the upper and lower limit of the extent of rooted green plants with a subdivision corresponding to the upper part of the zone that is subject to fluctuations in water level (the part that can be flooded). The *deep zone* is characterized by a degree of darkness in which green plants *cannot* grow. Its upper part, characterized by the presence of shell debris on the bed, is called the *sublittoral zone*. The *abyssal zones* of great lakes are at depths of more than 600 m (DUSSART, 1966).

Piscicultural zoning is related to the profile along the length of hydrological basins, especially to the gradient of the water course and the width of the bed. According to HUET (1949), in a given biogeographical region, flowing waters of equal sizes with regard to depth and with comparable gradients have analogous biological characteristics (especially fish populations). This general rule must, however, take other parameters into account such as the origin, the flow, sudden variations in the gradient, and even the insolation of the water course.

Variations are recorded, depending upon climatic conditions, as studied in 1969 by HUET, LELEK, LIBOVARSKY and PENAZ in respect of water courses in Moravia and, in 1972, by ARRIGNON for the water courses of Normandy.

In both these cases, the overriding effect of temperature reported by HUET (1949) was clearly observed. Salmonids colonize water courses of higher cretaceous regions with a slight gradient and a high rate of flow, without, however, the water channel being wider than 50 m. The reason for this particular zoning is based on the preponderant effect of a temperature that is constant and low (9–11°C), subjacent to or very near these water courses with a high rate of flow and a slight annual variation.

We must, therefore, describe clearly the biogeographical region to which we wish to apply the gradient rule; it is, initially, absolutely necessary to carry out a detailed pedological study and also adopt seasonal thermal and hydrological measures (ARRIGNON, 1972).

D. TYPOLOGY

Studies conducted on flowing water systems have dealt chronologically with observations of the succession of species along water courses, then with the longitudinal and altitudinal zonations referred to earlier (HUET, 1949), and with the proposal for a typical reference structure in the abstract plan of a typological analysis (VERNEAUX, 1974).

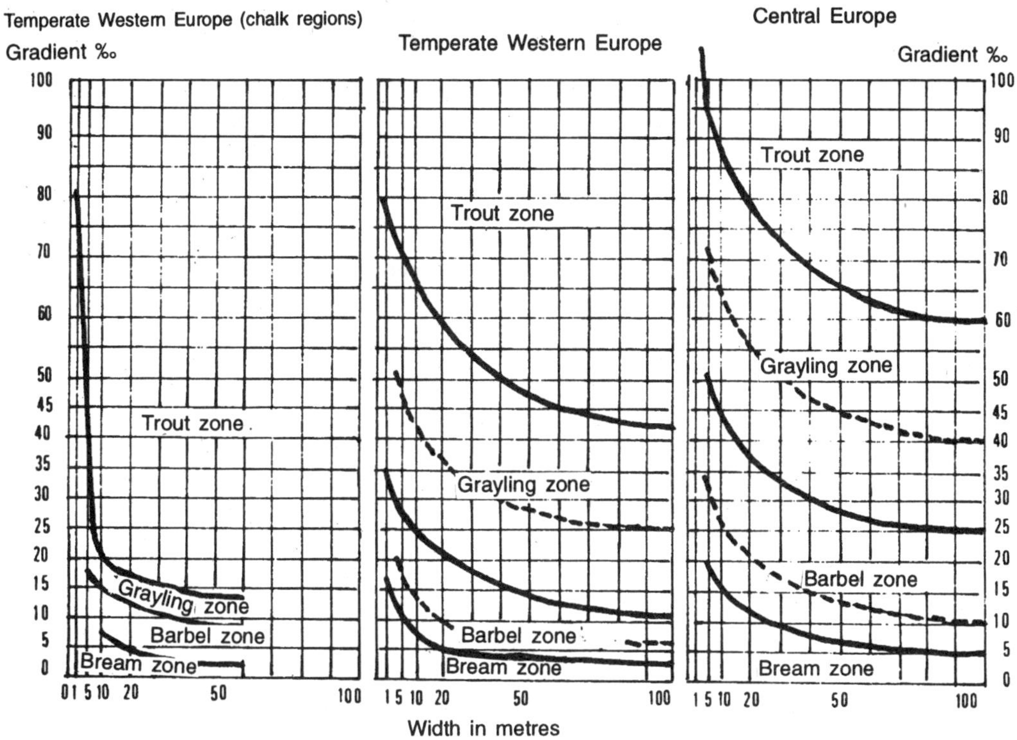

Fig. 4. Graphs of gradients for European water courses (after HUET, LELEK, LIBOSVARSKY and PENAZ, 1969; ARRIGNON, 1972)

1. THEORETICAL REFERENCE OF BIOLOGICAL STRUCTURE

A theoretical reference of biological structure was established after a statistical analysis of quantitative zoological data (of benthic invertebrates and fish) noted during a methodical survey of the hydrographic network of Doubs and finalized after examination of data relating to other French water courses.

VERNEAUX (1973) observed that a species is identified on the basis of a U curve in the plane of the first two axes of a **factor analysis**. Calculation of the proximity between species enables us to identify 10 typological levels that succeed each other along the structure in the order of succession of stations in a theoretical system from the sources to the mouth.

Each typological level corresponds to a group of species with somewhat similar ecological characteristics: this is a **biocoenotype**. The initial model of biogeographical zones is extended to progressively more extensive zones by determining the greatest possible number of equivalent ecological species. Once typological analysis has

Table 1. Populations of piscicultural zones (after HEUT, 1949)

Trout zone	Grayling zone	Barbel zone	Bream zone
Salmonids	Mixed fauna salmonids predominating	Mixed fauna cyprinids predominating	Cyprinids (with carnivores)
Trout	Trout (grayling) running-water cyprinids other cyprinids other carnivores	Trout (grayling) running-water cyprinids other cyprinids other carnivores smooth-water cyprinids	Running-water cyprinids other cyprinids other carnivores smooth-water cyprinids

enabled the establishment of a hierarchy of species based on their ecological spectra for determining their typological succession, it is possible to think of a practical procedure that would help to establish approximately the typology to which a given population belongs. Furthermore, a study of morphodynamic and physicodynamic variations in a water course that has an overall ecological significance helps in an approximate identification of the extent to which a station or a section of water course is similar to one or other of the ecological levels.

2. IDENTIFICATION OF TYPOLOGICAL RELATIONSHIPS

Typological relationships are identified using a grid based on the ichthyological fauna. Species that constitute the fish population of a station are compared with the horizontal groups and, next, with the vertical ones shown in Table 2, the identification being done from left to right (supergoups) and from top to bottom (groups). The group present in the sample with the highest identification number in both cases serves as a reference.

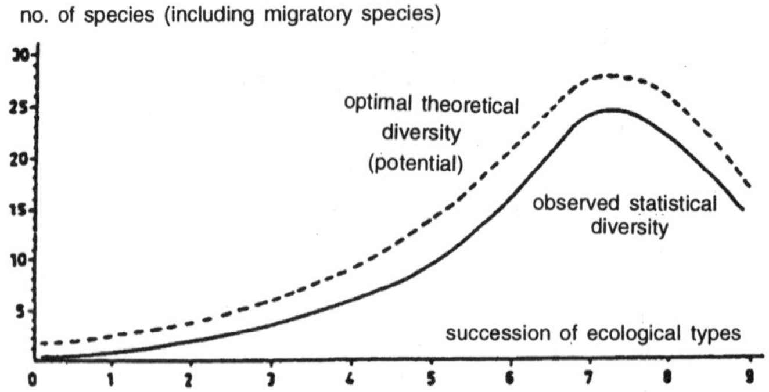

Fig. 5. Diversity and typology

Table 2. Composition of potential ichthyological populations associated with types of water courses (after VERNEAUX, 1981)

TYPOLOGICAL LEVEL		Trout zone (Upper)		Trout zone (Lower)	Grayling zone		Barbel zone		Bream zone
	B0–B1	B2	B3	B4	B5	B6	B7	B8	B9
TYPE OF MEDIUM	Springs and small streams, little or no fish culture	Streams emerging from hill sources	Mountain streams	Small cold rivers	Pre-mountain rivers	Cool rivers	Water courses in plains with warmer waters	Major water courses in plains	Dead arms filled with water major slow-flowing and warm water courses

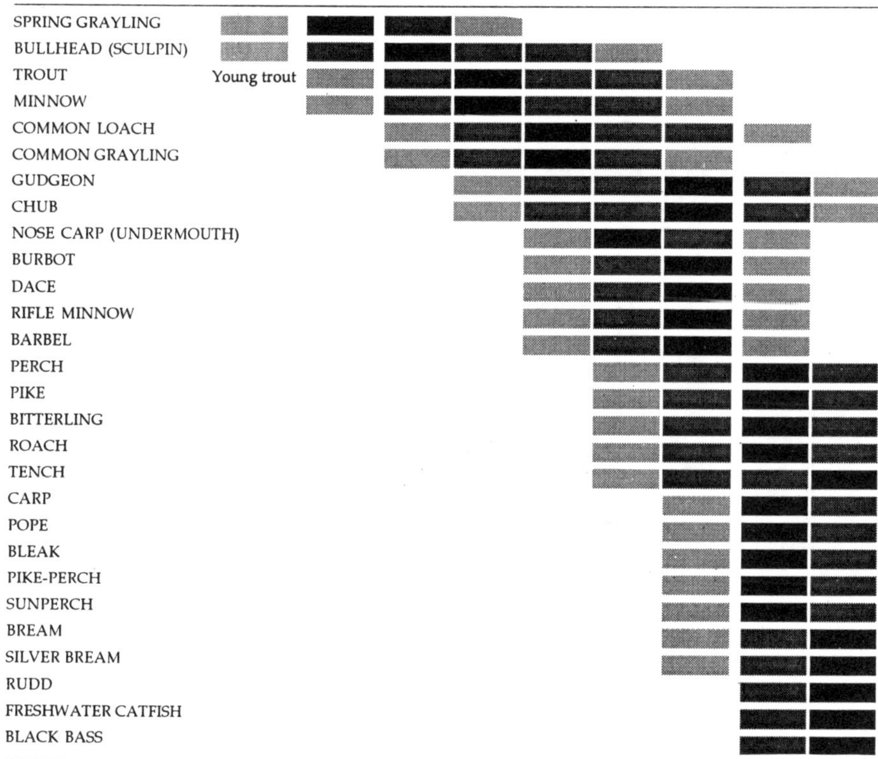

Central species Optimal abundance — Intermediate species Moderate abundance — Marginal species Limited abundance

VERNEAUX and LEYNAUD (1974) very correctly explained that discordances between theoretical similarities (**mesological** graph) and approximate **ichthyological** similarities (table) may be due to historical conditions (biogeographical, paleogeographical), or particular ecological conditions (geomorphological, climatic, thermal . . .). They may also be due, in most cases, to the prevalence of abnormal geological conditions with somewhat severe effects on the elective aquatic populations of the typology under consideration: in such cases, a thorough investigation is necessary.

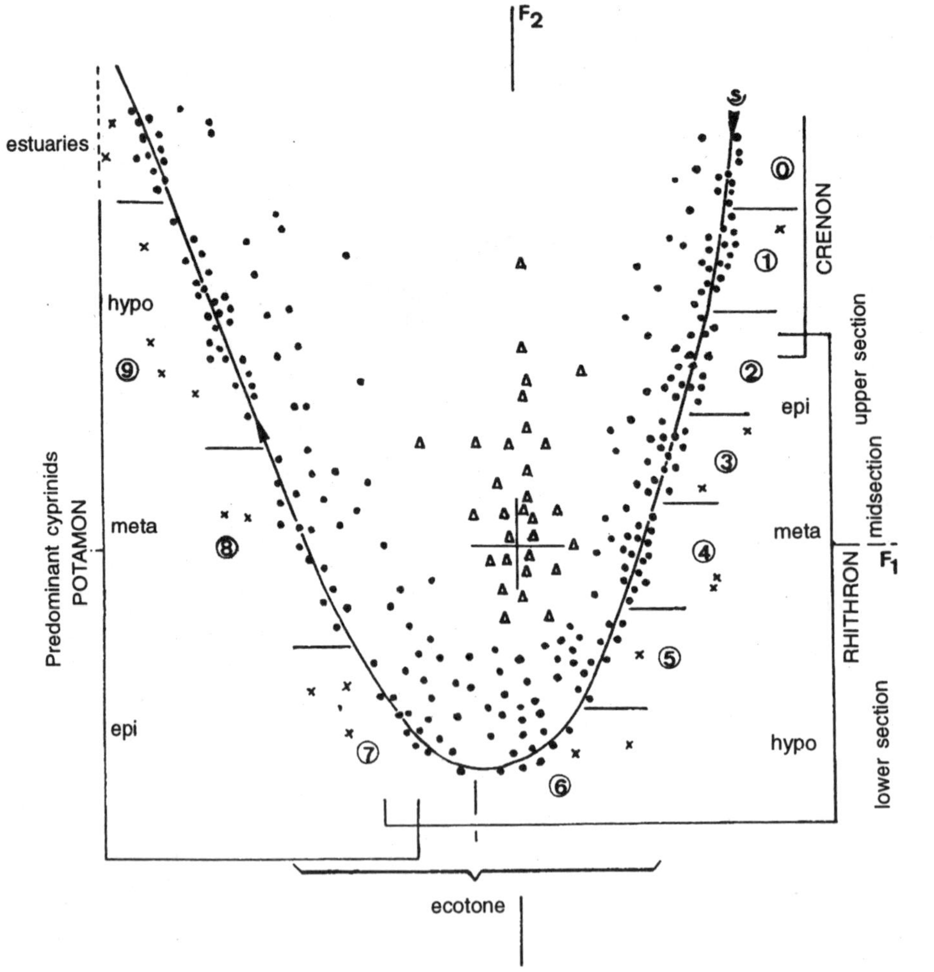

Fig. 6. Typological structure of a theoretical hydrological network corresponding with HUET'S zones (1949) (after VERNEAUX and LEYNAUD, 1974)

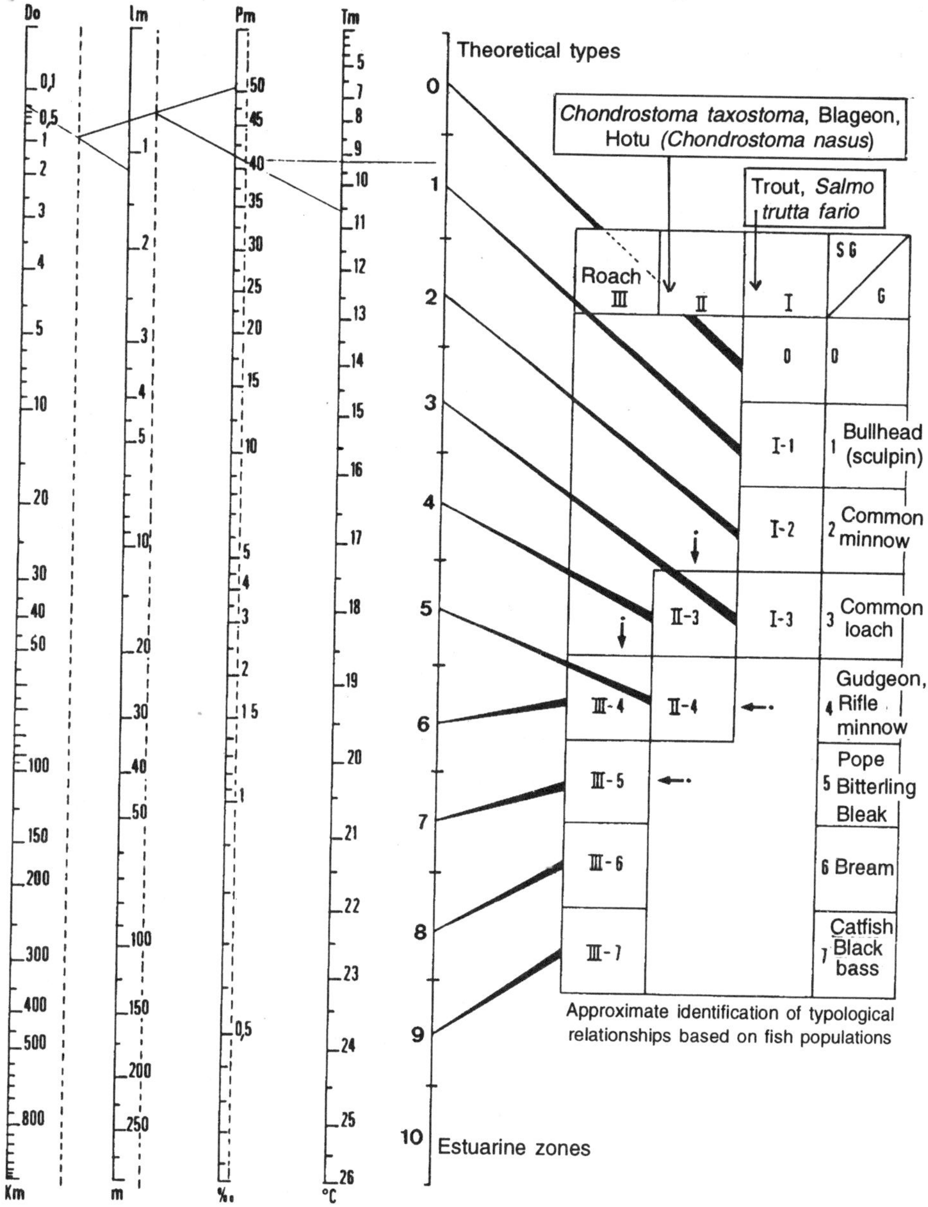

Identification of typological relationships
Do : distance from sources
Im : average width at low water level
Pm : reduction in level per km (gradient ‰)
Tm : maximum average temperature during the hottest month

Fig. 7. Approximate identification of typological relationships (after VERNEAUX and LEYNAUD, 1974)

E. FLUVIAL HYDROSYSTEM

1. IDENTIFICATION

In addition to the classical gradient between the upper reaches and downstream, in major water courses there is a considerable heterogeneity of habitats and populations: This heterogeneity is a result of an interaction between the natural processes (river dynamics, eutrophication, succession of populations, alluvial deposits) and the effects of human activity that may reduce, or even increase, this heterogeneity. AMOROS *et al.* (1988) observed the following around a natural or restored principal course of a river:

• active secondary arms, in braids or anastomosed,

• secondary arms somewhat separated from the main course (a natural result of an alluvial deposit or the artificial effect of a dyke),

• old meanders, with damaged embankments abandoned by the flowing waters of the river,

• semi-aquatic ecosystems on deposits of alluvium after a reduction in the water depth due to the combined effect of a physical process (sedimentation) and biological processes (accumulation of litter),

• terrestrial ecosystems on islands, embankments and filled-up channels.

To this may be added:

• ecosystems in the underground runoff of the river and the adjacent and interdependent water tables as well as in the ecotones of the two underground resources.

Water, as a surface or underground fluid, ensures an excellent liaison between all the parts of a hydrological system. The interactions between aquatic and underground mediums are of considerable interest.

From the main channel to the oldest abandoned arms, the functional role that this "interstitial compartment" plays at the hydrological and biological levels is considerable. For example, it provides oligotrophic and buffered water to the surface mediums in the process of eutrophication or even of dystrophy; some organisms complete their biological cycle, or part of it, in this compartment (crustaceans, beetles, stoneflies, dragonflies); others may migrate temporarily, passively or actively, during floods or when the water level is low.

2. FLUVIAL SPACE

Perception of fluvial space may actually highlight—often at the human chronological level—the link between its development and the duration of major phenomena that have conditioned it. AMOROS *et al.* (1988) noted three hierarchical levels in the spatio-temporal perception.

a) *Functional sectors* separate a river channel depending on its natural (or anthropic) heterogeneity: a sector with a gorge (or a canyon), a braided sector, an anastomosed sector, a sector with meanders, a channel, follow each other theoretically from upstream to the mouth of a river, ending in an estuarine or deltaic sector.

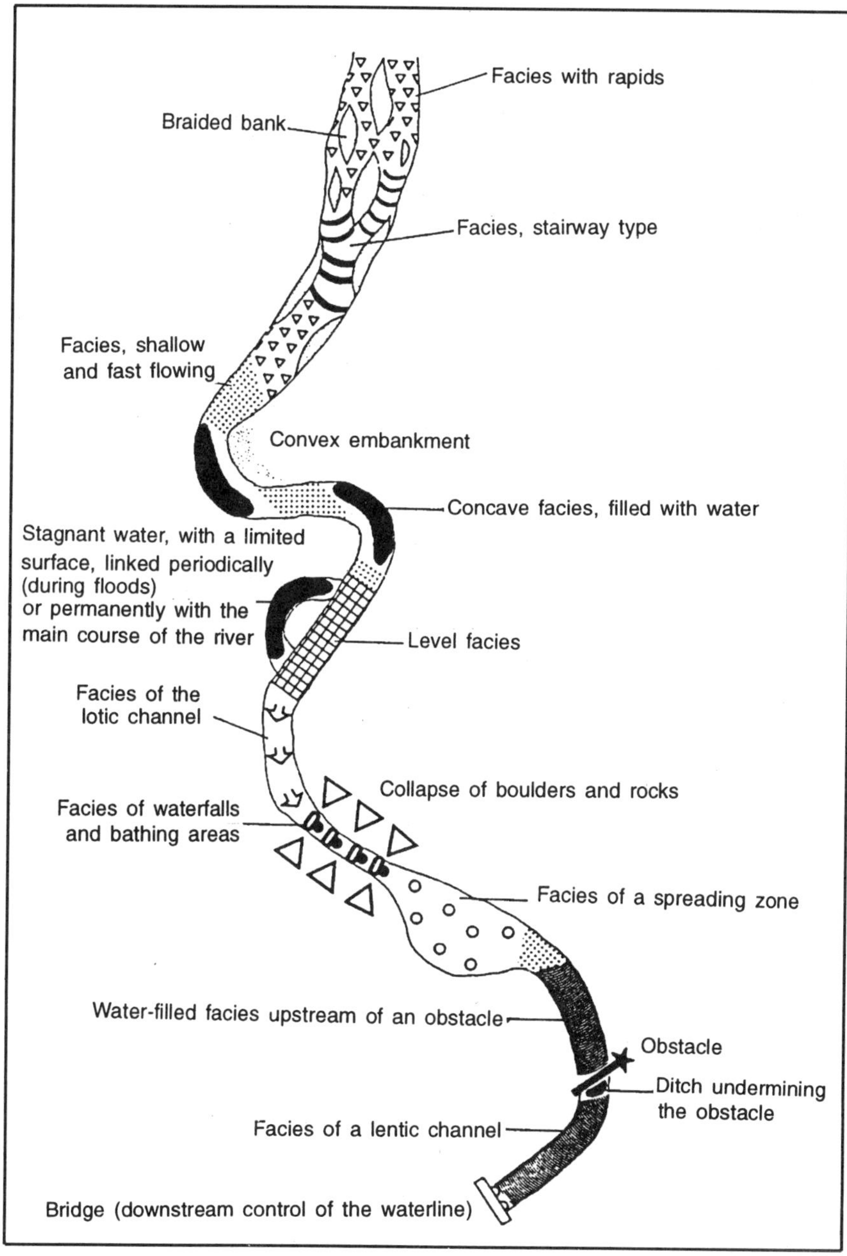

Fig. 8. Example of spatial distribution of types of facies

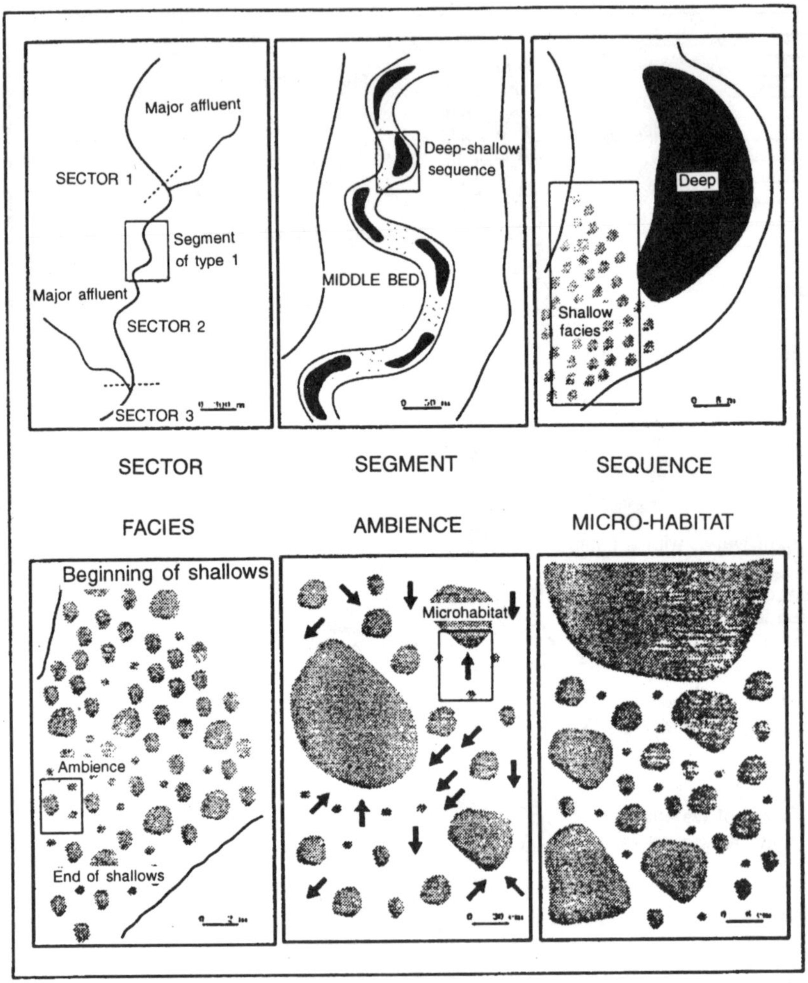

Fig. 9. Morphoecological sectorization of a water course (after MALAVOI, 1989)

The various modes of fluvial dynamics that are a result of structural constraints, gradient, hydrological regime, and flow of solid matter identify, within the hydrological systems, the subsystems that authors have called "functional sectors", the area of which may vary from 10 to 100 sq km as, for example, in the upper Rhone valley.

It is mainly at the level of the functional sector that there is a difference in the modes of appropriation and use of space, where conflicts of interests and uses may be clearly noted and where corrective measures may be planned and implemented.

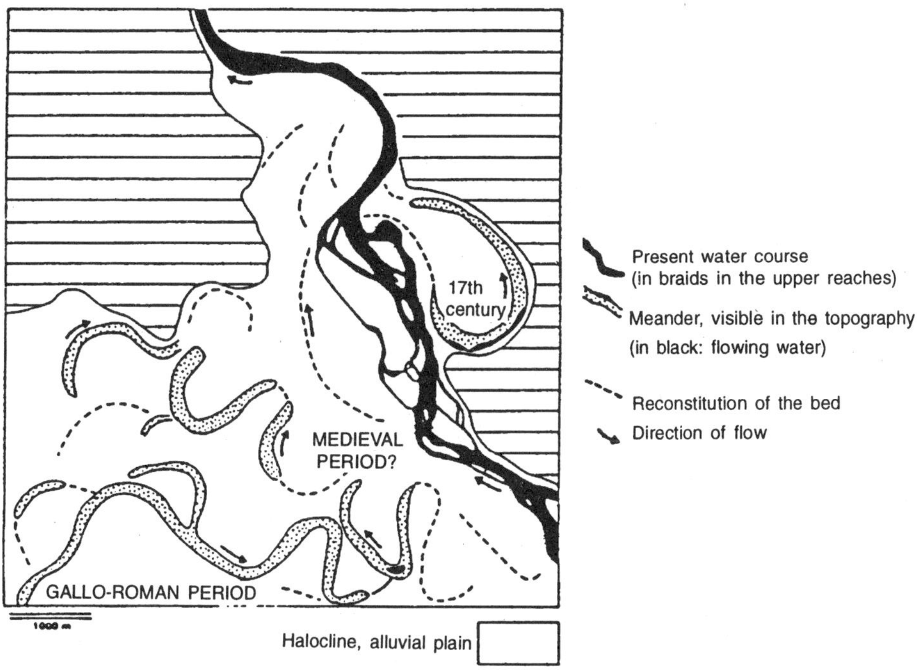

Fig. 10. A sector with meanders: the Brangues plains (upper Rhone valley at km 92 to km 82): the abandoned meanders bear witness to a historical dynamism, and they have not been regenerated since the 18th century (after Cl. AMOROS *et al.*, 1988).

b) *Functional groups* compartmentalize the sectors and contain ecosystems occupying a continuous geographical space subject to the same development process (cutting off of a meander, upstream isolation of a braided arm . . .). All the elements that constitute a functional group have the same origin, resulting in common properties: all ecosystems of an old meander (paleopotamon), for example, have a larger amount of organic matter than in a secondary arm (parapotamon) that is connected with the river.

This compartmentalization is of operational interest: this is how anti-malaria units make use of the knowledge of the hydrological operation of functional groups to forecast possible breeding places of mosquitoes (AMOROS *et al.*, 1988).

c) *The functional unit,* lower in the scale, comprises the biotope and biocoenosis of a given site: it corresponds, in adequate measure, to the definition of an ecosystem.

In a functional sector with meanders, for example, the river dynamics, erosion of a concave embankment, and deposits on convex embankments result in a cutting off and subsequent isolation of loops of some meanders creating crescent-shaped water surfaces: the stagnant water biotope and associated communities constitute a functional unit.

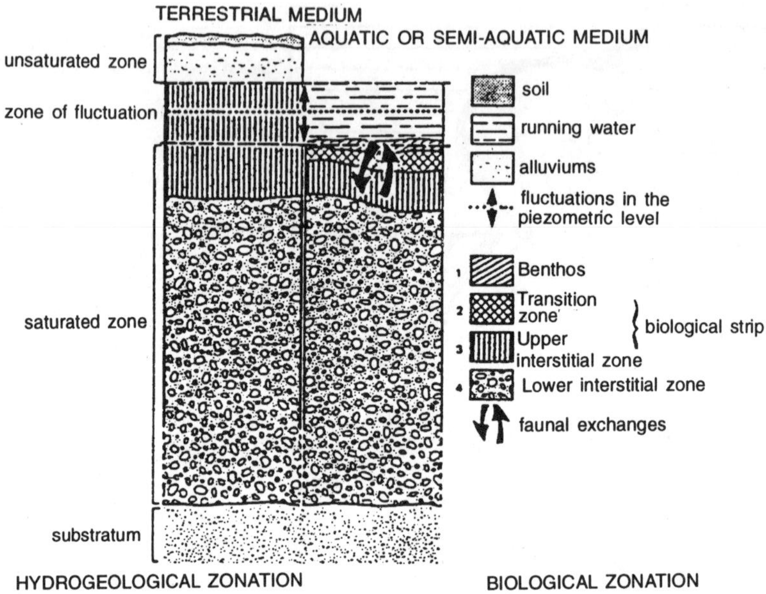

Fig. 11. Sectional profile of a hydrosystem in the valley of the Rhone illustrating the localization of the interstitial biological strip and its subsequent connections with epigeal mediums (after AMOROS *et al.*, 1988)

Recordings of variations in the medium, sampling of the communities living in it, study of their interactions, follow-up of their dynamics, and final assessment are carried out at the level of functional units.

In the field of application, perception of the ecological functioning at typological levels has, for example, resulted in decisions to preserve or reestablish connections between the main course of the upper Rhone and what are customarily, in piscicultural terms, called "annexes": these are secondary arms, meanders, areas with water or humid zones. Managers clearly take developmental processes into account during improvement planning in the study of possibilities of maintaining the capacities of ecological successions—including piscicultural capacities—while preserving the processes of river dynamics (AMOROS *et al.*, 1988).

F. LIMNOLOGICAL ASPECTS OF LAKES

1. STRUCTURE

The structure of lakes is highly variable. The shape, depth, and volume of a lake is fairly often related to its origin. A lake section is subject to modifications due to movements of the water that result in a line of the bank with zones of alluvium and zones of erosion; wind and the mineralogical structure evidently play an important additional role depending on the case.

Life in lakes is created by the action of sunshine on the water, by both the light rays and heat rays.

Heat is essentially from the light absorbed, by the lacustrine water, in the wavebands from red to infrared. The heat from the soil, from rain water coming through the atmosphere, and from the water of affluents is minimum.

The light absorbed depends on the angle of incidence of the rays and, therefore, on the season, the latitude and the time of day. On Lake Leman, 2.5% of the light is reflected in summer but 14% is reflected in winter. Light diffused by clouds is also absorbed.

The amount of light absorbed depends upon the nature of the water sheets. Lacustrine waters absorb light faster than others. When there are large and regular temperature variations we observe the phenomenon of thermal stratification.

During summer there are three temperature zones with different gradients:

—The *epilimnion* corresponds to a surface layer in which the temperature is high; the currents are active and the gradient is moderate.

—The *metalimnion*, at a certain depth, is a zone of rapid temperature increase, or thermocline in which the gradient is high.

—The *hypolimnion* is at the depths; the gradient here is almost nil and the temperatures are cold and stable.

Heat losses are due to radiation, evaporation, conduction and downstream movement of layers of warm water.

2. SEASONAL CYCLE

At the end of winter, the water temperature is homogeneous and very close to 4°C; the lake has no stability and the least gust of wind causes a movement of the entire mass of the lake, resulting in a mixing of the water.

In the spring there is a *first cycle of circulation* (**overturn**). The light is intense, and the water layers are warmed. This warming is concentrated if the weather is calm but, if it is cloudy and the wind is violent, the water is stirred and the temperature at the bottom rises; this depends on the wind force in the spring.

In summer, there is a large heat gain, and also a thermocline: surface waters that have become less dense may sink a little but there is a clear threshold below which, at a certain depth, the water suddenly becomes colder.

At the beginning of autumn, heat loss is greater than the gain; the water becomes colder and sinks, the epilimnion is homogenized, stability is destroyed, the entire mass begins to move and the temperature becomes uniform from the surface to the bottom: this is the *autumn circulation—or overturn*.

In winter the surface water becomes cold and may freeze: the water at the bottom stabilizes at about 4°C. This is an inverse stratification.

Lakes with such a seasonal circulation are called *holomictic*. On the other hand, others in which there is only a partial circulation are called *meromictic*. In meromictic lakes there is no seasonal variation and the stratification is due not just to the temperature but also to the water density when it has some salts in it. The increase in temperature is due to the active oxidation of organic matter at the bottom or even the inflow of waters with a salt content, for example, selenitic waters. According to DUSSART (1966) we have here two superimposed lakes with different properties.

3. CHARACTERISTICS

The characteristics of lakes, such as their thermal cycles, transparence, turbidity, colour, nature of currents, and development of chemical compounds, determine their animal populations and fish production capacity.

3.1 Currents

Currents are due to a disturbance of the thermal stratification by wind, differences in density because of variations in temperature, and inputs of dissolved salts; they are also due to lunar attraction.

a) Non-periodic currents

Non-periodic currents comprise drift currents created by wind. Their velocity reaches 2% of that of the winds that caused them. They are deviated by the Coriolis effect of the earth's rotation. These currents cause whirlpools with a considerable effect on the distribution of living matter. Also aperiodic, gradient currents are due to differences in depth or density; they are weak, are also subject to the Coriolis effect, and originate at the depths with an increase in velocity at the surface. Currents observed during navigation are the result of a combination of gradient and drift currents. Convection currents are of thermal origin; they are caused by sinking of water layers cooled by certain phenomena that cast shadows, such as clouds or a mountain overhang. The surface temperature becomes lower than that at the bottom, causing an inverse stratification. Currents created by the entrance of tributaries in a lake result in lapping of water against the bank.

b) Periodic currents

Periodic currents are created by tides, not very perceptible in large stretches of water (3 cm in Lake Superior), and by internal and external tidal waves. Superficial tidal waves cause a periodic rocking motion, the period being determined by the shape of the lakes and the axis of oscillation. There are binodal and multinodal tidal waves. The interference from these waves results in highly complex movements due to an excess of pressure, rainstorm on a particular site, or winds. According to MERIAN the period of these waves is inversely proportional to the square root of the lake depth (73 minutes for Lake Leman, 56 for Lake Constance, and 10 to 12 for Lake Balaton, which is not very deep). The origin of internal tidal waves is not clearly understood.

Currents cause a redistribution of plankton and planktotrophic fish, they have an effect on the spawning areas of salmonids (especially the arctic char—*Salvelinus alpinus*), and sometimes they cause a considerable drift of fishing nets.

3.2 Colour

Colour is one of the principal characteristics of lakes. It depends on the selective transparence of the water. Radiations are absorbed by some types of matter (colloidal silica, clay) as well as by plankton. Maximum transparence is observed during winter when the low temperatures are not favourable for plankton. The colour of the water also depends on the colour of the sky, whether it is clear or cloudy, as well as on the colour of the bed, the quality of the incident light, and relief of the surrounding land area.

The true colour of the water is due to the dissolved substances or those in suspension. Its assessment provides an indication of the productivity in plankton: yellow or green indicates a high productivity; blue a limited productivity. Waters with a high calcium content are generally blue (calcium salts coagulate humic substances).

3.3 Chemical Phenomena

Chemical phenomena are dependent upon the amount of oxygen present. In a littoral zone, planktonic algae and aquatic phanerogams cause an intense oxygenation that may reach supersaturation. Elsewhere, the oxygen cycle is variable depending upon whether the lakes are holomictic or meromictic, oligotrophic or eutrophic. The consumption of oxygen is by phytoplankton, zooplankton, and fish. In winter the metabolism of living creatures slows down while the solubility of oxygen increases: this is a good situation. It is likely to deteriorate as soon as the oxygen content is reduced to the extent of causing complete destruction of plankton. Oxidation of decomposing matter is faster in summer while the solubility of oxygen is low. It tends to move from the surface to the bottom: on the surface living matter is elaborated by photosynthesis in a somewhat thick layer, or *trophogenic layer*, and it is destroyed at a depth in the *tropholytic layer*. These two layers are important in eutrophic lakes and negligible in oligotrophic lakes. The processes of nitrification, which needs oxygen, and denitrification, which is helpful for anaerobic bacteria, are actually even more important than the organic matter content, which itself is important.

4. EVOLUTION OF LAKES

Evolution of lakes is specifically dependent on these phenomena. A poor lake, oligotrophic since the glaciations, in the course of time has a progressively larger biomass, with phenomena of production and degradation of living matter that cause it to reach a stage—if we carry this logic to an extreme—of total abiotic condition due to organic pollution, after a period of maximal productivity, and to the final stage of its disappearance as a lake, by being silted up (Fig. 237).

4.1 Oligotrophic Lakes

Oligotrophic lakes are young lakes the state of which is characterized, according to Dussart (1966), by a predominance of physical and chemical factors and a relatively limited role played by organisms in their existence.

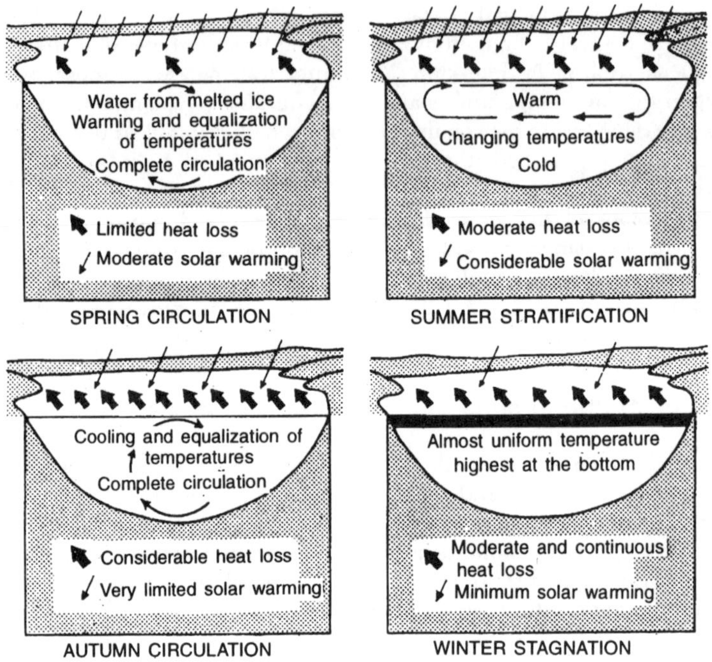

Fig. 12. Seasonal cycle of a holomictic lake

The littoral flora is limited, the phytoplankton has a limited requirement of oxygen, and primary production is modest, but oxygen is present even in the depths and helps organisms that require large amounts of it to exist in these waters (for example, *Coregonus*).

There are also ancient lakes that, as a result of external inputs, have characteristics similar to the aforementioned ones (inflow of highly oxygenated water during periods of thermal stratification in the deeper zones from large tributaries). In such cases their productivity may also be high without a subsequent proportionate degradation.

4.2 Dystrophic Lakes

Dystrophic lakes are oligotrophic lakes that produce little, but the waters have no oxygen. They develop slowly in acid terrain and with a high content of humic matter, like the Lispach lake referred to by DUSSART.

4.3 Eutrophic Lakes

Eutrophic lakes are oligotrophic lakes that have developed. THIENEMANN (1925) identified them as being shallow, containing brownish to green waters, slightly or very slightly transparent, with a high content of nutritive substances and calcium.

Plankton is abundant in the superficial layer; according to DUSSART it is made up more of blue-green algae (Cyanophyceae) than green algae (Chlorophyceae). The bottom contains putrescible substances and the number of faunal species is very limited but dense (*Chaoborus, Chironomus* sp.). It is, however, not much used as fish are unable to stay in this poorly oxygenated zone. Eutrophication is hastened by organic pollution.

4.4 Silting of Lakes

Lakes are filled up by sedimentation from water courses entering them and by the phenomena of vertical sedimentation inherent in the destruction of the biomass and precipitation of mineral compounds.

The littoral zone becomes larger than the pelagic zone. The lake begins to resemble a pond. The emerging vegetation colonizes the entire bed and makes the lake appear like a marsh, later a marshy area, and eventually a humid grassland.

In an acid impluvium the littoral belt forms a boggy peat ring that gradually becomes a floating carpet on which palustrine vegetation may develop, with many extremely dangerous pits. When the climate is favourable boggy areas are themselves colonized by forest trees.

Table 3. Trophic typology of macrophytes in Swiss lakes according to LACHAVANNE (1985)

Trophic state	Most common species	
Oligotrophic	*Nitella* sp.	
	Chara sp.	
	Ranunculus sp.	
	Potamogeton graminaeus	
	P. praelongus	
	P. alpinus	Mountain lakes
Mesotrophic	*Chara* sp. (to 15 m)	Littoral zone
	Potamogeton perfoliatus	
	P. pectinatus	*Phragmites australis*
	P. filiformis	*Scirpus lacustris*
	P. graminaeus	*Nymphaea alba*
	P. pusillus	
	P. lucens	
Eutrophic	Plants limited to 5–6 m depth	Littoral zone
	Potamogeton pectinatus	
	P. perfoliatus	*Phragmites australis*
	P. crispus	*Typha* sp.
	P. lucens	*Nuphar luteum*
	Zannichellia palustris	
	Myriophyllum spicatum	
	Ceratophyllum demersum	
	Nittellopsis obtusa	
Hypereutrophic	Plants limited to 2 m depth	Littoral zone
	Najas marina	
	Potamogeton crispus	*Phragmites australis*
		Nuphar luteum

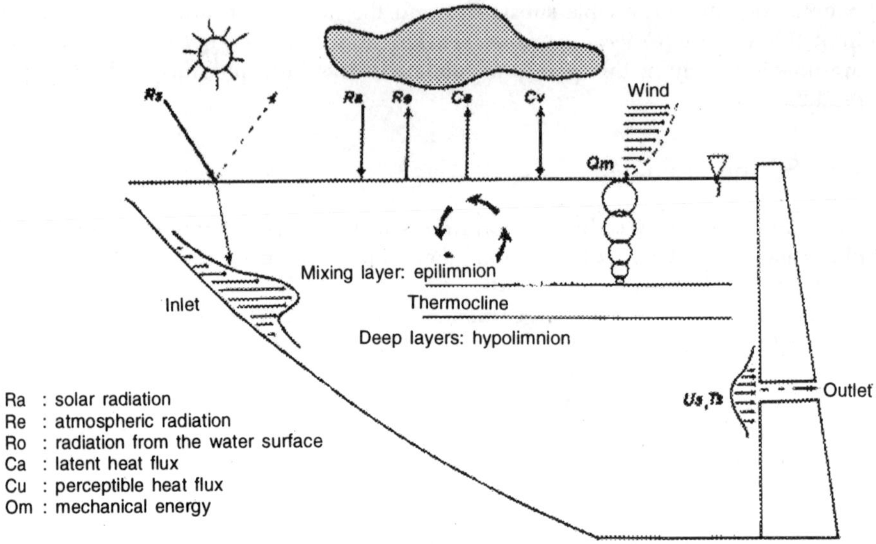

Fig. 13. Energy balance of a dam and internal dynamics

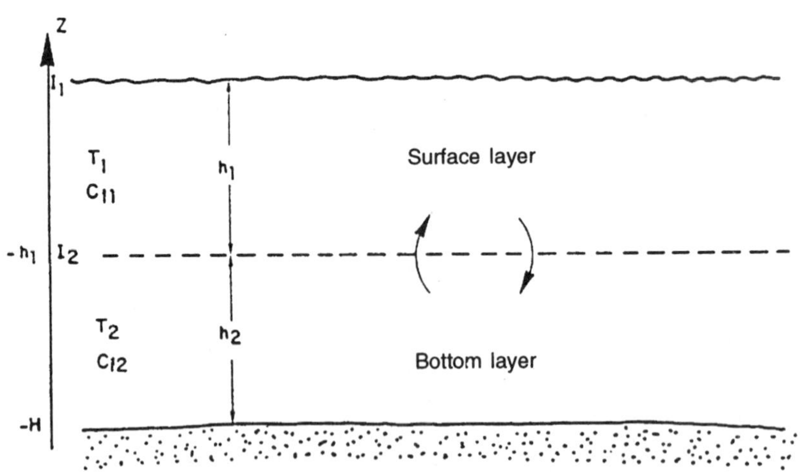

Fig. 14. Vertical structural diagram of the model (after PURCHER and SALENCON, 1990) I_1, I_2: intensity of solar radiation at the level of the upper limit of each layer; T_1, T_2: temperature of the surface layer (bottom layer); C_{11}, C_{12}: concentration of element i in the surface layer (bottom layer); H: depth of water column; h_1, h_2: depth of the surface layer (bottom layer)

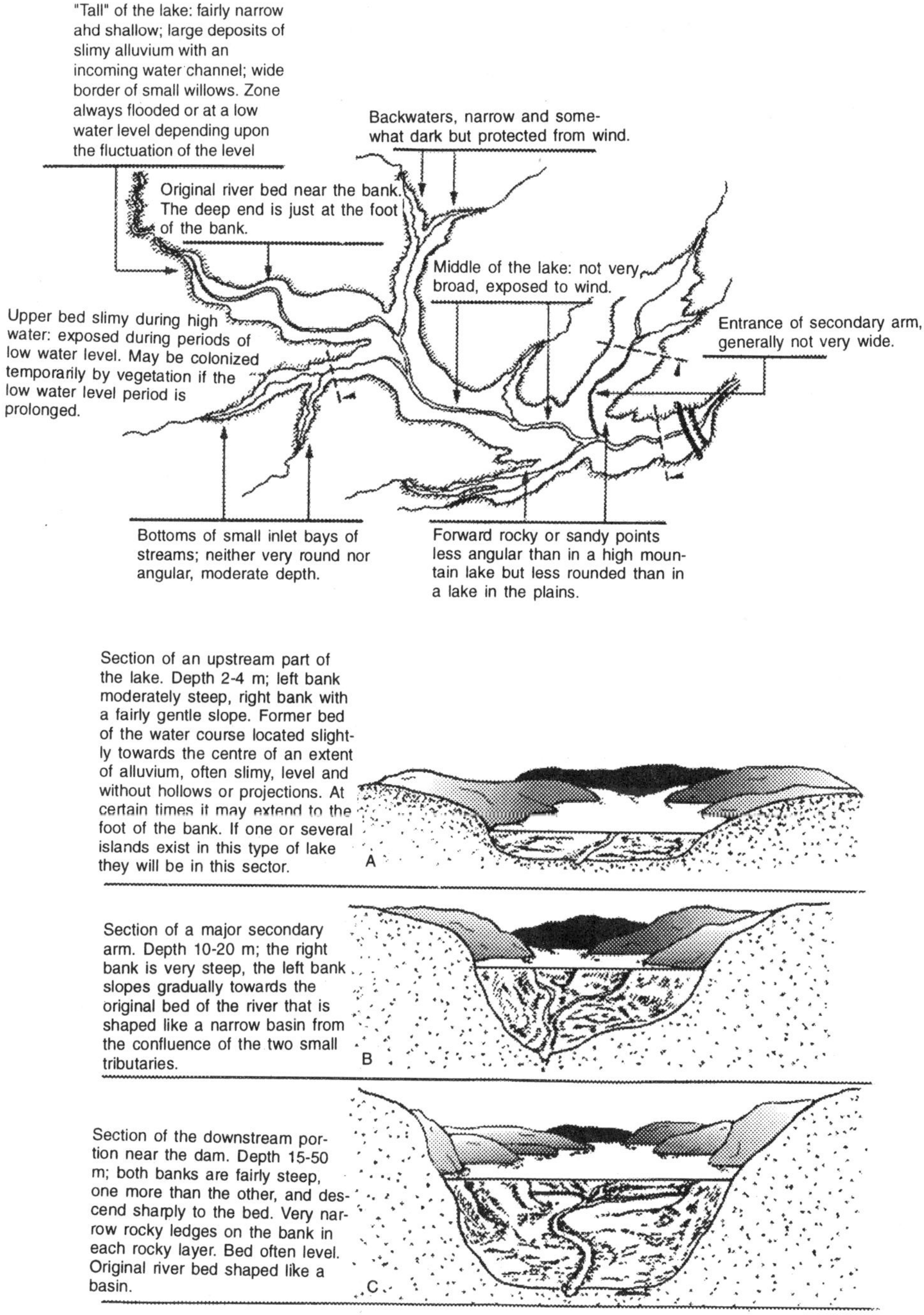

Fig. 15. Theoretical configuration of a lake dam

2 NATURE AND DYNAMICS OF THE COMPONENTS OF A MEDIUM

Ecological studies and estimations are based on examination of a certain number of abiotic components as well as biotic ones because of the antinomy, interaction, and coaction resulting from their own dynamics that create a succession of balances and imbalances or a fragile climax in various aquatic ecosystems.

Knowledge of the nature and the dynamics of components in aquatic systems, limited to the main and more incidental ones, is necessary to understand certain mechanisms and justify our intervention in the medium.

A. TERRESTRIAL ENVIRONMENT

The terrestrial environment of a body of water has an influence that is even greater if it is allowed to develop, either periodically depending upon the seasons, especially with regard to the plant cover, at a rate related to growth in the aquatic life or from time to time as a result of fundamental disturbances such as deforestation in the catchment area of a lake, cutting down of an area of woodland, or building of a dam.

The climate, permeability of the terrain, and gradient determine the flow.

Waters contain organic substances and mineral salts depending upon the areas they have passed through. Plant cover has a direct effect on a water course or a stretch of water as a result of the shade it provides or by the leaves that accumulate in the autumn and an indirect effect due to released substances or inflows.

While the shape of a water body varies only in exceptional circumstances, that of a water course may be altered to a considerable extent in both its plane and its profile where the regime is no longer uniform or regular, depending on the sinuosities such as meanders, dunes, or folds.

According to Lebreton (1974), depending upon the erosive nature of the banks and the general slope, the bed may be one of three principal types:

— a bed with meanders, with the meanders increasing downstream in regular curves of which the wavelength Δm is equal to approximately 10 times the width of the bed (e.g., the Seine);

— a bed with tresses, characterized by many islets and channels in a network (e.g., the Loire);

— a straight bed, fairly uncommon, with only somewhat short reaches (10 times the width). The thalweg remains sinuous from one bank to the other, forming sills and ponds.

Instability in the profiles of banks and beds results in ecological disturbances and reduces fish productivity.

B. WATER MOVEMENTS

Water movements comprise horizontal, vertical (both ascending and descending), and convection currents. They have a mechanical effect on beds and banks and a biological effect on the aquatic medium depending upon their origin, their cause, and their extent.

Surface movements erode banks by an **undertow** when a water body is subjected to the effect of prevailing winds and by the **wakes** of boats due to fluctuations caused by navigation.

The flow characterizes lotic mediums. There are three main factors involved: the liquid flow, the solid flow, and the current velocity. The liquid flow is determined by the formula $Q = V \times S$, where Q is flow (m^3/s), V is velocity (m/s) and S is section (m^2).

1. LIQUID FLOW

According to Lebreton, a flow with a liquid phase and a solid phase in the form of granules that are not cohesive may be identified by a certain number of physical measurements relative to the fluid, the non-cohesive granules, and a uniform flow.

The principal sources of replenishment of water courses are rain, snow, glaciers, and ground water; their relative amounts, depending upon the relief, the geological, pedological, and photogeographical components, determine the liquid and solid flows.

Water courses are categorized according to the **seasonal** variations in their flow as:

—water courses with a simple regime, characterized by a high-water period during winter in an oceanic pluvial regime and during summer in a snow and glacial regime;

—water courses with a complex regime that have a mixed system of replenishment: pluvionival with two maxima in spring and autumn.

Irregularities in a flow are caused by variable high- and low-water periods and their consequences depending upon the manner of replenishment. Periods of low-water level may lead to drying but their effect as well as the effect of high-water levels, though they disturb the existing communities, may be more beneficial than harmful for fish. Temporary streams in the plains may be more productive than permanent ones and even flooded zones, by being rendered suitable as spawning grounds for cyprinids and esocids.

2. SOLID FLOW

Erosion in the bed and the banks leads to a carrying away of heavy material near the bottom in a series of surges in the flow.

QUESNEL (1964) gave the velocities for loosening (perturbation), movement, and transportation of individual elements depending upon their sizes (Table 4).

Table 4. Characteristic velocity of individual elements (cm/s) (after QUESNEL, 1964)

Diameter of elements (cm)	Velocity Characteristics (cm/s)		
	Loosening	Initial and subsequent movement	Transportation
0.2	8	15	11
1	39	70	51
3	78	157	105
7	100	196	130

Fine elements in suspension in a higher water level are carried to a longer distance than those given in Table 4.

The quantities transported vary considerably and, like deposits, depend upon the impluvium and the gradient. The stability of beds is closely related to the size, shape, and nature of the constituent elements.

The polyhedral shape of stone blocks, the existence of fixed plants, and the cohesive effect of clays or colloidal sludges are among the most important factors in the cohesion of beds.

3. CURRENT VELOCITY

Current velocity depends, also, upon the shape of the bottom and the width and depth of the bed. According to BERG as cited by DECAMPS (1971), there are several such velocities:

- very low, less than 10 cm/s,
- low, 10–25 cm/s,
- average, 25–50 cm/s,
- high, 50–100 cm/s,
- very high, more than 100 cm/s.

The flow in a water course (Q) is the sum of the inflow (R) and ground water (B) and represents the gross hydraulic potential that can be used to provide energy.

Precipitations, the starting point of a hydrologic cycle, occur at random and are highly variable from day to day, season to season, and year to year.

After a rain shower, depending upon the characteristics of the receiving mediums, a typical hydrogram and a variable distribution of the parameters of the hydrologic balance in terms of time may be drawn as shown in Figs. 17 and 18.

Within the water there are unequal rates of flow; as a result of friction they are reduced near the banks and the bottom. The contrasts are greater in a longitudinal section due to a series of pools and sills.

There is a turbulence in the flows depending upon whether the medium is a lotic or a lentic one. When lentic, the liquid veins may flow side by side without much mixing, which explains why some may, over a fairly long distance, affect only

Table 5. Characteristic rates of flow in various regimes (after M. PARDE)

Regimes	DCE	DC 11	DC or 75%	DC or 50%	DC or 25%	DC 1	DCM 10 d
Glacial	0.04–0.15	0.05–0.18	0.09–0.25	0.25–0.50	1.55–1.75	2.75–3.25	3.80–4.50
Nivo-glacial	0.12–0.25	0.15–0.30	0.20–0.40	0.50–0.60	1.40–1.60	2.40–3.00	3.20–4.00
Mountain snow	0.15–0.25	0.20–0.30	0.25–0.40	0.55–0.65	1.30–1.45	2.30–2.80	3.00–3.70
Plains snow	0.15–0.25	0.20–0.30	0.30–0.40	0.40–0.55	1.30–1.45(?)	2.75–3.50	4.00–5.00
Transitional mountain snow	0.15–0.30	0.18–0.35	0.35–0.50	0.65–0.75	1.25–1.45	2.10–2.50	2.50–3.00
Oceanic nivo-pluvial	0.12–0.20	0.20–0.30	0.25–0.40	0.60–0.75	1.20–1.35	2.10–2.50	3.80–4.20
Oceanic pluvio-nival	0.08–0.16	0.15–0.25	0.30–0.40	0.60–0.80	1.20–1.35	2.00–2.50	3.50–4.50
Mediterranean pluvio-nival	0.02–0.10	0.05–0.15	0.13–0.25	0.30–0.50	0.90–1.20	2.25–2.75	1.50–6.00
Oceanic pluvial	0.15–0.25	0.25–0.35	0.35–0.45	0.68–0.75	1.20–1.35	2.10–2.50	3.00–5.30(?)
Mediterranean pluvial	0.01–0.10	0.05–0.15	0.08–0.20	0.30–0.50	0.80–1.00	2.50–3.00	5.00–6.50
Complex regimes of major water courses with a highly nival influence and a pluvial influence in cold weather	0.30–0.45	0.40–0.50	0.55–0.70	0.85–0.92	1.20–1.35	1.65–1.90	2.30–2.60
Effluents from large lakes	0.30–0.50	0.45–0.60	0.60–0.80	0.80–0.90	1.20–1.40	1.65–1.85	1.90–2.20
Large karstic reserves that drain slowly in pluvial to nivo-pluvial regimes or effluents from several large lakes	0.65–0.72	0.70–0.77	0.80–0.85	0.85–0.92	1.08–1.20	1.40–1.50	1.65–2.00

The coefficients in the table provide, in a simple and condensed form, the general slope of the flow curves as well as an initial estimate of the extreme annual flows for various regimes. We observe that the DCM, which we may consider the "ordinary high-water level", is about four times the module in glacial and nivo-glacial regimes, while it may reach five times the module for an oceanic pluvial regime (more than six times in a mediterranean regime). The low-water level indicated by the DCE is often hardly more than 1/100 the module in a mediterranean pluvial regime, while it is about 15–20% of the same value for some regimes of the nivo-pluvial type of the Pyrenees or the nivo-glacial type in the Alps.

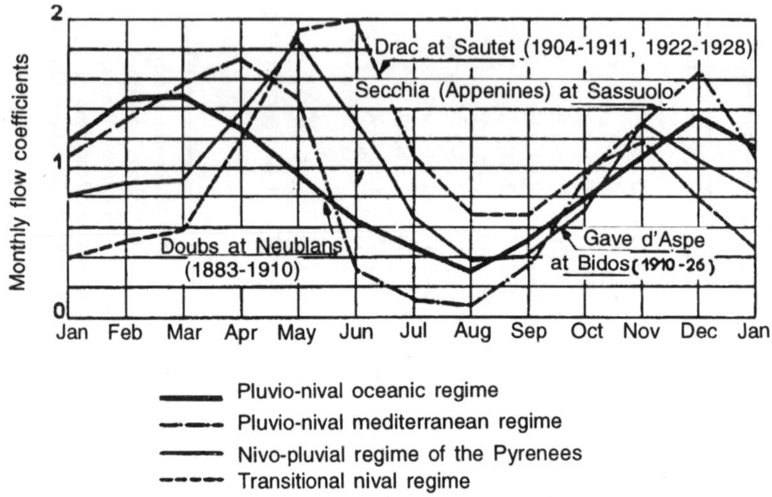

Fig. 16. Different profiles of mixed-flow regimes

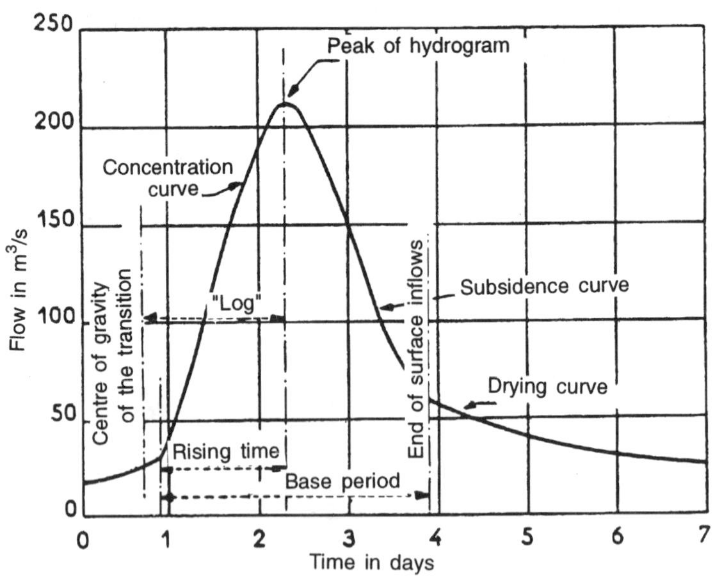

Fig. 17. Various characteristics of a typical hydrogram (courtesy G. REMENERIAS, Publ. Eyrolles)

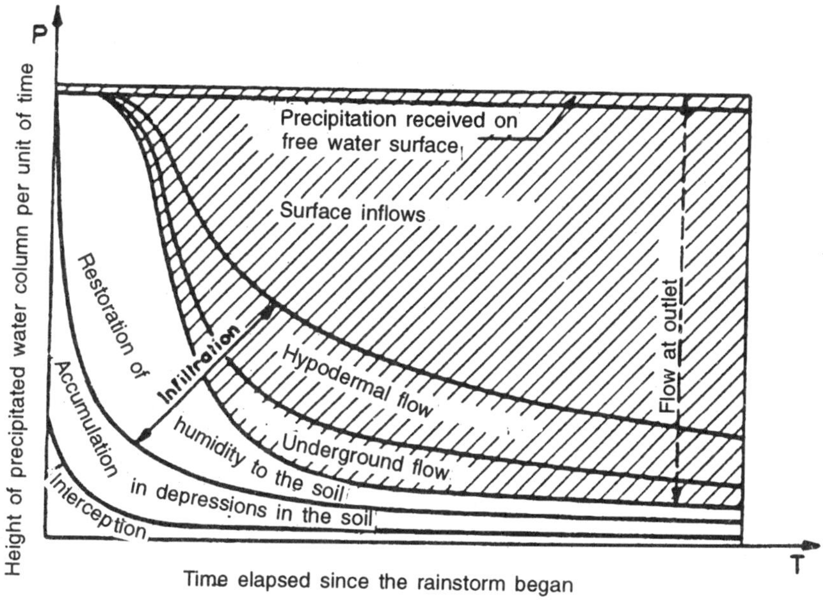

Fig. 18. Distribution of atmospheric waters during a rainstorm of constant intensity (after LINSLEY)

a single marginal zone or only the median zone. The turbulence in a lotic medium, on the other hand, enables mixing, which is generally less intense near the bottom.

AMBUHL, TRIVELLATO, and DECAMPS have shown that near the bottom of a river, the physical phenomena transform the living conditions at the very level where there are communities that develop in flowing water, because of the existence of a transition zone in which the current velocity is reduced to zero at the level of the substrate; the same applies to "still waters" sheltered from the main current by obstacles and irregularities at the bottom.

The current tends to carry living creatures downstream, depending upon their morphology and behaviour. It determines the diversity at the bottom of water courses and, consequently, the distribution of communities. It facilitates gaseous exchange and transfer of energy-producing materials as well as the elimination of waste products.

C. WATER

Water, which in its three states has played and still plays an important role on the earth, is an element upon which all creatures that breathe in it rely heavily for support.

Nothing can live in chemically pure water because it offers no means of subsistence. But an aquatic medium contains water that is never chemically pure, only relatively pure. It has static physical properties such as its specific heat, density, and transparence, chemical properties such as its solubility and stability, and dynamic characteristics, such as the lentic facies of still waters and the lotic facies of flowing waters.

Natural water contains:
- dissolved gases
- mineral compounds
- organic compounds

In the form of **rain water** it has, in the atmosphere, come in contact with gases and solid particles which it has partly dissolved and carried downwards in its fall. This is why the water of a first rain shower has a much higher content of gases and compounds than the rain water that falls later:

- carbon dioxide (CO_2), 54 mg/l
- oxygen, 9 mg/l
- phosphates (P_2O_5) } in fairly large amounts
- nitrous oxide (HN_2O) } in fairly large amounts
- traces of sulphur

Water from melting snows, on the other hand, has very few contaminants and may even be very pure in crystalline formations, except after atmospheric pollution.

Water from inflows or infiltrations dissolves some soluble matter but leaves behind, in areas that it passes through, some suspended matter brought down by precipitations.

Water that emanates from springs and feeds streams, depending on the terrain through which it passes, is therefore a solution with a certain amount of gases, salts, and other substances.

1. PHYSICAL CHARACTERISTICS

1.1 Temperature

The temperature of water affects its density and viscosity, the solubility of gases, especially oxygen, and the rate of chemical and biochemical reactions.

Its variations may destroy certain aquatic species but also be favourable for the development of other species, resulting in an ecological imbalance. Each species, in order to exist, can do so only within a certain temperature range and is otherwise likely to disappear; it has its thermal preference that corresponds to the temperature zone in which it finds it easiest to exist.

1.2 pH

pH is a symbol which, by an accompanying number, indicates the acidity or alkalinity of a particular water.

- the range 0 to 7 corresponds to values of acidity
- the range 7 to 14 corresponds to values of alkalinity.

pH is a negative logarithm of the concentration of hydrogen ions in water (refer to the law of mass action). The pH of pure water, neither acid nor alkaline, containing

Table 6. Thermal limits for certain types of fish (°C)

Species	Acclimation	Min. temp.*	Max. temp.*
Dicentrarchus labrax	20	5	32
Bass	30	11	34
Lepomis macrochirus purpurescens	15	3	31
Sun perch	30	11	34
Ictalurus melas	15	0	30
Catfish	25	6	34
Perca fluviatilis	5	/	21
Common perch	25	9	32
Alosa sp.	25	11	34
Shad	35	20	37
Salmo trutta gairdneri	3	/	23
Rainbow trout	20	/	25
Sarotherodon mossambicus	20	11	40
Tilapia	15	6	36

*Temperature at which the survival rate is 50%.

Table 7. Tolerances

pH < 5.0	lower limit for survival of most aquacultural species with the exception of certain tolerant habituals
5.0 < pH < 9.0	tolerable limits for most species
6.0 < pH < 7.2	optimal zone for reproduction of most species
7.5 < pH < 8.5	optimal zone for productivity of plankton
pH > 8.5	some algae are destroyed beyond this value
pH > 9	lethal threshold for many species (especially salmonids)

the same number of H^+ and OH^- ions resulting from the dissociation of a certain number of water molecules ($10^{14.14}$) is exactly 7.07, the extreme values, therefore, being 0 and 14.

Determining the pH is important because, combined with the measurement of dissolved CO_2 and the total and temporary hardness, it helps to estimate the extent of aggressiveness of a particular water and also whether it is suitable for higher animal life or otherwise.

Measurement of the pH is done by colorimetry or potentiometry.

In colorimetry we use sensitive papers that are effective for a fairly short period but can provide results accurate to a ± 0.1 unit of pH or thereabouts.

It also uses colorimetric estimations by optical comparators with the addition of coloured indicators. It may, however, be noted that the colour of the dye depends upon the salt concentration of the unknown waters, that colloids may affect the reading, that strong oxidants in polluted waters may also affect the reading, and that buffer solutions are affected by the dissolved CO_2.

Measurement of pH by electrometry involves estimation of the electromotive force between a calomel electrode and an indicator. The potential is a linear function of the pH. The indicator is a glass electrode that needs to be checked (it may be "contaminated" by contact with colloidal residues).

1.3 rH

The battery-powered pH meters used in fieldwork have a needle that moves on a dial. They are sometimes used with a redox cell that gives the rH or oxidation-reduction potential, the relationship between the rH and pH being given by the formula

$$rH = \frac{Eh}{29} + 2\mathbf{pH}.$$

Eh is the potential recorded by a hydrogen electrode (expressed in millivolts and with its sign).

Measurement of the oxidation-reduction potential is extremely useful when the water that is being examined contains organic matter. The amount of dissolved oxygen may be negative and the BOD may indicate the amount of oxygen needed for the degradation of organic matter without, however, indicating the rate at which this used water will consume oxygen.

The redox potential is based on the fact that reduction and oxidation are transfers of electrons, with oxidation corresponding to a loss of electrons and reduction to a gain in electrons and also because within a liquid there is an electronic and thermodynamic balance between reducers, oxidants, and various other substances (COLAS, CABAUD, VIVIER).

In practice the rH is represented by a single figure between 0 and 35.

A low value indicates a medium that is more reducing than does a high value.

—In pure waters, with very little organic matter, the rH is between 30 and 32; it is improved by the synthesis of chlorophyll.

—In lagoon waters, above the water plants, the rH is from 30 to 31.

—In a rough water course it is from 25 to 27 (as a disturbed flow will circulate reducing compounds).

—In zones rich in hydrogen sulphide it varies from 10 to 12.

1.4 Electrical Conductivity

Electrical conductivity, expressed in microsiemens/cm, is the conductance of a water column between two metallic electrodes with a surface of 1 cm², separated from each other by 1 cm.

The electrical conductivity of absolutely pure water is about 0.036 × μS/cm (HOHLRAUSCH and HEYDWILLER, 1894). The conductivity of water in a river, however, increases with the content of dissolved electrolysable salts and increases further with the mobility of its ions as a result of a rise in temperature.

There is an increase in the content of electrolysable salts when the regions through which a water course has passed have a high content of various salts, when the water has been on such terrain for a long time, and when the water-terrain contact has been extensive in relation to the water course. On the other hand, there is a reduction in the content of alluvial deposits when there is a large inflow of almost chemically pure water, for example, water from melting snow.

The following provide an example of considerable variations in the electrical conductivity of natural waters (P. LAMARQUE):

—sea water, 35,000 × μS/cm
—water from a limestone stream, 400–500 × μS/cm
—water from a primary terrain stream, 20 × μS/cm
—water from certain mountain lakes, 10 × μS/cm
—distilled water in ordinary conditions, 3.3 × μS/cm
—chemically pure water, 0.036 × μS/cm

Table 8. Table for calculating resistivity of water depending upon temperature

Degrees	Coefficient	5/10	Degrees	Coefficient	5/10
5	1.427	1.404	16	1.048	1.035
6	1.381	1.359	17	1.024	1.012
7	1.339	1.318	18	1.000	0.989
8	1.299	1.280	19	0.978	0.967
9	1.261	1.243	20	0.956	0.946
10	1.225	1.209	21	0.936	0.926
11	1.192	1.176	22	0.916	0.906
12	1.160	1.143	23	0.897	0.888
13	1.130	1.115	24	0.879	0.870
14	1.101	1.088	25	0.861	0.852
15	1.074	1.060			

Example: water temperature = 10°C; conductivity = 3200 ohms (Ω)
3200/1.209 = 2640
resistivity = 1/0.00264 = 378 mhos/cm or 378 μS/cm

1.5 Mechanical Properties

Among the mechanical properties of water it may be noted that its density reaches a maximum at 4°C and 1 atm. This property forms one of the bases of the metric system. Expansion above the point of maximal density results in water bodies freezing in winter with ice on the surface and not at the bottom.

Water has the highest specific heat among all usual solids and liquids as well as the highest latent heat of fusion (except for ammonia) and of evaporation among all liquids. Temperature changes in water are always gradual and slow.

Dissolved salts increase the density of water and reduce its freezing point.

Sound is transmitted at 1435 m/s at 8°C.

With regard to its optical properties, water absorbs orange and red rays, whence the blue colour of the light transmitted by a thick layer. Light, therefore, increases the number of calories in a water mass. The absorbed infrared light causes a warming. The transmitted light provides an illumination on which photosynthesis is dependent.

Each type of fresh water has a particular reaction and absorption spectrum.

Movement of organisms as well as masses of water (convection currents) is easier in warm water than in cold; pressure reduces viscosity as opposed to what happens with other liquids.

2. CHEMICAL CONSTITUENTS

2.1 Classification of Waters Based on Their Chemical Properties

Natural water and water from water courses are classified as follows:
- Sea water contains 32–37‰ of salts, especially sodium chloride.
- Fresh water, a general term, comprises:
  - distilled water containing only dissolved gases, O_2, CO_2 and N,
  - natural rain water that contains dissolved minerals,
  - water from streams:
    - crystalline: 10 mg/l of calcium salt
    - limestone: Lake Leman, 160–170 mg/l of $CaSO_4$
      Doubs, 150–200 mg/l of $CaCO_3$
      Mont-Cenis Lake, 400 mg to 1 g/l of $CaSO_4$
      Rhine, 1–3 g/l of chlorides

Classification of waters results in different terminologies depending upon whether we are considering the sodium chloride content, the content of calcium salts, or fermentable organic matter.

Depending upon the sodium chloride content we have:
- salt marshes, salts > 40‰, hyperhaline
- sea waters, 40‰ > salts > 30‰, euhaline
- waters of some lakes, 30‰ > salts > 5‰, mixohaline

There are also a number of intermediate types in coastal lagoons.

It is considered that 5 g/l of salts is a constraint for typical freshwater fauna except for fish that have a system of osmoregulation.

In inland waters, we refer to soft and hard water depending on whether it contains less than 20 mg/l or more than 100 mg/l of calcium (in the forms of bicarbonates and sulphates).

2.2 Oxygen

a) Origin

The amount of oxygen in water depends upon temperature: if there is an increase in temperature the solubility of oxygen is reduced. It also depends upon atmospheric pressure: if there is an increase in pressure the solubility of oxygen is increased. Table 9 gives the solubility of oxygen in water (in mg/l) at normal pressure (76 mm Hg) and at temperatures ranging from 0 to 35°C.

The oxygen comes from contact of water with the air. The coefficient of absorption of water is 1/32 for oxygen and 1/65 for nitrogen (there are 210 cm^3 of oxygen and 790 cm^3 of nitrogen in a litre of air). At 1/32 there are 6.4 cm^3 of oxygen in a litre of water. Dissolution is facilitated by stirring. There may be a supersaturation where, in fish culture, we use a compressor or a GIFFARD injector; the water, with a milky appearance, may cause a gaseous embolism in fish.

Oxygen in water is also of biological origin, due to the chlorophyll activity of plants of the periphyton in fast-flowing streams, planktonic algae in ponds and lakes, and aquatic phanerogams in the littoral zones of stretches of water. It also leads to a supersaturation if the aquatic flora is abundant and the level of insolation high.

b) Consumption

Respiration: plankton, plants, fish, and crustaceans breathe. They have no heat regulation systems, and it is the temperature that regulates their respiration (VANTHOFF law).

Plankton grows at a very low temperature; the rate of metabolism is slow, the oxygen solubility is high, and conditions for the proliferation of plankton are very good. When, however, the amount of dissolved oxygen decreases, there is a high death rate, a "slaughter" of plankton. Some culicids (*Chaoborus*) and some metazoans such as *Oligochaetes* and *Tubifex* can exist without oxygen.

The requirement of oxygen for fish depends upon the species; salmonids, for example, need more than do cyprinids; the critical concentration is, however, higher in summer than in winter because of the greater activity of organisms that consume oxygen. It may be assumed (M. NISBET) that in piscicultural waters it should not be less than 5 mg/l for more than 8 hours in a day and in salmonid waters it should always be at least 6 mg/l, preferably 7 mg/l.

Table 9. Amounts of dissolved oxygen (after MORTIMER, 1974)

Temp., °C	Cs, mgO_2/l	ΔCs, mgO_2/l	Temp., °C	Cs, mgO_2/l	ΔCs, mgO_2/l
0	14.64	0.0925	20	9.08	0.0481
1	14.22	0.0890	21	8.90	0.0467
2	13.82	0.0857	22	8.73	0.0453
3	13.44	0.0827	23	8.57	0.0440
4	13.09	0.0798	24	8.41	0.0427
5	12.74	0.0771	25	8.25	0.0415
6	12.42	0.0745	26	8.11	0.0404
7	12.11	0.0720	27	7.96	0.0393
8	11.81	0.0697	28	7.82	0.0382
9	11.53	0.0675	29	7.69	0.0372
10	11.26	0.0653	30	7.56	0.0362
11	11.01	0.0633	31	7.43	
12	10.77	0.0614	32	7.30	
13	10.53	0.0595	33	7.18	
14	10.30	0.0577	34	7.07	
15	10.08	0.0559	35	6.95	
16	9.86	0.0543	36	6.84	
17	9.66	0.0527	37	6.73*	
18	9.46	0.0511	38	6.63	
19	9.27	0.0496	39	6.53*	

*Values not provided by Mortimer and calculated with the help of a regression formula.
Column 1: Temperature, in degrees Celsius.
Column 2: Solubility (Cs) of oxygen in milligrams of O_2 per litre in pure water in the presence of air saturated with moisture containing 20.94% (v/v) of oxygen and at a pressure of 1 013 mbar (MORTIMER, 1974).
Column 3: Variation in solubility (ΔCs) for a total salinity of 1 g/l (MONTGOMERY, 1964).*

The dissolved oxygen is normally 35% of the volume of gases dissolved in water. The coefficient of absorption of water is 1/32 for oxygen and 1/65 for nitrogen. At 1/32 there is 6/4 cm^3 of oxygen in one litre of water.

For the same absolute value of dissolved oxygen content the percentage of saturation decreases with temperature.

c) Sampling and measurement

There are some kits used for sampling and measurement of oxygen in water, either by titration (WINKLER method) or by colorimetry or by analysers with an electrolytic cell.

Analysis by the WINKLER method is the most frequently adopted one and also the cheapest. The method involves filling a flask of 125 ml in a stream, stretch of water, or reservoir, holding the flask horizontally in such a way that no air bubble is formed, and filling the flask to the top. We then insert the stopper, ensuring that absolutely no air bubble has entered the flask. If this first attempt is not successful, we carry out the same operation again. The oxygen fixation must be immediate, as well as the record of temperature in the flask.

The WINKLER fixation technique involves the following steps:

– Open the flask carefully.

– Introduce 0.5 cm^3 of manganese chloride ($MnCl_2 4H_2O$) 50% followed by 0.5 cm^3 of iodized soda (100 g NaOH + 200 cm^3 H_2O + 30 g KI), always using the same pipette for the same product (unless measuring flasks are available).

– Put the stopper back on the flask, **ensuring that there is no air bubble** in it (if there is one, begin all over again).

– In the flask a reddish-brown flaky precipitate is formed that is left to settle for 15 min.

– Open the flask and, with a clean pipette, add 2 cm^3 of sulphuric acid (H_2SO_4, 50%).

The precipitate dissolves and the liquid becomes brownish-yellow.

The flask is then classified and listed.

Measurement can be carried out in the field or in a laboratory.

The WINKLER measurement technique consists in:

– taking 50 cm^3 from a flask of 125 cm^3 that is introduced in a beaker in the presence of a paste of starch or preferably thiodene.

– titrating, using a burette filled with a solution of sodium hyposulphite (N/80 $Na_2S_2O_3$) prepared in a measuring flask of one litre with 10 cm^3 of amyl alcohol (or isobutyl alcohol) till the 50 cm^3 that is being titrated becomes colourless.

Calculation:

The volume of $Na_2S_2O_3$ noted $\times$ 2 = the number of mg of oxygen contained in a litre of the water sample; the temperature level in the water enables us to assess the percentage of oxygen saturation.

Equipment:

The kit for fixation of dissolved oxygen usually contains three flasks for sampling the water to be measured, three flasks containing products needed for the fixation, and, in the stopper, pipettes needed for measurement and introduction of these products in the sampling flasks together with a thermometer.

d) BOD

The biochemical oxygen demand is measured by comparison between the immediate dissolved oxygen content and what remains five days after preservation of the second 125 cm^3 sample in a dark place within an incubator regulated at 25°C.

Pure waters, generally, have a very low BOD as compared to residual waters with a high organic matter content, which uses up a large amount of oxygen.

2.3 Carbon Balance

a) Effect of CO_2

Carbon dioxide, free and dissolved in water, is a necessary balancing factor to prevent the precipitation of carbonates. By dissolving, it forms a weak acid, H_2CO_3, that reacts with bases to form acid carbonates and bicarbonates $(HCO_3)_n$ – acid carbonate – $(CO_3)_n$ – bicarbonate. Carbonates are almost insoluble, while bicarbonates are highly soluble. There is a chemical balance between the two salts and the free carbon dioxide

$$\underset{\text{bicarbonate}}{Ca(HCO_3)_2} \rightleftarrows \underset{\text{carbonate}}{CaCO_3} + \underset{\text{dissolved carbon dioxide (biacid)}}{CO_2 + H_2O}$$

The solubility of the bicarbonate is 13 mg/l (NISBET).

In pure water CO_2 dissolves, causing a decrease in the pH: on the other hand, in natural water, depending upon the calcium or magnesium content, we observe that the neutralization of carbon dioxide by one or other of the bases results in a progressive increase in the pH.

During a 24 hour cycle, at night when the respiration of aquatic plant and animal organisms results in the release of CO_2, there is a solubilization of the existing carbonate and a transformation to a bicarbonate. During the day, in contrast, some portion of the CO_2 is used up by plant organisms for photosynthesis. A part of the bicarbonates is transformed to carbonates resulting in an increase in the pH, as noted at the end of the day, for example, during the summer in ponds. This part is the "aggressive" part of the CO_2; the other part, which ensures the aforementioned chemical balance, is the "balancing" part of the CO_2.

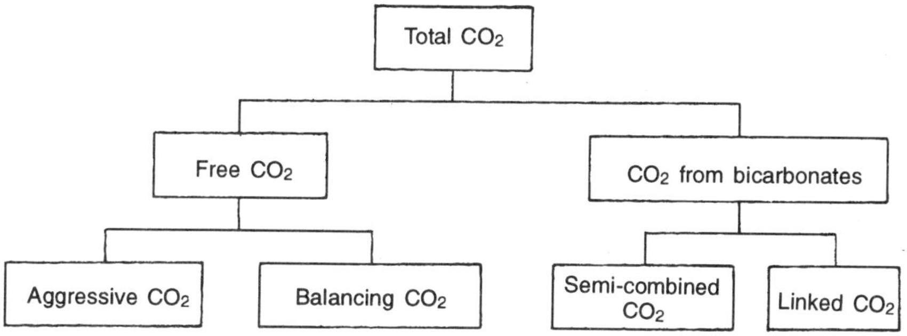

Fig. 19. Forms of CO_2 according to BREMOND and VUICHARD (1973)

Figure 20 shows the two points of neutralization of the biacid at pH 6.4 and pH 10.25. Below pH 8.3 there are no carbonates and above it there is no free carbon dioxide; the bicarbonate is observed between pH 9.5 and pH 11.4.

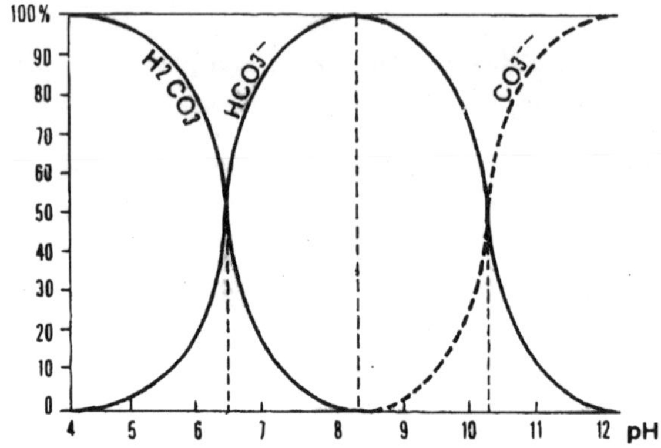

Fig. 20. Changes in carbonates depending upon pH, according to DUSSART (1966)

Since these combinations are with a base it may be assumed that the amount of free CO_2 enabling photosynthesis depends on the amount of dissolved calcium and it is, therefore, the latter that must be ascertained.

b) *Hardness*

Total hardness—TA—corresponds to the total amount of calcium and magnesium salts (carbonates, nitrates, sulphates of calcium or magnesium).

Temporary hardness—TAC—alkalinity, disappears on boiling. It corresponds to the bicarbonate $Ca(HCO_3)_2$.

Permanent hardness is the difference between total and temporary hardness: calcium and magnesium salts other than carbonates and bicarbonates.

c) *Measurement*

Free CO_2: Collect a sample without any bubbles. In 100 cm^3 of water, pour 20 drops of 1% phenolphthalein and after this with the special burette introduce N/25 soda till a pink colour is observed that persists for 10 min. after the last addition of soda.

Let N be the volume of this soda.

Conduct the same operation with 100 ml of distilled water, boiled for half an hour and cooled.

Let N′ be the volume of soda used.

The amount of CO_2 in the water is: $(N - N') \times 8.8$ mg/l.

Total hardness—TA

Fill the special burette keeping the level of the alkalimetric fluid at the zero mark.

Pour a few drops of phenolphthalein in the 100 cm^3 sample of the water to be analysed.

With the burette, pour the N/25 alkalimetric fluid, drop by drop, till the pink liquid becomes colourless.

The TA is then read off directly from the burette.

Note: If, after addition of a few drops of phenolphthalein in the water that is being examined, the liquid remains colourless it is because the TA is zero: this is generally the case for natural waters where the pH is lower than 8.3.

Temporary hardness—TAC

The same process is used, with phenolphthalein being replaced by methyl orange.

If the titre is more than 30°, take only 50 cm^3 of water and multiply the result read off the burette by 2.

2.4 Nitrogenous Substances

Nitrogen is useful in an aquatic medium in the forms of its combinations that constitute a veritable cycle with mineral compounds: ammonium nitrites and nitrates.

It comes, with rain water, through the soil (percolation of nitrates) and by fixation of atmospheric nitrogen (symbiotic bacteria of leguminous plants and aquatic Cyanophyceae (*Anabaena*); it comes also from animal residues (large quantities of dead plankton release urea). The proteins that result from this are sedimented and released subsequently in solution by **ammonization**.

$$R - CH \begin{matrix} \nearrow NH_2 \\ \searrow COOH \end{matrix} \rightarrow R - CH \begin{matrix} \nearrow OH \\ \searrow CO_2H \end{matrix} + NH_3$$

regarding the attack of amino acids

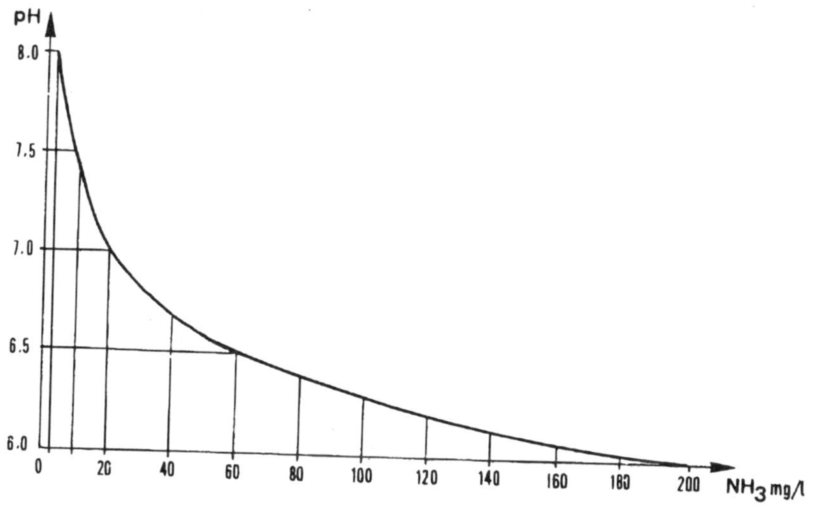

Fig. 21. Concentration of NH_3 depending upon pH according to BREMOND and VUICHARD (1973)

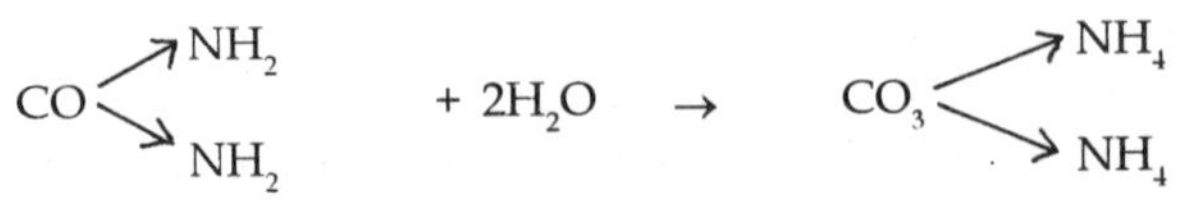

regarding the transformation of urea.

By **nitrification**, which is only possible in the presence of oxygen, ammonia NH_3 becomes a nitrite NO_2 and another nitrite NO_2 becomes a nitrate NO_3.

Denitrification occurs in aerobiosis; bacteria are responsible for reduction, from which they draw their energy in the deep zones near the bottom of lakes and ponds.

Nitrates, the most oxygenated forms of nitrogen, are found in natural waters. Their content varies with the season and, depending upon the origin of the waters, it varies from 1 to 15 mg/l with an optimal content of 2 to 3 mg/l.

Nitrites, intermediary forms resulting from the oxidation of organic matter, are undesirable. They remain only in mediums where there is very little oxygen because, since they are unstable, they have a tendency to oxidize to nitrates.

Ammonium salts, reducers, are found in artificial lakes and in newly constructed ponds and dams and are also due to the decomposition of organic matter in flooded terrain. Since aquatic vegetation generates a large amount of oxygen the medium is favourable for a rapid transformation of these salts to nitrites and nitrates, except in the deep zones.

In water courses they are, on the other hand, indicators of pollution, especially in waters that are poor in oxygen and have a heavy inflow of ammonium salts (M. NISBET).

2.5 Organic Matter

Organic matter is seen in the form of primordial molecules (e.g., proteins, glucosides, lipids, vitamins) or, more frequently, at various stages of degradation by oxidation.

It is detected clearly by chromatography; most often the overall amounts are given by measurement of the oxidizability and the biochemical oxygen demand (BOD), which, instead of permanganate, uses potassium dichromate in a sulphur medium.

Normal river water absorbs less than 1 mg/l of oxygen. Normal pond water absorbs 2 to 5 mg/l. In polluted rivers the oxidizability ranges from 2 to 20 mg/l and sometimes more (M. NISBET).

2.6 Metalloids

a) *Phosphorus* present in water is from the dissolution of rocks; soils firmly retain phosphates and very few phosphates are carried away by water.

It originates from agricultural wastes (the Rhine carries more than 1800 t of phosphates every year to Constance) and urban effluents: detergents containing foam-producing adjuvants (polyphosphates of soda). It originates also from bacterial activity (phosphatases) and organic phosphorus is also found (the nucleoproteins).

The limited amounts of phosphorus in clean streams (less than 0.1 mg/l) may increase considerably (to as much as 200 mg/l), which, without being directly harmful, causes an excessive growth of algae (which concentrate as much as 10 times the amount of normally utilized phosphorus). The algae form a thick carpet on the surface of stretches of water, decompose, and cause a dangerous reduction, for fish, in the amount of dissolved oxygen. These algae are also responsible for an unpleasant taste in the fish. Excess phosphates are almost impossible to eliminate because of their stability. It may be noted that increasing amounts of phosphorus compounds are being used in agricultural pesticides: all these compounds are more or less poisonous.

b) *Sulphur* is present in the forms of sulphates and sulphides. Sulphates come from inflows or infiltrations in gypsum terrains ($CaSO_4$). At 18°C, water dissolves 2 g/l of sulphates. They result also from oxidation of pyrites and bacterial activity such as that of chlorothiobacteria, rhodothiobacteria, and the leucothiobacteria at the bottom of lakes and ponds. This activity may, in two stages, oxidize H_2S (hydrogen sulphide) to SO_4 (sulphate):

$$2H_2S + O_2 \rightarrow S_2 + 2H_2O$$

$$S_2 + 3O_2 + 2H_2O \rightarrow 2H_2SO_4$$

c) *Chlorine* comes as a result of leaching from rocks and soils by natural waters. It is important to know the chloride content because of its effect on some stenohaline species affected by the extent of "chlorinity" in water.

It is measured by titration with a solution of silver nitrate and potassium chromate, as an indicator that results in a reddish colour of silver chromate.

2.7 Metals

a) Calcium and magnesium

As already mentioned, calcium, magnesium, and carbon dioxide are closely linked in very important chemical reactions for elaboration of living material contained in water at the expense of mineral elements.

Waters with less than 6 mg/l of calcium are unsuitable for fish life.

Those with 6–20 mg/l are not very productive.

Those with 20–60 mg/l are fairly productive.

Those with 60–160 mg/l are the **best waters for fish culture**.

Beyond 160 mg/l, waters are hard, encrusting, and not very suitable for aquatic life (M. NISBET).

Calcium and magnesium are measured by complexometric titration in two stages:

1. The total amount (calcium + magnesium) can be determined using complexon III (disodium salt of ethylene-diamine-tetra acetic acid) in a buffer medium with a small amount of ammonia (pH = 9); eriochrome T black is used as an indicator (changeover from red to blue).

2. The calcium alone is measured using the same complexon with a soda medium (pH = 12) and murexide as an indicator.

The difference gives us the content of magnesium (Colas, Cabaud, Vivier); it may be noted that in the Paris basin there are relatively high contents of magnesium, especially in the Valois (from 18 to 32 mg/l).

b) Iron and manganese

Iron is not frequently found in water but is sometimes present in the form of ferric oxides and black sulphides. Iron in ponds acts as a sterilizer in the form of humates that are difficult to detect and the content of iron is especially high in boggy terrain.

The iron cycle is linked to those of CO_2 and oxygen; in water we find soluble ferrous carbonate that may be precipitated when:

the pH is 7 or less or

the oxygen is 0.5 mg/l or less.

Ferrous carbonate may be found in acid water with more than 0.5 mg/O_2/l, but there is no direct attack or immediate reduction: this occurs above a pH of 6.5 in the presence of organic matter.

$4Fe(HCO_3)_2 + O_2 + 2H_2O \rightarrow 8CO_2 + 4Fe(OH)_3$, which is precipitated.

Manganese, even less frequently observed, is likely to oxidize or be reduced but, unlike iron, it is more easily reduced than oxidized.

From a biological point of view it is important for certain genera of molluscs (*Ancylus* and *Ancyllastrum*). As a catalyser in water it improves fish yields.

2.8 · Suspended Matter

Water carries small particles of solid matter in suspension that can be assessed, in terms of weight, by centrifugation and sedimentation.

This matter affects fish in an aquatic medium directly, thickening the epithelial cells of the gills (Herbert and Alabaster), or by a harmful effect on the eggs, changes in the natural body movements or movements from one place to another, or even a reduction of the biomass produced ordinarily by the medium.

This effect is noted whenever the amount of suspended matter is more than 25 mg/l, and productivity in terms of fish is extremely low, or even nil, when it is more than 400 mg/l.

D. BIOTIC COMPONENTS

1. PLANT FORMATIONS (Barbe, 1984)

1.1 Free-floating Plants

The root system is poorly developed, since it plays no role in fixation: these are small plants (1 mm to 5 cm) specially adapted for floating because of the spaces in their tissues. They develop exclusively in lentic facies.

– Pteridophytes (ferns), e.g., *Azolla* sp., *Salvinia natans*.

– Spermatophytes (or phanerogams), e.g., *Lemna* sp., *Spirodela* sp., *Hydrocharis* sp., *Wolffia arrhiza*.

Phytoplankton is composed of unicellular or colonial algae that live freely within the water, their relative mobility being due to the existence of flagella or, most often, to gaseous exchanges with the ambient medium.

These algae grow in calm waters: lakes, ponds, water meadows, and dead ends of large water courses in the plains. In deep lakes they remain in the superficial layers where there is an adequate penetration of light to enable photosynthesis.

The proliferation of some species results in various colours in the water and they may also form large masses on the surface or be deposited on the banks; they are referred to as "water flowers". A colour of wine lees is observed for *Oscillatoria rubescens*, and blue or green for some Cyanophyceae (such as *Aphanizomenon*) or Chlorophyceae (such as *Pediastrum-Scenedesmus*).

All these organisms are among the primary producers that elaborate their own material from dissolved salts, carbon dioxide, and the energy of light; they provide food for small invertebrates (rotifers, cladocerans, copepods) and for some planktotrophic fish (coregons, roaches, dace).

1.2 Benthic Plants

a) Fungi and bacteria

Fungi and bacteria are organisms with no chlorophyll that, as opposed to all other plants, are heterotrophic, can live in darkness, and synthesize their own material from dissolved organic substances or those in the course of transformation. This particular feature explains why they sometimes develop on a massive scale in residuary effluents or in systems where there is a high organic content. Some species specialize in transforming particular substances such as cellulose (cellulobacteria), iron (ferrobacteria), and sulphur (sulphobacteria), but the most easily observable forms in polluted aquatic systems are macroscopic colonies. These colonies look like flakes, cotton wool, downy filaments called "sheep tails" or "lamb tails", or even "bird lime". Their formations colonize all the substrates by forming somewhat filamentous masses, generally whitish or greyish, and viscous to the touch. The most frequently observed groups are:

among the fungi,

—*Leptomitus* with a milky colour

—*Fusarium aquaeductum* of a brick-red colour, covering canalizations and the crests of dams (with a preference for high velocity flows)

among the bacteria,

—*Beggiatoa, Sphaerotilus, Cladothrix, Leptothrix, Crenothrix, Zoogloea*

Based on the fact that some organisms develop selectively in waters polluted by organic matter we may suggest a list of species considered to be indicative of certain degrees of organic pollution.

Among these indicators are filamentous algae that form macroscopic colonies, and bacteria and fungi whose development corresponds to extremely high contents of organic matter, nitrogen, or phosphorus.

b) Algae that form the primary biological cover of submerged supports

In flowing waters and the borders of lakes, these algae, among which are diatoms, colonize all the supports; they form a brownish slippery film (of ≤ 1 mm) on the surface of stones and pebbles. Some of these, which cover the macrophytes with a type of sheath, are part of the periphyton.

Diatoms are unicellular or colonial algae, solitary or filamentous, with a finely decorated siliceous structure formed of two valves fitted together that contain the organism. Groups of species may be used to evaluate the quality of streams.

c) Algae that form non-filamentous macroscopic colonies

This type of formation includes colonial algae that belong to different groups:

– Chlorophyceae such as *Palmella*,
– Rhodophyceae such as *Batrachospermum*,
– Cyanophyceae such as *Nostoc*,
– Chrysophyceae such as *Hydrurus foetidus*.

In all these cases the thallus forms a gelatinous mass, loose or globular, attached to benthic supports.

Hydrurus foetidus develops mainly in salmonid waters, the forward portion of the population moving downstream in cold weather and confining itself progressively to upstream sectors when the waters are warm.

Some colonies form gelatinous green or bluish masses that have irregular lobes (*Palmella*) or are globular (*Nostoc*); others are somewhat irregularly branched in the form of fingers (*Hydrurus*) or a string of beads resembling amphibian eggs (*Batrachospermum*). All these forms develop generally in cold or cool waters.

d) Algae forming filamentous macroscopic colonies

Filaments, branched or otherwise, constitute colonies of variable shapes, colour, and texture.

• Filaments grouped in the form of cushions on the surfaces of stones and pebbles—rough to the touch—with a frequent alternation of light and dark green rings (*Vaucheria*)

• Long filaments (5–40 cm) green in colour
– unbranched, viscous to the touch (*Spirogyra*)
– irregularly branched (*Cladophora*)
– dichotomously branched (*Dichotomosiphon*), of a violet, black, or brownish shade, rough to the touch (*Lemanea*)

• Short filaments in small colonies (2–5 cm)
– branched, red or violet (*Audouinella*)
– branched, green (*Stigeoclinium*)
– unbranched, pale green (*Ulothrix*)

e) Macroscopic algae containing calcium forming a carpet at the bottom of still waters (ponds and lakes)

By their external morphology and size, these algae resemble more developed plants such as the ceratophylls and horsetails.

The plant itself has a principal "stem" with regular whorls, "branches", and "leaves". On the other hand, the structure of these elements with a simple shape cannot be compared with that of higher plants.

Incrustation of all the growing parts results in a rough and rigid texture, often brittle; these benthic algae belong to the family of **Characeae**.

The depth, associated with the transparence at which these algae grow, provides a synthetic indication of the quality of water, which improves when they are found at a low depth.

f) Liverworts

The growing vegetative structure is seen in the form of green leafy blades (liverworts with a thallus), which may be wide, or with a "stem" and "leaves" in two rows (except for *Fissidens*—moss).

- Liverworts with a thallus:

—thallus in the shape of a bifid blade, plant floating freely (*Riccia fluitans*),

—thallus trailing over stones or exposed alluvium,

—upper side of the thallus with no stomata or air cavity, plant often submerged (*Pellia*),

—upper side of the thallus with stomata and air cavities, plant rarely submerged,

—stomata visible to the naked eye (*Fegatella conica*),

—stomata visible only at high magnification (*Marchantia polymorpha*).

- Liverworts with leaves:

—bilobed leaves, dorsal leaf smaller than the ventral (*Scapania*),

—non-lobed leaves (*Chiloscyphus polyanthus*).

The presence of this species, found in water sources and streams, indicates the freshness of water (stenothermal cold-water species).

g) Mosses and peat mosses

Mosses have stems and leaves arranged in at least three rows (except for *Fissidens*) and are attached to the substrate by rhizoids (holdfasts) that enable them to resist high current velocities.

During periods of low water level they dry up and are reactivated at a more favourable period. Generally grouped in very dense populations, they are in this way able to retain the slight humidity needed for survival. They provide the preferred habitat for many benthic vertebrates.

Some species form brushes (of a few cm) on the surfaces of rocks, while others have ribbon-like structures that move with the currents (*Fontinalis*).

In marshes and boggy areas there are dense populations of peat mosses, elements that grow continuously, contributing to the formation of peat.

Where there are seepages, in damp and shady areas near water sources, on paving stones and rocks, we find mosses belonging to the genus *Cratoneurum* or *Cinclidotus*.

Within the currents there is a growth of constantly submerged mosses such as *Fontinalis, Leptodyctium,* or *Plathypnidium.*

h) Phanerogams attached to submerged leaves: Submerged hydrophytes

Strictly aquatic plants whose existence depends on the permanence of a water layer, these plants are attached to the substrate and their entire vegetative structure is under water: on the surface of the water we only see their reproductive organs (for sexual reproduction, flowers).

Many representatives of this category have slender stems and filiform leaves that offer limited resistance; this is, for example, noted in *Ranunculus fluitans,*

Potamogeton pectinatus or *P. mucronatus, P. trichoides*, capable of growing in the entire volume of a pond, *Ranunculus aquatilis*, or *Myriophyllum spicatum*.

Among the forms with spreading or well-developed leaves are many species of the genus *Potamogeton*, such as *P. densus, P. crispus, P. lucens*, and *P. perfoliatus*, as well as many other mainly lacustrine plants such as *Elodea canadensis* or those in water courses such as *Callitriche obtusangula*.

i) Attached phanerogams with floating leaves: Floating hydrophytes

Attached to the substrate, these species spread the lamina of their leaves on the water surface. They are found in lentic waters at fairly low depths (1–7 m).

The leaves are generally large and have stomata and air lacunae on the upper side, e.g., *Nuphar luteum, Nymphaea alba, Potamogeton natans, Polygonum amphibium*.

j) Semi-aquatic phanerogams: Helophytes

In these species the root system is in a medium constantly engorged with water but the vegetative parts develop to varying extents out of the water. These are semi-aquatic or amphibious species; among the common species are *Phragmites communis, Typha latifolia, Carex riparia, Equisetum limosum, Ranunculus lingua, Helosciadium nodiflorum, Menyanthes trifoliata, Oenanthe.*

1.3 Plant Groups

Plants are not distributed randomly in aquatic ecosystems but are found in groups, the elements of which have somewhat similar ecological requirements.

Although there may be some common species, the plant groups are different in still waters and running waters.

a) In the ecosystem of running waters

Depending upon the mode of flow and the variation in certain correlated parameters such as the gradient, the current velocity, or the texture of the bed, plants are distributed longitudinally, a flora of beds with alluvium changing progressively to one of eroded beds.

• rheocrene emergence:

Populated with liverworts such as *Fegatella conica* or *Marchantia polymorpha* and incrusting mosses that result in the formation of tufts (*Cratoneuron*).

• limnocrene sources:

Located in depressions forming puddles or small water surfaces. These sources are populated with lentiphilous cold-water species such as *Nasturtium officinale, Helosciadium nodiflorum, Mentha aquatica, Veronica anagallis, V. beccabunga*, and duckweeds (*Lemna*).

• torrential sectors and hygropetric surfaces:

Paving stones and rocks provide shelter to an often limited flora of benthic algae (diatoms) generally stenothermal, of cold water: in the less turbulent sectors there are a few mosses such as *Plathypnidium*.

• sectors with changes in flow (predominantly salmonid water courses—Rhithron):

Characterized by changes in habitats in lotic (fords) and lentic facies (deep areas and pools).

Strong currents on a substrate of rocks and pebbles are colonized by rheophilous bryophytes: *Cinclidotus aquaticus, C. fontinaloides, Fontinalis antipyretica, Calliergon giganteum, Leptodyctium riparium.*

Sandy or alluvial elements in slow currents are populated by phanerogams of water courses where there are variations in flow: *Ranunculus fluitans, Potamogeton crispus, P. perfoliatus, Helosciadium nodiflorum,* Callitriches.

• lower sectors of water courses (with a predominance of Cyprinids—Potamic):

In sectors with a gradient and a low current velocity, sediments enable the development of plants of lentic waters. Fixed flowering hydrophytes (*Nuphar, Nymphaea, Potamogeton natans, Polygonum amphibium*) colonize the riverine zones and, where the banks have a gentle slope, a succession of species are observed identical to those in ecosystems of calm waters ("water plants" of major water courses in the plains like that of the Saone or the lower area of the Doubs).

b) *In a dormant-water ecosystem*

Three zones, clearly differentiated by the nature and size of plant populations, are observed here:

• **littoral zone** colonized by macrophytes arranged in somewhat clear belts that may join up in shallow ponds,

• **well-lighted pelagic zone**, with phytoplankton, and

• **deep, dark zone**, where there is only a flora of bacteria and fungi together with a few Cyanophyceae.

• In the **littoral zone** there are plants of biologically different types identified by their position in relation to the water surface; the species are distributed, depending upon the depth, in a somewhat concentric manner (plant belts).

—*Helophytes* are amphibious with the base normally in the water, and their reproductive parts require contact with the atmosphere to develop (there may be aquatic forms but they will be sterile). Among these species, successively from the outside moving inwards, are: *Phragmites communis, Typha* sp., *Equisetum limosum,* and *Scirpus lacustris.*

—*Fixed hydrophytes with floating leaves,* bearing flowers, and having a root system; their vegetative parts grow throughout the water column on stems or leaf stalks and spread out over the water surface (leaves): *Nuphar luteum, Nymphaea alba, Potamogeton natans, Polygonum amphibium.*

—*Fixed and totally submerged hydrophytes* develop their vegetative parts within the water mass without any contact with the atmosphere. Among this group we find species that form vast grassland-like areas at the bottom of reservoirs (*Helodea canadensis, Potamogeton densus, Hippuris vulgaris, Chara* sp.).

—*Free-moving hydrophytes* without any system for attachment to the substrate can either float, like duckweed, *Salvinia natans,* or *Azolla* sp., or move about under water, like *Utricularia* sp.

• The **pelagic zone** is the preferred zone for the development of free-moving microscopic organisms that form plankton.

Plankton populations, much more complex in terms of their composition and succession than plant groups, are subject to a two-fold distribution in space and time.

Vertical distribution: Nearly all populations are confined to the first 10 m, where the metabolic processes are more common than catabolic ones. Below this zone, the

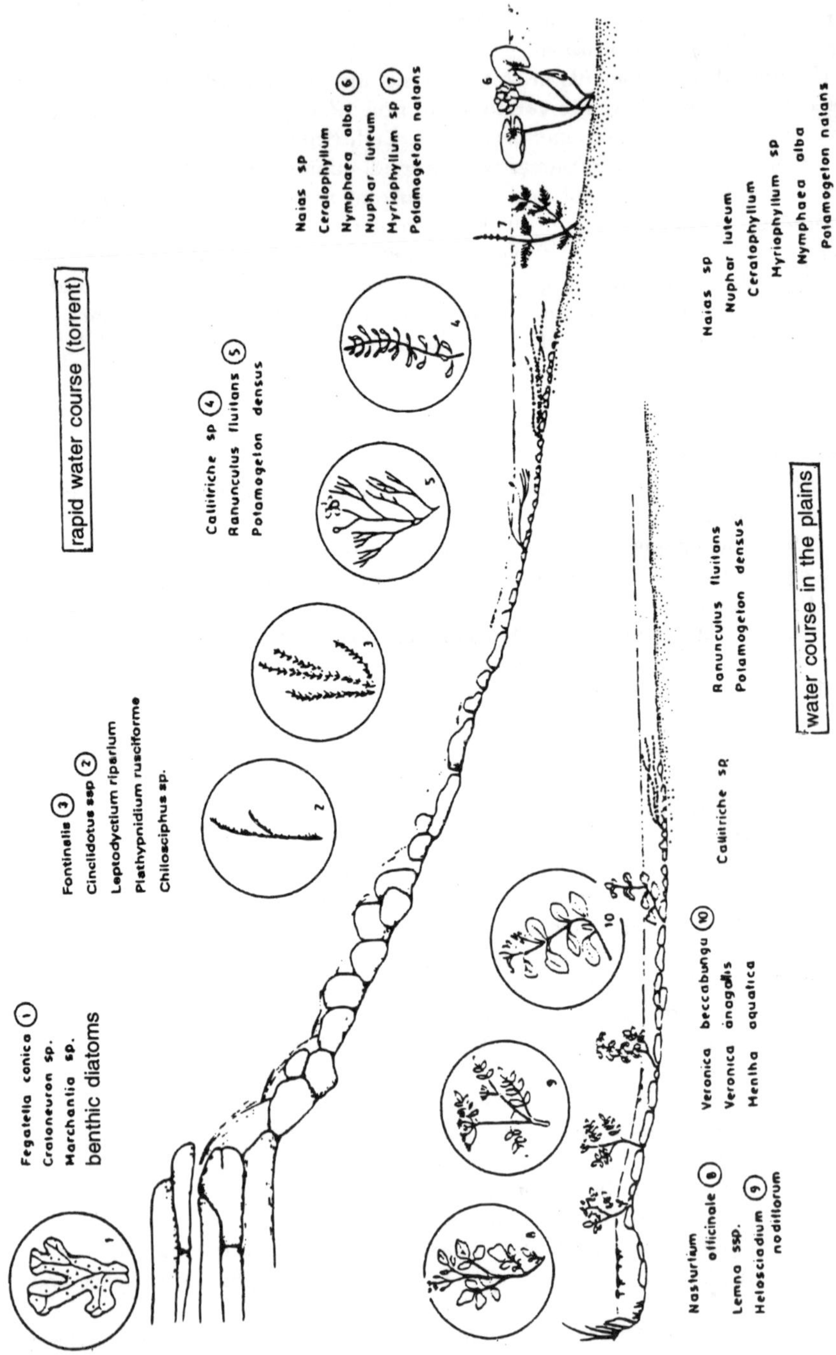

Fig. 22. Distribution of plants (lengthwise profile) in an ecosystem of flowing water (J. Barbe, 1984)

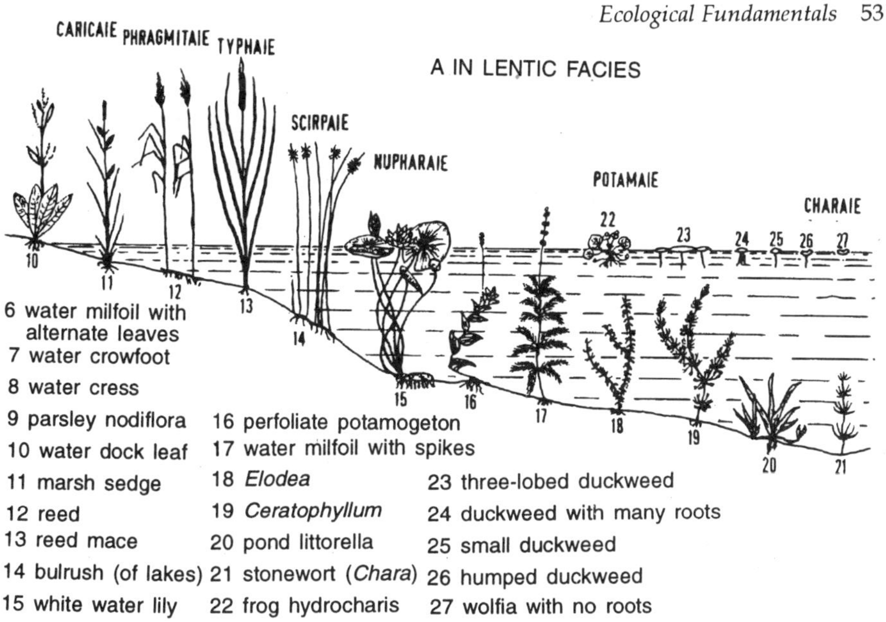

Fig. 23. Plant groups in a lentic medium (transverse section)

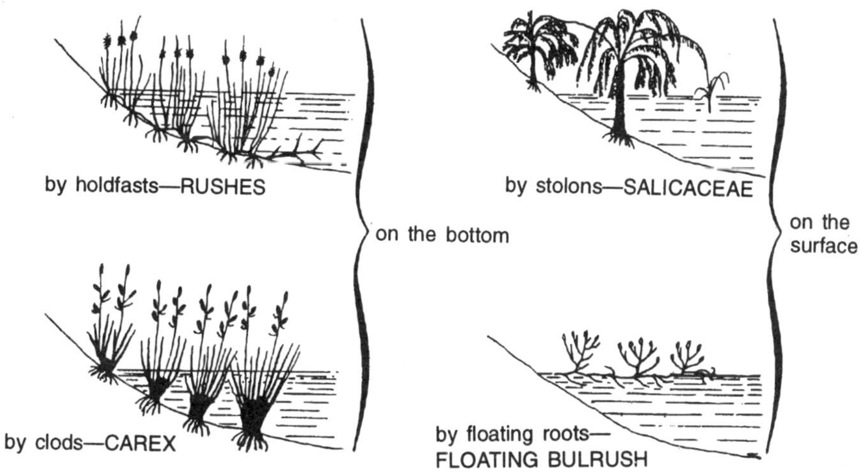

Fig. 24. Colonization of the bank in a pond

amount of incident light energy is very limited and does not enable the development of photosynthetic organisms; it is the deep zone.

Distribution in time: Because of their size and structure, plankton organisms are highly sensitive to variations in certain components of the medium (such as temperature or nutritive salts) and, therefore, are short-lived, resulting in a series of different populations in the course of an annual cycle.

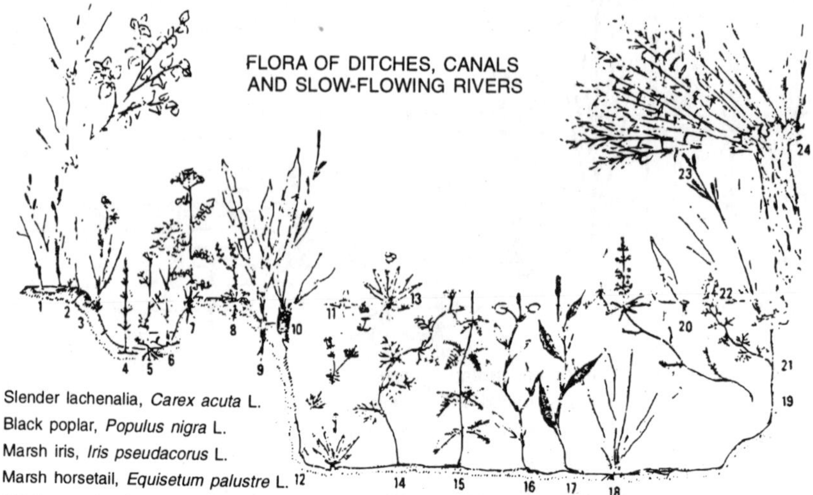

1 Slender lachenalia, *Carex acuta* L.
2 Black poplar, *Populus nigra* L.
3 Marsh iris, *Iris pseudacorus* L.
4 Marsh horsetail, *Equisetum palustre* L.
5 Fistulose water dropwort, *Oenanthe fistulosa* L.
6 Reed with pointed flowers, *Juncus sylvaticus* Reichenbach
7 Meadow sweet, *Filpendula ulmaria* L.
8 Forget-me-not, *Myosotis scorpiodes* L.
9 Water dock, *Rumex hydrolapatum* Hudson
10 Lachenalia, *Carex stricta* Good
11 Three-lobed duckweed, *Lemna trisulca* L.
12 Hornwort, *Ceratophyllum demersum* L.
13 Water soldier, *Stratiotes aloides* L.
14 Divaricated ranunculus, *Ranunculus divaricatus* Schrk.
15 Water milfoil, *Myriophyllum spicatum* L.
16 Pondweed with grassy leaves, *Potamogeton gramineus* L.
17 Glossy potamot, *Potamogeton lucens* L.
18 Arrowhead, *Sagittaria sagittifolia* L.
19 Marsh hottonia, *Hottonia palustris* L.
20 Duckweed with many roots, *Lemna polyrhiza* L.
21 Common bladderwort, *Utricularia vulgaris* L.
22 Small duckweed, *Lemna minor* L.
23 Sedge, *Carex riparia* Curt.
24 Velvet osier, *Salix viminalis* L.

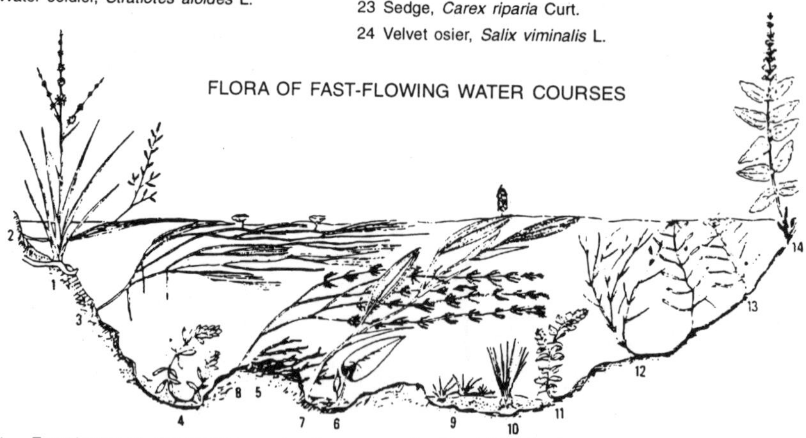

1 Erect burr reed, *Sparganium erectum* L.
2 Float grass, *Glyceria fluitans* (L) Brown
3 Floating ranunculus, *Ranunculus fluitans* Lamarck
4 Canadian elodea, *Elodea canadensis* Rich.
5 Water moss, *Fontinalis antipyretica* L.
6 Yellow pond lily, *Nuphar luteum* Sibth.
7 Glossy potamogeton, *Potamogeton lucens* L.
8 Water milfoil with alternate flowers, *Myriophyllum alternifolium* D.C.
9 Pond littorella, *Littorella lacustris* L.
10 Pond quillwort, *Isoetes lacustris* L.
11 Dense pondweed, *Potamogeton densus* L.
12 Capillary pondweed, *Potamogeton trichoides* Chamisso and Schlechtendal
13 Marsh starwort, *Callitriche palustre* L.
14 Common loose-strife, *Lythrum salicaria* L.

Fig. 25. Ecological distribution of higher aquatic and subaquatic plants (after Montegut, 1973)

These seasonal variations have immediate effects on the transparence and colour of the water. The proliferation of some algae may cause a rapid and intense colouring of the water mass. They also result in a minimal winter biomass with a predominance of diatoms, and a succession of "water flowers" after the spring warming, till the autumn.

2. ROLE OF AQUATIC PLANTS

2.1 Physicochemical Role

The daytime photosynthetic activity of plants with chlorophyll results in the production of oxygen and absorption of carbon dioxide. Whatever their forms and dimensions, plants are essential in every aquatic ecosystem.

At night there is no activity involving chlorophyll and plants, like animals, use the oxygen dissolved in water.

The amount of oxygen produced during the day depends upon the characteristics of the plant (physiological state) and the parameters relevant to the aqueous substrate (insolation, temperature, percentage of saturation of the medium).

The oxygen released, apart from enabling animal respiration, is essential in assisting oxidations (nitrifications). Fixation of carbon from carbon dioxide or bicarbonates affects their contents in the water and is accompanied by an increase in the pH. During the period of rapid growth we observe daily cycles of oxygen, pH, carbonates, and bicarbonates. Oxygen concentrations are highest at the end of the day (1900 h) and lowest at the end of the night (0600 h). Concentrations varying from 25 mg/l (200% saturation) to 3 mg/l may be noted in a 25 hour cycle in mediums with a large amount of phytoplankton. The screen formed by duckweed (*Lemna* sp.) or attached hydrophytes with floating leaves (Nymphaeaceae, *Trapa natans*) limits the penetration of light rays and the development of plants beneath it (submerged hydrophytes, phytoplankton). Simultaneously, this carpet of plants acts as a barrier between the water and the atmosphere, limiting heat exchanges and thereby causing a slight summer heat stratification (Juget and Rostan, 1973).

Nitrogenous and phosphoritic nutrition of plants takes place by direct absorption of nutritive substances in the water or sediments. In the case of macrophytes, the nutrients are consumed mainly during the period of growth (May to October).

Till fairly recently it was thought that this nutrition was due only to a diffusion of elements through the cell membranes of stems and leaves. Various experiments have since shown that some of these plants with roots can also draw their food from sediments in the same way that terrestrial plants do. Nevertheless, most of their nutrition is extracted from the ambient medium, thus enabling an improvement in the quality of the water. According to several authors, populations of vascular plants may contain 0.2–16% of the nitrogen and 1–37% of the phosphorus that is generated every year. These results have led us to estimate that a growth of plants could be a means of preventing the eutrophication of mediums.

Plants release organic subtances in water in two ways:

— One is a continuous release of excretory products in the form of organic matter dissolved by leafy stems. The phenomenon depends on various factors (Wetzel, 1969) including the concentration of cations in the water (calcium, magnesium, sodium, iron, etc.). This release may reach 20% of the amount of carbon fixed by photosynthesis.

—The other is associated with decomposition of organic matter of plant tissues. It may occur naturally during an annual cycle or be the result of certain actions (clearing of the beds, chemical treatment). These products are eventually added to the superficial sediments and re-enter the cycle of matter through the intermediary of decomposers.

Exchanges between the aquatic medium and the atmosphere take place directly at their surface of contact. The evapotranspiration of plants with floating leaves is more than evaporation from the open surface. This evapotranspiration assumes considerable importance in systems where the renewal capacity is low.

2.2 Biological Role

a) Primary production

Plants are the basic element in the food chains of aquatic biocoenoses. Production of organic matter from dissolved or colloidal substances in water is an indication of synthesis of a living organism from elementary compounds.

Vascular plants may constitute 0.7–5.1% of the total primary production of stagnant ecosystems. This annual production may appear to be limited as compared to that of planktonic or periphytic algae but, if considered only with regard to the period of growth, it is clearly greater.

Table 10. Production of plant biomass (after WETZEL, 1964)

	Average prod., mg $C/m^2/d$	Values, mg $C/m^2/d$
Phytoplankton (of the year)	249.3	10.4–524.5
Periphyton (of the year)	731.5	0.0–5760.0
Macrophytes (of the year)	76.5	0.0–982.2
Macrophytes (period of growth: 75 d)	372.3	0.0–982.2

The extent of primary production of macrophytes in the total production of a lake depends mainly on the water depth.

Concentrations of nutritive substances in waters and sediments also influence the amount of biomass produced: WESTLAKE (1963) estimated that the net annual primary productions of submerged plants in fertile lakes varied from 4 to 7 t/ha, while in a poor medium it was only 1 to 2.5 t/ha. The production of aquatic plants (helophytes) may reach 20–46 t/ha with an extreme value of the order of 75 t/ha for the gramineous *Arundo donax*.

The biomass of submerged plants (hydrophytes in the general sense) is rarely more than 1 kg of dry matter per m^2, while for aquatic macrophytes (helophytes) it may be as much as 4.5 kg of dry matter per m^2.

In lakes, plant matter is decomposed, stored in the sediments, and recycled fairly rapidly depending upon the activity of the decomposing organisms.

In flowing waters this organic matter is carried by the current, deposited, decomposed in calmer areas and, sometimes, taken downstream later during a high-water period.

b) Diversification of habitats

Plant and animal populations in an aquatic medium are closely associated not only because of the food that the former provide the latter, but also because of the support and shelter they offer. Many microscopic benthic algae (diatoms) are attached to stems or leaves of macrophytes (epiphytes).

Oxygen produced by plants may vary from 0.13 to 7.36 $g/m^2/d$ (SCULTHORPE, 1967), enabling the introduction of species that need a large amount of oxygen.

The density of microinvertebrate populations increases considerably in the presence of plants. GAUDET (1974), in England, reported that, in rivers with pebbly beds, the density of organisms was 3–4 $\times$ $10^3/m^2$; in mosses and other plants it may be as much as 40 $\times$ $10^4/m^2$.

The presence of plants also ensures an increase in the potentially useful area for benthic fauna: 1 m^2 of sediment may, depending on the nature of the vegetation, provide more than 20 m^2 of leaf surface. Plants also serve as places for egg laying and spawning of invertebrates and fish. They are also used as building material for larval sheaths of some caddis flies and cocoons for the metamorphosis of some lepidopterans.

It may also be borne in mind that a plant mass shelters organisms from their predators or from the heat of the sun in summer.

In the plant world, there is an interspecific competition. Plants with floating leaves and those that grow above the water line have an advantage in respect of light that may be a limiting factor for submerged species. PHILLIPS *et al.* (1978) have shown by experiments conducted in controlled and natural mediums that a disappearance of hydrophytes from mediums rich in nutritive substances had to be linked with a considerable development of epiphytic algae, which also disappeared after the destruction of their supports.

Plant populations in such mediums are, therefore, composed mainly of phytoplankton.

c) Source of food

Plants may be consumed directly by phytophagous organisms or indirectly by predators of the second or third order. Planktonic or benthic algae provide food for young and some adult fish (nose carp, roach, Coregonids) that form the essential mass in the food chain. Some species of fish (bream, carp, asiatic cyprinids) are herbivorous and consume leaves and stems of phanerogams. Molluscs, crustaceans, and the larvae of insects feed on aquatic plants. The coypu (*Myopotamus coypus*) has a preference for rhizomes of Nymphaeaceae or certain heliophytes.

2.3 Mechanical Role

a) Obstacle to flow

The volume occupied by plants may reach considerable dimensions in some water courses. By reducing the size of the original water section, plants cause a reduction in the flow velocity and raise the water level. In England, DAWSON (1978) indicated a reduction in flow velocity from about 0.3 to 0.1 m/s and an increase in water level of 0.2 to 0.4 m. The CHEZY-MANNING coefficient, which takes into account the roughness of the substrate and obstacles to the flow, increased from 0.03 to 0.3. Variations in this coefficient are directly connected with the plant biomass.

The existence of water plants that fix movable substrates during a period of low water level may result in changes in the beds and banks by creating erosive turbulences during a high-water period. A dense plant growth helps in sedimenting suspended particles. Organic or mineral debris trapped in it contributes to the formation of obstacles that have an adverse effect on the flow.

b) Consolidation of movable elements and fixation of banks

Deposited sediments may subsequently be fixed; plants grow on and stabilize them. Roots and rhizomes effectively consolidate layers of fine material which, in normal conditions of the flow, would have been carried downstream.

Around stagnant waters, helophytes resist the erosive effect of waves by both weakening them and fixing the elements of the substrate.

3. PROTOZOA

Like aquatic flora, aquatic fauna is examined from the ecological point of view: that is, with regard to the relationships with the medium of living organisms, both unicellular protozoa and invertebrate metazoa, which are more elaborate than the former.

3.1 Rhizopoda

Amoebae, free-moving, 100-500μ in size, are found in stagnant waters and crawl on a support (silt or the lower sides of leaves of the water lily).

Testacea are amoebae encysted in a shell, a theca. The genera *Difflugia* and *Arcella* are found in large numbers in acid waters and peat bogs.

Heliozoa are beautiful amoebae that look like suns and live among aquatic plants.

3.2 Flagellata

Flagellates move with the help of a flagellum or several flagella.

Free-moving flagellate: *Euglena*

Parasitic flagellate: *Costia necatrix* with four flagella, a parasite that attaches itself to the skin and gills of salmonids.

Octomites, an internal intestinal parasite of salmonids.

Trypanosoma cyprini, transmitted by *Piscicola*, causes anaemia in carps.

3.3 Ciliata

Sometimes invisible to the naked eye, their bodies covered with very short vibratile cilia, ciliates are abundant in stagnant water. Extremely important, because they are food for young fish. They are classified according to the arrangement of cilia on the body.

a) Holotricha

Paramecium, in water plants submerged in floods.

Spirostomum (the largest infusorian, 400 μ), in tufts of spirogyra.

Ichthyophthirius, rounded or oval, a harmful parasite on the skin of trouts.

Chilodon cyprini, on the skin, fins, and gills of carps.

b) Oligotricha: a few cilia on the body.

Tintimopsis lacustris, a small shell commonly found among plankton.

Heterotricha: cilia all over the body, some of which form a series of small collars.

Stentor, found in very pure and acid waters of mountain peat bogs. Green stentor is seen in symbiotic algae (zoochlorella), shaped like a horn attaching itself to a support by the point.

c) Hypotricha

Stylonichia, 350 μ, with cilia joined together and forming filaments, cirri; they live on spirogyra.

Peritricha, with a single collar of cirri.

Vorticella, with a pedicel that contracts like a corkscrew, found in both pure and polluted waters.

Carchesium, branched vorticella in sticky colonies in highly polluted waters.

d) Sporozoa (all parasites, causing diseases). The egg provides a spore from which one individual emerges.

Coccidia:

Eimeria cyprini develops in the intestines of carps, causing haemorrhages and anaemia.

e) Cnida or Myxosporidia (extremely important because many of these species are parasites on fish)

Myxobolus attaches itself to the skin or gills of fish and causes fish plague by ulceration.

Henneguya sporospermica sterilizes the ovaries of the pike.

Glugea infects the ovaries of trouts, causing degeneration of the eggs.

Lentospora cerebralis causes a disease like staggers in trouts (*Ichthyophorus*, a fungus, also causes this disease).

4. METAZOA

4.1 Spongiae

The body mass forms a jelly surrounded by cells: this mass is held together by rod-like cells (spicules) that may be calcareous (calcareous sponges), siliceous (siliceous sponges), or fibrous (natural bath sponges).

Spongilia: as a white crust on pebbles, this sponge lives in clean water with some organic matter.

Ephydatia lacustris: lives in the deeper parts of lakes.

Ephydatia fluviatilis: zoochlorella, green crusts in clean running waters and trout waters.

4.2 Coelenterata

The freshwater hydra, on plants and under duckweed.

4.3 Annelida (with an annulated body)

- **Oligochaeta:** with relatively few chaetae (setae) on the body.

Lumbricus or earthworm.

Tubifex: 4–5 cm long, slender, with red blood; these worms contain haemoglobin. They live in groups in the mud in highly polluted waters and emerge above the water depending upon the amount of oxygen in it, which they do not tolerate well (a phenomenon of osmosis). *Tubifex* is often mistaken for *Lumbriculus*.

Lumbriculus: This genus is larger (up to 8 cm); although generally found in polluted waters, it may also be seen in clean waters.

- **Hirudinea**

Leeches, with no chaetae, have a sucker at each end of the body. Like other annelids, they are hermaphrodite. On the dorsal side of the rings there are eyes, the number and position of which enables identification of different genera: there are two groups, one with jaws and the other with a proboscis.

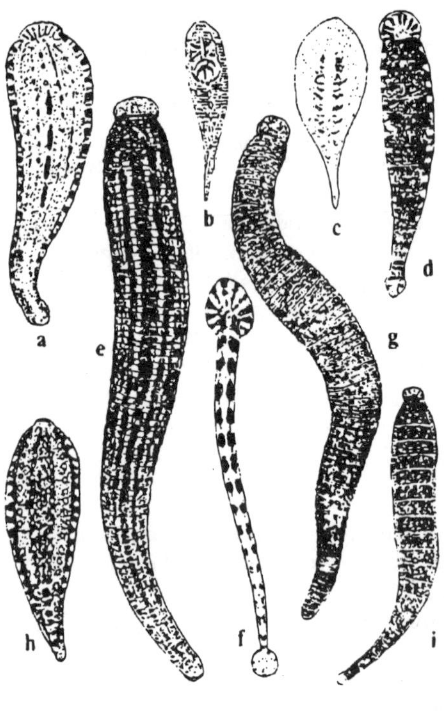

a: *Haementia* (70 mm).
b: *Helobdella* (10 mm).
c: *Glossosiphonia heteroclita* (10 mm).
d: *Hemiclepsis marginata* (30 mm).
e: *Haemopis sanguisnga* (120–150 mm).
f: *Piscicola geometra* (20–50 mm).
g: *Hirudo medicinalis* (100–150 mm).
h: *Glossosiphonia complanata* (30 min).
i: *Herpobdella octoculata*.

Fig. 26. Hirudinea

Gnathobdellida: mouth with no proboscis, three jaws, red blood.

Herpobdella atomaria: eight eyes, lives on pebbles, in slightly polluted waters, sometimes found in trout rivers.

Hirudo medicinalis: ten eyes, black, grey, white with red bands on the body, yellow abdomen, 10–15 cm long. Lives in polluted rivers and ponds, feeding on the blood of amphibians and fish.

Hirudo officinalis: green all over, similar to *H. medicinalis.*

Rhynchobdellida: with a proboscis, no jaws, white blood.

Piscicola geometra: very slender, 2–3 cm long, causing anaemia in fish on which it is a parasite (often as many as 100 on a single fish).

Hemiclepsis marginata: 15–20 mm, two pairs of eyes, sucks the blood of fish on which it is a parasite.

Glossosiphonia paludosa: 30 mm, two pairs of eyes.

Glossosiphonia complanata: 15–30 mm, three pairs of eyes on three consecutive segments.

Glossosiphonia heteroclita: 5–10 mm, three pairs of eyes on three non-consecutive segments.

Helobdella stagnalis or clepsin: with two eyes and a small mark between the 10th and 11th segments; very active parasites.

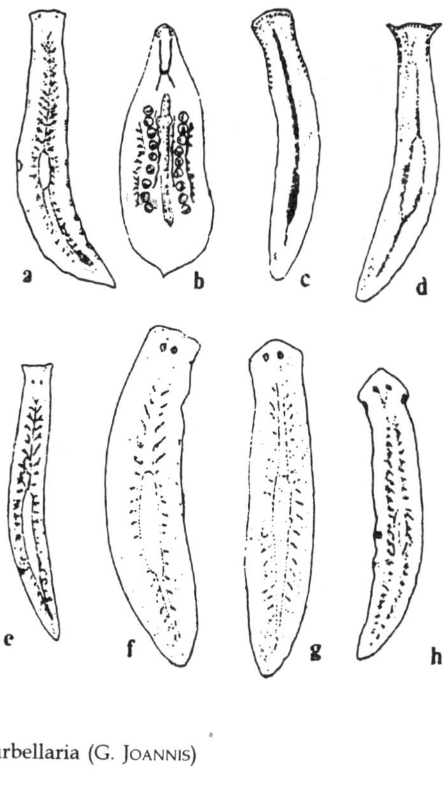

a: *Dendrocoelum* (25–30 mm).
b: *Mesostoma* (15 mm).
c: *Polycelis nigra* (13 mm).
d: *Polycelis cornuta* (18 mm).
e: *Planaria alpina* (16 mm).
f: *Planaria torva* (20 mm).
g: *Planaria lugubris* (20 mm).
h: *Planaria gonocephala* (25 mm).

Fig. 27. Turbellaria (G. Joannis)

- **Flatworms or Platyhelminthes**

Free-living worms or **Turbellaria:** These are planarians, are small (approximately 1 cm), and appear to slide over submerged objects. They are hermaphrodites. There is no anus. Some are carnivorous, others detrivorous.

Dendrocoelum lacteum or white planarian, in stagnant waters on mud or pebbles; the body is surrounded by rounded lobes.

Polycoelis nigra or black planarian has many eyes and lives in ponds and slightly polluted waters.

Polycoelis cornuta is found in the same places.

Planaria gonocephala

Planaria torva and *P. alpina:* both species have two eyes, but the shape of the head differs in each species. Their presence indicates very clean water.

Planaria lugubris

Parasitic flatworms: Trematoda

– **Liver fluke** at the embryonal stage or *miracidium* is found as a parasite in *Lymnaea* and changes into a cercaria later attached to aquatic plants before being ingested (for example, by sheep).

Gyrodactylus: a parasite on the gills of fish.

Segmented parasitic flatworms: Cestoda

– **Bothriocephalus:** its intermediate hosts are, successively, *Cyclops* and fish, the third host being man: extremely dangerous because it secretes toxic substances.

Unsegmented round worms: Nematoda

– **Filarioidea:** one of its intermediate hosts is *Cyclops* (found in ponds).

– **Eelworms:** planktonic in ponds.

4.4 Phoronoidea

Rotifera are very important in hydrobiology; these microscopic organisms (0.1 mm) have a transparent body. They have two crowns of cilia divided in two that appear to mesh with each other when they vibrate. The wheel organ is an organ for swimming and adduction of food particles to the mouth. Behind the mouth is the *mastax*, a masticatory organ on the basis of which different species are determined.

Rotifers crawl on plants, swim, or are just parasites. The females reproduce by parthenogenesis and may proliferate under favourable conditions. If conditions are unfavourable only males emerge from the eggs; the eggs are, therefore, a resistant form of these 2000 to 3000 species.

There are no rotifers in very clean waters.

In relatively clean, oligosaprobic waters we find:

– *Notholca longispina:* the body is covered with a hard shell from the shape of which the species may be identified

– *Conochilus volvox*

– *Fluscularia*, which can retract into a gelatinous sheath

In somewhat polluted, β-mesosaprobic waters:

– *Anurea (Keratella cochlearis)*, with a hard shell on which there are hexagonal designs

– *Anurea quadrata*, with two posterior points

– *Brachionus*

— *Philodina*, without a shell
— *Callidina*, closely resembles *Philodina*

Common in both oligo- and β-mesosaprobic waters:
— *Pedalion*
— *Asplanchna* and *Schizocerca*, loricated (with a kind of tail)

Common in α- and β-mesosaprobic zones:
— *Rotifer vulgaris*

In highly polluted zones, α-mesosaprobic and polysaprobic:
— *Rotifer neptunuis*, the most common type, and *Rotifer citrinus*, with three terminal appendages
— *Diglena biraphis*, with two terminal appendages

4.5 Mollusca

Molluscs have a soft, segmented body in three parts: the head, the dorsal part, which contains the viscera covered with a mantle that secretes a shell, with a ventral part, and muscular part or "foot". The characteristic larvae are called **veligers**. There are two groups of molluscs, the Gasteropods and Lamellibranchs (or Pelecypoda).

a) *Gasteropoda*

—**Pulmonata**

Planorbia cornuta: the horned planorbis. It crawls among aquatic plants and swims upside down under the water surface. The foot is ventral and above the head there are two cylindrical tentacles with two eyes at the base of these tentacles (in *Helix* the eyes are at the end of two small differentiated tentacles, stylommatophora). The respiratory organ is pseudobranchial. Above the head there is a mouth with a cutting jaw and a rough tongue. The digestive tract—the oesophagus and the intestine—is folded back, reappearing at a side of the shell with the anus; there is a hepatopancreas and a simple heart, and the nervous system comprises several ganglia linked by a network of nerves. There are male and female genitals. The eggs are horn-shaped and flat. The respiratory cavity is 3–4 cm in diameter.

—*Planorbis* is smaller (1 cm in diameter). The shell is flat and coiled. It is found in polluted waters.

—*Lymnaea*

—**Lymnaea** has no pseudobranchia and must rise to the surface from time to time. The eggs are agglomerated in a gelatinous mass shaped like a black pudding. The feet are covered with microscopic cilia that help in locomotion.

Radix limosa (maximum 1 cm): their presence is indicative of clear and clean waters.

Physa: while in *Lymnaea* and *Radix* the shell has a right hand twist, in *Physa* it has a left hand twist. The mantle is very small, 8 mm in size. It is found in clean waters, springs, and trout waters.

—Among **Ancylids**, the shell resembles a Phrygian cap:

Ancylus: the tip of the cap is turned to the left.

Ancylastrum: the tip of the cap is turned to the right. Their presence is indicative of very clean water with a considerable biogenetic capacity. These animals breathe through pseudobranchia.

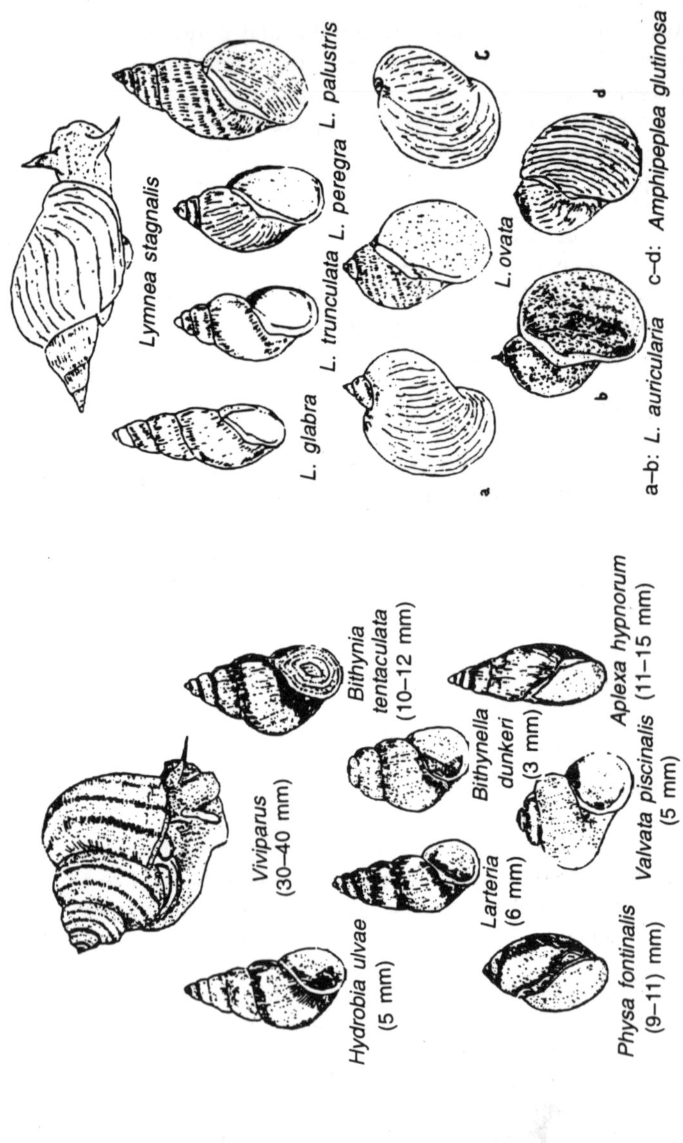

Fig. 28. Mollusca (G. Joannis, after "Was lebt in Tumpel, Bach und Weiher?")

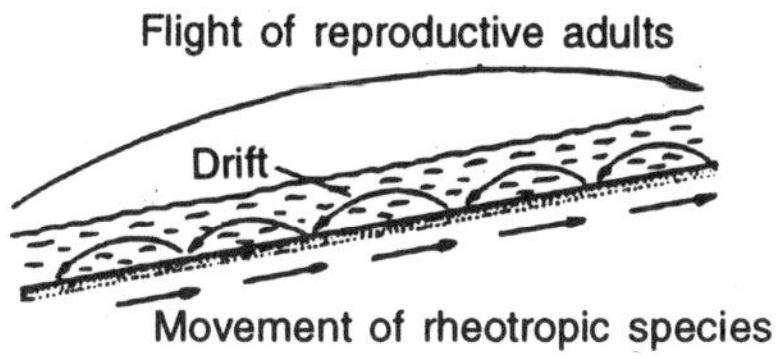

Fig. 29. The benthic drift and colonization

—**Prosobranchia** have branchia and an operculum permanently attached to the foot; they close the shell when the foot is retracted. Among these there are:

Neritina, with a mottled shell 1 cm long and a small incomplete operculum of an orange colour. The waters in which they are found are suitable for trout. *Neritina* lay their eggs over each other (the white spots often observed on their shells are eggs).

Bythinia resembles a very small *Lymnaea;* it lives in clean waters.

Paludina may be more than 3 cm in size. The globular shell is covered with dark orange spots. *Paludina* live in stagnant waters that are relatively clear and clean. They are viviparous and can be used as fish feed.

b) Pelecypoda (bivalves, lamellibranchs)

The females may lay 2 million eggs, which develop on the gills of fish. These give rise to an embryo or *glochidium* that looks like a small bivalve, each valve of which ends in a hook; these embryos are carried about by the fish.

—**Unionids**

Anodonts measure as much as 15 cm; the shell is thin and the hinge is simple. They breathe through two siphons and are edible.

Unio: these mussels are small with an elongated shell (7–8 cm). The teeth are extended on the hinge. They live in ponds and muddy rivers.

Margaritina margaritifera or freshwater mussels, with thick, nacreous shells and a large hinge, are found in streams in primary mountains.

—**Dressenids** or freshwater mussels have a byssus. The velliger larvae can swim. They live in rivers and canals of average β-mesosaprobic purity.

—**Spherids** are very small.

Dressenia polymorpha is host to a parasite that causes a very high death rate of cyprinids in the basin of the Seine: *Bucephalus polymorphus* (larval bucephalosis).

Spherium, with an equilateral shell, is found in rivers that are in the process of being cleaned.

Pisidium, with unequal sides, lives in trout waters.

These two aforementioned genera, which have a fragile shell, are eaten by fish.

4.6 Arthropoda

Arthropods include animals in which the body is composed of articulated elements covered by a thick and resistant layer, thin and supple at the articulations. This layer is formed of chitin and may be encrusted with lime. The animals are not capable of continuous growth and undergo a process of **ecdysis**. There is often a change of form and appearance when the integument is shed (metamorphosis).

There is one pair of appendages per segment but some may be small or absent. The segments may also be joined together.

—cephalic appendages, sensory or prehensile (antennae, antennules, mandibles, jaws)

—thoracic and locomotor appendages, those closest to the head being prehensile (these are maxillipeds or jaw feet)

—abdominal appendages, nearly always present, of small size, play a role in reproduction: they hold the eggs

The following is a simplified classification:

—No antennae 4 pairs of legs for locomotion 1 pair of poisonous or biting appendages or **chelicerae**	Arachnid
—2 pairs of antennae and branchia	Crustacea
—1 pair of antennae, legs on all segments	Myriapoda
—1 pair of antennae, 3 pairs of legs	Insects or Hexapoda

a) Arachnida, includes an aquatic spider

Argyroneta makes a bell-shaped structure under water; it dives carrying an air bubble, fills its bell with air, and lies in wait for its aquatic prey.

—**Free-living acarians:** these are benthic, commonly found at the bottom of the water depth, and are not eaten by fish.

b) Crustacea

Crustaceans have one pair of antennules and one pair of antennae, are all aquatic, and breathe through branchia that are always associated to some extent with their legs. On the head there are eyes, which we do not consider appendages, and also 5 pairs of anterior and posterior biting appendages (mandibles).

- **Entomostraca**, generally small, number of segments variable
- **Branchiopoda**

Phyllopoda

Branchipus (25 mm), found in temporary puddles.

Apus, found in the same habitat. The eggs may hatch even if they have desiccated.

Artemia salina, in salt marshes, indicative of the extent of salinity.

Cladocera: very important organisms, small but often visible to the naked eye. The body is enclosed in a bivalve shell. Outside the shell the antennae are used as oars. They have 4–6 pairs of feet and they swim with jerky movements. The segments on the antenna and the shape of the post-abdomen help in identification of the species. There is a single large eye in the middle of the head. Reproduction is by parthenogenesis.

Daphnia pulex is found in pools and ponds; it feeds on bacteria. The parthenogenetic phase occurs under favourable conditions and sexual reproduction in unfavourable conditions (the ephippium contains 1 or 2 eggs). There are 3 upper segments and 4 lower segments on the antenna.

Daphnia magna measures 4–5 mm.

Daphnia longispina, found in ponds and lakes, is an excellent source of planktonic food for fish fry and even for carp in ponds.

Sida: the antennae have fewer segments and more bristles; they stay attached to aquatic plants by a mucal organ (a sucker).

Diaphanosoma have 2 plus 3 segments on the antenna and no teeth on the post-abdomen.

Bosmina: the rostrum is elongated like a beak. The organism's silhouette is like that of a small elephant and it is found in lakes and ponds.

Scapholeberis: on the rostrum there is a small horn-like structure that gives the organism the appearance of a black rhinoceros; it lives in ponds.

Holopedium gibberum has a body with a gelatinous covering; its silhouette is similar to that of *Bosmina.* It is found in waters with a low calcium content.

Chydorus has a smooth, globular shell and is found in lakes and ponds.

Eurycercus: the post-abdomen is wide and lamellar. The anus is within a deep groove. There are 3 segments on the antenna.

Leptodora: a predatory cladoceran 1 cm long; together with *polyphemus* (4 pairs of legs instead of 6), it forms the major plankton in lakes.

• **Copepoda:** no bivalve shell; the trunk is ovoid with 5 thoracic segments that are separate in females and joined in males, each with a pair of branched feet with swimming bristles. The abdomen is somewhat cylindrical and apodal and ends in a fork (a furca). They are excellent swimmers.

Cyclops has antennae that are not longer than the body.

Cyclopos viridis has egg sacs close together on each side of the abdomen.

Cyclops bicuspidatus has egg sacs separately placed on each side of the abdomen.

Diaptomus has antennae longer than the body.

Many Copepods are parasites, such as:

Argulus or the fish louse, which has appendages transformed into suckers. It attaches itself to fish at the base of the fins and sucks their blood through a stylet.

Brachiella, a parasite on cyprinids.

Lernaeopoda, a parasite on salmonids.

Ergasilus, an occasional and temporary parasite.

• **Ostracoda** have a bivalve shell covering the body; the feet extend beyond the shell while they swim and are retracted at rest.

Cypris, very common, about 1 mm in size, is found near the bottom in stagnant waters.

• **Malacostraca:** few species are observed in fresh waters; these are higher crustaceans with a body of 20 segments.

Isopoda: no true shell, one pair of thoracic maxillipeds, 7 pairs of feet for locomotion.

Asella: 6 abdominal segments joined together (telson). The abdominal appendages act as branchia. The females carry their eggs under the thorax, protected by an incubative lamina. They resemble wood lice.

They feed on all types of debris and are in turn eaten by fish. Living in the mud of ponds or running streams, they are indicative of polluted waters.

Amphipoda: the body is compressed laterally. The thoracic feet are divided into two groups: the first 4 are prehensile and the remaining 3 are for swimming. On the head there are eyes with facets.

Gammarus, incorrectly called freshwater shrimps, **are among the most important animals in the aquatic medium**. From their abundance we can estimate the biogenetic capacity of a river and since they are a direct source of nutrition for trout they are responsible for the "salmonization" of trout flesh due to the carotenoid pigments in the shell; *Gammarus* are found mainly in tufts of Callitriche or wild watercress; though detritivorous, they also feed on algae. The male is about 20 mm long and the female 12 mm long.

Decapoda: the thoracic appendages comprise 3 pairs of maxillipeds and 5 pairs of feet for locomotion. The head and thoracic rings form the cephalothorax and cover the branchia. The eyes are pedunculate.

Caridina: the real freshwater shrimp, with a bluish, transparent body, 5–6 cm long. It lives in clear waters with aquatic plants. Much less common than *Gammarus*.

Crayfish (see section 4.7 below).

c) Insecta

This most important group of the animal world plays a major role in aquatic biology, not because some adult insects are typically aquatic but mainly because the aquatic larvae of insects are valuable indicators of water quality and an important link in the trophic chain of fish.

Insects breathe through tracheae. The insect body is formed of a head, thorax, and an abdomen. Under the thorax there are 3 pairs of legs. There are 1 or 2 pairs of wings. On the head there are antennae and antennules, a pair of mandibles, a pair of jaws, and a lower lip.

Apterygota: no wings in the adult state and no ecdysis. Among the collembolans there is an aquatic genus that lives on water:

Podura aquatica, found almost everywhere, generally widespread among duckweed. The abdomen ends in a *furca*, which when triggered causes the animal to jump.

Pterygota: with wings in the adult state.

Group 1: with incomplete or progressive metamorphosis. The larvae are not very different from the adults but there are no wings on them and the animals have branchia. There is no ecdysis.

–**Hemiptera** (bugs):

Hydrometra, filiform, moves over the water surface.

Velia and *Gerris*, which run like spiders over the water surface, are harmless.

Notonectes, which swims on its back, is found in stagnant waters.

Corixa is smaller and swims in the normal way.

Naucoris looks like a fairly round bug. It is often observed in fairly clean waters and sometimes in ponds.

The three aforementioned harmful genera are difficult to eliminate.

Nepe or water scorpion has claws for grasping. It lives in dirty mud at the bottom of ponds. Its sting is painful and often dangerous.

Ranatre has a narrow, elongated body and is also harmful.

–**Odonata:** Dragonflies and damselflies. The carnivorous types are characterized by a "mask" (buccal parts that fold back under the head) ending in two sharp curved teeth for catching their prey.

In the family of dragonflies we have *Aeschna* with a large carnivorous larva, dangerous to alevins, which it eats.

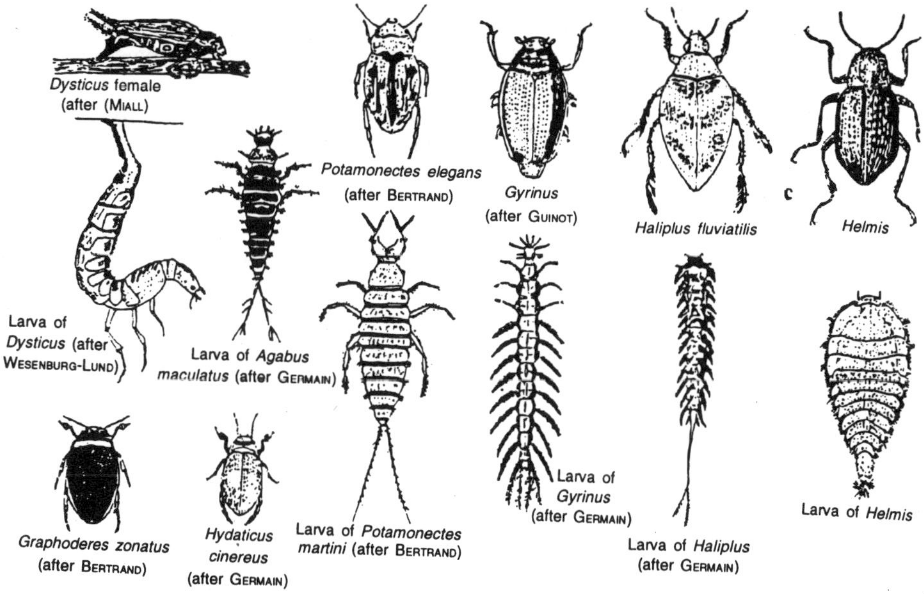

Fig. 30. Coleoptera (G. JOANNIS, after "Was lebt in Tumpel, Bach und Weiher?")

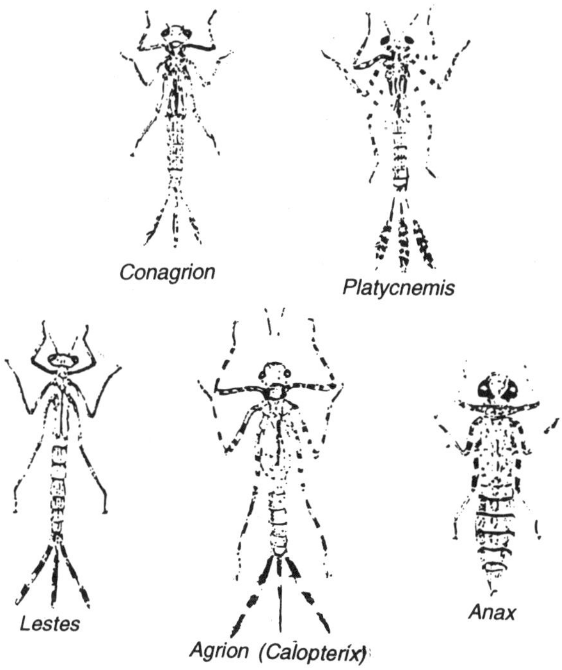

Fig. 31. Odonata (G. JOANNIS, after "Was lebt in Tumpel, Bach und Weiher?")

In the family of Agrionidae we have *Agrion,* which forms part of the exogenous food of fish.

—**Plecoptera** or "stonefly", with wings folded on the back. The abdomen ends in 2 large filaments or cerci; the branchia are connected with the thorax. The larvae live in very clean waters; they are vegetarians and feed on the biological cover of pebbles (e.g., algae, diatoms). They are much sought after by fish and of considerable nutritive value, and their presence greatly increases the biogenetic capacity of mountain torrents.

—**Ephemeroptera**, with erect wings on the back, have an abdomen that ends in 3 broad cerci. The branchia of the larva are under the abdomen; the legs end in a claw. The wings develop progressively in the water. The animal flies after the second last ecdysis (sub-imago). The life of the imago is very short, although the larva may live for two or three years.

—In very clean waters: *Rhitrogena, Exonurus.*

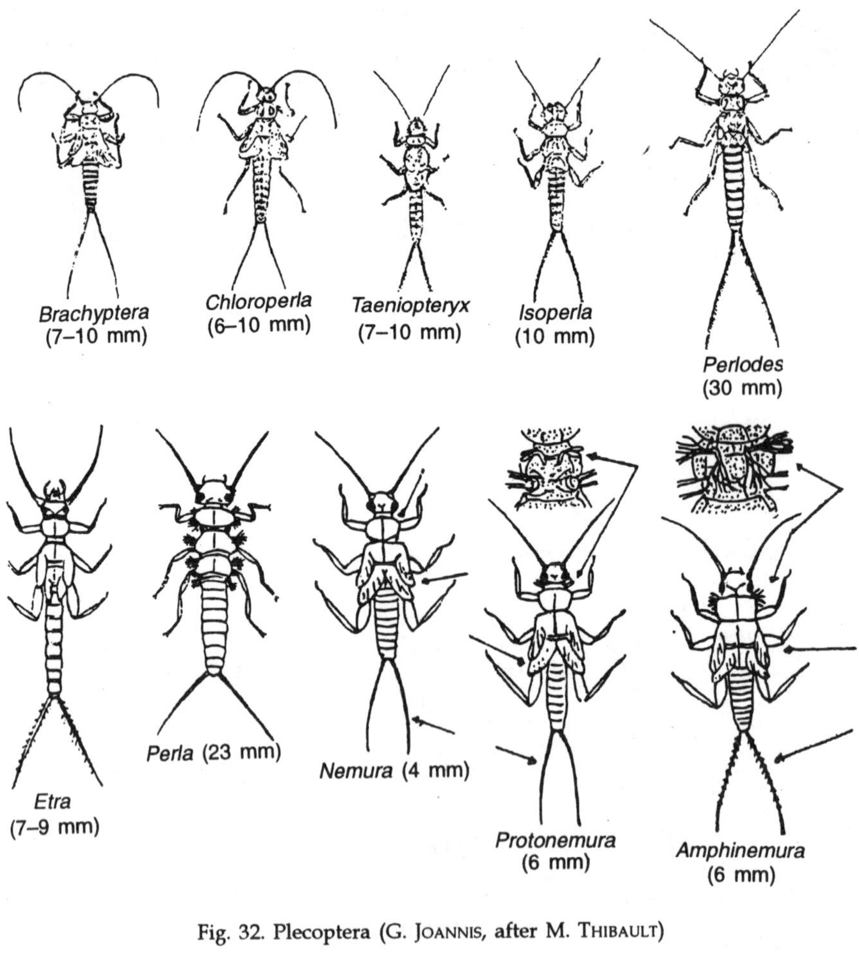

Fig. 32. Plecoptera (G. JOANNIS, after M. THIBAULT)

—In very clean, fairly calm waters: *Baetis, Caenis.*

—In running waters: *Epeorus* (extremely flat, attached to stones), *Ecdyonurus, Prosopistoma.*

—In less clean waters, oligo- and β-mesosaprobic: *Ephemerella, Baetis.*

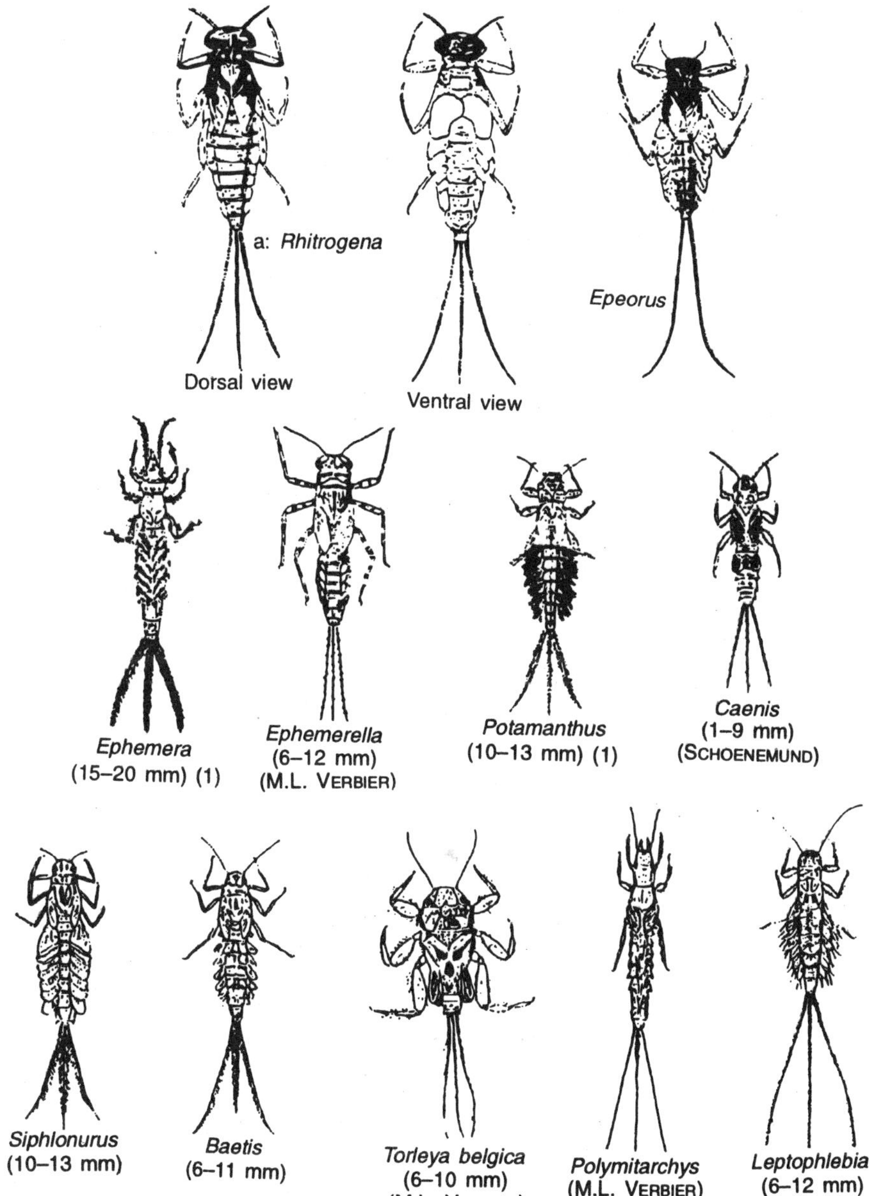

Fig. 33. Ephemeroptera (G. Joannis): (a) after M.-L. Verrier; (b) source unknown.

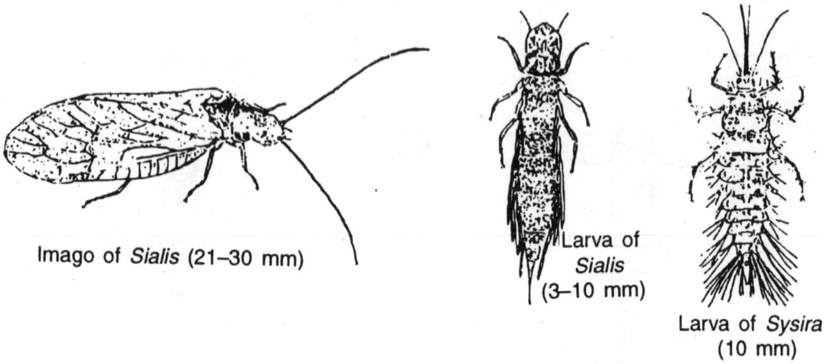

Fig. 34. Trichoptera (G. JOANNIS, after "Was lebt in Tumpel, Bach und Weiher?")

The large ephemerids are burrowers that live in mud. The feathery branchia are folded on their backs.

Group 2: metamorphosis ends with the nymph and chrysalis forms.

–**Neuroptera:** with clearly visible, thick veins on its wings.

Sialis: the adult form resembles a small fly with black wings. The larva has an elongated body and a soft abdomen bordered with long filaments. It is found in slightly polluted waters and lives in the mud at the bottom of streams and lakes. When caught it bites. It lives for two years in water.

–**Trichoptera** (Phryganea): The adults look like small moths. The larvae are covered with a sheath and are commonly called "caddis worms". They are omnivorous, vegetarian, or carnivorous. Three pairs of true legs emerge from the sheath. The false legs enable the animal to hold on to a support and end in hooks that may be considered an identifying characteristic.

Generally, one type sheath corresponds to one type of larva, though this is not strictly applicable in all cases.

Anabolia: sheath ornamented with twigs arranged lengthwise over it.

Table 11. Resistance of some benthic organisms to currents (cm/s)

	A	B	C
Larvae of Blepharoceridae (dipteran)	240	240	220
Larvae of Simuliidae (dipteran)	240	117	200
Larvae of *Epeorus* (ephemerid)	240	230	220
Larvae of *Protonemura* (plecopterid)	200	147	145
Gammarus (crustacean)	100	44	40

A: maximal resistance to the current.
B: maximal current against which these species can move.
C: maximal current observed in which these species have been observed under natural conditions.

Table 12. Relationship between current velocity (cm/s) and presence of some species (after DORIER and VAILLANT in DECAMPS, 1971)

Species	V (1)	V (2)	V (3)
Agrion sp. (Odonata)	< 10	54	77
Glossiphonia complanata (Hirudinea)	< 10	37	240
Crenobia alpina (Turbellaria)	14	140	143
Ancylus fluviatilis (Mollusca)	24	109	240
Heptagenia lateralis (Ephemera)	28	140	188
Gammarus pulex (crustacean)	40	44	99
Simulium ornatum (Diptera)	114	117	240
Rhyacophila sp. (Trichoptera)	125	100	200
Liponeura cinerascens (Diptera)	220	> 240	> 240

(1) Maximum velocity at which they were found under natural conditions.
(2) Maximum current velocity observed in experiments.
(3) Velocity at which they were carried away during experiments (after a resistance of least 1 min.).

Phryganea, 4 cm long, builds its sheath with pieces of plants rolled in a spiral on stones. It is found in trout waters but can also live in slightly polluted waters.

Rhyacophila does not build a sheath and is found in very clean waters. It is identified by its lateral branchia.

Stenophylax builds its sheath with irregular grains of sand. The sheath itself, which is slightly curved, is found whole in the stomach contents of fish.

Philopotamus, instead of a sheath, forms a funnel-shaped net arranged between pebbles to catch its prey. It lives in running water, even in the main current.

Goera builds a sheath made from small pebbles, two of which are arranged in the form of wings on stones in torrents.

Limnophila builds its sheath with the debris of shells and grains of sand.

—**Diptera:** one pair of wings reduced to the role of a mere stabilizer. Among the Nematocera there are mosquitoes. Only the females bite.

Culex is the common mosquito.

Anopheles is an agent of malaria.

Dixa has a larva bent in a U shape on a support and is found in slightly polluted waters.

Corethra and *Chaoborus* are 1 cm long and found in lakes. The larvae are transparent and lie horizontal in the water; 4 small air-filled vesicles play a hydrostatic role.

—**Chironomidae:** extremely important organisms. The adults are small, non-biting mosquitoes. The larvae, commonly called "mud worms", are red (because of the presence of haemoglobin): *Chironomus plumosus*. All of them are not indicative of polluted waters.

Rheotanytarsus builds a tube attached to stones with a web spun at the entrance. This is a trap.

—**Simuliidae** (black flies): the adult is a biting fly. The larva resembles a maggot. The head is surrounded by filaments that are used to retain food particles. Larvae and nymphs are excellent fish food. Their presence considerably improves the biogenetic capacity of rivers.

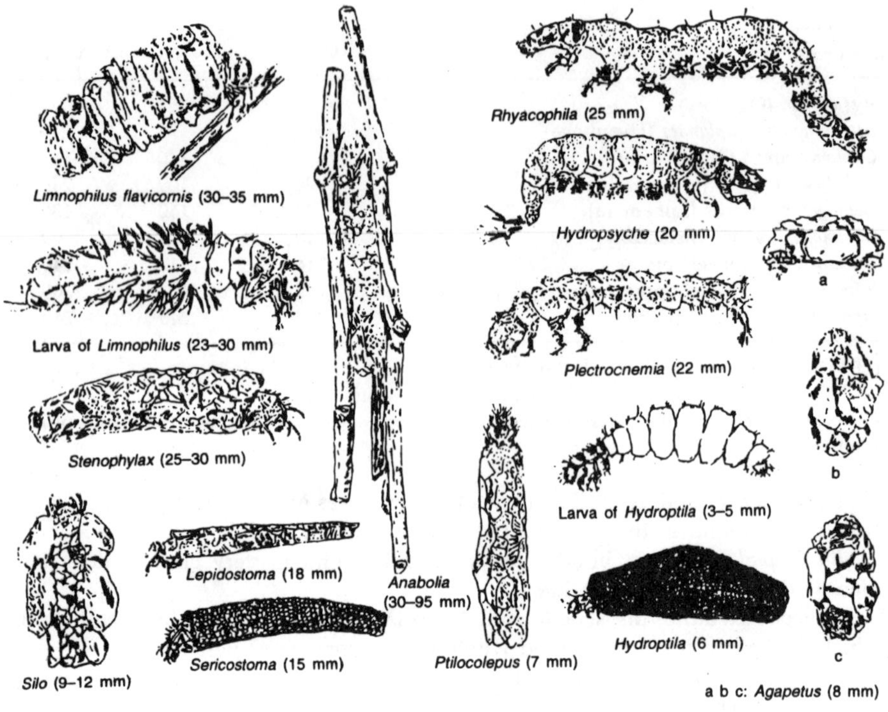

Fig. 35. Trichoptera (G. JOANNIS, after "Was lebt in Tumpel, Bach und Weiher?")

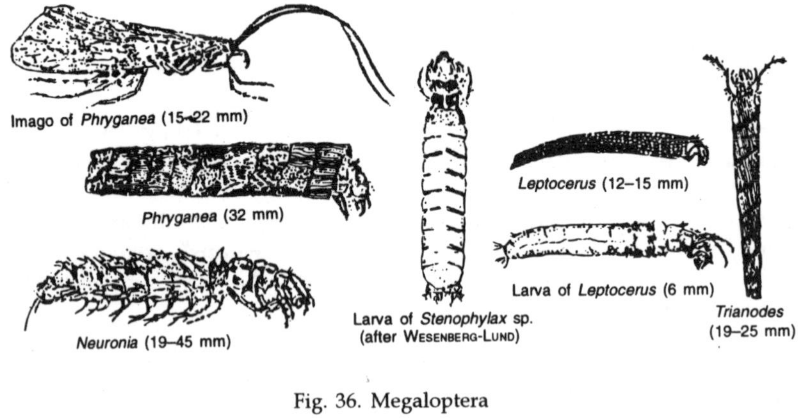

Fig. 36. Megaloptera

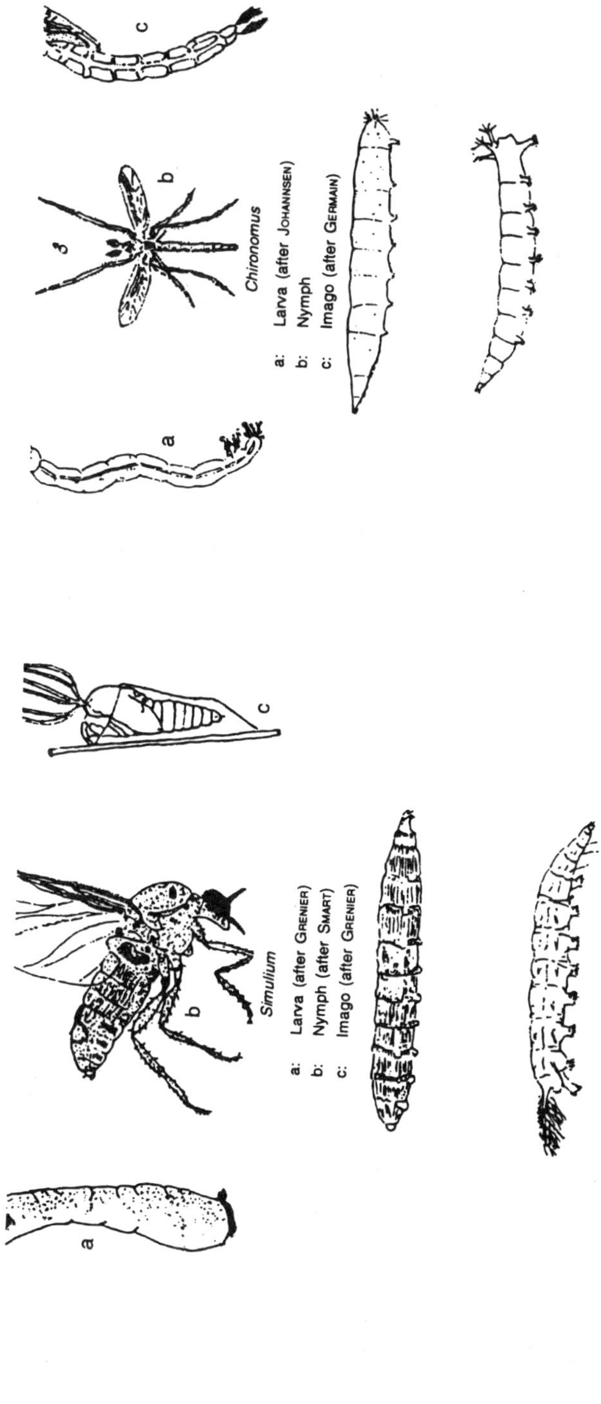

Fig. 37. Diptera (G. JOANNIS)

Among the Brachycerae:

Blepharocera and *Liponeura* have flat aquatic larvae with suckers under the body. They are found in mountain torrents.

Atherix has spindle-shaped larvae with pseudopodia under each segment of the abdomen and a number of filaments at the end. It lives in clean waters.

Stratiomys has a large, spindle-shaped larva 5 cm long. It lives in clean or slightly polluted stagnant waters. It floats on the surface with the aid of hairs on the top of its head.

—**Tabanidae** (gadflies): the larvae look like maggots. They live in highly polluted waters.

Eristalis lives in cesspools and highly polluted, shallow waters, and its larva is a maggot with a tail resembling that of a rat.

4.7 Major Crustaceans

Crayfishes mainly comprise two indigenous species: (1) *Astacus astacus* or the red-legged crayfish found in still, almost stagnant waters and living generally in holes in the banks and the network of roots of trees and shrubs around them and (2) *Austropotamobius pallipes pallipes*, the white-legged crayfish, undoubtedly the most widespread species in France, which lives in limpid cool waters with a fast-flowing current and a gravel bed.

There are also four exotic crayfishes: *Orconectes limosus* or the common American crayfish has colonized 90% of the entire area in France including, especially, most of the river basins of the Loire, Seine, Rhone, and Garonne with a preference for canals, the major slow-flowing water courses, and lakes, where it populates the banks even in mesosaprobic zones. *Astacus leptodactylus*, the slender-legged or Turkish crayfish, originally from the Black Sea area, has been acclimated in several river

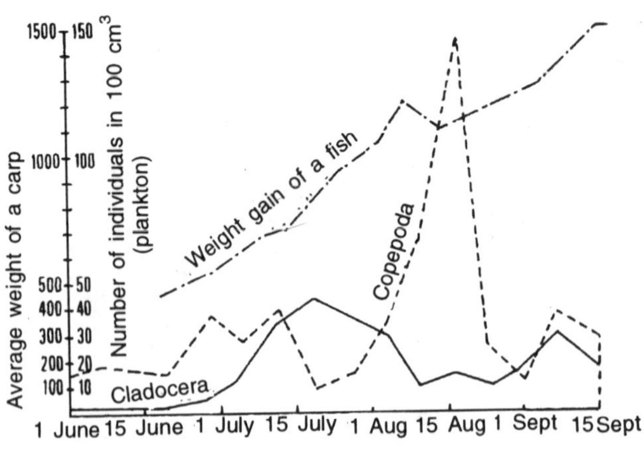

Fig. 38. Variation in the number of Chironomidae in one litre of *Potamogeton lucens* (after WUNDER in VIVIER, 1972)

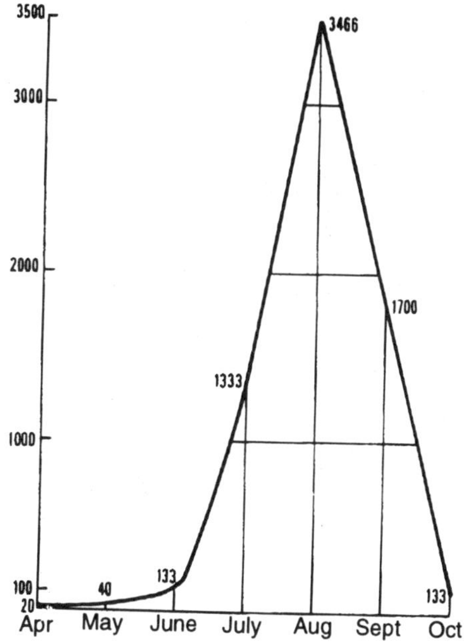

Fig. 39. Comparative table of variations in the abundance of Entomostraca (Copepoda and Cladocera) and average weight gain of a carp in a pond in Silesia (after WUNDER in VIVIER, 1972)

basins, lake dams, and water-filled mines. *Pacifastacus leniusculus* or the Pacific crayfish is found in about 20 French departments and is extending its area, with an ecology comparable to that of the two indigenous species. *Procambarus clarkii* or the red crayfish from the Louisiana marshes, introduced about 1875 in France, has adapted rapidly to temperate climatic conditions (ARRIGNON, 1990a).

A crayfish, depending upon its age and according to the season, has different effects on the trophic chain. It is omnivorous but carnivorous by predilection. It feeds on mosquitoes, trichoptera, leeches, gammarids, tadpoles, even grown frogs, small benthic fish (mainly tench and loach), and occasionally water rats. It is also detrivorous and necrophagous as well as herbivorous, feeding on autumn litter and cress.

Exotic crayfishes have an advantage in not being seriously affected by epidemic fungal diseases such as aphanomycosis and thelohaniosis, which explains their proliferation in astacicultural mediums. The invasion of *Procambarus clarkii*, a burrower, is as much a cause for concern as that of the muskrat and more so than that of the chinese crab (ARRIGNON, 1990b).

According to HOESTLANDT (1955, 1975), the exotic chinese crab (*Eriocheir sinensis*), which arrived accidentally from northern Germany, has entered the Atlantic seaboard of France, which is favourable to its collective migration, and has also entered the Mediterranean coast. It appears that an intensive migratory period was followed by

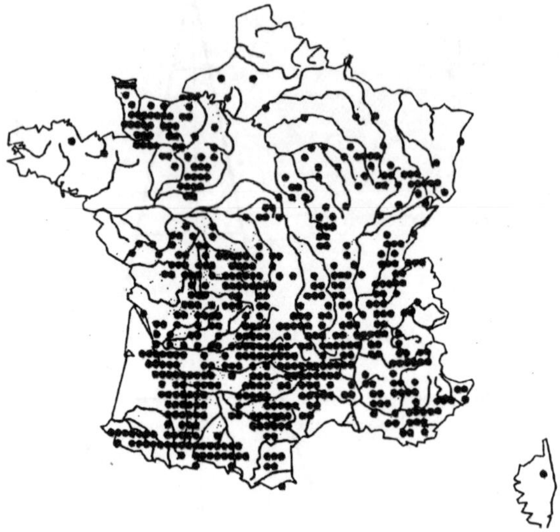

Fig. 40. Distribution in France of the white-legged crayfish (*Austropotamobius pallipes*) (after VIGNEUX, 1997)

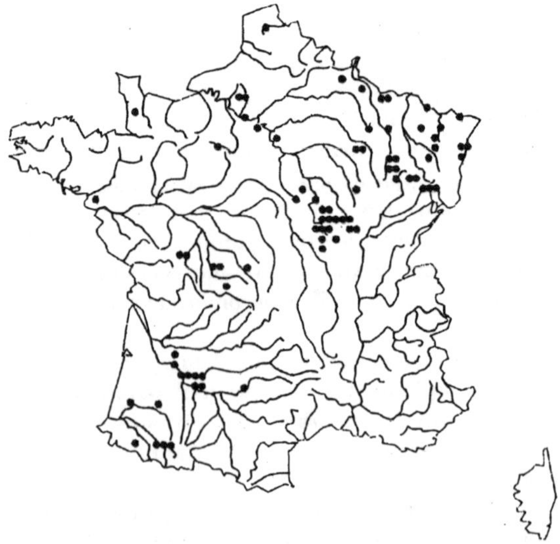

Fig. 41. Distribution in France of the red-legged crayfish (*Astacus astacus*) (after VIGNEUX, 1997)

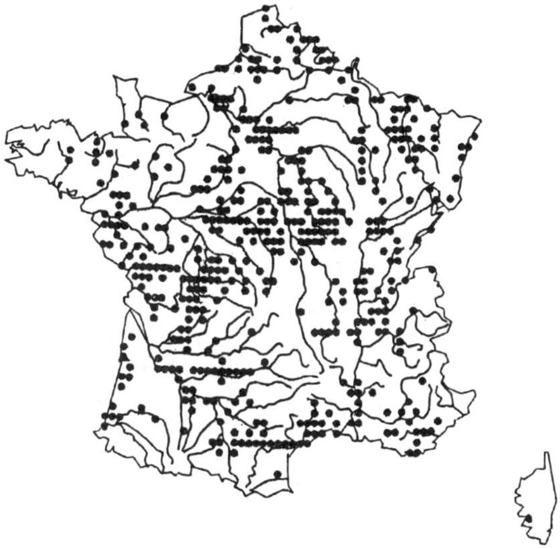

Fig. 42. Distribution in France of the American crayfish (*Oronectes limosus*) (after VIGNEUX, 1997)

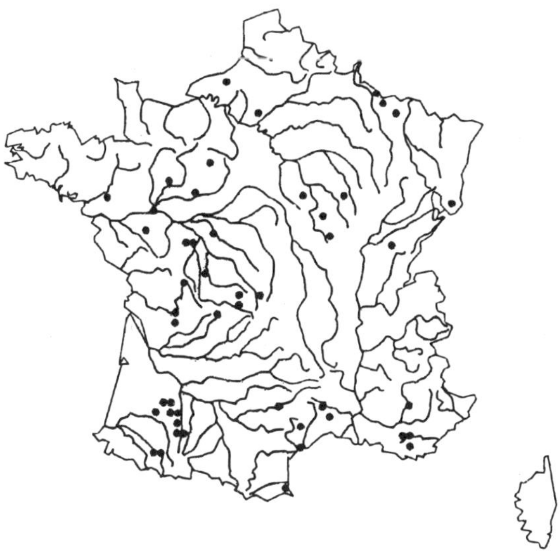

Fig. 43. Distribution in France of the slender-legged crayfish (*Astacus leptodactylus*) (after VIGNEUX, 1997)

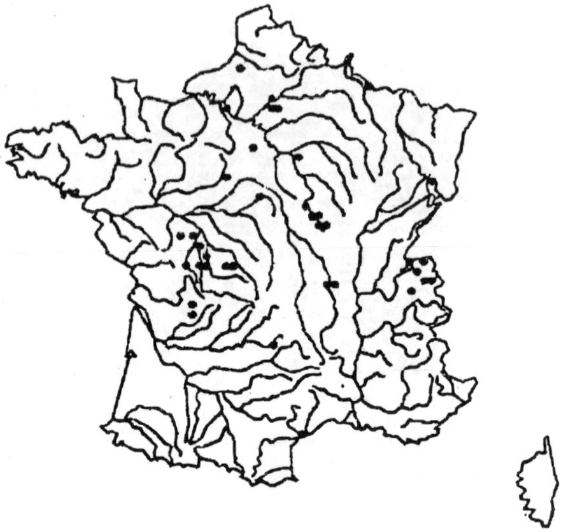

Fig. 44. Distribution in France of the Californian crayfish (*Pacifastacus leniusculus*) (after VIGNEUX, 1997)

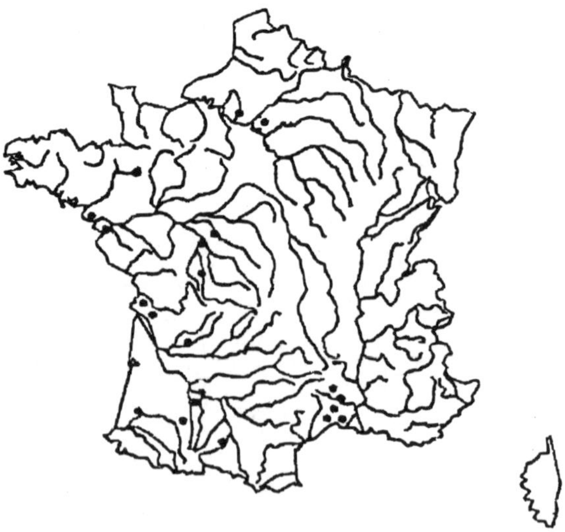

Fig. 45. Distribution in France of the red Louisiana crayfish (*Procambarus clarkii*) (after VIGNEUX, 1997)

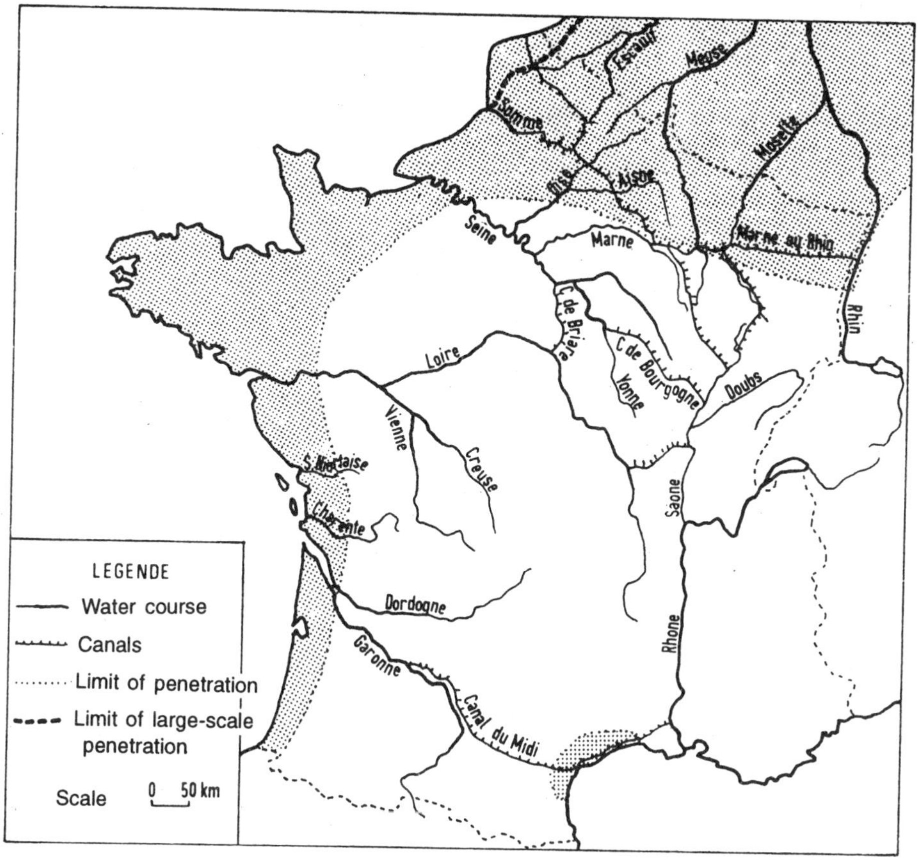

Fig. 46. Spread of the Chinese crab (*Eriocheir sinensis*)

a notable endemic period without causing any alarm. The effect of its digging is now a cause for concern. In the aquatic medium it competes with Cyprinidae in bream and barbel zones and is a predator on them.

4.8 Invertebrates in the Food Regime of Fish

While ending this chapter on water as a support and the section dealing with invertebrates that live in it, it may be useful to examine briefly the role of these invertebrates in the food chain.

Among the zooplankton there are protozoans, rhizopods (*Difflugia*), heliozoans (*Acanthocystis*), and ciliates (*Stentor niger*), which predominate, together with cladocerans, copepods (*Cyclops, Diaptomus*), rotifers, and a few hydracarians.

In ponds, the composition of plankton varies with their management, which directs production according to the desired yield of fish.

Plankton is both a producer and a consumer of organic food. Its distribution and density vary with the depth and season, mainly on the basis of temperature, light, oxygen content, and currents.

The importance of a study of regimes and food habits is best understood by zoological specialists who, for some years now, have been conducting detailed investigations on them.

These investigations have had recourse to stomach contents rather than direct observation of habits, which is difficult because of the limitations under which they would have to be carried out in the medium.

The fisheries manager, the amateur angler, and the naturalist may, however, acquire an idea of these habits and benefit from it in terms of their objectives by an elementary study of the stomach contents of fish available to them.

The stomach contents are examined after a fish is killed or by a stomach wash carried out without killing the fish.

a) *Killing the fish*

The examination should be carried out as soon as possible (because digestion continues after death).

The subject is cut with a pair of small scissors along a line from just ahead of the anus till below the neck. This incision should be only along the abdominal wall.

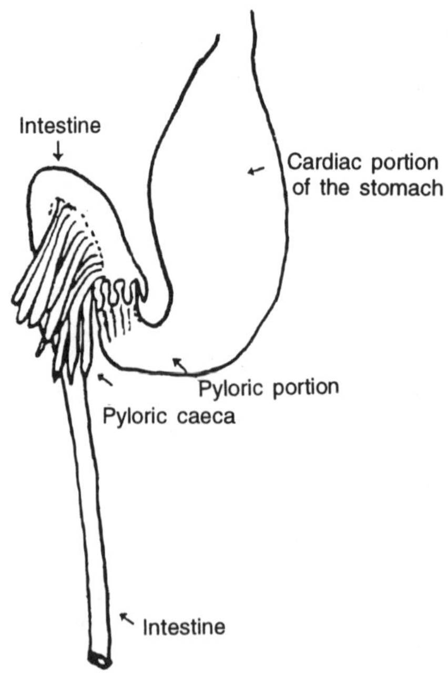

Fig. 47. Digestive system of a fish

By separating the two sides of this long incision we observe the digestive tract with the heart located high above it, behind which the whitish stomach is, to a large extent, covered, especially on the right, by the dark red liver. We detach the liver and the gall bladder, remove the entire digestive apparatus (stomach and intestine) by cutting it off with scissors, high up behind the mouth and lower down near the anus. It is placed separately on a sheet of polyvinyl (or stiff paper) so that it can be examined.

Two distinct parts can be seen: the stomach, with a thick wall, whitish, and curved in a U shape, and the intestine, with a thin wall, almost transparent, and for the most part straight till it reaches the anus.

The stomach begins directly from the back of the mouth (the fibrous oesophagus is short) and is in two parts:

—an anterior part, the cardiac portion, and

—a posterior part, the pyloric portion.

We are concerned mainly with the anterior part because the prey in it is still fresh.

It is much less fresh in the pyloric portion, closed by the pylorus from where the intestine begins and containing only fragments that are difficult to identify.

In the pyloric portion there are many elongated sacs, often covered with fat, the pyloric caeca (40–50 in the trout) which open at the entrance to the intestine and secrete gastric juice.

We separate the intestine and keep it aside.

We first examine the stomach by cutting it with scissors along the length of its two branches, and following its curve. The contents, made up of the prey, often sticky with mucus, are kept in a small flask filled with a 5% solution of formaldehyde. This preparation enables its preservation for subsequent examination by an expert. The attached label should indicate the following: date and place where caught, approximate weight, size, and sex. If possible, a few scales removed with a knife from the shoulder of the fish should be attached. Some additional information may also be supplied regarding the fishing conditions, such as the state of the water (high or low, clear or troubled) and of the atmosphere (e.g., temperature, clear or cloudy weather, rain, storm).

With the help of a small brush we may often be able to separate the prey in the stomach and count and identify the various elements.

We may also collect fairly large indigestible elements, shells and molluscs, sheaths of phryganeids, and shells of insects, that can be placed in the flask.

b) Stomach wash (see Fig. 127)

Stomach wash is carried out using a stomach pump (SEABURG, 1957). The device has two vinyl tubes, 10–15 cm long and 1–4 mm in diameter, joined together over a length of 5–7 cm. These twin tubes form a probe that is introduced into the mouth and, from there, into the oesophagus of the fish.

The smaller tube is connected with a rubber bulb filled with water and the larger tube ends in a small container in the cover of which there is a hole for inserting the tube and another hole covered with gauze to let out the air and, later, the excess water without allowing the prey carried in the tube to escape.

The fish is tranquilized. The tube is inserted in the stomach. When the rubber bulb is pressed, water is injected into the stomach. This water together with the contents is forced into the larger tube and collected in the container. The operation ends when the operator sees that nothing more is passing through the vinyl tube.

The content is collected as already indicated.

Analysis of these results leads to a qualitative interpretation of a "meal"; it may be used for a study of the food cycle, in which case the synthesis must take into account the average number of organisms ingested by the fish, the percentage of each category of organisms in the total volume of food, and other factors. This is how MacCORMACK (M. THIBAULT, 1967) carried out several observations on the habits of trout of different ages.

c) *Food habits of salmonids*

Alevin* less than 1 year old (trout)

—On resorption of the vesicle

57% of the total organisms consumed are Diptera (chironomids),

10% small gammarids,

10% Collembola,

10% larvae of Ephemera.

—After resorption till the end of the year we observe a seasonal variation: ephemerids in May–June and larvae of Trichoptera during midsummer.

—In May–June:

35% chironomid larvae,

14% ephemeropteran larvae,

40% gammarid larvae,

11% tichopterans and plecopterans.

Alevin of one year (trout): consumption of exogenous fauna

In winter, gammarids, larvae of dipterans with a predominance of earthworms,

In March, gammarids and larvae of ephemerids,

In April–May, gammarids,

From May to October, the average for the year is 30% exogenous food and 26% gammarids. No chironomids are found.

Adult trout

The consumption of exogenous food increases from April to June and continues during the autumn:

64% are trichopterans,

6% ephemerids and a few water slatters (*Asella*), average for the year,

molluscs (negligible),

minnows, from May to October.

Salmon alevin (1-year-old smolts)

50% are trichopterans,

30% ephemerids,

11% *Ancylastrum* (eaten by 50% of salmons).

d) *Food habits of some fish, commensals of the trout.*

Gudgeon: identical to the food habits of trout less than 1 year old. There is, therefore, competition if the two species of this age are present together.

**Alevin* is used in French to mean young fish. Here it is used interchangeably with fry—Technical editor.

Minnows: also competitors.

Loaches: larvae of Trichoptera, Plecoptera, and Ephemeroptera in the case of young loaches. The same prey and their own fry for adult fish.

Eels: no terrestrial organism.
32% are ephemerids,
27% trichopterans,
7% minnows,
17% young trout.
(ARRIGNON, 1964, average of 57 individuals)

5. OTHER AQUATIC VERTEBRATES

In European aquatic ecosystems, reptiles, amphibians, and aquatic mammals form the bulk of animals in the predatory chain that eat fish eggs, fry, or adult fish.

5.1 Reptiles and Amphibians

Among reptiles, the freshwater turtle of the Mediterranean coast, though mainly herbivorous, occasionally eats young fish. The common grass snake (*Natrix natrix*) and the grass viperine (*Natrix maura*) live near streams, puddles, and ponds where they feed on amphibians and fish (NAULLEAU, 1973).

The Florida turtle (*Trachemys scripta elegans*) has been imported into France as an animal for breeding in aquaria since the 1980s (4,200,000 from 1985 to 1994). It has since then been released into natural mediums and is observed in all French departments (SERVAN and ARVY, 1997). Signs of reproduction have been obtained indicating that the species not only has been acclimated but is also in the process of being naturalized (HAFFNER, 1997). It is a source of concern for two reasons: it is prolific, which makes it a formidable competitor for fish, and it transmits salmonellosis.

Among the amphibians, the green frog (*Rana esculenta*) consumes fish eggs. Tadpoles compete directly with alevins of the pike, which hatch at the same time but are smaller. These small alevins are also eaten by adult pike. The toad (*Bufo vulgaris*) does not live in water but lays its eggs in water; its tadpoles, which are smaller than those of the frog, play the same role in the ecosystem.

5.2 Aquatic Avifauna

a) The kingfisher (*Alcedo ispida*) is a constant predator on young fish. Since it lives near spawning grounds, streams with young fish, or fisheries, it causes serious damage because the daily consumption of a single bird is more than ten troutlets. It nests in holes that it makes on the banks and, because of its abundance, it is probably one of the major predators of fish fauna in both lotic and lentic zones.

b) Herons (*Ardea cinerea, A. purpurea*) have an extremely varied diet including insects, shrimp, micromammals, young muskrats, fish, amphibians, and reptiles. In terms of biomass, they consume mainly fish in the spring, but during the rest of the year, especially in winter, they hunt mammals, sometimes exclusively. The preferred fish are the eel, roach, and tench, which are caught in slow-flowing streams. Most of these fish are small (less than 30 cm for the eel, 10–15 cm for whitefish). The heron hunts by stealth, day and night, on the ground or in shallow water not deeper than 30–40 cm; its rate of capture is very slow and its average daily requirements are not more than 240–300 g of all types of prey (MARION, 1990).

c) Grebes (*Podiceps minor, P. auritus, P. cristatus*) live exclusively on the water but rest and nest near the banks. They consume large numbers of small fish and tiny aquatic animals, which they catch by diving. They kill more than they eat.

d) Ducks and teals are abundant on water reservoirs, which they colonize temporarily or permanently. They therefore intervene actively in the aquatic ecosystem by eating some water plants, including duckweed and myriophylloid plants, and are eupotamic. They are one of the causes of eutrophication of ponds by a notable increase in faecal matter. According to HUET (1970), the droppings of ducks may result in an excess of organic matter when their population is above 250 birds/ha. They may occasionally be indirect predators on the fish by eating the eggs on aquatic plants. They intervene frequently by populating virgin waters, arriving on them and depositing eggs of cyprinids, pikes, or perches that they have carried on their feet.

e) Cormorants (*Phalacrocorax carbo, P. sinensis*) exist in two different populations, one marine and the other continental, that have no contact with each other except in the estuaries. The carbo nests on cliffs in Normandy and Brittany and winters within a radius of 200 km near the coasts and estuaries. The sinensis is continental and formed mainly of wintering birds. In France, this wintering is limited mainly to Camargue, the course of the Loire, major lakes in the plains (Grand-Lieu, Champagne), and estuaries. The sinensis did not nest till 1981, when the first pairs arrived on the Grand-Lieu lake. Wintering birds arrive mainly in October and the maximum numbers are observed in November. This is followed by a minor to major decrease from December

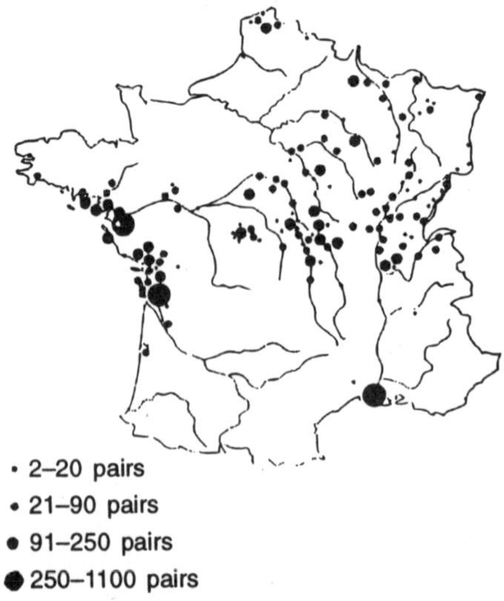

Fig. 48. Distribution and populations of common heron colonies in 1981

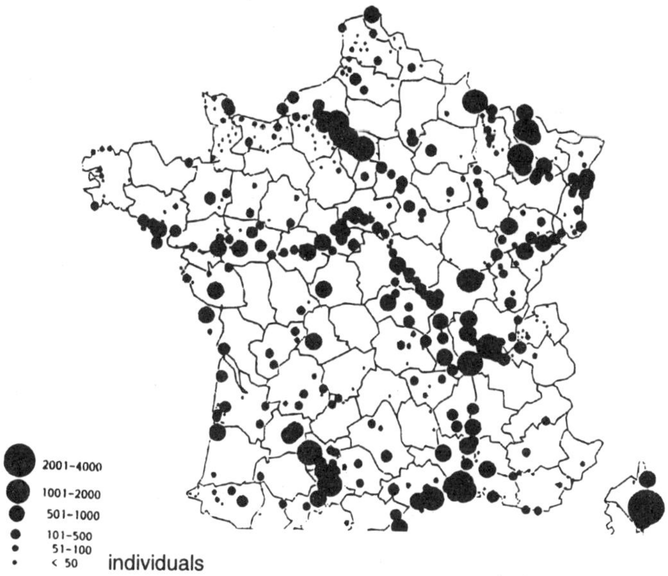

Fig. 49. Distribution and numbers of the great wintering cormorants (after L. Marion, 1997)

onwards on large water bodies, with birds remaining on the smaller water bodies. The last of the wintering birds leave in April.

Apart from the coasts and estuaries, the large cormorant is seen on major water bodies surrounded by trees and where there are islets on which it can spread its wings to dry and establish common living areas. Unlike the heron, it hunts in large groups, swimming below the water level to catch fish. It looks for prey of average size, about 20 cm. Its daily requirement, on the average, may be as much as 320 g (Marion, 1990).

f) Gulls (*Larus* sp.) were earlier present only near water courses. Now they are active everywhere, except on high mountains. Their extension is related to the proliferation of waste dumps. They are predators mainly in intensive fish farms and ponds.

5.3 Mammals

The **otter** (*Lutra lutra*), well adapted to life in water by its body shape, its sense of smell, and the tactile sensitivity of its fur, lives a sedentary life near its burrow with two entrances. A cautious animal, it stays near open beaches and dry plants, where it leaves its pug marks. It feeds on fish of all sizes that it catches while swimming; it actually performs the job of an undertaker in water by eating many sick or abnormal fish. In view of its limited numbers and poor resilience, it does not constitute a danger to fisheries.

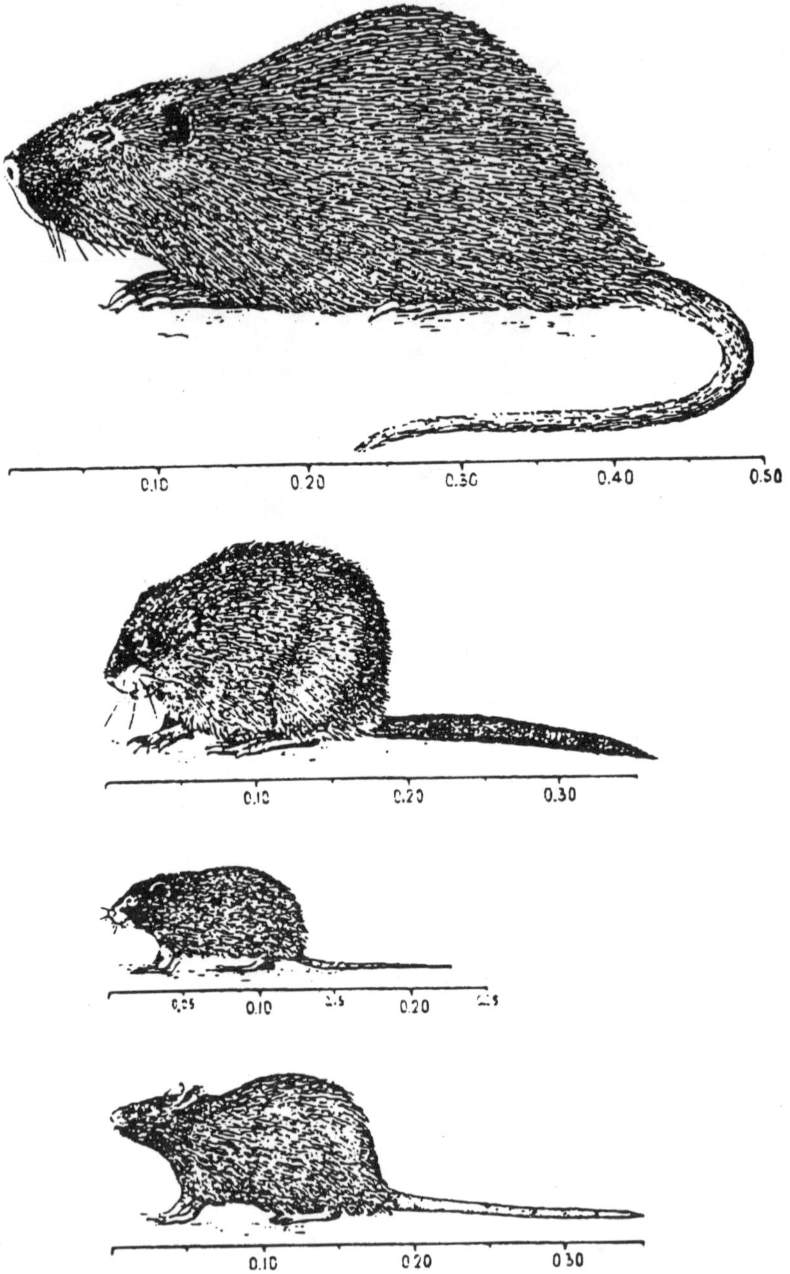

Fig. 50. Comparative sketches of (top to bottom) the coypu, muskrat, water vole and brown rat

The **European water shrew** (*Neomys fodiens*) is not often seen. It frequents lakes, torrents, and streams with variations in the flow velocity. Being carnivorous, it hunts aquatic fauna consisting of insects and their larvae, crayfish, fish eggs and fry. In winter, it even attacks large fish.

The **mink** (*Mustela lutreola*) swims and dives like an otter. Like the otter, it eats frogs but its diet consists mainly of fish. In this respect it would be a major predator if it were numerous. It is found, having escaped from mink farms, in the Loire basin, in the Jura, and in some valleys of the Ile-de-France.

The **water vole** (*Arvicola amphibius*) is found at the sides and in the dykes of reservoirs, where it causes serious damage by digging tunnels. In the water it eats eggs, fry, and fish of average size.

The **beaver** (*Castor fiber*) alters the aquatic medium by building dams on water courses. Rare in France, it is only found in the lower valley of the Rhone and at a few places in Brittany, Morvan, and the Ile-de-France, where it has been reintroduced on an experimental basis.

The **coypu** (*Myopotamus coypus*), introduced from South America, is a strictly herbivorous rodent, eating aquatic plants especially phragmition and scirpion. Unlike the muskrat, it does not burrow but builds a shelter using plants. Pond owners generally consider it useful. As a biological clearing agent, it increases the productivity of reservoirs and hastens the mineralization of silt. This is, however, not always beneficial unless the numbers of the species are strictly controlled; otherwise it will result in destruction of the habitat and serious damage, as reported in southwestern France.

The **muskrat** (*Ondatra zibethica*), imported in 1905 from America to be raised for its fur, is found in stagnant or slow-flowing waters rich in aquatic plants. According to Giban (1960), its essentially vegetarian diet is supplemented by mainly bivalve molluscs (Anodonta and Unio) and, occasionally and exceptionally, crayfish and fish.

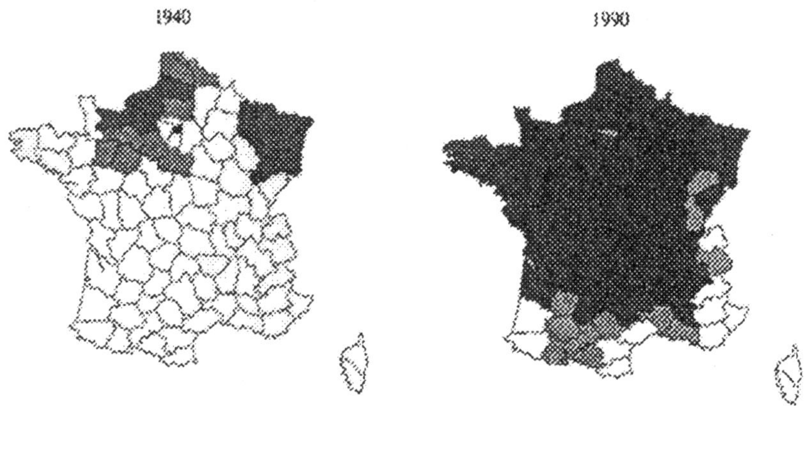

■ Common, sometimes localized
□ Rare, occasional, or to be confirmed

Fig. 51. Distribution of the muskrat (*Ondatra zibethica*) in France (after Maurin, 1997)

This animal intervenes in ecosystems mainly by its effect on the vegetation and, thus, indirectly on the fish fauna by moving about in spawning areas and destroying plants that support the eggs. It also has a mechanical effect on banks and retaining dykes due to its burrowing.

It is a constant menace, since it causes damage to dykes and disturbs the hydraulic system, being responsible for leaks and a fall in water level of reservoirs.

The muskrat is polygamous and extremely prolific and is spreading progressively over Europe from the north to the south.

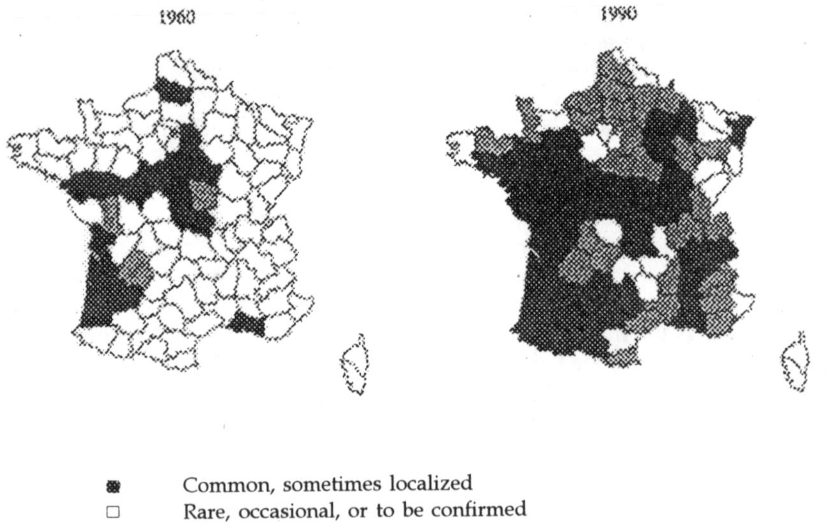

Fig. 52. Distribution of the coypu (*Myopotamus coypus*) in France (after MAURIN, 1997)

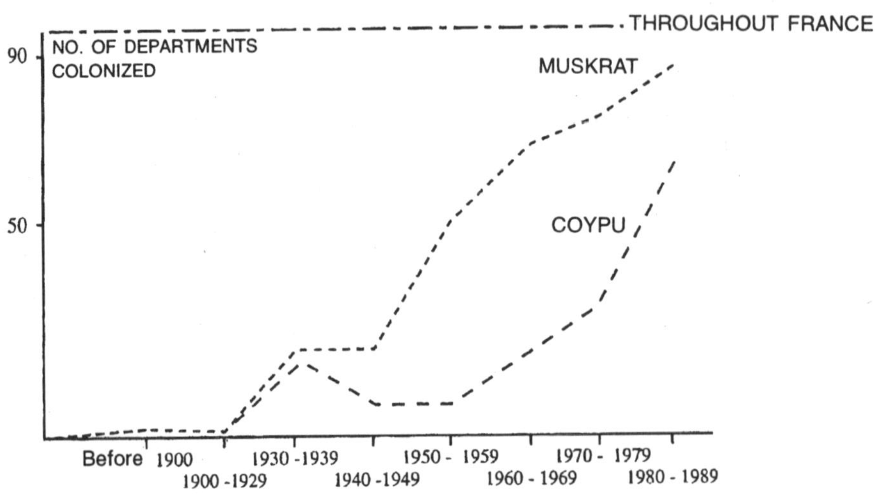

Fig. 53. Comparative development in the spread of muskrat and coypu in France (after MAURIN, 1997)

3 FISH

We often hear the word "fish" being used to include all animals living in fresh or salt waters. Many people, therefore, include porpoises, seals, sharks, rays, tuna fish and other animals under this term, but porpoises and seals are mammals. In fresh waters it is noted that people include not only chub and trout but also frogs and crayfish under fishes.

Like aquatic invertebrates, the crayfish, which is a crustacean, the frog, an amphibian, and the chub, which is a fish, are part of the **aquatic fauna** since they live in water or need water to live, and **freshwater** fauna because they need fresh water.

A fish is a lower vertebrate living in water, with fins and a body that is generally covered with scales.

Our knowledge about the class is inadequate. A large number of identified species (more than 2500) are fairly well known, but many remain to be discovered: more than a hundred new species are found and described every year.

It is precisely because of various morphological, anatomical and physiological characteristics that new species can be differentiated, sometimes very similar to known species, which may have a different incidence in the community as well as the aquatic habitats.

A. MORPHOLOGY

1. BODY SHAPE

The body of a fish is generally elongated and spindle-shaped. It may, however, be compressed laterally or depressed from the back to the abdomen.

Each genus has a different shape and differences may be found within each genus and sometimes, within a species, among individuals of different sexes. The way of life and the habitat condition the shape. Large, athletic long-distance migrating fish such as the salmon, sea trout, and nose carp have a hydrodynamic shape, like a spindle, unlike a sedentary fish such as the bullhead.

The following are some examples:

— spindle-shaped: salmon, trout, pike
— flat: flounder
— serpent-shaped: eel
— conical: bullhead
— oblong: carp, roach

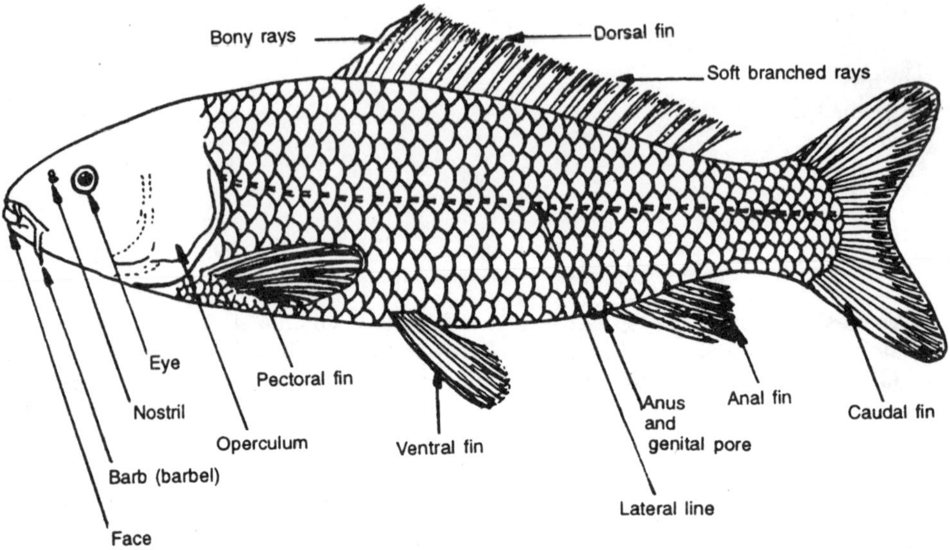

Fig. 54. General appearance of a fish

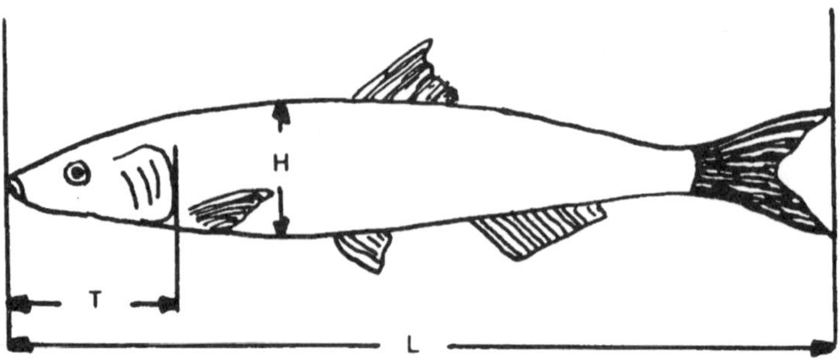

Fig. 55. Measurement of a fish
L = length; T = length of head; H = body height

– disc-shaped: sunperch

As mentioned earlier, there are local subspecies of a particular species with forms that are short or long (trout from the Ource, short pike from the Vendee and the Overijssel).

Selection also enables us to obtain forms of good market value (for example, carp from Galicia).

Finally, some fish have juvenile and adult forms (the eel is flat – leptocephalus – before attaining its adult serpent-like shape; the flounder is first symmetrical, then turns and swims on its side and drops to the bottom, the eye on the lower side moving to the upper side due to a localized torsion of the skull).

The following measurements are taken in a fish:

– the body height is measured at a third of the length from the snout;

– the total length is measured from the extremity of the snout to the end of the tail fin;

– the length of the head is measured from the tip of the snout to the rear of the operculum;

– the tail is measured onwards from the anus.

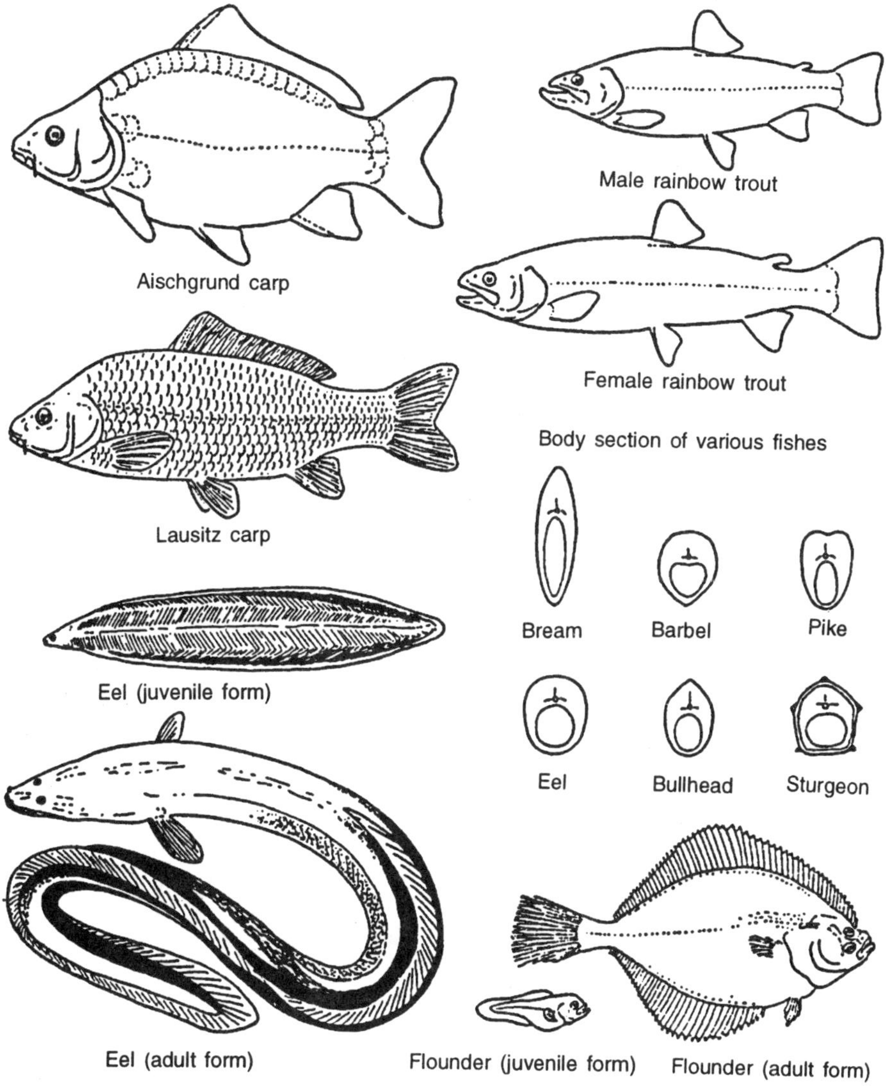

Fig. 56. Morphology of fishes

2. EYES, MOUTH, NOSTRILS

In the head of a fish there are eyes, a mouth, and nostrils. Here again, depending upon the species, there is an infinite variety in their arrangements and characteristics, useful for purposes of identification.

a) The eyes are generally without eyelids, except in some fishes that have a nictitating membrane, such as sharks, or two vertical eyelids, such as grey mullet.

b) The mouth is terminal or at the ventral side of the head (undermouth—*Chondrostoma nasus, C. toxostoma*). In the latter case the snout is prominent and is sometimes called a rostrum.

The upper jaw may be shorter than, as long as, or longer than the lower jaw. Each of them may have fleshy extensions called barbs or barbels.

Within the mouth are teeth that are developed to different extents and sometimes virtual. Depending upon their position they may be:

—maxillary teeth, on the maxillary bones;

—palatine teeth and vomerine teeth, the numbers of which are extremely useful for identification of species, especially among the salmonids;

—pharyngeal teeth that are also useful for identification, especially of cyprinids;

—lingual teeth found in the trout and the pike;

Fig. 57. A: Eye of a mammal (changes in shape of lens). B: Eye of a fish (movement of lens)

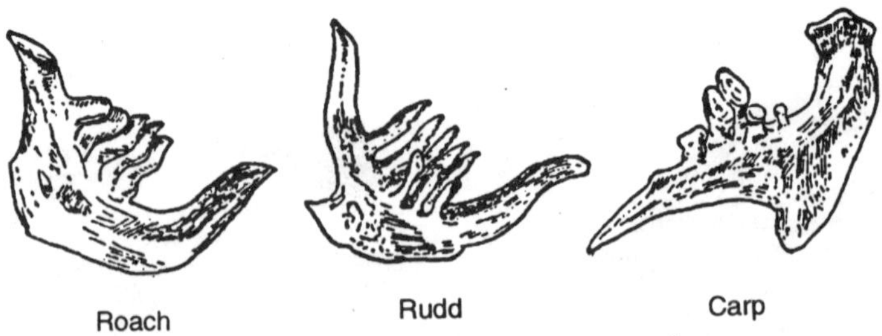

Fig. 58. Jaws and teeth of different fishes (after BOURGEOIS and GALLAND, *La Peche*, 1955, with the kind permission of Editions Larousse)

– teeth on the branchial arches of some fish such as the perch and the pike.

Generally, the functional teeth are worn out. In the pike they are movable: they tilt backwards so as to provide the widest possible passage and then become upright again.

The set of teeth, as in the case of mammals, is an indication of food habits:

– piscivorous: pike, perch, and the pike-perch with strong jaws

– herbivorous, granivorous, vermivorous: the cyprinids, which have no maxillary teeth

– insectivorous: trout

When the teeth are pointed, numerous, and closely arranged, one against another, depending upon their size, they are referred to as soft teeth or combs.

c) Nostrils: In an aquatic medium olfaction enables detection from a distance of soluble or suspended substances. This is rendered possible by a nostril or nostrils. The lamprey has only one median nostril. Most fish have two nostrils, generally not in communication with the mouth.

3. FINS AND INTEGUMENT

a) Fins are the limbs of fish: paired fins correspond to the limbs of mammals. Pectoral fins correspond to forelimbs and pelvic fins to hind limbs. In addition to paired fins there are unpaired fins:

– one dorsal fin, sometimes two (perch) and even three (cod)

– the caudal fin

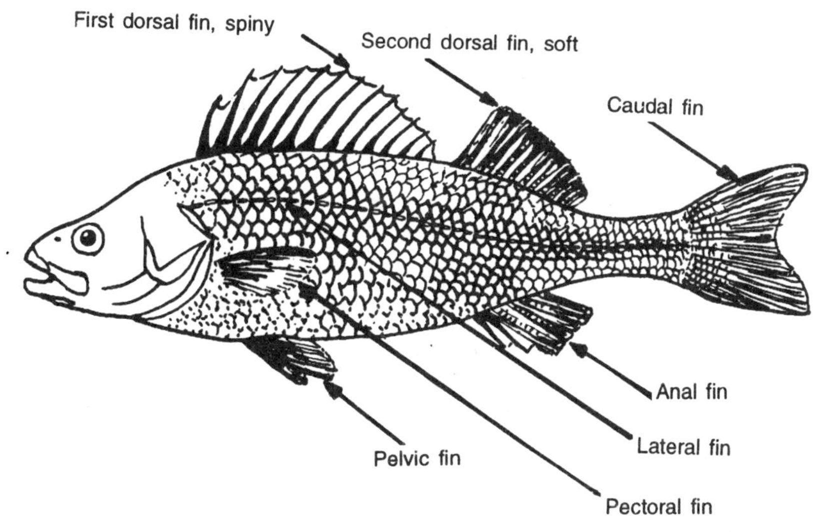

Fig. 59. Fins of a fish

—the anal fin located between anus and caudal fin

—the caudal fin, a sort of scull at the end of a muscular lever, ensures propulsion of a fish by rotation and torsion of the tail and the fin. The fin, like an oar, describes a figure of eight and propels the fish.

—the pectoral and pelvic fins are rudders for both direction and depth and their bilateral erection enables the fish to stop.

—the dorsal and anal fins act as stabilizers.

There are also many varied types. Some so-called **apodal** fish (without feet) such as the eel have no ventral fins. The dorsal, caudal, and anal fins are joined in a continuous fringe. Others like the stickleback have pelvic fins reduced to spines or, as in the salmonids, have an adipose soft dorsal fin.

Pectoral fins are generally attached to the sides near the respiratory organs but the position of pelvic fins varies greatly. They are ventral, abdominal when they are under the abdomen, thoracic when they are under the pectorals (perch), or jugular when they are further forward, under the neck (cod).

—**The rays** on fins, extremely useful for the identification of species, are of two types: spiny rays, or joined or soft rays.

There are no rays on the adipose dorsal fins of salmonids.

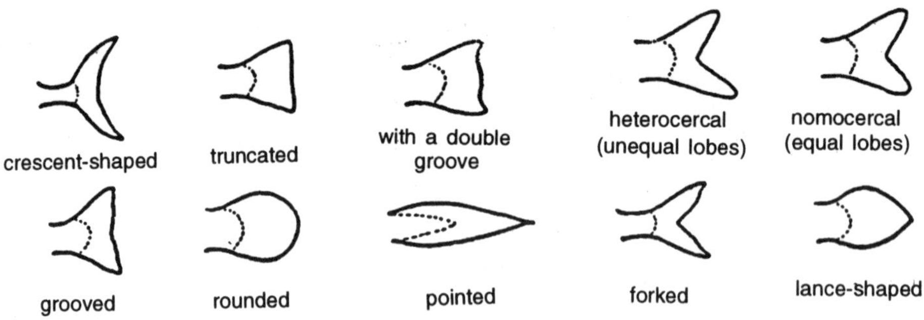

Fig. 60. Various types of caudal fins

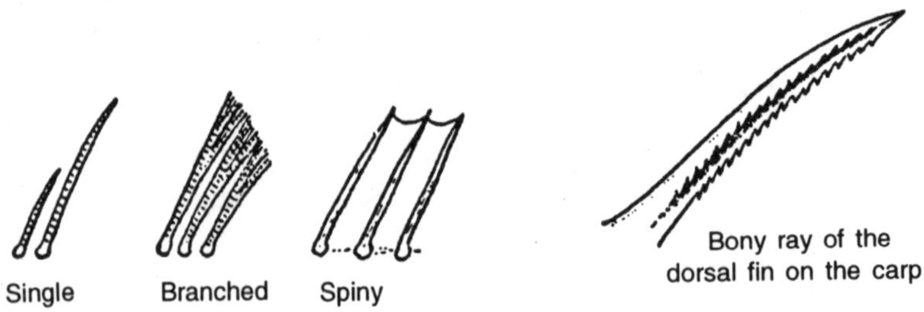

Fig. 61. Rays on fins

b) Integument

As in mammals, the integument, which forms the "skin" of a fish, is composed of a superficial epidermis and a deeper dermis.

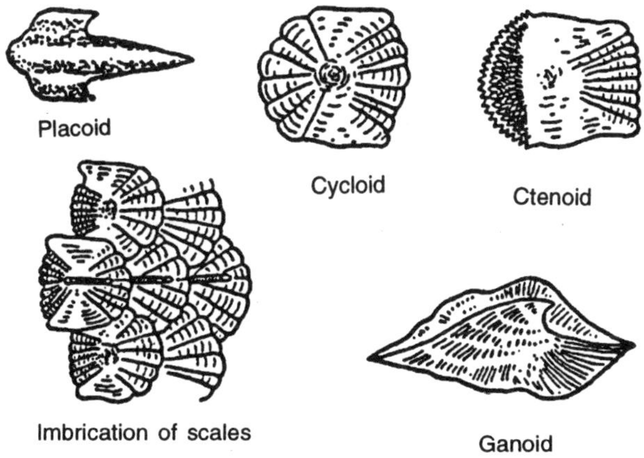

Fig. 62. Fish scales and imbrication

■ **The dermis** is formed of connective tissue containing chromatophores, which are pigment cells that give colour to a fish. The dermis generates scales, most often in association with the epidermis.

■ **The epidermis**, stratified in its thickness, contains glandular cells that secrete mucus. This mucus is somewhat abundant, depending upon the species and, it may be noted, upon the number and size of the scales. As a protective coating, a large amount of mucus is found in species that have no scales or only very small ones.

Some scales that we find, for example, on sharks, called **placoid**, are in all respects comparable to our teeth.

Other scales, called **ganoid**, composed of bony enamelled tissue, are joined together loosely (sturgeon).

There are also **elasmoid** scales, of interest to us because they cover teleostean fish of fresh waters. These elasmoid scales are

—**cycloid** if their external borders are smooth and rounded and

—**ctenoid** if the uncovered portion has one or several rows of small spines.

On each side of the body, about halfway up the side, there is ordinarily a duct that communicates with the exterior and at the bottom of which are sensory organs. This is the **lateral line.** The scales through which it passes are perforated; depending on their length and their number they are useful in systematics.

Scales increase in size at the same time as the body and this growth is concentric. There is a relationship between the increase in size of a scale and the different annual phases in the life of a fish, whether it be an active or dormant phase. This relationship is determined after measuring the scales.

B. ANATOMY

After a rapid examination of the visible characteristics of a fish, we need, by dissection, to acquaint ourselves with the major aspects of its internal anatomy.

1. SKELETON

The framework of the body, the skeleton, is usually bony and sometimes cartilaginous (lamprey-sturgeon).

The skeleton of the head comprises the skull, which protects the nerve centres, and the face, which forms the jaws and supports the branchial system. This does not exist in the lamprey, which has no jaws.

The **vomer** is a bone that helps in differentiating salmonids.

For the **bones of the trunk**, the vertebral column also helps in a more detailed determination of subspecies: we compare the number of vertebrae in some apparently similar individuals.

The other bones of the trunk, separated from the vertebral column, are supports for the fins and their relationship with the skeleton.

The bones in fins are somewhat bony rays.

2. MUSCLES

When we break up a piece of cooked tunny-fish we observe that the muscular mass is arranged in chevrons within the surrounding elements; each chevron is called a **myomere** and the arrangement of the muscular mass is said to be **metameric**.

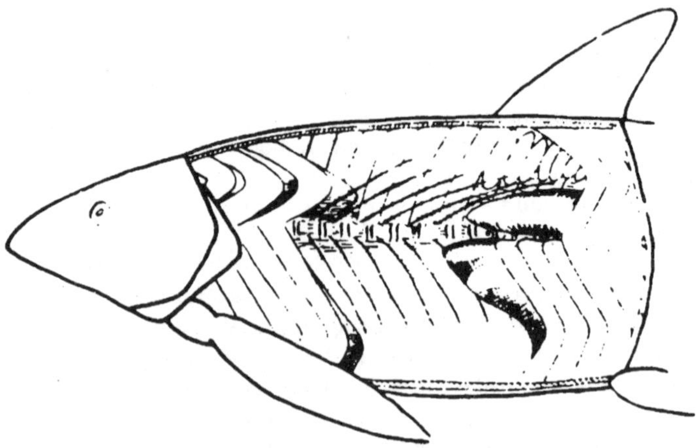

Fig. 63. Oblique backward arrangement in the myomeres of a fish. The spinal nerves follow the inclination of the myomeres.

This metameric muscular mass forms the main mass of flesh and enables a fish to move.

Apart from this mass there are some differentiated muscles, especially in the head:

—the masseter, muscle of the lower jaw, powerful in carnivores,

—the levator and depressor in the temporal arch,

—constrictors of the pharynx, which alter the opening at the back of the mouth,

—the levator, depressor and attractor of the operculum, responsible for the functioning of the respiratory organs,

—the muscles of the branchiostegi,

—the slender upper and lower muscles that control the various fins.

3. DIGESTIVE SYSTEM

The digestive system comprises:

—a mouth,

—a tube that links the mouth to the anus, and

—digestive glands in them that release gastric secretions: some are integral parts of the tube and others are separate (liver and pancreas).

Examining from front to rear, we note:

—mouth and teeth,

—pharynx and oesophagus,

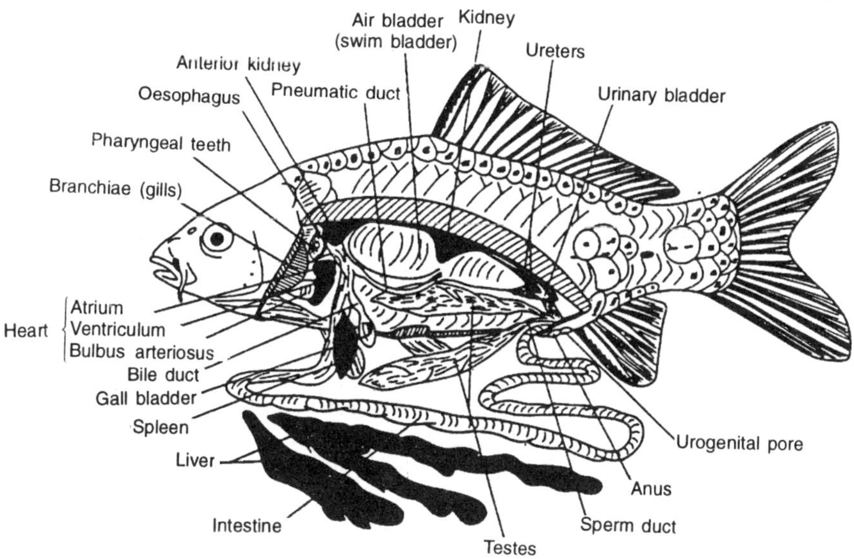

Fig. 64. Schematic diagram of the internal organs of an omnivorous fish, the carp (*Cyprinus carpio*) (sketch by M. Dorson) in De Kinkelin *et al.* (1985) (courtesy INRA)

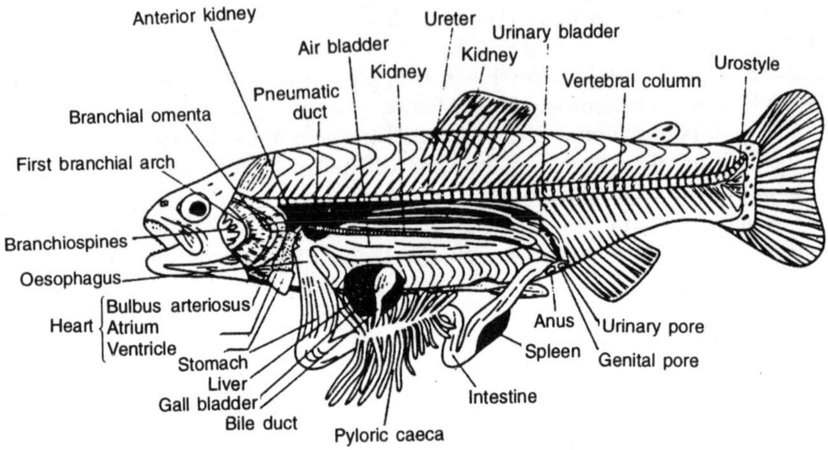

Fig. 65. Diagram of the internal organs of a carnivorous fish, the rainbow trout (*Salmo gairdneri*) (sketch by M. Dorson) in De Kinkelin *et al.* (1985) (courtesy INRA)

– stomach,
– pylorus,
– intestine and anus.

The **mouth** is functional. It is a sucker in the lamprey, a funnel in the sturgeon, telescopic and rummaging in the carp (**protactile**), and very wide in the pike.

The lower jaw is frequently deformed in salmonids and, especially in older males as opposed to females, shows a hook-like deformation entering the upper jaw.

The **teeth** are also functional.

The **pharynx** is behind the buccal cavity, a type of crossroad into which the branchiae open out, and is followed by the **oesophagus** and the **stomach** generally in a U shape. The thickness of the stomach wall depends on the species and the type of food consumed. It may be noted that digestion in fish is more of a chemical rather than a physical type and the stomach walls secrete active gastric juices.

Between the stomach and the intestine, the **pylorus** and pyloric caeca, which are often numerous, are seen as filaments that should not be mistaken for parasitic worms: there are no caeca in cyprinids.

In the anterior portion of the **intestine** we observe the **bile duct** coming from the liver and the pancreatic duct. The intestine is fairly long, longer in herbivores than in carnivores. Its main role, as in mammals, is to introduce nutritive elements into the blood.

The **liver** is a large brown gland, located behind the heart and often accompanied by a gall bladder. The appearance of the liver often helps us to assess the health of dissected fish.

The **air bladder** (swim bladder) is part of the digestive tract, in which it forms a sort of goitre in the upper half, linked to the intestine in certain fishes by the pneumatic duct, totally independent in others, and sometimes not present. These are respectively referred to as physostomi, physoclisti, and aphysi.

—The flounder and the sculpin (bullhead) do not have an air bladder and are said to be aphysic.

—In other cases, this bladder acts as a hydrostatic apparatus that is compressed by the fish to an extent that depends upon the level it wishes to occupy in the liquid mass. It sometimes has a role in respiration and works as a lung (loach).

The **anus** is ahead of the urinogenital pore and the first ray of the anal fin. It may be sited differently and is sometimes used to determine the sex of the fish: in the carp, the anus of the male is concave while that of a female is convex and turgescent.

4. RESPIRATORY SYSTEM

The gills are essential organs in the respiratory system of a fish. They comprise:

—a bony arched frame, the **branchial arch**, between the pharynx and the cheek,

—and, on either side of this arch: **branchiostegi**, generally known as gills, on the convex portion, and **branchiospines** (gill rakers) that look like small soft teeth on the concave portion,

—bony fish have four gills—four branchial arches—on each side of the body,

—cartilagenous fish (the ray) have five,

—the cyclostomes (lampreys) have seven.

The gills open on the side of the pharynx by pharyngeal clefts and towards the outside by branchial clefts. The latter are generally protected by parts of the operculum, some of which are hinged. The **operculum** is also called a gill cover. Selachians (sharks) do not have opercula. It is easily observed that a fish appears to swallow continuously; the current of water passing through the mouth irrigates the gills, which fix oxygen and release carbon dioxide. The operculum acts as a valve that opens and closes.

It has already been explained that the air bladder may play a role in respiration; this is observed in the pond loach, which buries itself in mud during the summer and breathes through its mouth.

Respiration may also take place by exchanges from the skin, as in the case of *Periophthalmus*, the mudskipper.

5. CIRCULATORY SYSTEM

The circulatory system is a closed circuit comprising arteries, capillaries, veins, and a pump, the heart, located behind the gills.

The simple heart corresponds to the upright heart in mammals; it is formed of four successive cavities:

—the sinus venosus, a conjunction of veins that takes the blood to the heart,

—the atrium, which corresponds to the two auricles in mammals,

—the ventricle, and

—the bulb which is the antechamber of the ventral aorta.

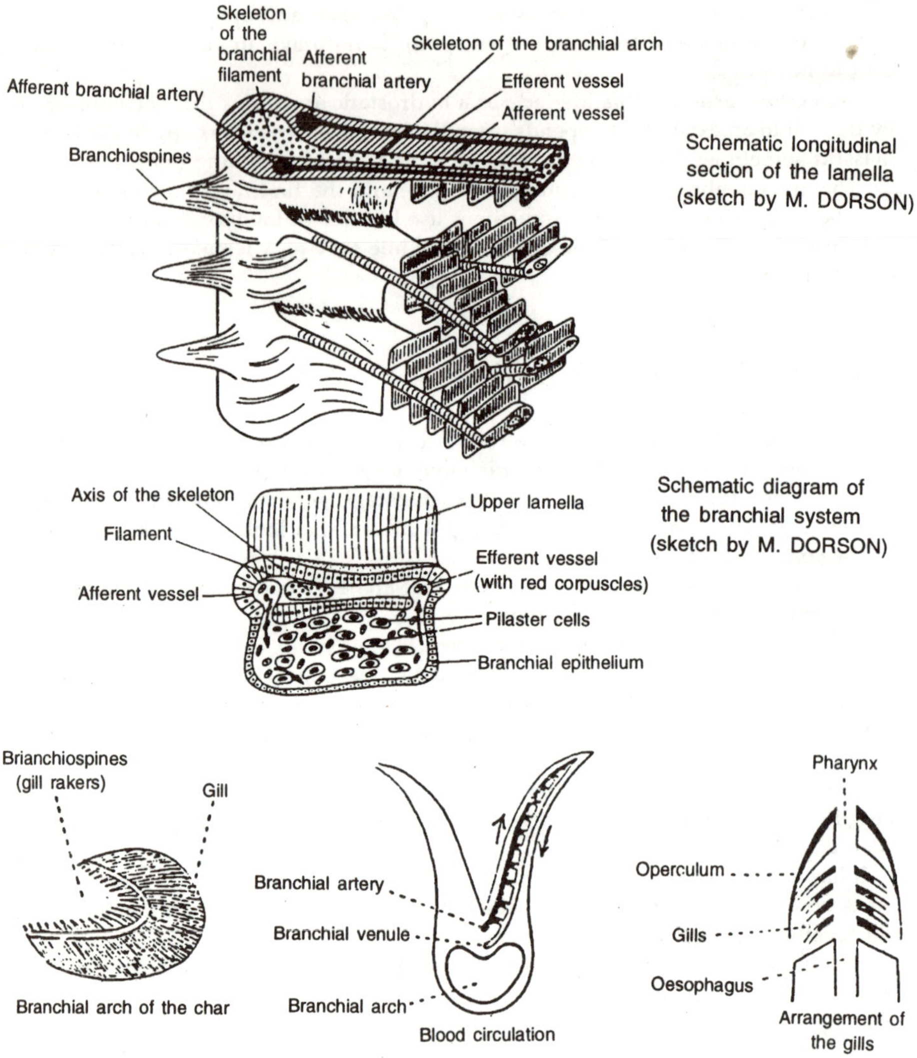

Fig. 66. Respiratory system of a fish (from DE KINKELIN *et al.*, 1985, courtesy INRA)

This aorta carries blood to the gills on the left and the right through 4, 5, or 7 pairs of branchial arteries.

From the gills, **the blood does not return to the heart**, but converges towards the artery below the vertebral column in the hemal arch, from which many secondary arteries originate, which irrigate the viscera and the muscles.

The blood containing CO_2 and waste products is carried to the heart through:

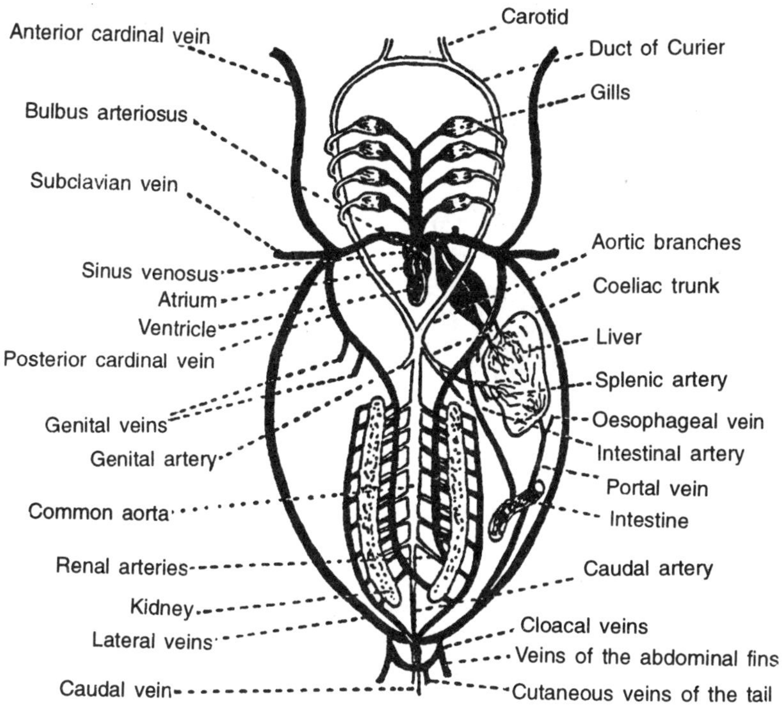

Fig. 67. Circulatory system of a fish

—the anterior cardinal veins carrying blood from the head,

—the posterior cardinal veins carrying blood from the rear portion of the body,

—the capillaries from the intestine forming the intestinal vein, which subdivides into capillaries in the liver, forming the **hepatic portal system.**

—similar capillaries forming the **renal portal system**.

There is a **lymphatic heart** in some fishes such as the eel, in which it is situated in the caudal region. It is well known that to kill an eel we only have to cause a bursting of the heart by beating the tail against a stone or a post.

6. EXCRETORY SYSTEM

The kidneys, essential organs of the excretory system, are not exactly like those in mammals. They are brown glands, highly elongated, sometimes greatly ramified, somewhat jointed together, covering the dorsal portion of the visceral cavity. Two ureters carry the waste products to the urinary pore, sometimes through a terminal bladder which is only an enlargement of the ureters.

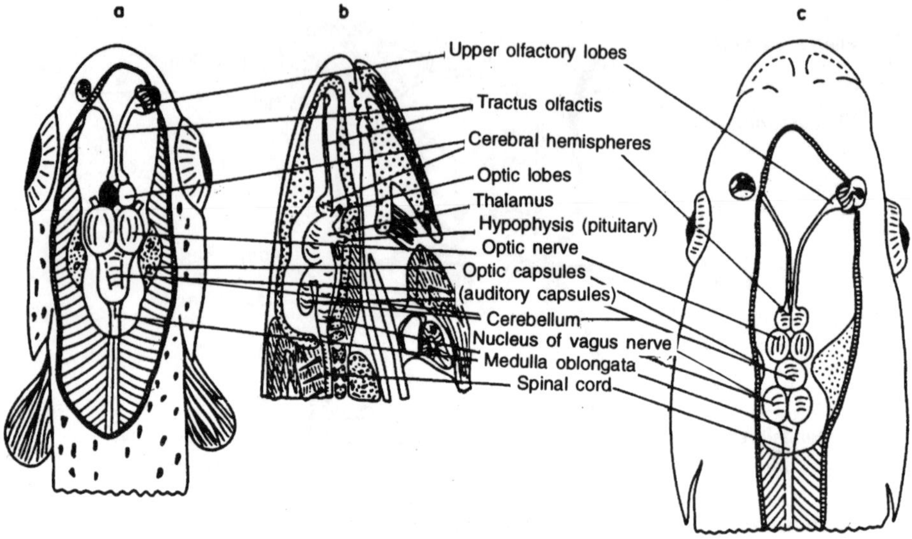

Fig. 68. Schematic diagram of the nervous system of a teleostean fish, the rainbow trout (sketch by M. DORSON) in DE KINKELIN *et al.* (1985) (courtesy INRA)

C. CLASSIFICATION

1. GENERAL CLASSIFICATION OF THE ANIMAL KINGDOM

Table 13. General classification of the animal kingdom

Sub-kingdom	Branches	Classes	Orders
	Flagellata		Dinoflagellates – Polymastigina Chromomonadina – Hypermastigina Phytomonadina – Euglenina Pantostomadina – Protomastigina
	Rhizopoda		Heliozoa – Mycetozoa Radiolaria – Foraminifera Proteomyxida – Amoebina
	Ciliata		Holotricha – Hypotricha Heterotricha – Peritricha Oligotricha – Tentaculifera
	Sporozoa		Cystosporida – Sarcosporida Cnidosporida

	Coelenterata		
Protozoa	Sponges	Calcareous sponges Ascons, Sycons, Leucons Corneosiliceous sponges	 Hexa-, Tetra-, Monactinellida Ceratospongea
	Echinodermata		
	Monomerida	Rotifera Bryozoa	
	Vermes	Annelids	Hirudinea Chaetopoda Gephyria
		Platyhelminthes	Turbellaria Trematoda Cestoda
	Nemathel- minthes	Nematoda Acanthocephala	
	Arthropoda	Crustacea Myriapoda Insecta Arachnida	
Metazoa	Mollusca	Amphineura Gastropoda Lamellibranchia Scaphopoda Cephalopoda	
	Protochordata	Acraniata Tunicata	
	Vertebrata	**Pisces** Amphibia Reptilia Aves Mammalia	

2. IDENTIFICATION

2.1 Anguilliform Body

a) Several gill openings, not covered by an operculum, at the sides of the neck. Mouth in the form of a sucker, on the lower side of the head. No pectoral fins:

- Family PETROMYZONIDAE

b) A simple gill opening, not covered by an operculum, at each side of the neck. Pectoral fins present:

- Family ANGUILLIDAE

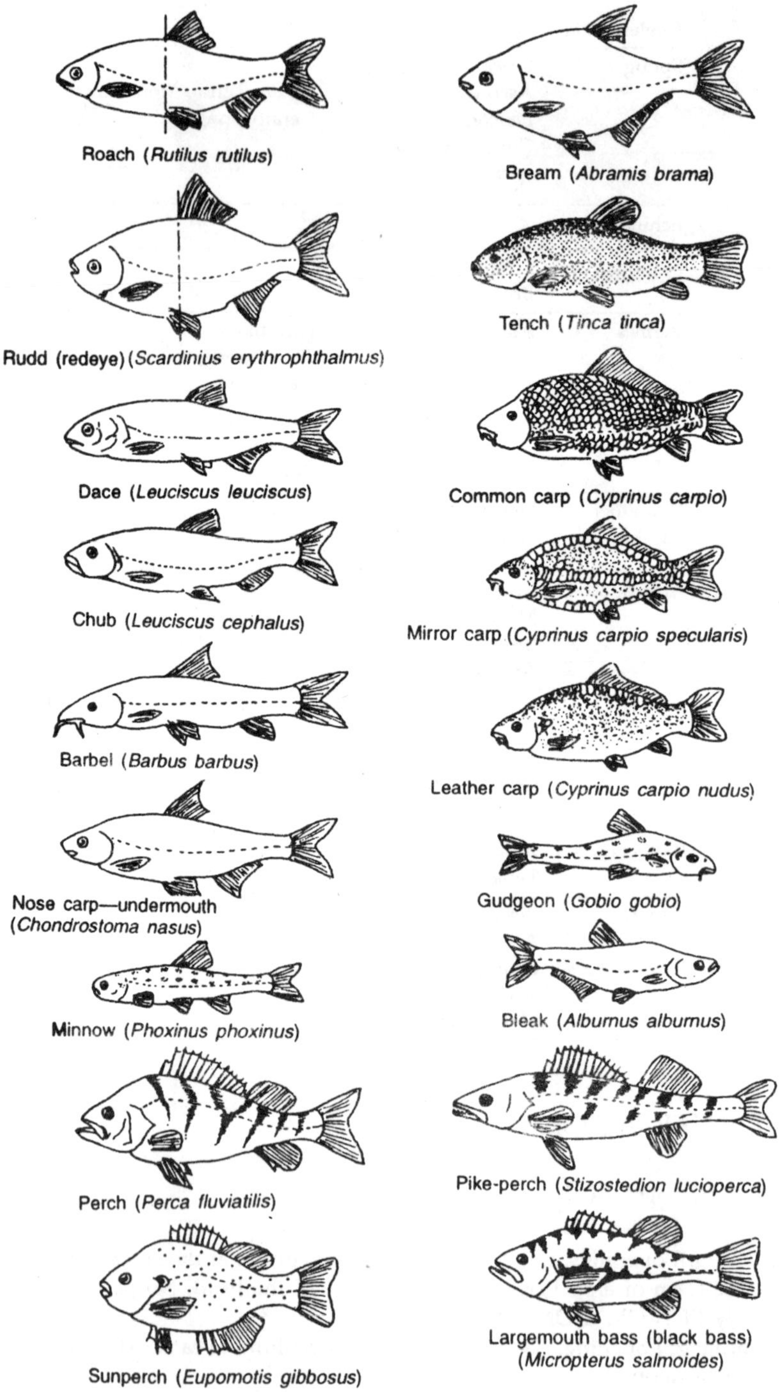

Fig. 69. Some species of fish

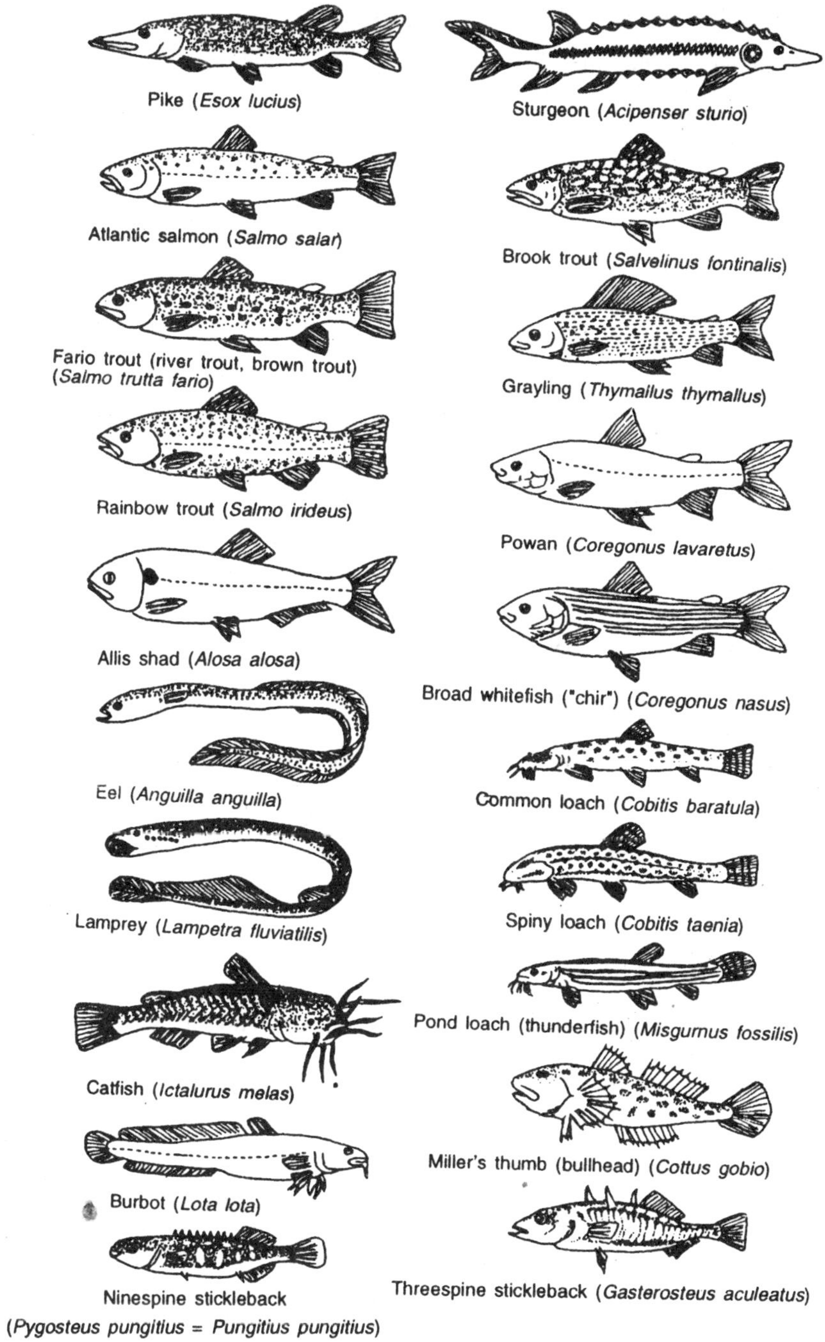

Fig. 70. Some species of fish (contd)

2.2 Asymmetrical Body

—Both eyes on the same side of the body (pigmented face):
• Family PLEURONECTIDAE

2.3 Symmetrical Spindle-shaped Body

a) Small shields (bony plates) on the body, arranged longitudinally. Mouth on the lower side of the head.
• Family ACIPENSERIDAE
b) Separate spines ahead of the normal dorsal fin:
• Family GASTEROSTEIDAE
Bare body:
—Pelvic or ventral fins directly below the insertion of the pectoral fins:
• Family COTTIDAE
—Pelvic fins in the shape of two rod-like structures directly below the insertion of the pectoral fins. No barbels on the lower jaw:
• Family BLENNIDAE
—Pelvic fins inserted behind the line of insertion of the pectoral fins. Barbels on the snout and under the chin:
• Family SILURIDAE
Body covered with scales of various sizes but always visible.
—Pelvic fins of normal shapes, slightly ahead of the insertion of pectoral fins. A barbel on the middle of the lower jaw:
• Family GADIDAE
—Pelvic fins attached at the level of insertion of the pectoral fins:
—The first two rays of the anal fin are spiny:
• Family PERCIDAE
—The first three rays of the anal fin are spiny:
• Family CENTRARCHIDAE
—Pelvic fins attached behind the level of insertion of the pectoral fins:
—Two dorsal fins with rays:
• Family MUGILIDAE
—Two dorsal fins, the second small, soft, and with no rays:
—Large mouth, very wide; upper jaw extending beyond the vertical diameter of the eye:
* Anal fin with 10–13 rays:
• Family SALMONIDAE
* Anal fin with 13–15 rays:
• Family OSMERIDAE
—Narrow mouth. Upper jaw not extending beyond the vertical diameter of the eye.
* Dorsal fin about twice as long as the anal fin with 20–25 rays:
• Family THYMALLIDAE
* Dorsal fin almost equal to the anal fin with 9–17 rays.
• Family COREGONIDAE
—A single dorsal fin:

—Anal fin opposite the dorsal fin.
* Dorsal fin inserted far back. Very wide mouth.
• Family ESOCIDAE
* Dorsal fin inserted slightly to the rear. Small mouth.
• Family CYPRINODONTIDAE
—Anal fin not opposite the dorsal fin:
* A ventral notched keel.
• Family CLUPEIDAE
* No ventral keel. No teeth.
—6–10 barbels on the mouth:
• Family COBITIDAE
—Mouth, bare or with only 2–4 barbels:
• Family CYPRINIDAE

3. MAJOR FAMILIES

3.1 Anguillidae

General characteristics: The body is long, snake-like, rounded in front and flattened towards the tail. The skin is covered with a thick sticky mucus, above very small scales.

The head is long, jaws with teeth, free tongue; the gill openings are very small, situated at the base of the pectoral fins. Dorsal and anal fins are united at the end with the caudal fin. The pectoral fins are small.

Anguilla anguilla L., the common eel, lives anywhere in salt, brackish, or fresh waters, estuaries, rivers, lakes, ponds, or wells.

The colour varies considerably: the back is of an olive or yellowish-brown shade; the abdomen is yellowish-white. The anal fin is normally white with a rose-coloured border; the dorsal fin is greyish and other fins yellowish: these are yellow eels.

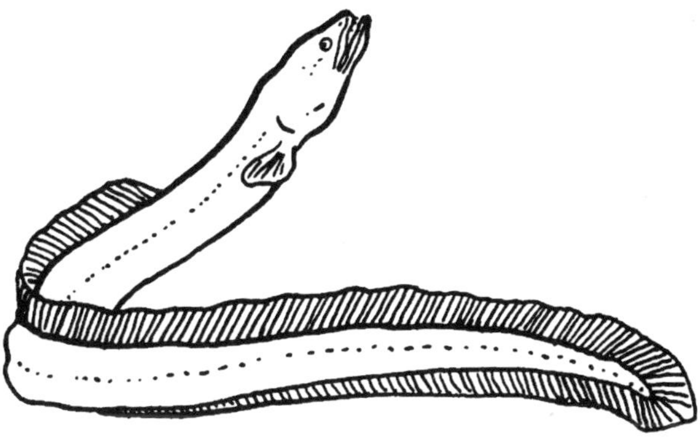

Fig. 71. General view of eel

Sexually mature individuals are black at the back: the abdomen is a silvery white. These are silver eels; the fins are dark.

The eel is lucifugous, with an amazing vitality, and also extremely supple. It swims slowly by undulations and by creeping. During winter it buries itself in mud and remains in a lethargic state.

It is carnivorous and a heavy predator; during the autumn, at the end of their period of growth (4–7 years for males and 7–15 years for females), eels acquire a strong urge for migration and stop feeding; catadromic migration leads them to the sea. We know, from the works of J. SCHMIDT, that all eels of Europe and North Africa move to the central region of the Sargasso Sea where spawning and incubation occur at a depth of 400–500 m and at a temperature of 16–17°C. The small larvae (leptocephalus) carried by currents to the surface are dispersed in different directions and only those carried to the northeast are likely to develop further. The larval migration continues for about 2 1/2 years.

The females can reach a length of 1.5 m. The flesh, highly palatable when fresh, especially at the time of the eel's downstream journey, can be preserved by salting or smoking.

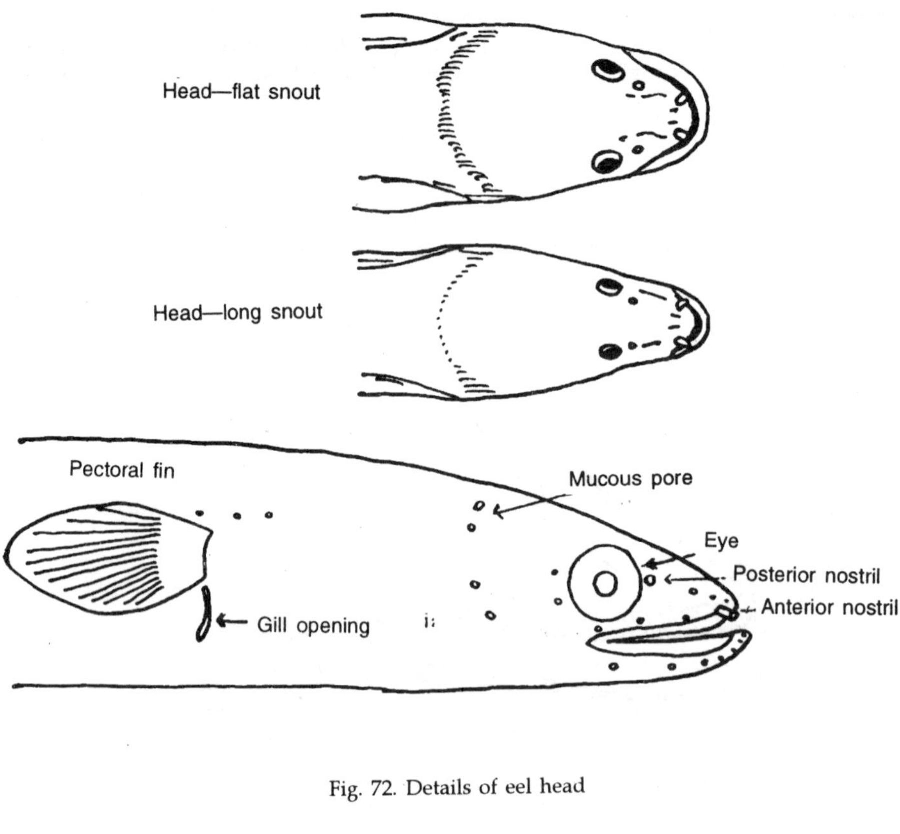

Fig. 72. Details of eel head

3.2 Percidae

General characteristics: There is a single dorsal fin formed of two dissimilar parts; sometimes there are two dorsal fins with the first one formed of spiny rays, joined by a membrane. It is as long as the second one or even longer. On the palate there are soft teeth.

Perca fluviatilis L., perch, has 13–16 spiny rays on the dorsal fin and 8–9 rays on the anal fin. The colour is a golden green with about 6 brown transverse stripes on the back and sides. The normal size is 20–40 cm. Spawning occurs from March to June in shallow areas when the water temperature is 14°C. A female lays 200,000–300,000 eggs, 2–2.5 mm in diameter, in long mucous strings attached to water plants. The incubation period is 8–14 days.

Stizostedion lucioperca L., the pike-perch, differs from the perch in that the anal fin has 12 soft rays.

The coloration is greenish-grey with narrow brown transverse stripes. It is commonly observed to be longer than 1 m. It is a bottom dweller and lucifugous.

Spawning occurs from April to June in a water temperature of 15°C. The eggs are small, 1–1.5 mm in diameter. The female lays 200,000 eggs per kg body weight. The average incubation period is 10 days.

3.3 Centrarchidae

General characteristics: The front rays of the dorsal fin have spines; the others are soft and jointed. There are soft teeth on the palate. On the dorsal fin there are 6–11 spiny rays and on the anal fin there are 7–12 articulated rays behind 3–8 spiny rays.

Eupomotis gibbosus, the sun perch, has a length (excluding the tail) that is twice its height. It has a rich coloration.

An introduced species, it has adapted everywhere and is harmful. Its voraciousness leads to the destruction of young indigenous fish.

The species spawns in May and June. The nest is guarded by the male during the incubation period. Several tens of thousands of eggs are laid by the female.

Micropterus salmoides Lacepede is the largemouth bass (black bass–trout–perch). The length of its body (excluding the tail) is three times its height. It is blackish-green and has a black horizontal stripe on the sides. The mouth is very large, extending beyond the eye. It prefers placid, warm waters. It is voracious and feeds on larvae, young fish (fry), and amphibians. Several tens of thousands of eggs are laid at the end of spring or the beginning of summer. The male guards the eggs during the incubation period.

Maximum size is 50 cm for a weight of 2 kg. The flesh is highly palatable.

Micropterus dolomieui Lacepede is the smallmouth black bass–black perch. It is identical to the afore-mentioned black bass, except that it has a smaller mouth. Not very common, it prefers cooler waters.

3.4 Salmonidae

Determination of species is based on the number of scales on the lateral line; it is also based on the structure of the vomer. Originally marine, in the Tertiary period

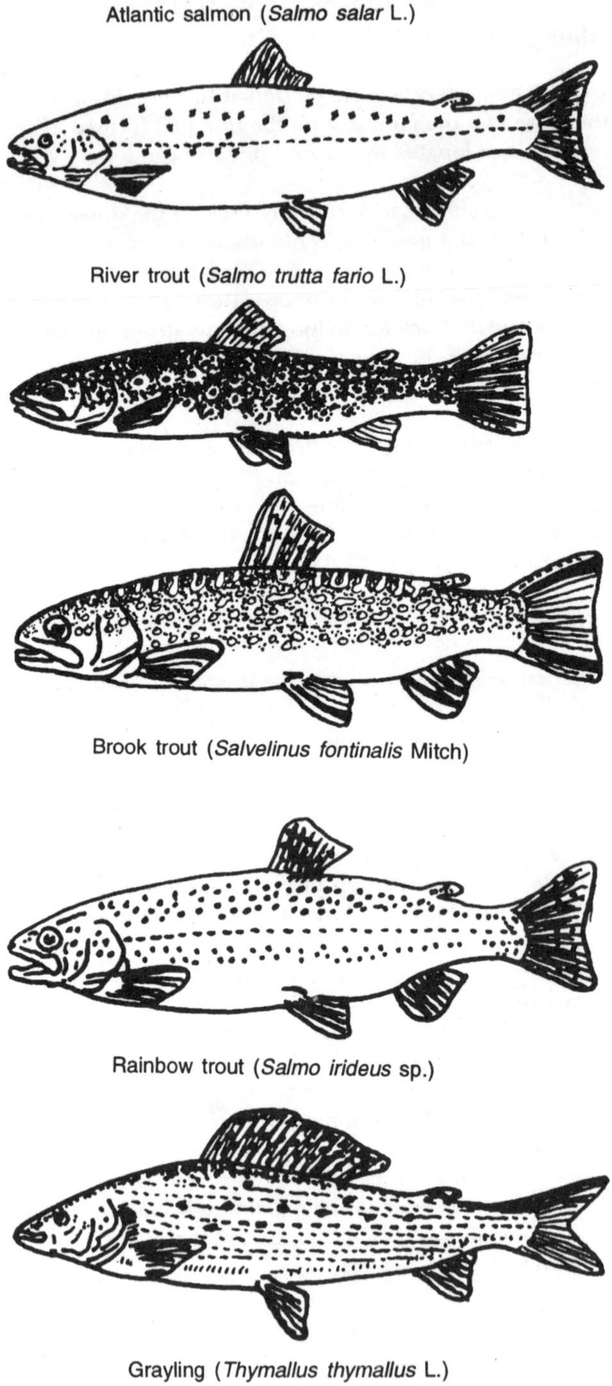

Fig. 73. Salmonids in running streams

(the Miocene), the ancestral stock must have been differentiated during the major geological upheavals of the Pliocene, resulting in migratory and sedentary lines.

Salmo salar L., the Atlantic salmon, is an anadromous migrator. The posterior angle of the upper maxilla is extended, not exceeding the rear portion of the eye. There are 120–130 scales between the operculum and the base of the tail and 10–12 between the lateral line and the anterior rim of the adipose dorsal fin. The rear portion of the caudal fin is concave.

It has a graceful shape and brilliant colours. It may be longer than 1.2 m and weigh 20 kg.

Spawning occurs in December and January. The female lays 1000–1600 eggs per kg body weight. These eggs are pale pink and 5-6 mm in diameter.

The eggs hatch at the end of February and early March. The alevins spend 1, 2 and sometimes 3 years near the spawning areas. When they are 15–20 cm long they move to the sea at the beginning of spring, after a change in coloration (parrs, smolts).

Salmo trutta L. is the river trout. The posterior angle of the upper maxilla extends beyond the back of the eye. There are 110–125 scales between the operculum and the base of the tail and 14–15 between the lateral line and the front part of the adipose dorsal fin.

The coloration depends on the water and the area. The back is usually of a dark olive colour, lighter at the sides. The abdomen is a bright golden yellow or yellowish-white. There are black spots on the back, sides, and fins. There are also bright orange-red spots with a pale blue border. The males have even brighter colours.

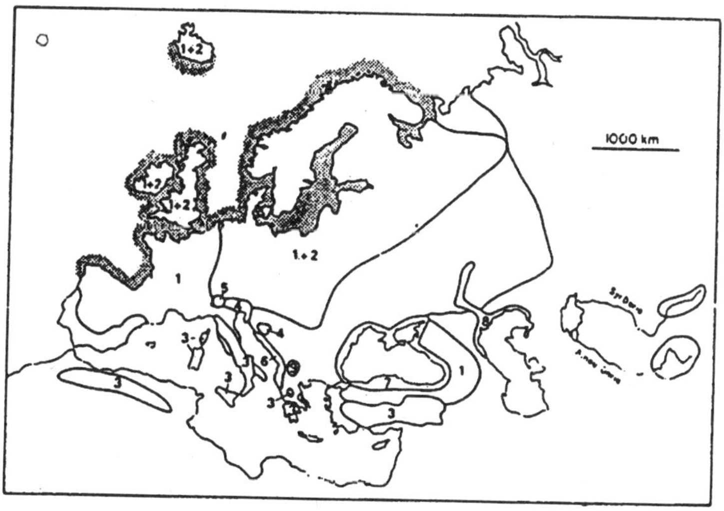

Fig. 74. Areas of distribution of some geographical and ecological "forms" of the common trout (after BLANC *et al.*). *Salmo trutta trutta* (sea trout). 1: *Salmo trutta fario* (river trout). 2: *Salmo trutta lacustris* (lake trout). 3: *Salmo trutta macrostigma*. 4: *Salmo trutta marmoratus*. 5: *Salmo trutta carpio*. 6: *Salmo trutta dentex*. 7: *Salmo trutta labrax* (Black Sea Salmon/ trout). 8: *Salmo trutta caspius* (Caspian trout). 9: *Salmo trutta letnica* (big Ohrid trout).

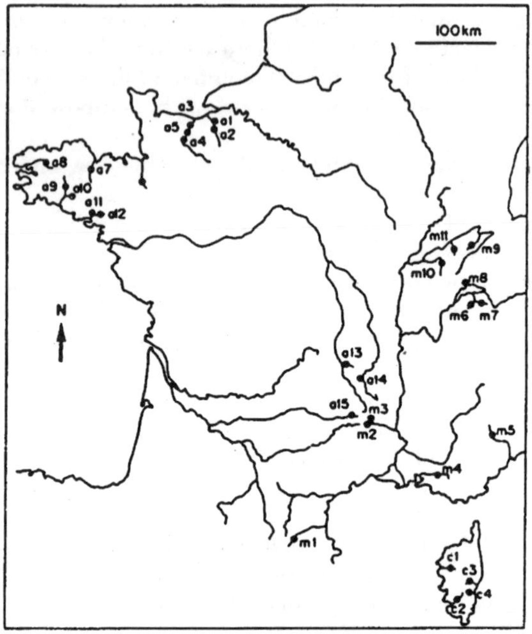

Fig. 75. Geographical locations of natural populations examined. a1: Calonne (sea trout). a2: Touques (smolts). a3: Orne (smolts). a4: Orne (sedentary trout). a5: Orne (sea trout). a6: Avion. a7: Leffe. a8: Elorn. a9, a10: Şcorff. a11, a12: Montgolerian. a13: Allier (tributary). a14: Loire (tributary). a15: Lot. m1: Tech (tributary). m2, m3: Ceze (tributaries). m4: Touloubre. m5: Var (tributary). m6, m7: Dranse (tributaries). m8: Aubonne. m9, m10, m11: Doubs (tributaries). c1: Aitone. c2: Rizzanese. c3: Taravo. c4: Solenzara (after GUYOMARD, 1989).

The trout spawns from October to December. Extremely voracious, it feeds on insects, spawn, and even fry of other fish or of its own species.

The "salmonid" trout is not a separate subspecies. It is merely its feed, which contains carotenoid pigments (small crustaceans), that gives its flesh the characteristic pink colour.

Apart from *Salmo trutta fario* (river trout/brown trout), which has already been described, there are several other varieties:

Salmo trutta (lacustris) (lake trout) has a silver coloration, is 50–85 cm long, and weighs 2–8 kg. It migrates at a low depth and there are at least as many subspecies as there are lakes.

Salmo trutta (marina) (sea trout), silver-coloured with black crosses, measures 50-85 cm in length and weighs 2–12 kg. It migrates seasonally to the sea and comprises as many subspecies as there are coastal rivers.

Salmo irideus Gibbons (*Oncorhynchus mykiss*) (rainbow trout) generally has 135–150 scales between the operculum and the base of the tail. Imported from America,

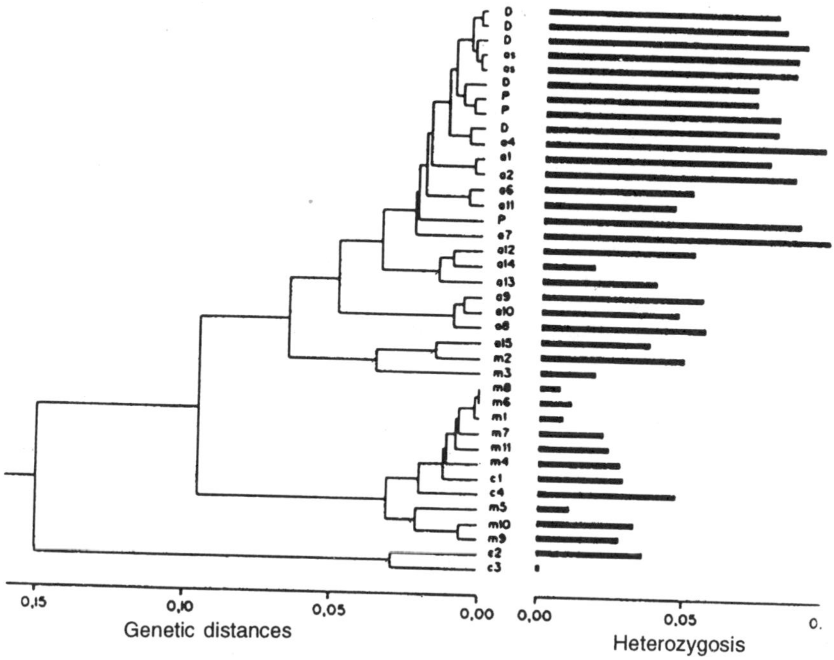

Fig. 76. Dendrogram obtained by hierarchical agglomeration (UPGMA) based on genetic distances (standard genetic distance of the NEI 1975) and extent of heterozygosis. D: domestic stock. P: Polish stock.
This dendrogram highlights phenetic relationships (degrees of genetic resemblance) between populations; their phylogeny ("genealogy" of populations) may be quite different.

it was the result of several crossings between various species very similar in appearance. Since then there have been other crossings subsequent to later imports: *S. gairdneri* (rainbow trout or steelhead), which is a migrator; *S. shasta*, a strain similar to rainbow trout introduced in Europe; and *S. roosevelti* (Everman). They are more akin to the genus *Oncorhynchus* than to *Salmo*.

The body is broad. The length is four times the height and the head is small. The colours are iridescent. The back is indigo blue verging towards olive green. The colour fades at the sides, becoming almost white on the belly. The entire body is speckled with black spots except on the lower part. The median part is iridescent, more so in the male, with a deep red shade.

Extremely voracious, it is constantly searching for food. The spawning period is from November to March and is almost exclusively conducted by artificial reproduction. It can tolerate higher temperatures better than *S. trutta*.

Salvelinus alpinus L. (arctic char) is a lake species with at least 200 scales on the lateral line and large branchial spines on the first branchial arch.

A bluish-green tint on the back changes to a yellowish-pink tint on the sides with small bright yellow spots.

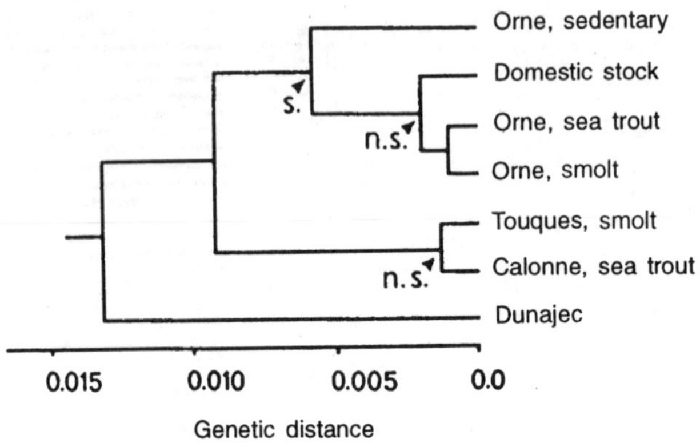

Fig. 77. Dendrogram (47 loci, standard genetic distances of the NEI, UPGMA) representing the phenetic relationships between migratory and sedentary ecophenotypes in the Orne and Touques (samples a1, a2, a3, a4, a5 in Fig. 75) and the two strains used for restocking in these rivers (domestic stock and Dunajec). s: significant at 5%. ns: not significant (after GUYOMARD, 1989).

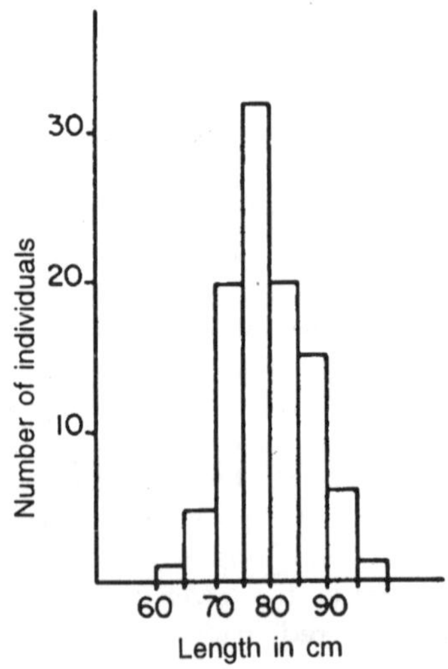

Fig. 78. Sizes of fario trout (*Salmo trutta fario* – river trout) at 6 months

The arctic char is 25–50 cm long and lives in deep water. It rises only to spawn from November to March in waters at a temperature of 6°C on gravel beds. The female lays 1600–1800 eggs, smaller than those of the trout. This char is considered highly palatable.

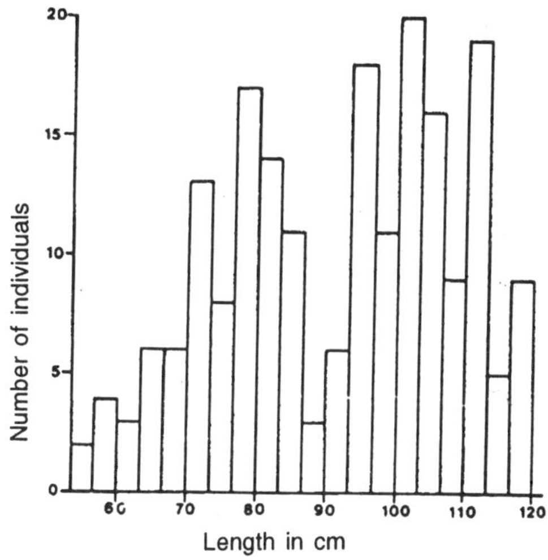

Fig. 79. Sizes of Atlantic salmon (*Salmo salar*). Appearance of bimodality associated with smolting (after KRIEG, 1989).

Salvelinus fontinalis (brook trout) is an introduced species. The scales are even smaller than those of the char (220–230 on the lateral line). The branchial spines are smaller and less numerous. The back is greenish-blue, mottled with irregular sinuous stripes. The sides are of a violet shade and the belly ochre-yellow. This fish prefers cool and clear waters. It grows rapidly and is highly valued.

– *Hucho hucho* L. was introduced in France from Central Europe and is known as the Danube salmon. It has a short vomer with 5 teeth across the vomerine plate, while there are no teeth on the vomer itself. The scales are relatively smaller than those on the common trout. There are 180–200 scales on the lateral line. The length may be 1.5 m and the weight 25 kg.

The major predators on the eggs of the Danube salmon are the graylings. When these young salmon emerge from eggs they hunt other young ones, especially those of cyprinids and particularly those of the nose carp, which hatch almost at the same time but are much smaller.

The *hucho* is not a migrator. The adult lives in deep water courses with adequate oxygen, downstream of the trout zone, and in grayling zones above the zones of barbels. Because of its large size it has no predators. It lives on the cyprinid fauna and especially the nose carp.

The flesh of the Danube salmon is considered excellent, better than trout and as good as salmon. It was acclimated in 1956 in the Rhone basin, apparently without much success, and by introduction in the river Usses, where it reproduced. It had been acclimated in Morocco by 1952.

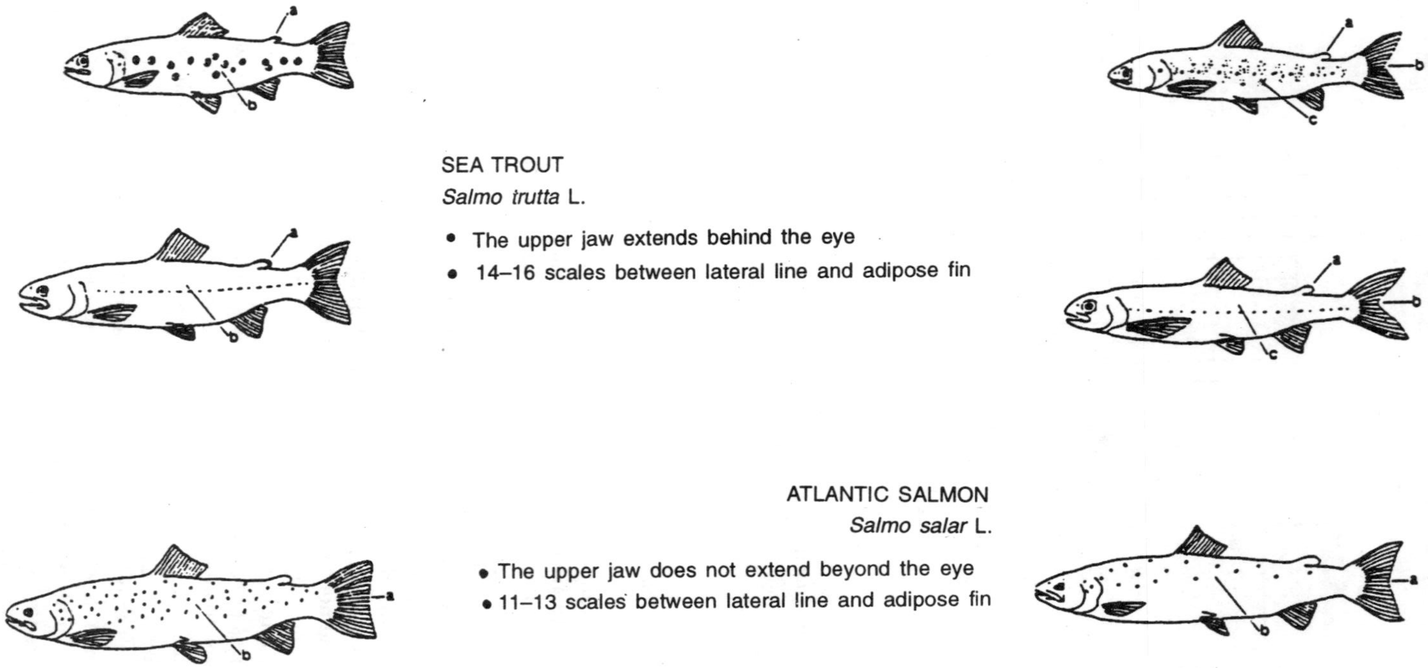

Fig. 80. Characteristics differentiating sea trout and salmon (after PORCHER, 1988)

3.5 Coregonidae

General characteristics: small mouth, brilliant colours, silver shades on the sides and belly. These are lacustrine forms that prefer cold, clean, and deep waters.

Coregonus lavaretus L. (powan), never more than 30 cm long, is specific to the Bourget lake. On the first branchial arch there are 32–36 gill rakers. It has a terminal mouth and small pectoral fins.

It has a greenish-blue coloration on the back. It spawns from mid-November to mid-December. The eggs are deposited along the bank of the lake.

Coregonus fera Jurine (large bottom-dwelling whitefish), is the largest of our whitefish (more than 50 cm). It has 21–30 gill rakers on the first branchial arch, a large snout, and a low mouth.

It has the same coloration as powan, with some blackish marks on the upper part of the body. This whitefish is found in Lake Leman. It spawns in deep water from February to March. The incubation period is 2–3 months.

Coregonus hiemalis Jurine, also found in Lake Leman, is smaller than the broad whitefish and has a lighter blue shade in its coloration. It does not appear in the upper layers of water during the summer. It is caught in December when it comes near the banks to spawn.

The meat of whitefish is delicate and palatable. They are caught with nets on a large scale.

3.6 Cyprinidae

General characteristics: the family Cyprinidae includes most fishes in the fresh waters of France. These are white fish, what fisherman call "white bait". Omnivorous and not fastidious (feeding on insects, worms, larvae, and plants), they reproduce in spring and early summer. There are many hybrids.

Identifying species based on the arrangement of the pharyngeal teeth is difficult, more so because of the facility of intrageneric or even intergeneric hybridization as observed in most members of the family. Some hybrids are fertile and may appear to be autonomous species.

Species of this family, of which there are approximately 1300, are found everywhere except in Australia and South America. On the other hand, they form the majority of freshwater fish in Asia, Europe, and North Africa.

Because of the large number of genera, a dichotomous table is necessary for their differentiation.

A) Anal fin with 2 or 3 single rays in front and not more than 5 or 6 branched and flexible rays
  a) 15–22 rays on the dorsal fin:
    1) 4 barbels around the mouth — *Cyprinus*
    2) No barbels — *Carassius*
  b) 7–9 rays on dorsal fin:
    3) 4 barbels, more than 45 scales on lateral line — *Barbus*
    4) 2 barbels, less than 45 scales on lateral line — *Gobio*

B) Anal fin with 2 or 3 rays in front and 7–12 branching and flexible rays
  a) More than 75 scales counted on lateral line:
    5) 95–110 scales — *Tinca*

6) 80–90 scales *Phoxinus*

b) Less than 70 scales on lateral line

–less than 40 scales, lateral line incomplete:

7) *Rhodeus*

–40 scales or more, lower buccal lip hard, horny:

8) *Chondrostoma*

–lower buccal lip soft, first ray of the dorsal fin much behind the vertical line of the beginning of the pelvic fins:

9) *Scardinius*

–first ray of dorsal fin above or very slightly behind vertical line of pelvic fins:

complete lateral line

* less than 53 scales on lateral line

no brown longitudinal stripe on sides:

10) 42–55 scales, total length (excluding tail fin) not more than 3.5 times body height *Rutilus*

11) 44–52 scales, total length (excluding tail fin) at least 4 times body height *Leuciscus*

12) Brown longitudinal stripe on sides, 15–18 cm *Telestes*

* more than 53 scales on lateral line:

13) *Idus*

complete lateral line, size 5–8 cm:

14) *Leucaspius*

C) Anal fin with 2 or 3 single rays in front and 13 or more branched and flexible rays.

a) upper jaw as long as or shorter than the lower one:

15) upper jaw shorter than lower: no black pigmentations on lateral line *Alburnus*

16) upper jaw as long as lower: black pigmentation on lateral line *Alburnoides*

b) Upper jaw longer than lower:

17) 40–50 scales on lateral line: diameter of eye larger than that of snout *Blicca*

18) 50–54 scales on lateral line: diameter of eye smaller than that of snout *Abramis*

Cyprinus carpio L. (carp)

General characteristics: On the anal and dorsal fins there is a ray that is hard and jagged at the back. The dorsal fin, which is long, has 16–26 rays. There are 4 barbels, of which two are on the upper jaw and two at the sides of the mouth.

The lips are thick. The pharyngeal teeth are arranged in several rows.

The coloration is extremely variable, generally greenish-brown.

The length may be as much as 50 cm, and more in selected subspecies such as:

–the mirror carp, with a few large scales,

–the leather carp, without scales,

–the chinese carp (hi goi), adipose and with an extremely fast growth.

Barbus

General characteristics: no hard and jagged ray on the anal fin. The body is somewhat cylindrical: the total length is 5–7 times the body height, the caudal fin is forked and

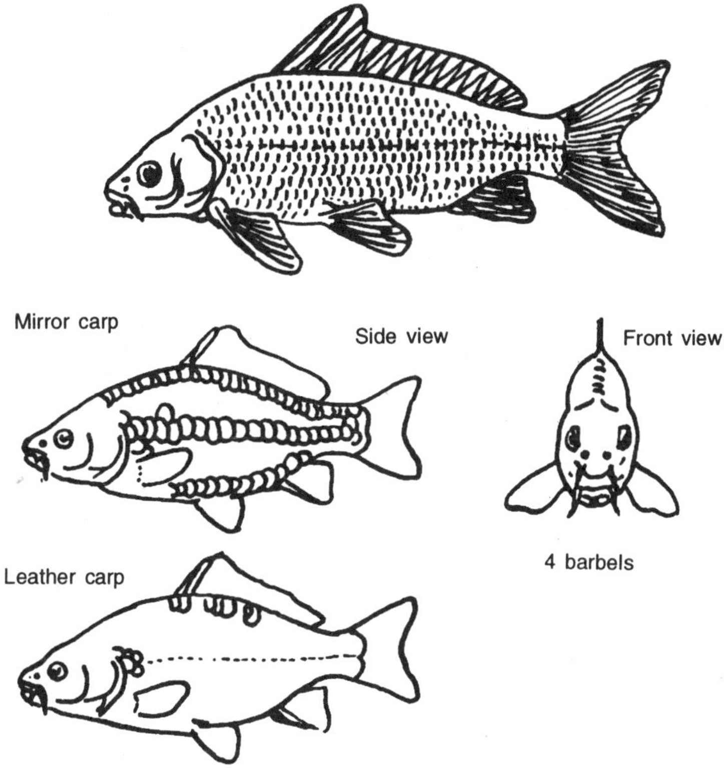

Fig. 81. Common carp (*Cyprinus carpio* L.)

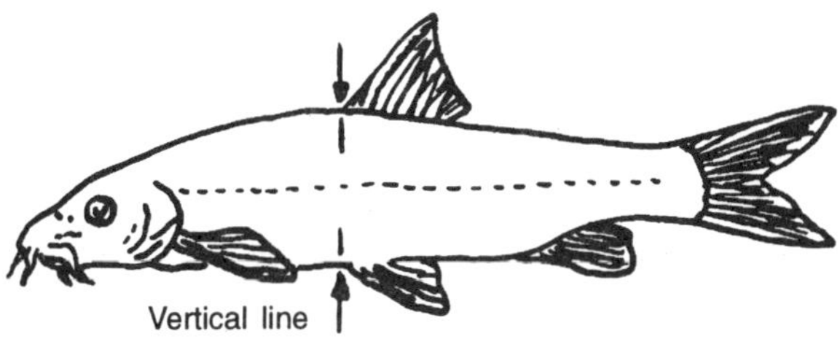

Fig. 82. Common barbel (*Barbus barbus* L.)

the border of the dorsal fin is concave; the pharyngeal teeth are arranged in several rows and there are 7–10 of them. The mouth is located below the snout, which is prominent.

Barbus fluviatilis C.V. (the river barbel) always has a hard and jagged ray at the end of the dorsal fin. There are no large black marks on the back and sides. The back is greenish-brown and the belly is silvery white. The length is 25–50 cm.

Barbus meridionalis Risso (the southern barbel) has no jagged ray on the dorsal fin. There are large black marks on the back and sides. The back is greenish-brown and the belly a silvery white.

This is the common barbel observed in all types of water collections. Many hybrids may be of a large size (as long as 75 cm).

Gobio gobio L. (the gudgeon) lives in schools on beds of sand or gravel where it can find molluscs and larvae that form its food. It prefers clear and fast-flowing streams. It is 12–18 cm long and pinkish on the back. The operculum is of a golden shade that is also seen in a longitudinal stripe on the upper part of the sides. The head and belly have glints of deep red. A bluish shade separates the dark colour of the back from the lighter colour on the sides.

Spawning is at the end of spring and beginning of summer. It extends over a month. The bluish eggs are 2 mm in diameter. The female lays about 100 of these, on pebbles or among water plants. Incubation period is 6–8 days.

Like the barbel, the male during the reproductive period has display spots on its body. The meat of the gudgeon is very tasty when fried.

Tinca tinca L. (tench) is found wherever carp is found and is often raised together with carp. Its coloration ranges from golden green to a dark brown wine shade. The belly is lighter in colour. Like the carp, the tench can live for a long period out of water in a humid medium. It remains always at the bottom, where it finds its food.

Spawning occurs when the water temperature reaches 18–20°C, which is from May to July. The female lays 400,000–600,000 eggs per g body weight. The eggs are greenish and 1 mm in diameter. The incubation period is 6–7 days.

The male differs from the female in having a thickening of the second ray of its pelvic fins. The average size of the species varies from 15 to 30 cm and weight from 500 to 1000 g. Its meat is tasty.

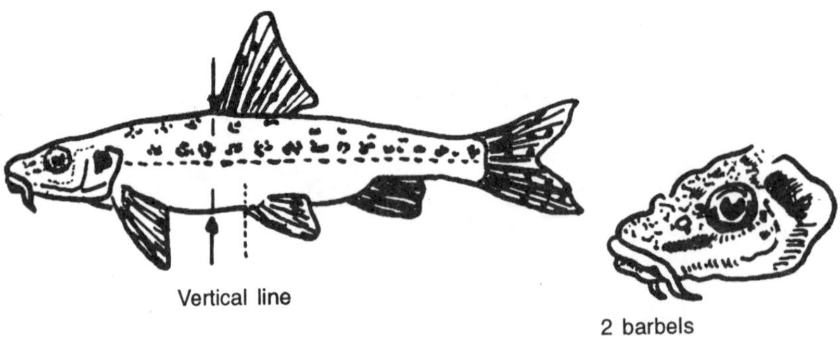

Fig. 83. Gudgeon (*Gobio gobio* L.)

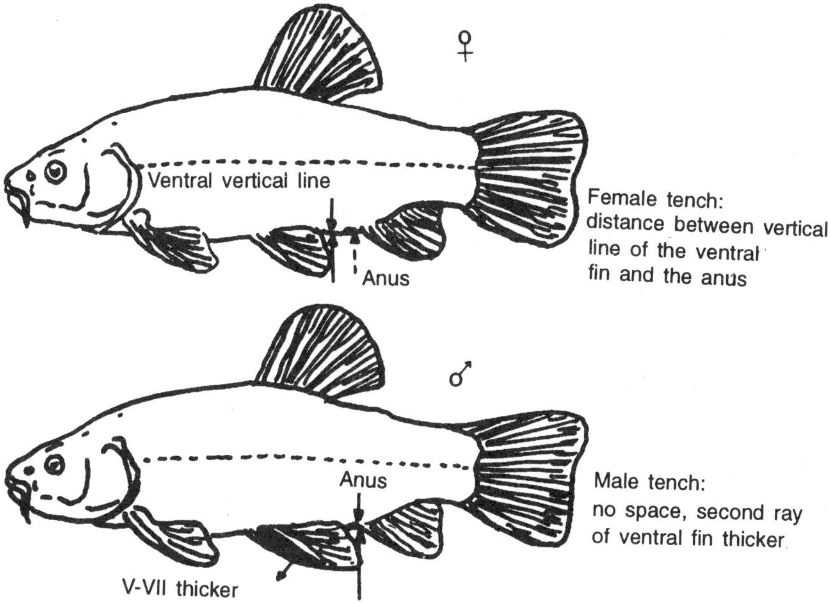

Fig. 84. Tench (*Tinca tinca* L.): sex differentiation

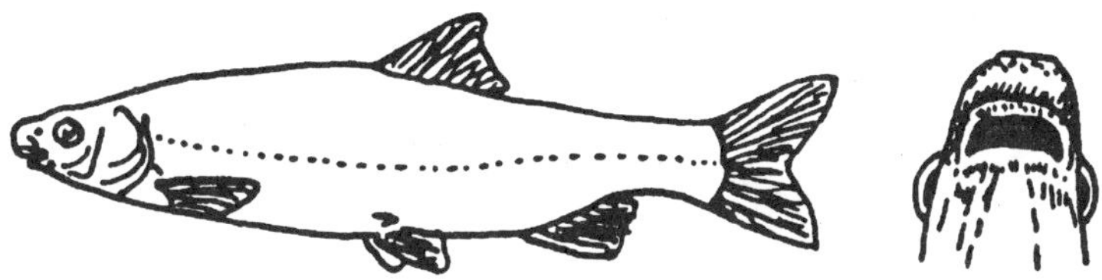

Fig. 85. Nose carp (*Chondrostoma nasus* L.)

Chondrostoma nasus L. (the nose carp), never longer than 50 cm and weighing 1500 g at most, has 55–62 scales on the lateral line. The mouth is very slightly arched, with thick lips. It destroys eggs and fry and is harmful in the waters of France. Originally from Central Europe, it reached the French hydrographical network (except in the southwest) through the Rhine and navigation canals.

The flesh is bland and soft, has many bones, and spoils easily. The fish is found in both minor and major water courses including waters with salmonids. It lives in schools.

Spawning occurs in spring from March to May, with 50,000–100,000 greenish eggs measuring 1.5 mm in diameter, on pebbles and stones at the bottom and near the banks of streams. The incubation period is 15 days.

Chondrostoma toxostoma Vallot (Rhone toxostome) is smaller than 15–25 cm in length and has 52–57 scales on the lateral line. It has a small mouth, arched like a horseshoe, with thin lips.

It is found together with nose carp in the Rhone basin, present only in the southwest. Its habits are identical to those of the nose carp. It also lives in schools.

Scardinius erythrophthalmus L. (rudd, "red eye") is found in placid bodies of water, water courses, canals, and ponds everywhere in France, especially in the southern regions.

The average size is 10–25 cm. The coloration varies widely, the dominant colours being yellowish, greyish, purplish, and pinkish.

The female lays 50,000–100,000 eggs, of 1 mm diameter, on aquatic plants to which they stick. The male acquires "display spots" on the back and the head during the reproductive period.

There are many hybrids. The meat is tasty but has many bones.

Rutilus rutilus L. (roach) is longer than the rudd. Its coloration is variable and the fins are red.

It is widespread in France, especially in the north and centre, in stagnant waters or those with a slow current. Being omnivorous, it consumes plants as well as molluscs, worms, and crustaceans.

Spawning occurs between April and June with 20,000–100,000 eggs attached to aquatic plants at the bottom. The eggs are 1–1.5 mm in diameter. The incubation

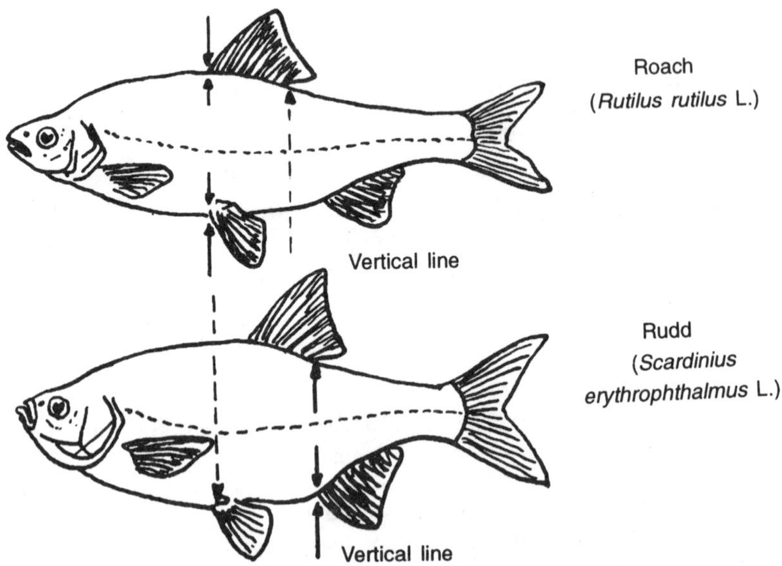

Fig. 86. Differentiation of the roach and the rudd

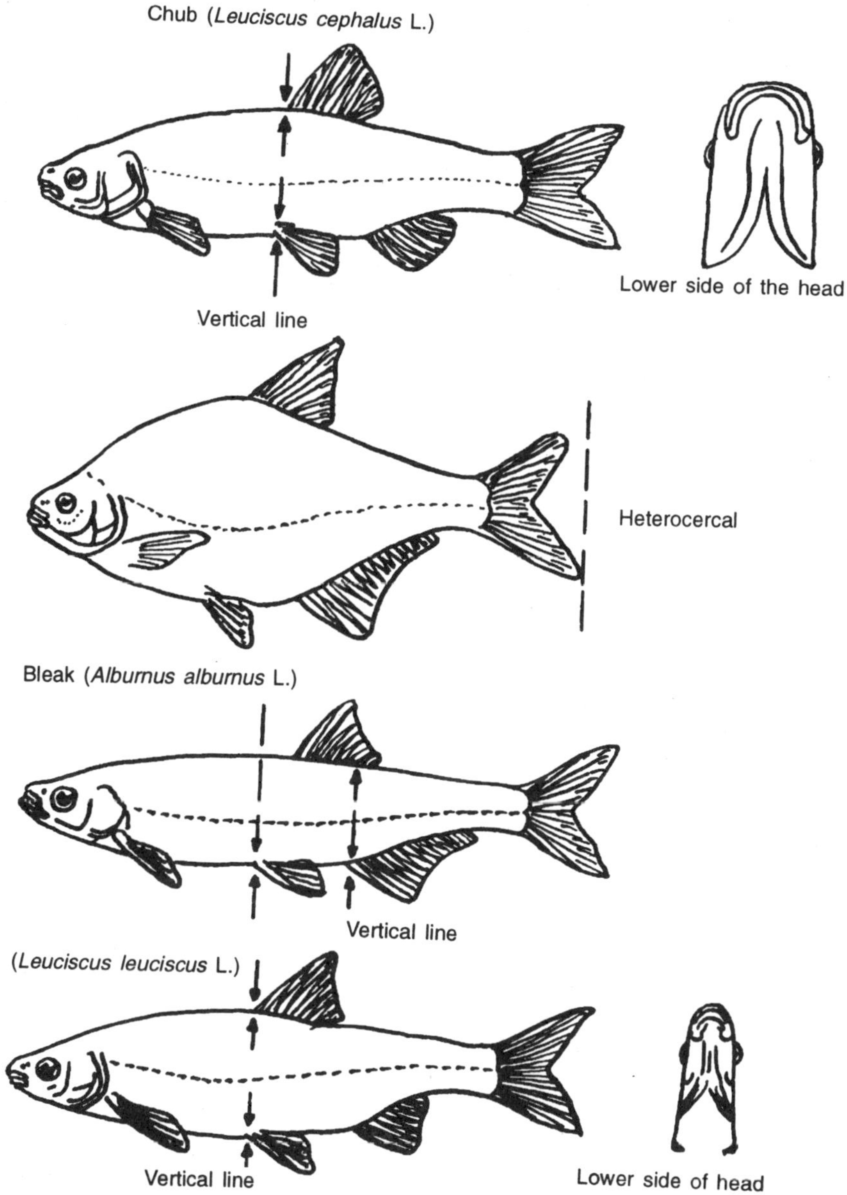

Fig. 87. Differentiation of other cyprinids

period is 8–15 days. During the reproductive period the male is covered with excrescences on its back.

There are many hybrids. The flesh is tasty in spite of the bones.

Leuciscus cephalus L. (chub) is found in all fast-flowing rivers with gravel beds. It is also found in low and medium altitude lakes. The length is 20–40 cm and the weight is 2–3 kg. The head is broad, rounded in front. It has a brownish-grey back and yellowish, sometimes greenish, scales with gold or silver glints.

Spawning occurs from April to June, in shoals in shallow currents. On gravel or sandy beds or on aquatic plants, the female lays 20,000–50,000 eggs, measuring 1.5 mm in diameter. The incubation period is 10–12 days. The male acquires a fairly bright coloration and is covered with "display spots".

There are many hybrids.

The voracious chub hunts by stealth, like the trout. It also feeds, apart from plants, on fruits that have fallen into the water, and on living prey: eggs, alevins, and young fish. It also eats gammarids, which give an orange-pink ("salmon") colour to its flesh.

Leuciscus cabeda Risso (cabede) is similar to the chub but smaller, and the front of the head is pointed. It has a higher body. It is found in the southern regions of France, sometimes together with the chub. It is sometimes called "chub-trout" because of the colour of its flesh, which is considered very good.

Alburnus alburnus L. (bleak) is 10–15 cm long. It has a green or blue back with metallic glints and a silvery white abdomen. It is found everywhere in France, especially in the east. It prefers water courses with a slow current and is also found in lakes.

Spawning occurs at the end of spring. Each female lays several thousands of eggs 1.5–2 mm in diameter on plants or gravel beds near the banks. The male, smaller in size, acquires "display spots" during the reproductive period.

There are many hybrids.

Apart from its highly valued flesh, the bleak, in the past, provided scales to the artificial pearl industry: it was the "essence of the Orient" that gave sheen and brilliance to artificial pearls.

Abramis brama L. (bream) can be identified by its laterally flattened body, convex at the back. It is widely observed in rivers and lakes of Central and Eastern Europe, in warm waters with slow currents, and stagnant waters in the plains.

It is found in muddy bottoms and among aquatic plants in ponds. It is more common in the north, east, and centre than in the south of France and is rare in the southeast. The bream is an omnivorous fish.

It may be 20–40 or even 60 cm long and weigh as much as 3 kg.

Spawning occurs during the spring, in shoals that frolic noisily, with each female laying 30,000–40,000 eggs per kg body weight. These eggs are 1–1.5 mm in diameter. They stick to aquatic plants or reeds near the banks. The incubation period is 8–10 days when the water temperature is between 18 and 20°C.

The species frequently hybridizes. It is not highly valued.

3.7 Esocidae

General characteristics: the dorsal fin is opposite the anal fin and behind the pelvic fins. The total length is 6–8 times the height of the body: the snout is flattened and elongated; the jaws, however, do not form an excessively long and slender snout. There is no carina at each side of the abdomen.

Esox lucius (pike) has the characteristics mentioned above. It has a wide mouth with strong teeth on the jaws, palate, and tongue. The coloration is greenish; the sides are mottled or marked, with a silvery colour on the belly. Its length is 30 cm to 1 m. It lives in placid waters with aquatic plants where it hunts by stealth; it is extremely voracious.

Spawning occurs early, beginning in February and sometimes continuing till May. The female lays 20,000–30,000 eggs per kg body weight. The eggs are toxic, sticky, transparent, and greenish-red and measure 2.5–3 mm in diameter. They are deposited on sandy bottoms or on aquatic plants in calm and shallow waters. The incubation period is 8–15 days.

3.8 Mugilidae

General characteristics: fish of this family have a somewhat elongated body, a slightly rounded snout, very small teeth, and two dorsal fins with visible rays; on the first of these fins there are four rays. The back and the head are broad, the eyes are widely separated, the scales are very large and cover the entire body, even the head. The lips on the mouth are somewhat thick. The opercula extend under the neck and almost completely cover it; there is an oval space in the centre, the jugular space.

The fish are found in brackish lagoons, ports, and estuaries. They always go to the sea, from July to October, to spawn.

They feed on organic matter suspended in water: the pharynx forms a kind of sieve that separates water and solid particles and sends them respectively to the gills and the oesophagus. They are difficult to catch because they jump out of the nets. They live together in shoals.

They are commonly known as mullets. The mullet of the genus *Mugil* has eyes that are vertically elliptic due to a double adipose eyelid.

Mugil cephalus L. (common grey mullet) has a longitudinal brown stripe on the body and may be as long as 75 cm.

It readily swims upstream in major and minor rivers, and is very common. Spawning occurs in September, at which time it is fished and the eggs are used to make a type of caviar called "botargo".

Liza ramada Risso (= *Mugil ramada*) (thin-lipped grey mullet), grey in colour, has a small head and a high body. It is found in salt, brackish, or fresh waters and is often seen in polluted water near sewers.

It spawns in the sea. The eggs float and are 1 mm in diameter. In the spring the young ones enter brackish coastal waters to grow during the summer. In the winter they return to the sea. Fish of this family are useful as large numbers can be caught in coastal regions.

4. SECONDARY SPECIES

Secondary species are those which even in the major families are not of considerable economic utility, nor of great interest for sport fishing, nor particularly beneficial by their coaction or interaction in the community of an aquatic ecosystem.

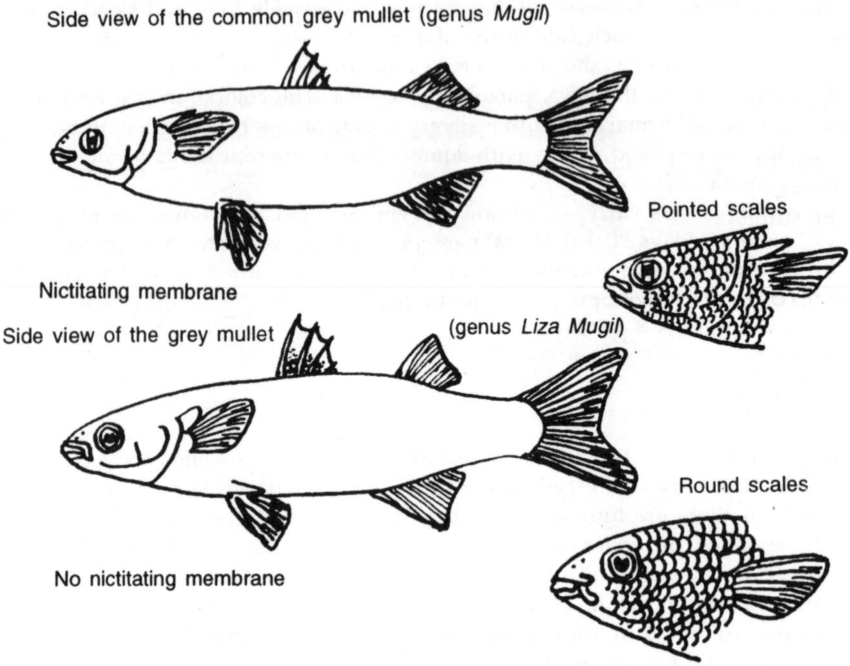

Fig. 88. Differentiation of mullets

Nevertheless, these species exist in European waters, are parts of communities in various aquatic ecosystems, and, for this reason, merit a mention.

Petromyzonidae

The **sea lamprey** (*Petromyzon marinus* L.) returns in March to spawn in the basins of the Rhone, the Saone, the Isere, and the Loire as far upstream as Orleans, the Gironde, and the Adour. It is 50 cm to 1 m long, weighs 1–2 kg, is highly valued and much in demand as food, and provides profitable fishing.

The **lampern** (river lamprey) (*Lampetra fluviatilis* L.), smaller than the sea lamprey, is found in rivers of the Atlantic and the English Channel, where it moves upstream in April and June to spawn. It is caught for food but is considered a predator as it preys on other fish.

The **brook lamprey** (*Lampetra planeri* Block) always remains in fresh water. It is found on sandy or muddy bottoms of small rivers and is not considered harmful.

Pleuronectidae

The **flounder** (fluke) (*Flesus flesus* L. = *Pleuronectes flesus*) moves fairly far upstream in rivers and their tributaries. This fish, 40–45 cm long, provides very tasty meat and is highly valued as food.

Acipenseridae

The **sturgeon** (*Acipenser sturio* L.), earlier common in France, is being rehabilitated in the Garonne basin. This is the largest species in French waters. It is 4–6 long and weighs 40–200 kg.

Spawning occurs from May to June in gravel beds in shallow water. A female of 200 kg may lay 4–5 million eggs. Caviar is made by treating these eggs. The flesh of the sturgeon is also greatly valued in Central Europe.

Gasterosteidae

The **threespine stickleback** (*Gasterosteus aculeatus* L.) is polymorphous, widely found in pools, ponds, slow-flowing streams, and even salt waters. It is extremely voracious, because the male, while guarding the nest, often eats eggs and newly hatched young fish. It is considered harmful like a similar genus, the ninespine stickleback (*Pungitius pungitius* = *Pygosteus pungitius*), which is smaller, with 10–12 dorsal spines instead of 3 in the threespine stickleback.

Cottidae

Cottus gobio L. bullhead (**sculpin**) is an excellent species to be raised together with trout when the population is not too dense. Voracious and lucifugous, it is found under stones in streams. It spawns from March to May and the male guards the eggs.

Blennidae

The river **blenny** (*Blennis fluviatilis* Asso) is found over the perimeter of the Mediterranean Sea, common in the southwest, southeast, and Corsica. It is edible.

Siluridae

The **sheatfish** (Danube catfish) (*Siluris glanis* L.), the giant of European rivers, is increasing in numbers in the Rhone basin (Seille-Saone) and has reached the basins of the Loire and the Seine. It is frequently 1.2–1.5 m long and weighs 20–30 kg (3 m long and weighing 300 kg in the Danube).

The freshwater **catfish** (*Ictalurus melas* Lesueur), a pest in cyprinid ponds, is prolific and voracious. It is not a useful fish because of the size of the head compared to the body and also because of the spines on its pectoral and dorsal fins. It is a harmful species.

Gadidae

The **burbot** (*Lota lota* L.) is widespread in the eastern regions of France, in ponds, lakes, and the basin of the Rhone. It may be as long as 1 m and weigh 3–4 kg.

Voracious and harmful, it has a very delicate flesh and a liver that it is in great demand by gourmets. Its eggs are poisonous.

Osmeridae

The European **smelt** (*Osmerus eperlanus* L.) is caught intensively when it moves up the estuaries in the spring to spawn.

Thymallidae

The **common grayling** (*Thymallus thymallus* L.) is found in the northeast, the upper reaches of the Rhone, Allier, Saone, Doubs, and Ain. It is excellent for sport fishing. Its flesh is considered to be good but difficult to preserve.

Cyprinodontidae

There are two somewhat similar genera, one in the maritime Alps – *Cyprinodon fasciatus* Val. – and the other, the killifish (*Fundulus hispanicus* Cuv. et Val.), in the Eastern Pyrenees.

A similar family, the **Poecilidae**, includes a fish that may be useful in the Roussillon. This is *Gambusia affinis* Baird and Giardr, a small fish 4–6 cm long, ovoviviparous like the **Cyprinodontidae,** voracious, and a destroyer of mosquitoes. Its dispersion is, in any case, restricted to waters with a temperature above 16°C.

Clupeidae

Two migrators of the same genus, the **allis shad** (*Alosa alosa* L.) and the **twaite shad** (*Alosa fallax* Lacep.) visit the basins of the Loire, the Garonne, the Adour, the Rhone, and coastal rivers. The spawners move upstream to breed in water courses.

The allis shad may weigh 3–4 kg; the twaite shad is seldom more than 1 kg. Its meat is also less appreciated than that of the allis shad, which is caught during summer by professionals using nets.

Family Cobitidae

Three fishes, loaches, of three different genera:

The **common loach** (*Cobitis barbatula* L.), a small animal, 12 cm long, with 6 barbels on its mouth, lives in clear fast-flowing waters of the northern and eastern areas of France. It spawns in the spring.

The **spiny loach** (*Acanthopsis taenia* L. = *Cobitis taenia*), is even smaller, not more than 10 cm long, with two bifid barbels on the head. It lives in the same waters as the common loach.

The **thunder fish** (pond loach) (*Misgurnus fossilis* L.), less common, lives in ponds in the northeastern region of France. It is larger, 25–30 cm long, with 5 barbels on its mouth.

Family Cyprinidae

In this important family, there are some secondary species not mentioned in the previous section:

The **crucian carp** and the **goldfish** (*Carassius carassius* L. and *C. auratus* L.) are found in stagnant and marshy waters in northeastern France. The former hybridizes with the carp and produces what we call the "Kollar carp". The latter, by selection, has given rise to monstrous forms: telescopic fish, some that look like sails, and of course the common goldfish.

The **minnow** (*Phoxinus phoxinus* L.) is a good species for raising with the trout. Not more than 10 cm long, it lives in shoals, spawns at the end of spring, becomes a predator if it proliferates, but is highly appreciated by fishermen while alive and by gourmets when fried. It is recognizable for its generally greenish colour, tending sometimes to pink, and its dark mottlings.

The **bitterling** (*Rhodeus amarus* L.) is known for its sexual dimorphism and the manner in which it lays its eggs on the branchia of freshwater mussels and unios. They are found in muddy ponds in the east, the north and the Paris basin. Somewhat like the ide, the stromer (*Telestes soufia* Risso) resembles the nose carp. It is seen in the basin of the Rhone.

The **ide** (orfe) (*Idus orfus* L. = *Leuciscus idus*) is a magnificent ornamented fish that lives in ponds. It has no food value.

Similar to the common bleak, *Alburnoides bipunctatus* is the **"Spirlin" bleak** (rifle minnow), a species found in streams and encountered mainly in the eastern and northern regions of France.

Similar to the bream, *Blicca bjoerkna* L. (silver bream), what the French call the **white bream,** is also found in the eastern regions of France.

Finally, we need to mention three genera included under the term "chinese carp": *Ctenopharyngodon idella* Val. (grass carp), *Aristichthys nobilis* Rich (bighead), and *Hypophthalmichthys molitrix* Val. (silver carp). These are herbivorous fishes found in France and acclimated in Russia and Poland, where they have been actively farmed with a view to propagating an extremely flexible fish with an effective means of clearing pond weeds.

Family Cichlidae

There are several species useful for Mediterranean countries as well as for utilizing hot-water wastes (nuclear electric plants). They are generally included under the term **Tilapia**, among the genera *Oreochromis, Sarotherodon*, and *Tilapia.*

D. ELEMENTS OF PHYSIOLOGY, BIOLOGY AND ETHOLOGY

1. FUNCTIONS

In **functions of relationship** certain aspects need to be examined in depth, especially those that pertain to the nervous and sensory systems.

In the **functions of nutrition** we will examine ideas relating to exchanges.

Finally, some useful details will be provided regarding the endocrine glands and taxes to which fish are subjected.

The very important **reproductive function** will be dealt with in a separate chapter.

1.1 Nervous System

The nervous system is made up of **nerves** containing fibres and **centres** where synaptic functions between neurons are formed.

The nerves comprise:

- **Spinal nerves** that emerge from each medullary segment. These nerves follow the inclination of the myomeres.
- **Cranial nerves**, of which there are 10 pairs.

Nerve I = olfactory nerve
Nerve II = optic nerve
Nerve III = that which innervates the oculomotor muscles
Nerve IV = effectors and non-receptors
Nerve VI = as above
Nerve V = mixed and a receptor of sensation in the head

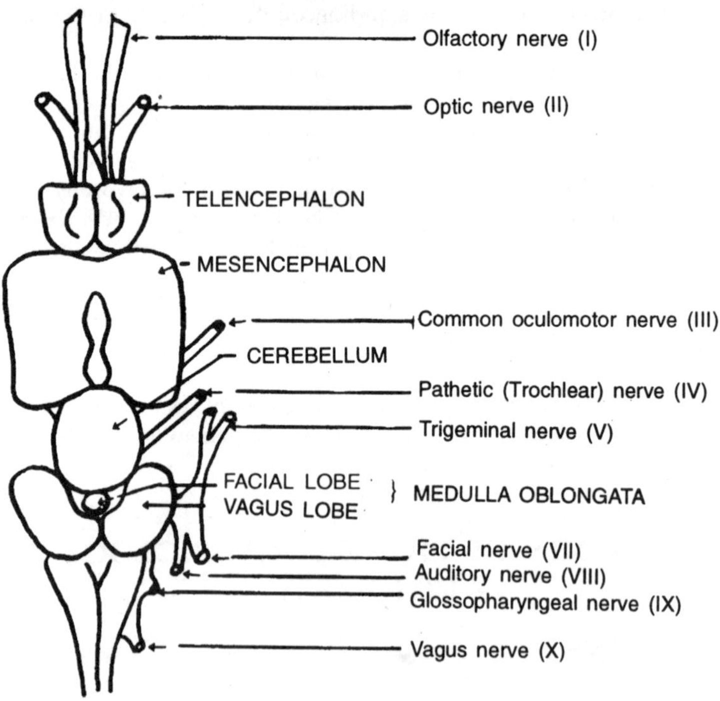

Fig. 89. Nervous system of fish

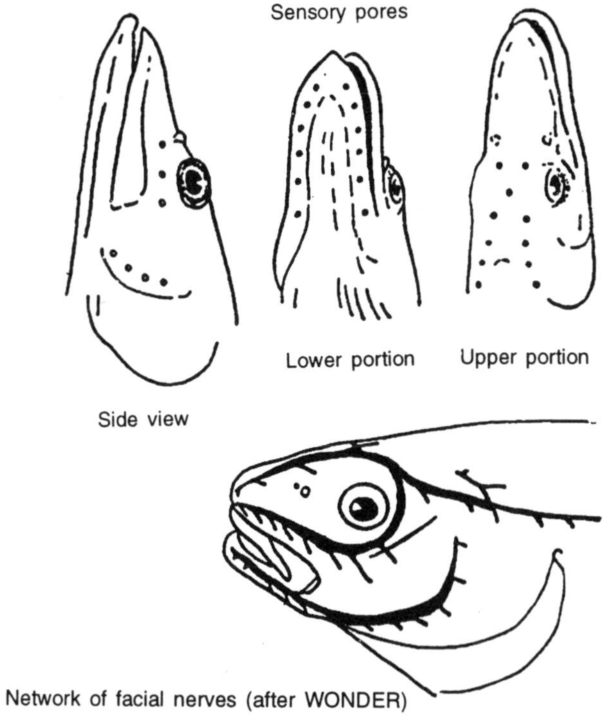

Fig. 90. Sensory pores and facial nerves of the pike

Nerve VII = receptor of the lateral cranial system

Nerve VIII = joined with Nerve VII, acoustico-facial. It is the receptor of sensation in the internal ear.

Nerves IX and X receive sensations of taste and those from the lateral system. Nerve X, or the vagus nerve, is composed of very long fibres that extend to the rear side of the body.

Nervous centres:

—A double sympathetic chain

■ The **spinal cord** contains the cells from which originate fibres of the spinal nerves and associated fibres at different levels that carry messages of sensation from the periphery to the encephalon (brain) or motor messages in the opposite direction. Motor fibres do not form a relay before they reach the motor neuron of the segment where they end.

On the other hand, fibres that carry messages of sensation form several synaptic relays. This latter observation is extremely important for an understanding of the phenomenon of attraction in electric fishing.

■ The **encephalon** (brain) has five enlarged portions which, starting from the spinal cord, are:

– the **medulla oblongata**, which is not a fundamental reflex centre because it is dependent upon the cerebellum and the optic tectum (mesencephalon).

It contains sympathetic reflex centres and the principal motor nucleus of the animal. It also receives afferent messages from the lateral line.

– the **cerebellum** receives messages of general sensation through the spinal cord as well as those from nerves V, VII, and VIII. It sends back reflex motor messages through the medulla oblongata. It ensures the equilibrium of the organism.

– the **mesencephalon** (optic tectum) is a visual centre

– the **diencephalon**, under the optic tectum and hardly visible, has a regulatory function in the sympathetic system through the medulla oblongata, nerve X, and the pituitary gland. It is a relay centre and does not give out motor fibres.

– the **telencephalon** is an olfactory centre from which olfactory tracts emerge.

1.2 Sensory System

a) Chemical Sensations

As already explained, the olfactory sense is highly developed; this is why an eel can detect a soluble compound at a dilution of $1/10^{16}$ and a salmon recognizes the river of its birth by smell, as each tributary of a major river is characterized by a particular odour. Such an olfactive memory is much keener than that indicated by the amazing possibilities of the olfactive sensitivity in some butterflies as observed by FABRE.

Olfaction also helps species that have lost the sense of sight to continue searching for food.

Taste is not limited to the buccal mucosa but is also manifest on certain organs such as the barbels on loaches.

b) Sight

The ability of a fish to see depends on its own optical system and the optical characteristics of aquatic and aerial objects that emit luminous rays, directly or by reflection.

The organ (WALKER, 1984), essentially the crystalline lens, is in the form of a spherical lens contained within a medium with a different refractive index. The refractive indices in various species of fish vary between 1.649 and 1.653 while the index of the humours in the human eye is the same as that of water, or 1.33. Calculation of local distances indicates that the pike and trout are somewhat shortsighted.

Assuming that a fish interprets a ray of light from an object above the water surface as a human eye would do, the object will appear to it to be higher than it really is, as if the light had been propagated in a straight line.

The ray subjected to the greatest refraction is the one of which the angle of incidence is close to 90°, in other words an almost horizontal ray. For this ray, the corresponding angle of refraction is approximately 48.7°. No ray from a point above the water surface will be observed by a fish if the angle of refraction is greater than 48.7°. All rays, therefore, that emanate from points above the water surface reach the eye of a fish in the cone of a vertical axis where the angle at the apex is twice 48.7°, or 97.4°.

The intersection of this cone with the water surface forms a circle called the "window of sight" of the fish. The size of the window varies with the depth at which the fish is found but the opening of the cone does not vary.

It may be assumed (WALKER, 1984) that a fish has an anamorphous vision of the world above the water surface: the magnification is not the same in all directions and we are not aware whether it mistakes this anamorphosis for reality and whether it interprets all objects above the water level as deformed corresponding objects, based on the laws of refraction.

Beyond the window the fish sees mainly a reflected image of the bottom of the river on the water surface. Some rays cannot be refracted and leave the water; others, of which the angle of incidence is less than 48.7°, are partly refracted and partly reflected.

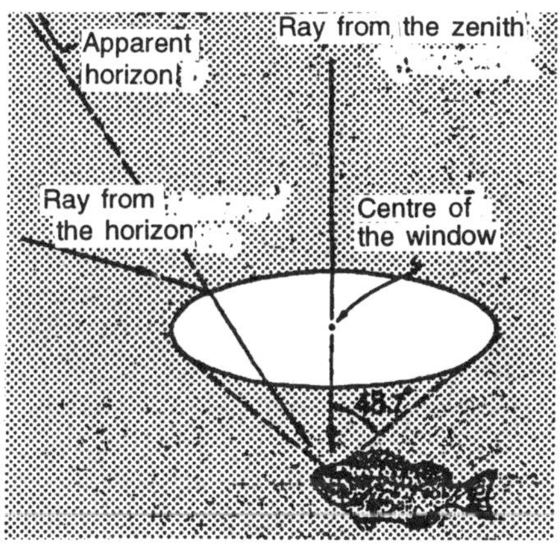

Fig. 91. Geometry of the window of sight of a fish (after WALKER)

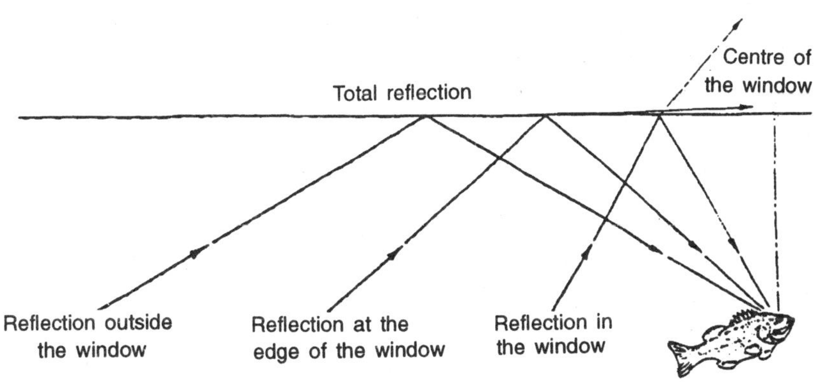

Fig. 92. Reflection of light rays emitted from the bottom of a river

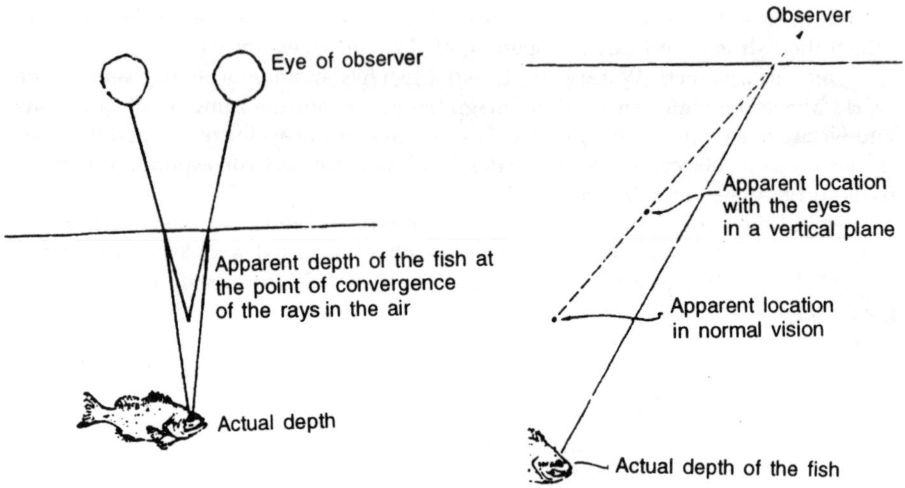

Fig. 93. Actual and apparent location of a fish

This information is useful, for example, to a fisherman while casting his lures in the window of sight of a fish.

c) *Equilibrium and Hearing*

The auditory organ is formed only of the internal ear contained within a cartilagenous auditory capsule.

In the Cyprinidae it is connected with the air bladder by a chain of ossicles.

The structure of the lateral sensory organ is complex. On each side of the body it comprises a longitudinal canal that starts from the operculum and ends in the tail, running below a row of perforated scales through which it communicates with the exterior. This longitudinal canal is continuous with a system of small canals in the bones of the head (Fig. 94).

The lateral line is innervated by a sensory branch that begins from the vagus nerve (X) and which receives the anastomoses of the spinal nerves. Under each scale there is therefore a sensitive plaque linked with the nerve. The sensory organs of the lateral line have a high mechanical sensitivity and operate like distant tactile receptors, recording pressure variations due to currents.

1.3 Exchanges

– **Energy exchanges**

The internal temperature of a fish is variable. Fish are **poikilothermal** but, due to differences in behaviour, some may tolerate sudden changes in temperature: these are **eurythermal**. Others may preserve their vital activity only within a limited temperature range; these are **stenothermal**.

Stenothermy leads some fish to undertake seasonal movements corresponding to variations in temperature of the surrounding medium, in order to remain in an environment where the water temperature is about the same.

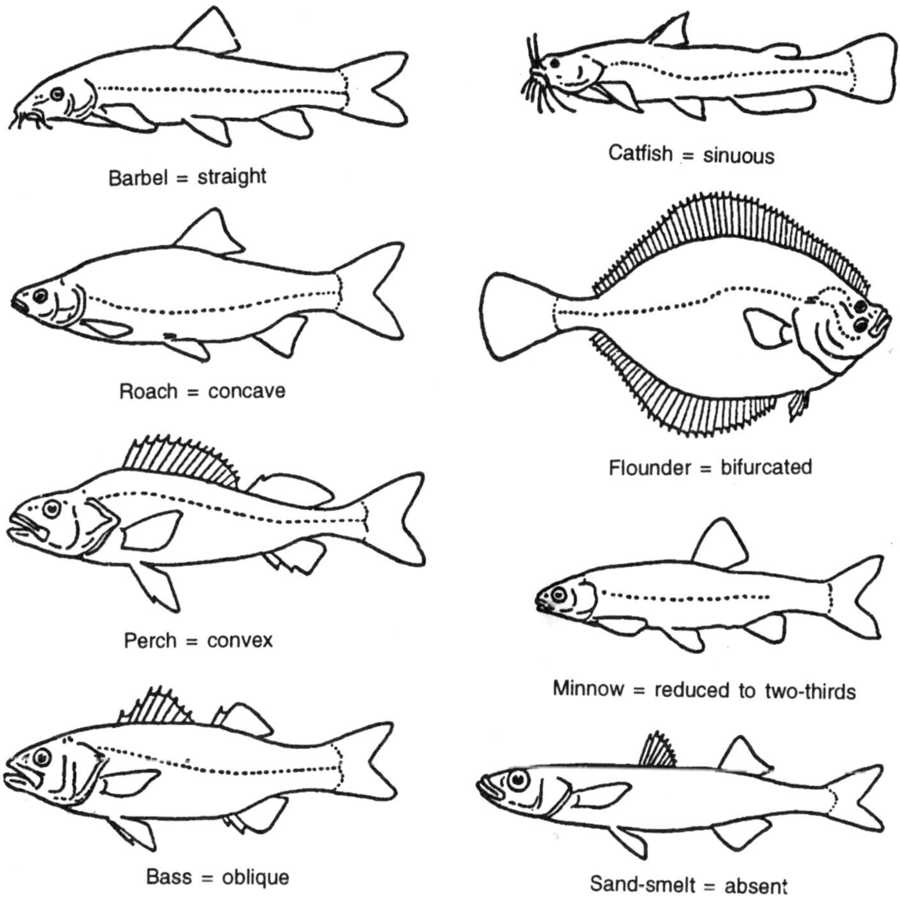

Fig. 94. Profile of the lateral line depending upon the species

It is explained by the fact that the enzymatic system has an optimal yield for a given temperature. Furthermore, a secondary incidence of stenothermy is also useful for the metabolism of a fish: the amount of oxygen dissolved in the water varies considerably with temperature.

– **Exchanges of water and mineral salts** (Figs. 96–98)

The semipermeable wall of the gills creates problems in osmosis because the molecular concentration in the blood of freshwater fish is much higher than that of the water in the surrounding medium: the blood is **hypertonic**. Dilution of the blood by water passing through the gills would be fatal if the kidneys were not able to eliminate the incoming water to ensure a constant concentration in the blood.

The opposite phenomenon in sea water (physiological changes in young salmon entering the sea), where the blood becomes **hypotonic**, is observed in the gills,

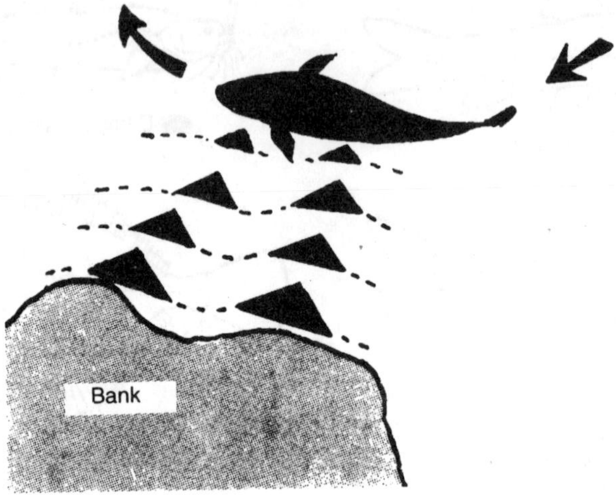

Fig. 95. Guidance system of a fish due to the effect of changes in pressure felt over the lateral line

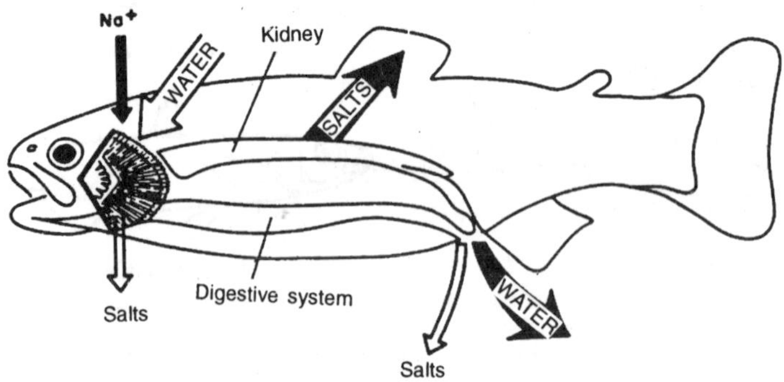

Fig. 96. Osmoregulation (hydromineral balance) in a fish kept in fresh water (after WEDEMEYER *et al.*, 1976); the area of the arrows indicates the extent of exchange (white arrows, passive phenomena; black arrows, active mechanisms)

which filter sea water so that only an isotomic liquid is allowed to pass through to the blood and, therefore, excrete the salts.

In fresh water a current of water passes through the fish in the gills, blood, and kidneys. In the sea a fish retains its water, and the gills act as a barrier.

Some species are **euryhaline**: the stickleback, the salmon, some trout, the mullet, and certain tilapias.

Most of them are **stenohaline** and die when they are taken out of fresh water and placed in sea water. Certain substances, such as **trioxymethylamine** and **urea**,

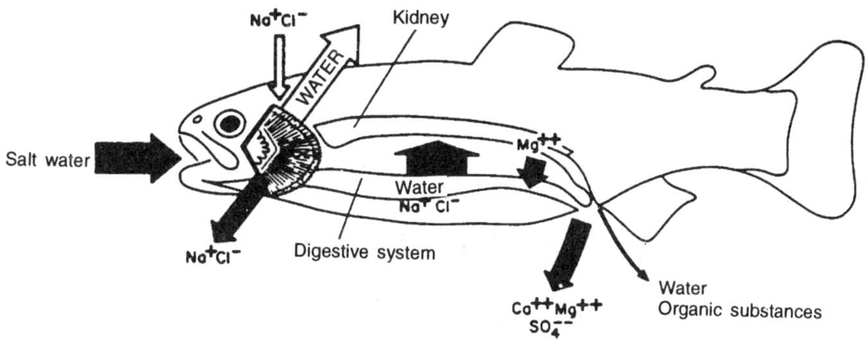

Fig. 97. Osmoregulation (water and salt balance) in a fish kept in sea water

enable isotonicity in euryhaline fish: during smolting, in the salmon, the trioxymethylamine concentration varies from 1 to 12.

Furthermore, in the cells, the variability of the lipocytic coefficient enables them to fix more water when in the sea and to maintain a constant internal osmotic pressure (the lipocytic coefficient is the cholesterol/fatty acid relationship).

1.4 Endocrine glands

Fish, like mammals, have endocrine glands, such as the pituitary, the thyroid, the suprarenal glands, and a diffuse endocrine pancreas.

Under the brain, the pituitary (hypophysis) produces a growth hormone and a stimulator for other glands; it is the most important gland in the endocrinal system. The secretions play an important role in osmoregulation (hydromineral regulation), as mentioned earlier.

The **thyroid** accelerates metabolism and accentuates motor activity. It is very active, for example, at the time of migration of salmonids (M. FONTAINE). The same applies to the Stannius corpuscles, which are small organs of the interrenal system: their ablation results in a state of debility for the eel.

1.5 Taxis

A taxis is a reaction of attraction or repellence in an animal by physical, chemical, and mechanical agents. **Phototaxis** is caused by light, **galvanotaxis** is caused by electric currents, and **chemotaxis** is caused by the chemical effect of dissolved substances in water.

When a taxis directs or leads an organism to where the stimulus begins, it is said to be **positive**. When it is manifest in an opposite manner it is **negative**.

—Phototaxis

Animal phototaxis is complex. Positive reactions are primary and observed in most of the fish in French waters, but for a certain amount of absorbed light there are secondary, negative phases: these are due to an adaptation and a reaction that tends to safeguard the organism against stimulation by light.

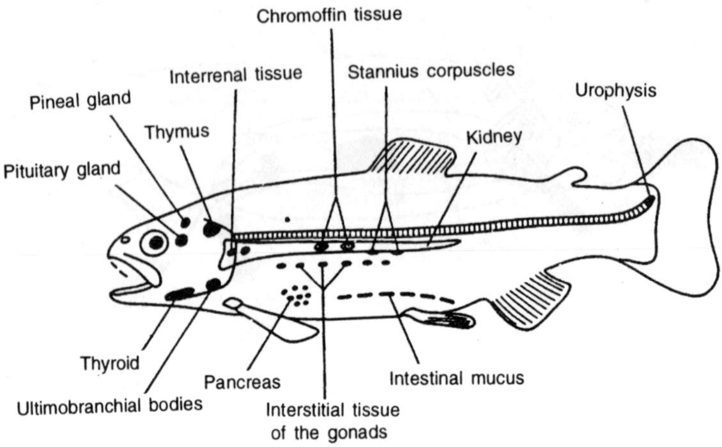

Fig. 98. Position of endocrine glands in a teleostean fish (after DE KINKELIN *et al.*, 1985, courtesy INRA)

Positive phototaxis is used in night fishing, especially at sea, in industrial fishing (sardine and anchovy with special lights). This phototaxis is specific and selective: several species "rise" somewhat rapidly towards a source of light. Nevertheless, in some fish, namely the sculpin (bullhead), the burbot, and the eel, there is a negative phototaxis. This primary negative phototaxis is also used, especially, for guiding eels into traps.

The galvanotaxis of vertebrates is generally **anodic** and that of fish is no different. The cathode has a repellent effect.

Physiological mechanisms which determine anodic galvanotaxis are complex. Let us say that anodic attraction is also a secondary manifestation, a **reflex effect** (P. LAMARQUE).

—Chemotaxis

It appears that the reactions of fish to various chemical substances are more of a morbid condition than taxis. There are, probably, genuine taxes among them that cannot be identified. The problem of being directed by perception of an infinitesimal amount of chemical compounds has already been discussed. That of being directed by an emission of ozone is more subtle, and trials to trigger a movement towards an ozonized zone have not been fully conclusive.

—Mechanical taxes

The most manifest ones are **barotaxis** and **rheotaxis**. Barotaxis is caused by water pressure. Rheotaxis is due to water currents: it is positive when fish move against the current (trout). It has been observed that minnows remain in a current to retain the same visual field. If they are kept in a bottle within a basin, and if the bottle is moved, they face in a direction opposite to the movement: it is, therefore, not friction of the water that causes them to face in a particular direction, but probably their visual perceptions: this is, therefore, not a genuine rheotaxis.

We may also refer to visual stimulus (cinetaxis) in the case of a fish that pounces on its prey moving at a given speed and not ahead or behind it; but is this a taxis or a perceptive reaction that occurs when the stimulus acts, at least under certain conditions, as a sign of the presence of a quarry?

A taxis, strictly speaking, is a **kinesis** caused and directed by stimulus and a kinesis, it should be understood, is a **random movement** caused by one or more external stimuli.

1.6 Locomotion

Most fish use undulatory or oscillatory movements for voluntary or involuntary swims (the "forced" swim induced by an electric field).

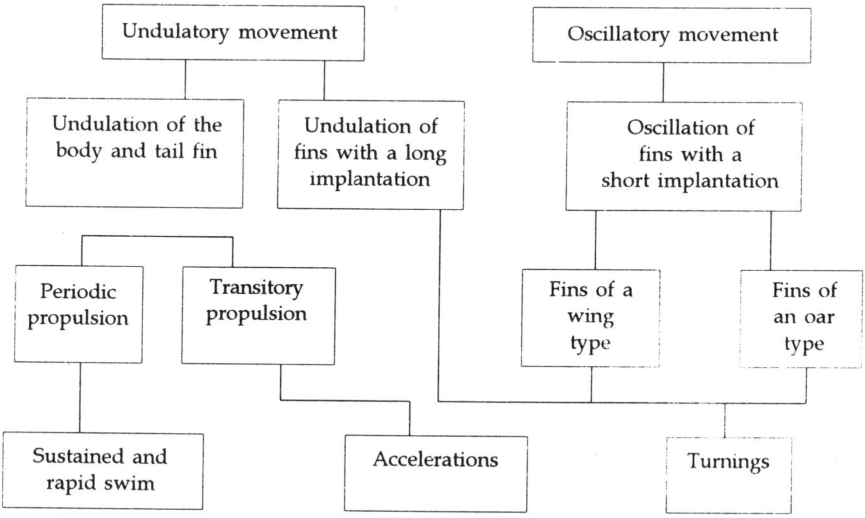

Fig. 99. The modes of propulsion used by fish are shown in the blocks (after WEBB, 1984). In undulatory propulsion a wave passes over the part of the body or the fin responsible for the propulsive force.

In oscillatory propulsion the anatomical structure moves from front to rear like an oar. For a sustained swim, a fast swim, and accelerations, the undulation of the body is combined with an undulation of the caudal fin (tail).

For periodic propulsion, used in a fast swim and accelerations, the swimming movements are cyclic. Fishes that turn at low speeds use the oscillatory movement of fins with a narrow base that acts as wings or oars, or the undulatory movement of fins with a long implantation.

When the body undulates, one or more half wavelengths move from the head to the tail at a speed higher than the relative velocity of the fish as compared to the water. The shape, the "fuselage" of the fish, therefore, has an effect on its performance that is dependent mainly on the body and the tail fin. According to P. WEBB (1984) the impaired fins with a long implantation (ventral and dorsal) play a secondary role, except in some fishes.

In oscillatory propulsion, a fish moves its fins: these are mainly fins with a narrow implantation. Movements of oscillating or undulating fins not supported by body movements are used in low speeds when a fish has to move and turn very precisely.

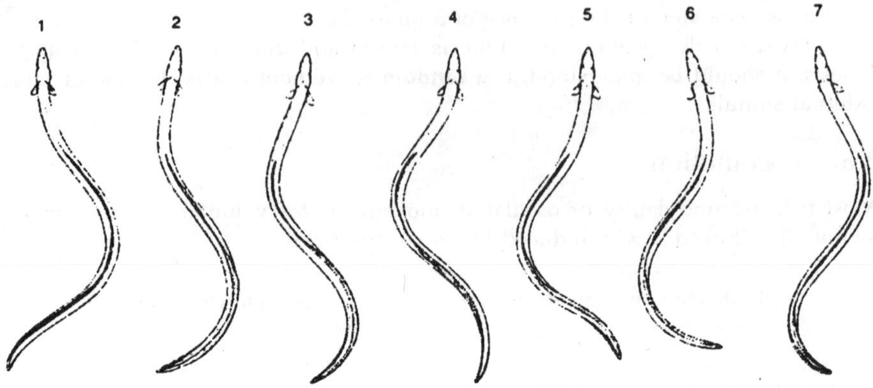

Fig. 100. In a sustained swim, the eel undulates over more than one wavelength when it moves in the water. In all types of swims where a fish uses the body and tail fin, the propulsive wave passes over the body with a velocity higher than that of the fish, in relation to the water. In periodic propulsion like that of the eel in a sustained swim, the movements are cyclic.

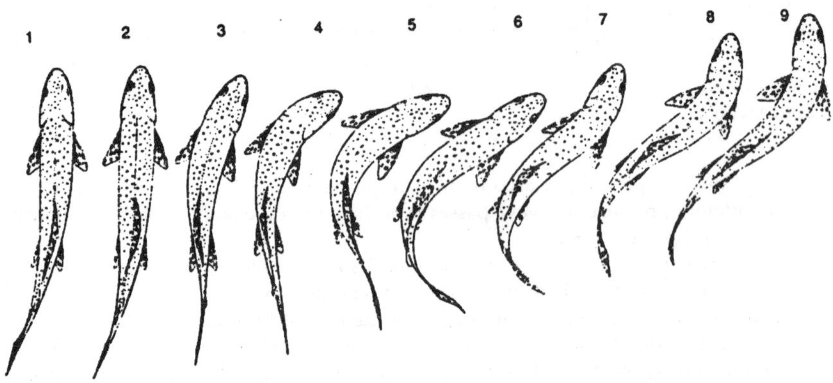

Fig. 101. A trout that accelerates from a stationary state bends only over a fraction of a wavelength. In this transitory swim, the overall movement is not cyclic. Like most transitory swimmers, a trout is capable of rapid starts (after WEBB, 1984).

The various swims based on movement of both the body and the dorsal fin are of two types: the transitory and sustained swims.

The **transitory swim** is a mode of movement involving sudden starts and sharp turns. It is based on short propulsive movements of wide amplitude.

The **sustained swim** is maintained by cyclic swimming movements, with several waves of the tail in each cycle: it may continue for an hour or more, but only for a few seconds during a sprint.

Consequently, fish that move mainly by rapid accelerations have a shape different from those that plough through vast extents of ocean at a constant speed (salmon).

In swims involving turns, all parts of the body are involved. A fish uses movements of the body and tail fin for acceleration and an oscillatory movement of the pairs of pectoral fins for sustained swims and turnings. There are three optimal profiles, served by very different types of fins that confer certain fish with performances that are also very different, making these "specialists" to some extent: the salmon "specializes" in sustained swims, the pike in acceleration, and the sunperch in turnings.

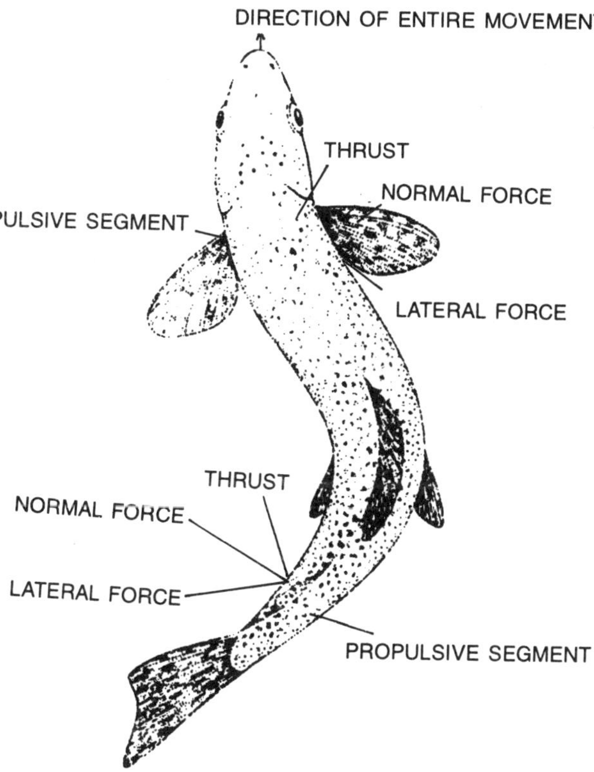

Fig. 102. A thrust is the sum of forces created by all the small propulsive segments of the body. Here we observe the forces acting on the two propulsive elements. When the propulsive wave passes, each element is displaced laterally and causes an acceleration in the water around it. This water movement is accelerated towards the tail. The force normal to the propulsive element, equal and opposite to the force exerted on the water, is applied on the propulsive element. We break up this normal force into two components. The lateral force is perpendicular to the mean displacement of the fish and the thrust parallel to the mean displacement. The thrust resulting from all the propulsive elements moves the fish forward. The intensity of the thrust due to each element increases when we approach the tail (after WEBB, 1944)

2. REPRODUCTION

Many remarkable possibilities and conditions of reproduction are observed in fish.

—There is considerable resilience with the eel and the burbot (2 million and 1 million eggs), very little in the bitterling (40 eggs), and even less in a sea fish, the brown cat shark (1 egg).

—No nesting in the roach or the perch, a simple nest for the trout (a single channel among pebbles covered by a few flicks of the tail), and a very elaborate, genuine nest for the stickleback.

—A total abandonment of the spawn by cyprinids.

—A vigilant surveillance till dispersion of the alevins by the black bass.

—Finally, oviparity in most fishes in French waters, but ovoviviparity in Cyprinodontidae, viviparity in the Gambusia, and even placentary viviparity in a sea fish, the smooth dogfish.

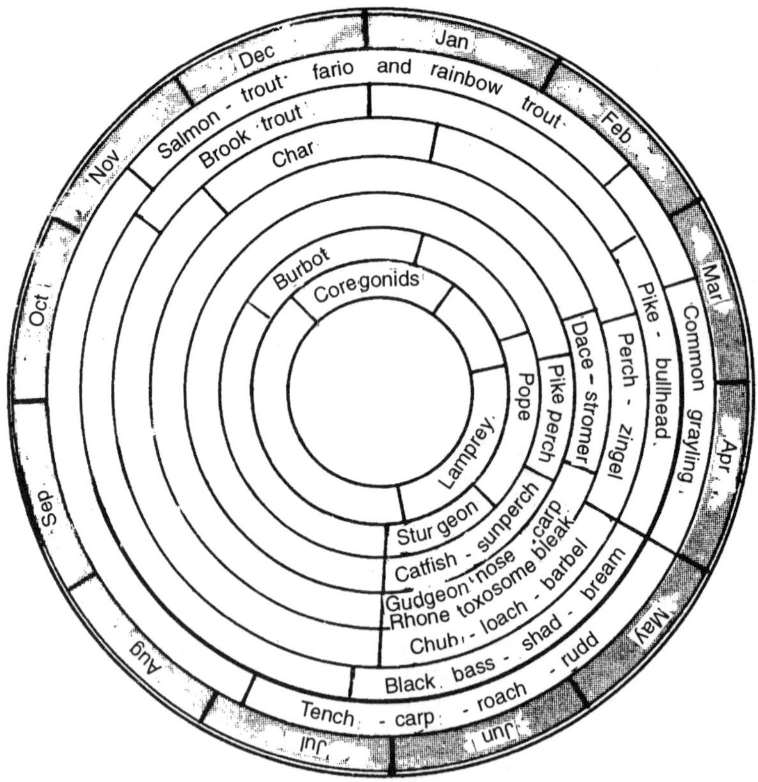

Fig. 103. Calendar of reproduction in fish

2.1 Biological Bases

An egg is the result of fusion of two gametes, one male, the other female, from sex cells that are located, depending on the sexes, in ovaries or testes.

During cell division, the chromatin in the nucleus assumes the shape of separate rods or filaments in numbers that are fixed. These rods or filaments are chromosomes, which are vectors of heredity factors or **genes**.

Since the number of chromosomes in the gamete of a living species is n and since an egg is the result of fusion of two gametes, a normal cell of this living species contains 2n chromosomes and is said to be **diploid**.

This is how the chromosomal formulae of certain species of fish have been determined; it is based on the diploid number of chromosomes before chromosome reduction:

Salmo salar	= 60 chromosomes of which 6 pairs are V-shaped
Salmo trutta	= 80 chromosomes
Salvelinus alpinus	= 80 chromosomes of which 8 pairs are V-shaped
Salvelinus fontinalis	= 84 chromosomes of which 8 pairs are V-shaped
Coregonus	= 80 chromosomes
Thymallus thymallus	= 102 chromosomes

An unfertilized egg is a large immobile cell with a special nucleus, the **pronucleus**, covered by an envelope with small canals and perforated with an orifice or **micropyle** through which spermatozoa can pass.

Fertilization is only possible during a very limited period of time because, in water, the egg swells up and the micropyle closes. Spermatozoa have also a very short life.

Some crossings result in hybridizations, which are frequent among cyprinids.

2.2 Sex Characteristics

a) Sex characteristics enable a visual differentiation of males and females. These involve several features:

- ***Primary***

Genital papillae, for example, of the carp are concave in the male and convex in the female.

Copulatory organs of the bitterling.

- ***Secondary***

Size: generally females are larger than males (for example, the eels), and heavier because of the large volume of the ovaries (trout).

Coloration: the males have a bright coloration, which is even brighter during the reproductive period, when they have their **display coloration**. At the same time, on some males, we observe excrescences or display spots (for example on cyprinids).

Dimorphism may affect all limbs (fins) (the male tench has a strong and thick second ray on its ventral fin). This is also a permanent feature, as is the transformation of the anal fin to a genopod in cyprinodonts.

b) Sexual behaviour is also a source of differentiation.
In species with a display coloration, the males court the females by dancing or twirling around them, inducing a release of the ova by a frenetic presentation of their bright display coloration.

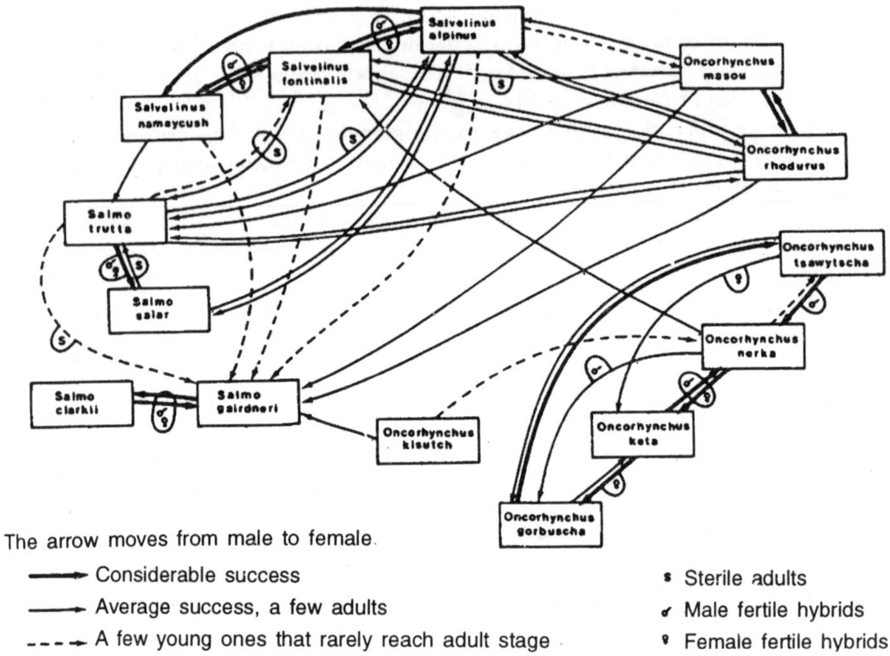

Fig. 104. Possibilities of artificial hybridization among the principal species of salmonids (after CHEVASSUS, 1976)

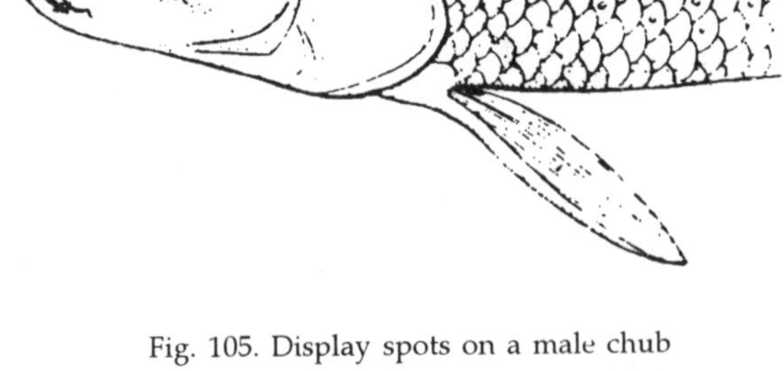

Fig. 105. Display spots on a male chub

In nesting species (for example, *Tilapia mossambica*), it is the males that select the location of the nest, which they prepare. They guard the eggs and later the fry (black bass).

In species which mate, there are fights between males for possession of the females (for example, *Tilapia mossambica*).

2.3 Genital Organs

The female organs are the ovaries, or roe, granular in appearance, extremely vascularized and of a pink colour.

The male organs are the testes or milt, elongated in smooth strings of a milky colour.

The genital system is separate from the urinary system at least in the teleosts in French waters: there are oviducts, spermducts, and ureters. In some cases, the oviducts and spermducts end in the ureter near the genital pore.

There are no genital passages in the lamprey, eel, salmon and trout. Eggs and milt are poured into the abdominal cavity and expelled through the genital pore.

2.4 Sexual Products and Spawning

For a given species, reproduction is possible only under certain conditions of the medium: environment, temperature, salinity, oxygenation. If, at the time of spawning, one of these conditions is not fulfilled, spawning may be delayed (temperature for the carp), the female may be rendered partly or even totally sterile (non-availability of a gravel bed for the trout) or even die (pike).

Particularly in the female, seasonal reproduction follows a long period of sexual inactivity during which the fish eats a lot of food and builds up reserves for its gonads, which become large, so large in fact that in the pike, a retention caused by the absence of a factor that could trigger spawning causes the death of the female. The animal does not feed near spawning time and therefore a serious muscular degeneration is observed.

The sexual products of the male form the **milt**. The sperm contains millions of spermatozoa that cannot survive in contact with water. In the case of a trout, the average life of a spermatozoon, once emitted, is about 30 seconds, about 2 minutes for the pike, and 3 minutes for the carp.

The ova are laid in numbers that depend upon the species and, it may be noted, depending on the spawning candidates. Ova released in the water and fertilized in the water are those that are emitted in large numbers: the percentage of fertilization is low. Where nesting is done, the number of ova is less and the fertilization percentage is higher. When there is viviparity, fertilization is not only internal but the spermatozoa are protected by spermatophores which open only near the gonads. In the subsequent spawning there are only a few eggs but all are fertile. A large number compensates for the difficulties in fertilization.

It is because of this incompatibility between water and spermatozoa that we undertake fertilisation by the "dry" method.

It may also be noted that the size of the ova—which together form the spawn—is inversely related to their number.

The amount of sperm emitted also depends on the species.

In the case of the pike, 3 to 4 males are required to fertilize one female.

For the carp, 2 males are needed to fertilize one female.

In the trout, 1 male is required to fertilize 2 females.

Spawning involves a sexual approach at the time of reproduction; it relates to collective approaches.

Mating involves the approach of two progenitors.

Eggs are separate and pelagic, adherent and demersal, separate and demersal, or parasitic.

Separate and pelagic eggs are of the same density as water—they are the result of a collective spawning. They circulate in suspension in the water moved by sea currents. In rivers, the shad releases pelagic eggs.

Adherent and demersal eggs are denser than water. This applies to the eggs of most freshwater fish:

—Adherent agglomerated eggs, of the carp and the roach, or those laid in dark places under stones by the sculpin.

—Adherent eggs in the form of a necklace laid by the perch; they are emitted in a long tube in an intercrossed web, sometimes as long as 2 m.

—Speckled adherent eggs of the dace and the chub are laid, individually, at the bottom of a stream where they stick to stones and gravel.

Separate and demersal eggs are those of salmonids, for example. They are:

—separate and covered by the trout and the salmon.

—separate and not covered by the char.

—parasitic eggs as in the case of the bitterling laid in anodonts and unios.

The eggs are generally spherical or oval and sometimes coloured.

2.5 Incubation

The incubation period is the time that elapses between fertilization of ova by spermatozoa and the emergence of alevins.

The incubation of pelagic eggs, which are poor in nutritive reserves, is short and that of dermersal eggs with a large yolk is longer: the survival rate of the young, which emerge at a later stage, is higher.

The duration of incubation varies with the species and the water temperature. This duration is expressed in degree-days: eggs of the arctic char (*Salvelinus alpinus*) need 450 degree-days or 30 days in water at an average temperature of 15°C or 45 days in water at 10°C to hatch.

We distinguish between the so-called formation of an embryo and total incubation.

The duration of embryo formation is the number of degree-days needed to incubate eggs from the time of spawning till the appearance of the two eyes in the egg. This is important to know because eggs of the pike and salmonids, as a general rule, should not be handled or transported until an embryo has been formed.

The degree-days constant, as mentioned above, depends on the species:

Common fario trout	400–410 degree-days
Rainbow trout	300–320
Brook trout	465
Arctic char	450

Common grayling	200
Coregonids (whitefish)	340–400
Carp	90
Pike	120

After formation of an embryo, the egg contains the embryo, lying on the surface of the yolk, of which the eyes are the most visible formation.

The embryo grows at the expense of the yolk and reaches a size greater than the diameter of the egg. The vitellus is then attached to the embryo only at the abdominal region.

There is next the digestion of the walls of the egg and the **hatching** of an alevin with a yolk sac whose size depends upon the species to which it belongs.

3. MIGRATION

By migration we mean a long and periodic voyage and by movement a short and aperiodic voyage.

3.1 Extent

Migratory behaviour, an expression of the internal dynamism of any particular organism, reaches its maximum in long-distance migrations of fish and birds.

This extreme range of outward and inward long-distance voyages may be explained by the fact that aquatic and aerial mediums are the ones in which there are the least numbers of physical obstacles to the movement of the animals.

Migrations may be for several thousand or several hundreds of kilometres, in the case of both anadromous fish such as the salmon and catadromous fish like the eel.

The range of migrations is considerable, in the sea as well as in fresh waters whether or not connected with the reproductive cycle.

The different types of migrations may be described as follows:

No change in the medium = Holobiotic

Living in the sea → Thalassophilous
Living in rivers → Potamophilous

Change in the medium = Amphibiotic

for reproduction of the species

↓

Gamodromous → in the sea → Thalassotocous

↓ { in fresh waters → Potamotocous

for other reasons

↓

Agamodromous

3.2 Analysis

We distinguish between two types of migrations:

—Those that take place over a wide front: sea fish

—Those that follow a well-defined route: eels, salmon

The factors responsible for the fact that a migratory fish, which has been sedentary for a long time, migrates suddenly are internal and external.

Among the **external factors**, we note the effect of the season, the meteorological conditions, floods, and lunar cycles, but these external factors affect individuals that are physiologically ready. The physiological state determines migration and the direction of migration.

In the autumn, therefore, in rivers and canals which link the marshlands of Poitou with the sea, we observe silver eels moving to the sea and young eels moving inland from the sea.

When they pass each other they are subjected to the same conditions but some move upstream and others downstream.

The same applies to salmon, in the same river, at the same time, in the same place.

The importance of the endocrinal state in premigratory physiology:

Migrations generally begin:

1. at the beginning or during the course of a genital maturation;
2. at the end of a growth phase;
3. after changes in the coloration or external morphology.

These three phenomena are dependent upon hormones.

Changes in coloration: a silver shade due to a deposit of guanine and a blackening of the fins can be obtained experimentally in both the eel and the salmon by an injection of thyroxine. This injection also causes a reduction in hepatic glycogen. In a young catadromous salmon (smolt) there is very little hepatic glycogen as compared to that in a young sedentary salmon.

The thyroid in a smolt like that in a catadromous eel is more active in sedentary individuals; there could be a threshold of hyperthyrodism that renders the fish sensitive to some external factors; it is seen to be in an unstable physiological state and this leads us to assume that:

—the premigratory period begins with a large secretion of thyroid-stimulating hormone,

—migration could be a period of pituitary and thyroid imbalance.

This is observed, especially in young salmon, in two ways:

—The young sedentary fish lies in wait for prey among pebbles and swims near the bottom.

—The smolt leaves its gravel bed, survives in the current, and leaps out of the water. It loses its visual identifications, and high waters in the spring carry it down to the sea.

On the other hand, reproductive hormones do not play a major role in this; the greatest diversity of reproductive states is observed in both females and males when moving downstream.

As a result of **internal factors**, among the various representatives of a particular genus, some have a migratory instinct, and others do not. This is why a seasonal change in thyroid activity affects some young trout in French rivers. They acquire a silver coating and may even migrate. These cyclic variations are qualitatively comparable but quantitatively different.

Let us say that amphibiotic migratory fish, during anadromous migration, have a thyroid tonus that may reach a more intense functional level than that in holobiotic species but in which, on the other hand, there are wider fluctuations (these are crises of hyperthyroidism).

Migrations begin when these fluctuations reach a level that results in certain neuro-endocrinal functions or hyperfunctions that cause an imbalance between the organism and the medium, rendering the organism sensitive to meteorological conditions. For smolts, therefore, it is the high-water level that triggers a mass migration.

Homing: Migrations, passive in rivers, are directed in the sea; fish follow a "laid-down" route; it appears that a particular population moves to a particular region in the sea (a region to feed or to spawn).

A return to the river of its birth, the "homing" of a fish, is very precise in the case of the salmon and the shad.

What factors lead adult fish to leave the sea and move upstream in a particular water course?

There is, certainly, a **hyperfunctioning of the thyroid** that causes the fish to look for waters that are less salty but the "guide" cannot be the salt concentration as this would vary depending upon the inflows.

As already mentioned, the **olfactory sense** may be responsible for the homing: the salmon, like the eel, has a powerful olfactive memory. If we remove salmon from two arms of a river which have an O-shaped confluence, block the olfactory sac of half of them, and release them all downstream of this O, the normal fish will return to the branch from which they were caught and the others will disperse randomly.

So much for guidance in a river, but what happens in the sea?

It is assumed that the semicircular canals could be in a state of preferential equilibrium as in the automatic guidance system of an aircraft. The fish, therefore, follow a **loxodromic line** (which makes a constant angle with the meridiens). This line, for eels from the Baltic moving to the Sargasso Sea, is N 120° W. It is precisely near the loxodromic line that the only catches of silver eels were made (near the Azores and South Cornwall in Britain).

According to Barlavo (1964), for its long voyage in the depths of the ocean, the salmon uses a system of two spatial coordinates that could be integrated in the brain in a feeling of inertia; in this way, the fish could have a sense of distance as well as a sense of direction. The receptor could be the internal ear and the semicircular canals.

3.3 Migration of the Eel

In fresh water, the eel is generally not mature. After 12 to 15 years in water courses as a yellow eel, it acquires a silver coloration and begins its move to the sea in October.

Before the winter, it reaches the mouth of a river and there begins its long sea voyage, probably at a great depth below the surface. It has been possible to follow

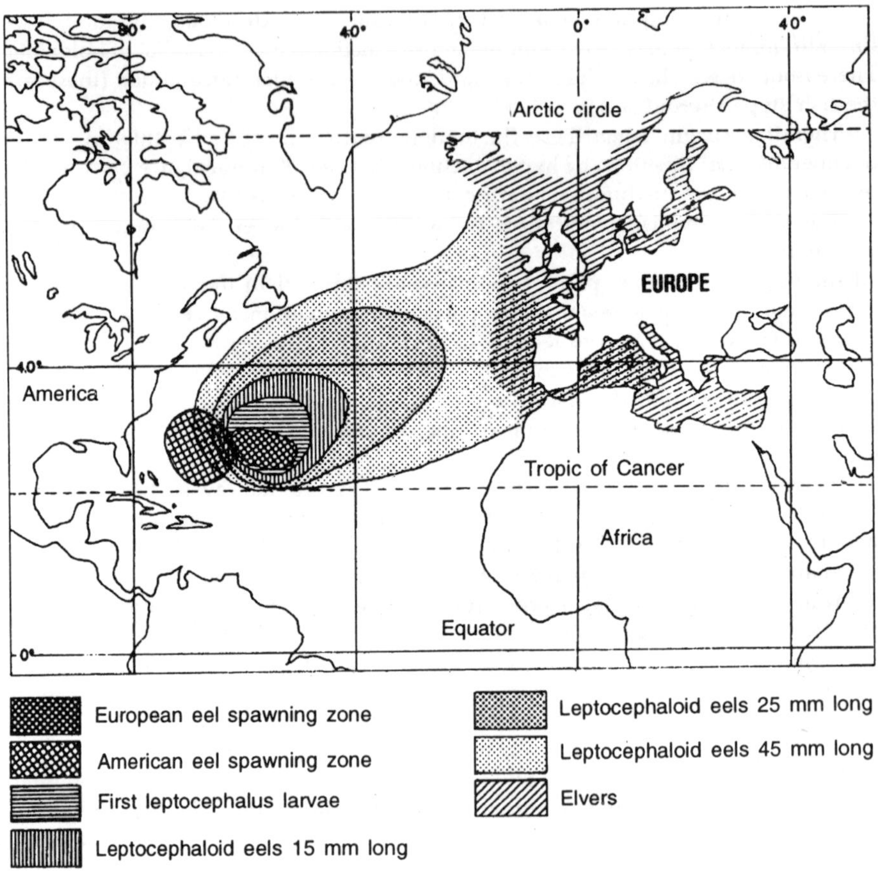

Fig. 106. Distribution of the eel (*Anguilla anguilla*)

its migration only partly. External and internal factors have contributed to this migration.

a) External factors

Darkness: it has been observed that if we illuminate the migration path of the eel at night, the movement stops.

The water currents: the eel has a positive rheotropism that increases to the point where it leaves the liquid medium and, to take a short cut, creeps over grasslands to reach the vector water course.

This rheotropism then subsides and may become negative. The eel allows itself to drift along with the current and even swims in the same direction.

The electric or magnetic states of the atmosphere: silver eels in aquaria are excited at a certain time in October. This agitation corresponds to the catadromous movement of silver eels in the wild. Is this not, however, a phenomenon triggered by the biological clock?

b) Internal factors

There is a hyperactivity of the thyroid and a disturbance in the osmoregulation, and the fish stops feeding.

There is also demineralization in the silver eel but not in the yellow one; this demineralization of muscle and blood causes the eel to move out of fresh water and reach a region of salt water.

The mucus surrounding a catadromous eel protects it from the sudden change in salinity; if it is plunged into salt water, it suffers no discomfort but if we wipe off the mucus, it dies. Subsequently, osmoregulation enables it to live in the sea.

Progenitors reach the Sargasso Sea, where it is probable that spawning occurs at depths of 400–800 m. The eggs are pelagic and the droplets of oil they contain enable them to rise to the surface, where they hatch.

The **leptocephalus larvae**, having reached the upper layers of the Sargasso Sea, drift slowly, some towards America and the major part towards the Northeast. Their voyage continues for 2 to 3 years. At the end of this period, having reached the continental shelf, they undergo a metamorphosis and become **elvers**.

Thousands of millions of these elvers approach the coasts, some moving into lagoons and coastal marshes, and others moving up water courses, even crossing grasslands to reach enclosed bodies of water. In the process, they lose their white coloration and "noodle-like" appearance and become young eels with a dark coloration.

Presumably, once the reproductive phase is over, exhausted by the voyage, the progenitors die on the spot or during a subsequent return voyage. It may be noted that male eels, smaller than the females, are observed near estuaries and migrate earlier than females, which are found in regions further inland.

3.4 Migration of the Salmon

The reproductive period is from October to January and spawning takes place in running water 15–50 cm deep on gravel beds with elements of 2–10 cm diameter. The female may prepare the spawning area, spawn, and cover the eggs in several separate sites.

The incubation period is 70–160 days, depending on the water temperature. After emergence, resorption of the yolk sac continues for six weeks, after which the alevins come out of the gravel bed and begin to feed, mainly on aquatic insects.

At the beginning of summer, they acquire a territorial instinct and look like trout alevins—these are parrs, measuring 5–8 cm.

During the next spring, the largest among these are more than 14 cm long and undergo transformations that are observed externally; they acquire a silver coating, the silver colour being due to a deposit of guanine. This is a smolt, ready to migrate into the sea, and it is one year old. The other part of the population will remain for another year or even two years or more in the cold countries of Europe before leaving for the sea. The smolt will then be 2 years old or more.

In the sea, a young salmon feeds actively on crustaceans and fish in the zones mentioned earlier. After one summer and winter in the sea, some salmon return to

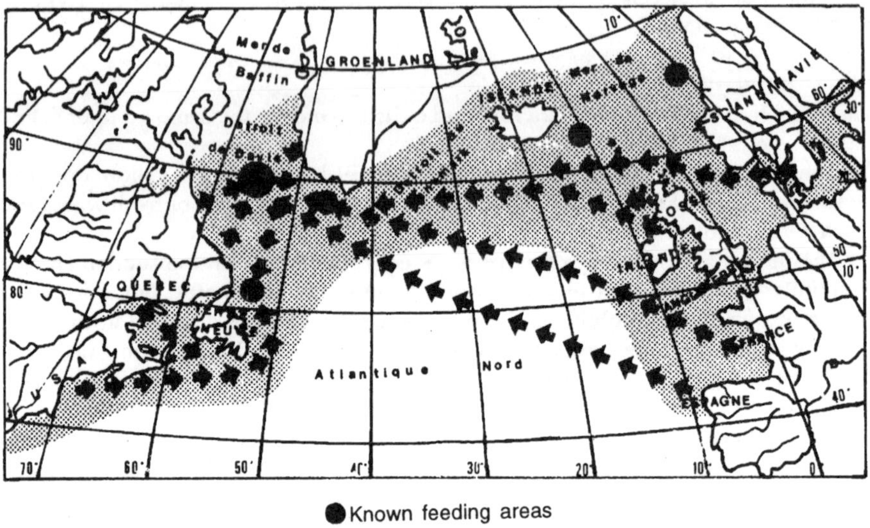

Fig. 107. Migration of the Atlantic salmon (*Salmo salar*) (after AFFRE, 1991)

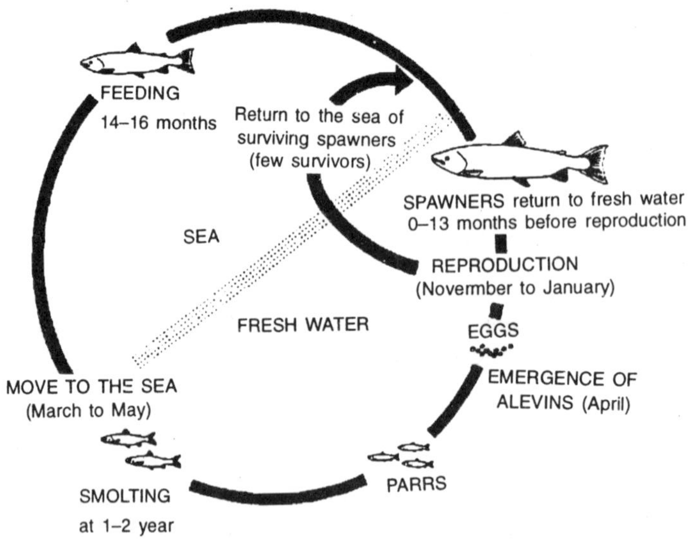

Fig. 108. Cycle of the salmon (*Salmo salar*) (after PORCHER, 1988)

the river to reproduce: these are **grilse**. Others remain for another year or two before returning to a river: these are the large spring salmon.

When it enters a river, a salmon loses its silver coating for a brighter one: it stops feeding.

After spawning, the mortality is very high, especially in the case of males. The survivors, called **kelts**, return to the sea for a new phase of nutrition before a second reproduction. A third reproduction phase is sometimes observed. Fifty per cent of the females and a much smaller percentage of males survive the first reproduction; sometimes 20% but often less than 5% of the survivors return for a second spawning.

3.5 Other Migrations

Sea trout: Like the salmon, the sea trout spawns in fresh water and feeds in the sea, albeit near the coasts around the continental shelf or estuaries where there is an abundance of food, especially in the form of small crustaceans.

The life cycle is different: after emerging from the egg the young trout lives in fresh water with the coloration of a sedentary young trout and, at the beginning of spring, acquires a silver coating and migrates. It remains for 1 to 3 years in the sea but frequently reappears in rivers; the movement from sea to river as well as from river to sea enables it to get rid of external parasites.

The range of migration is therefore not extraordinary except in the case of Polish sea trout, which travel more than 1000 km (900 km in fresh water), towards one of the upper tributaries of the Vistula, the Dunajec.

Each river basin has its subspecies of sea trout that return to the spawning areas of their birth. Some introductions of so-called sedentary trout that came from Danish coastal rivers were observed, after more than 30,000 of them were tagged, to undertake spectacular migrations clearly directed towards their region of origin: some of them, introduced in the upper reaches of the Marne and the Aisne, were caught for the second time off the coast near Dunkerque, having passed through Paris and Le Havre (Arrignon, 1967).

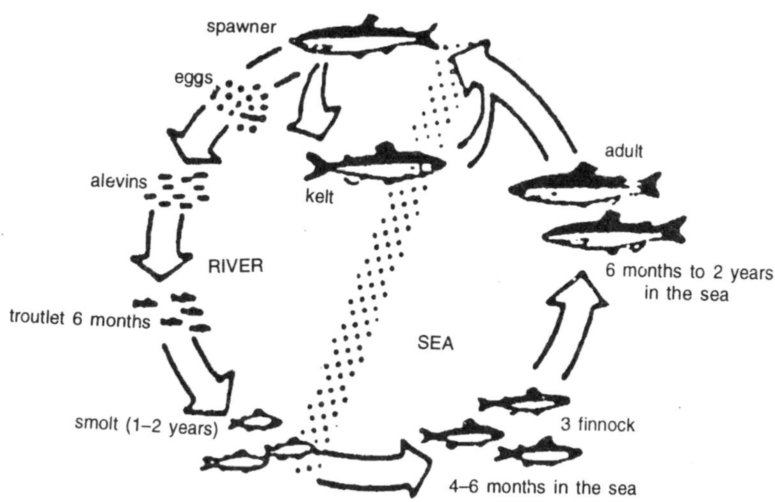

Fig. 109. Cycle of the sea trout (after Euzenat *et al.*, 1998)

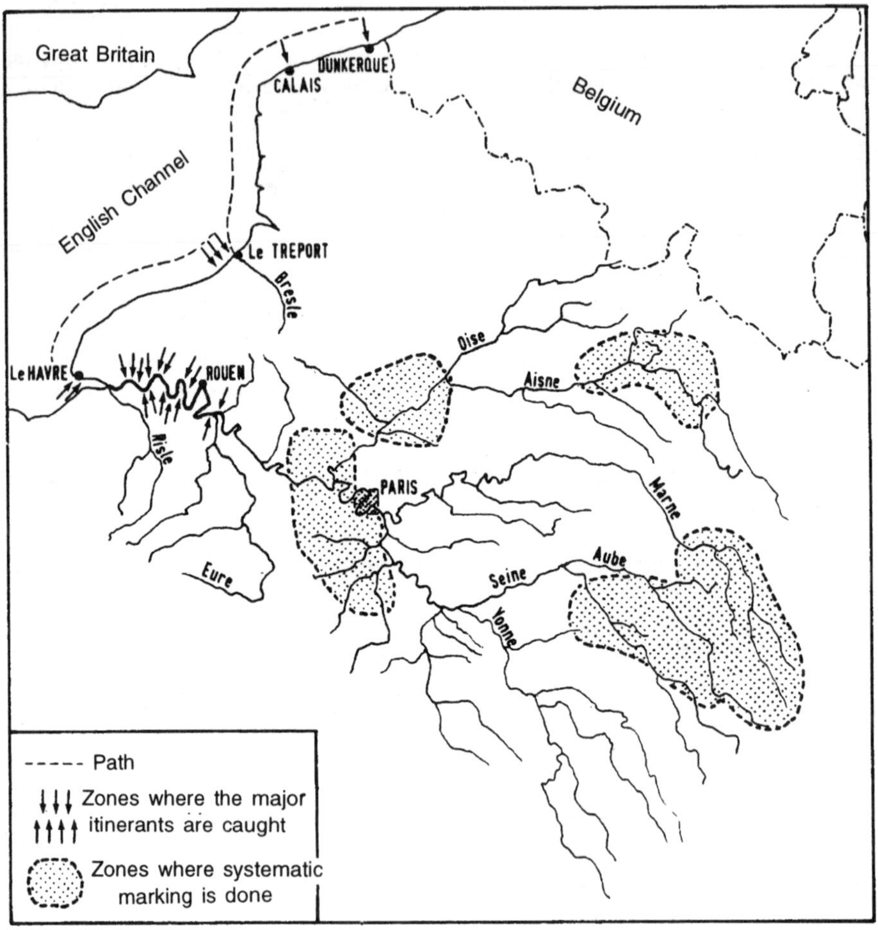

Fig. 110. Migration of salmonids in the basin of the Seine (after J. ARRIGNON, 1967)

The **shad** and the **sturgeon** have been referred to earlier.

The **nose carp** is holobiotic but a well-known migrator.

Finally, the **pike** and the **common trout** do not migrate but undertake movements with a view to reproduction in suitable zones: flooded grasslands for the pike and gravel beds of streams for trout. Tagging has revealed that reproductive individuals may return to their former hunting grounds with a precision of as much as one metre.

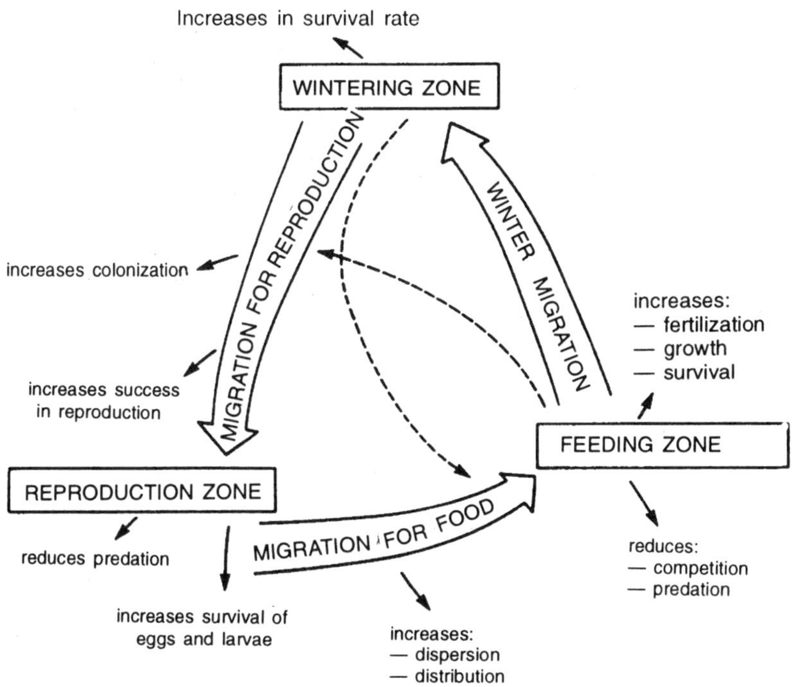

Fig. 111. Schematic representation of the cycle of migratory fish indicating the benefits that may be obtained during the course of various stages. The broken lines represent bypass loops (after NORTHCOTE, 1978).

4. SOCIAL HABITS

4.1 Instincts

Instincts may be offensive or defensive.

a) Aggressiveness is often intraspecific and is most frequently seen in solitary species as well as in older individuals especially during the changeover from a gregarious to a solitary existence; this gives rise to relationships of predominance and hierarchism (for example in the perch and black bass).

A fish, therefore, uses all the resources of this offensive instinct.

b) Defence may involve escape when a fish is dominated far from its nest (as during a fight between two sticklebacks) or refusal of prey of a doubtful type (as in black bass attracted by a yellow bait, refusing the yellow but accepting a white one and then attracted by the white bait and following it but not biting).

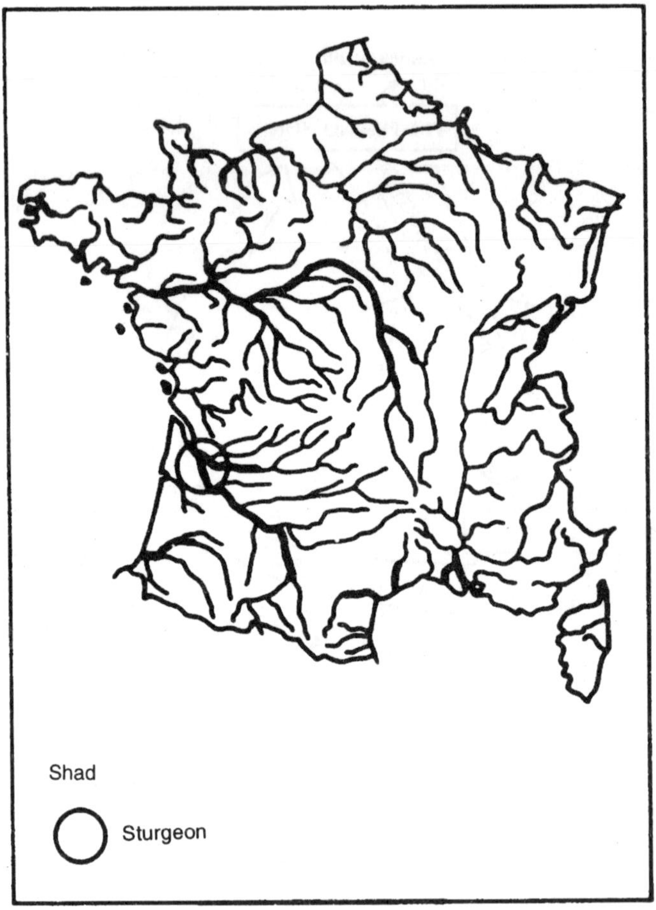

Fig. 112. Presence of shad and sturgeon in France

For fights against their enemies fish may be armed with spines (stickleback, catfish, the carp with its first ray like a toothed rack) or use expedients including mimicry (flounder, loach, sculpin).

4.2 Determinism

Is social interaction an innate phenomenon or something that is taught? It may be noted that alevins that have just emerged from eggs gather together immediately before they could have been taught anything and in the absence of any adult influence, but these alevins perhaps have an individual atttachment to the place of their birth. Reaction to a mirror reveals that every fish of a gregarious species is

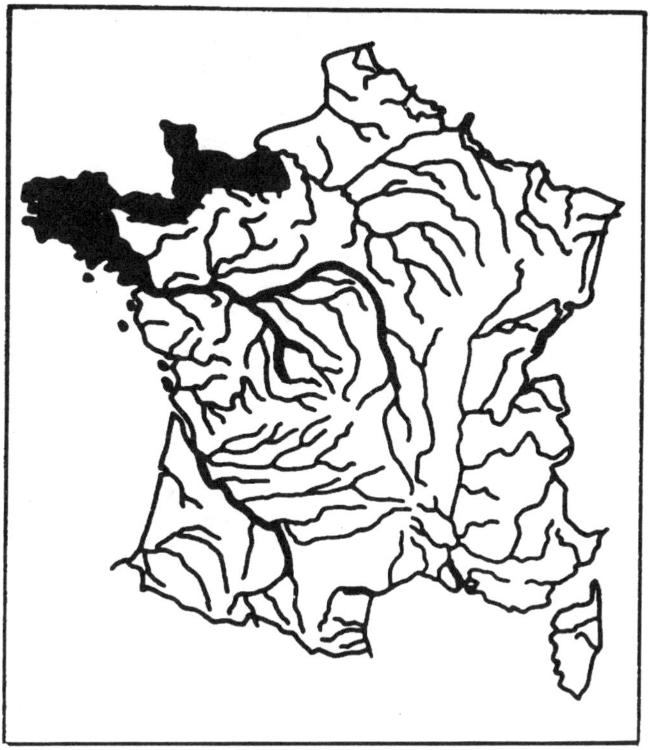

Fig. 113. Presence of lamprey (*Petromyzon* sp.) in France

attracted by those that resemble it; it is its own image or a part of it that attracts a fish and, in this part, a small, very specific anatomical feature: the **social signal**.

Biological sounds made by fish and chemical substances detected by minnows are also social signals.

Social behaviour appears to be helpful to individual fish and to the species. Gregarious fish, like other gregarious species, are most resistant to conditions in the medium.

4.3 Communities

The social organization of fish in an enclosed body of water is based on **communities** comprising preponderant species that impose a characteristic on the ecosystem: these are dominating species. We therefore talk of salmonid rivers, cyprinid/pike rivers, or grayling rivers depending on whether the domination is that of the trout, the carnivorous pike and the live-bait cyprinid, or the common grayling.

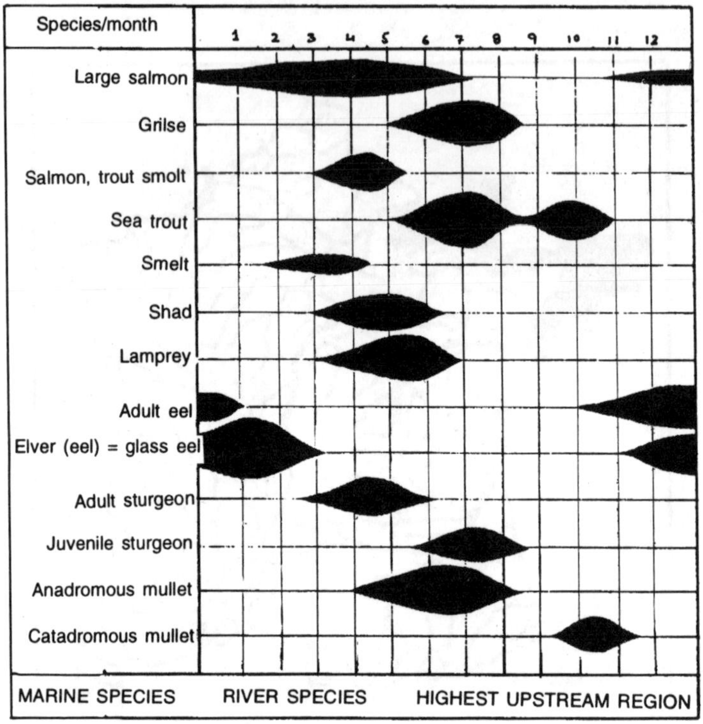

Fig. 114. Calendar of migrations

The changeover from one community to another occurs progressively over several kilometres or, on the other hand, suddenly from a lake to its tributary or from the head bay to the tail bay of a dam. There remain what are called "mixed" transition zones, for example, those in between cold fast-flowing waters in the upper reaches of a river with a predominance of salmonids and the temperate waters in the lower reaches with a predominance of cyprinids and pikes: this is an **ecotone**.

Generally an ecotone contains a larger number of species than the specific communities that it separates. According to VIBERT and LAGLER, due to a border effect the community living in the ecotone is denser and much more varied than in the typical communities to which it provides a transition.

In addition to the longitudinal ecotone there is also a lateral ecotone created by different conditions in the medium depending upon whether it is the median zone of a water course or the deep zone of a body of water or marginal or littoral zones. The latter are richer in fish both specifically and quantitatively.

An aquatic ecosystem also presents a vertical stratification of the communities: a cyprinid-pike community near the surface (carnivorous pike and live-bait cyprinids near the surface: bleak and roach) and a cyprinid—pike-perch community at the bottom (carnivorous pike-perch at the bottom and live-bait cyprinids at the bottom: gudgeon and tench).

A community is nevertheless a social organism sensitive to any changes in the habitat that may have a final repercussion on the respective degree of dominance of the species in the community.

The biological balance of a community in a fishery is due to the existence of balanced populations, not among themselves because the overall situation always results in a certain state of balance but because of direct or indirect human intervention.

5. POPULATION STRUCTURE

The structure, for each species, comprises age groups and age classes.

Age groups comprise all individuals that, at a particular time, have a certain age. **Age classes** comprise all individuals born in the same year. Depending upon the conditions in the medium, during a particular year there may have been an exceptionally large number in an age class: this would be a dominant age class.

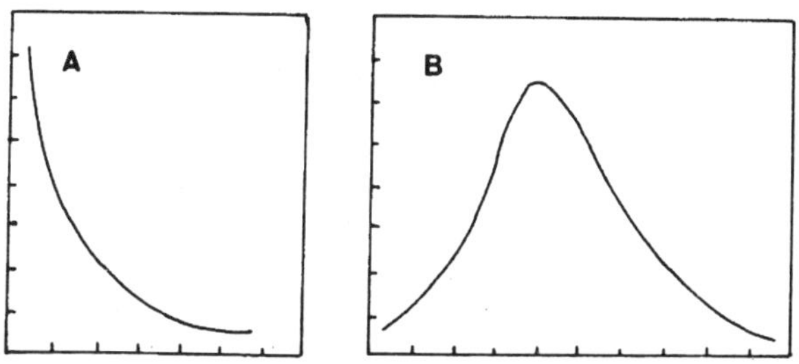

Fig. 115. Illustration of ALLEE'S principle (in VIBERT and LAGLER). Among some populations, growth and survival are much better when the population density is low (A); in others, due to the effect of an intraspecific protocooperation, the maximum growth and survival rate corresponds to an average density (B). In such cases a low population density is as harmful as overpopulation.

The spatial distribution in the medium is based on certain mechanisms. Very little is left to chance alone: this distribution is the result of competition between individuals or groups, for space and then for food, controlled by instinct and some aspects of social behaviour.

Aggressiveness is manifest very often in solitary species and among older individuals, especially during the changeover from a gregarious to a solitary life. It therefore creates relationships of dominance and hierarchism among fish.

Defensive action is often taken by escaping when a fish, far from its own territory, is dominated (as when two sticklebacks fight). It is also indicated by refusal of badly presented prey and by a withdrawal of a fish to its own habitat. All these are individual reactions.

Defence of their territory may also be undertaken by a pair or a group. In competition for space a pair that has selected a site intends to preserve it as its own territory and defends it against all intruders of its own species even more violently than against an individual of another species: this may be oberved by watching a pair of pike-perches during the reproductive period. In a particular habitat the

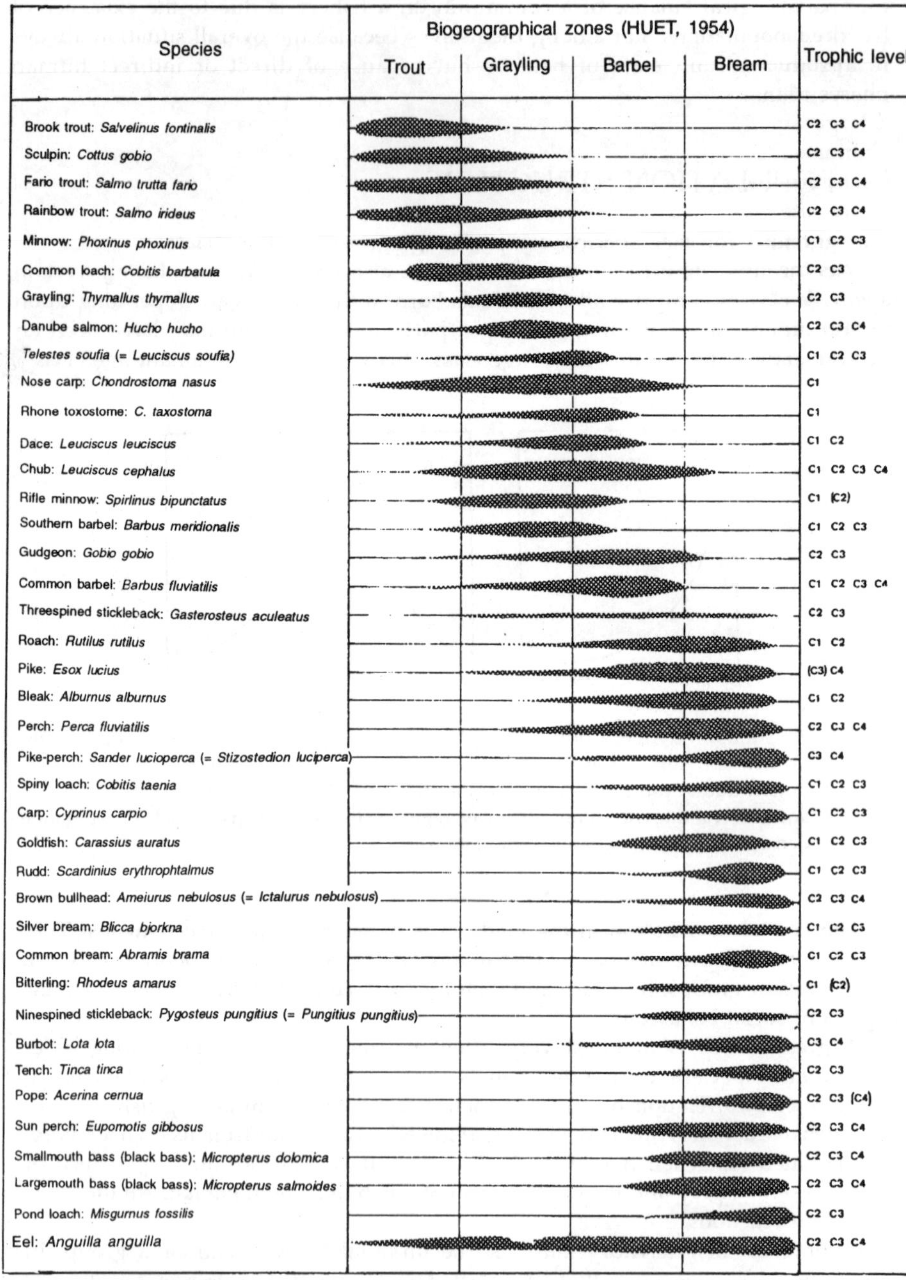

Fig. 116. Biogeographical distribution of the main species of fish in French rivers (trophic level at which there is an integration of species)

density of a population is initially limited by occupation by the strongest reproducing individuals of the sites they have chosen: the weakest are obliged to move away.

The most common species are to various extents gregarious. Aggregation helps in reproduction because intersexual selection is easier and the embryonal and larval phases of the group are generally limited to a short period of time. Predators have a large amount of prey, but for a very limited period, so they are not able to eliminate it completely. This is why, when restocking salmon, modest and repeated stocks are likely to fail, while the same number of eggs, if introduced together and at one site, will ensure an acceptable survival rate (ARRIGNON, 1972).

Aggregation is also an element in defence of a group due to its mass effect as well as the secretion of ectovaccines which condition the water biologically and, in a way, lead to a mithridatization of the group (AUBERT, 1960). It is also based on a certain organization of work in the group. Each shoal of nose carp (*Chondrostoma nasus*) has a leader, accepted or chosen for its considerable experience, which helps the group, especially in avoiding traps or escaping. The imbalance within communities, that of age classes in a species, and disorganization of aggregations of individuals lead to a weakness in fishery populations which, once they have been dispersed, cannot recover their earlier abundance even under favourable conditions: this is the principle, stated by ALLEE (1931), of **minimum population.**

4 INVESTIGATIONS IN THE MEDIUM

The diversity and the levels of intervention for protection and ecological improvements in all or part of the aquatic medium are indicated by investigations of the medium that are very different both in their nature and in their extent in terms of time and space.

A. GENERAL ARRANGEMENTS

Depending on the aim, the initial information will be specific or general; it will be adequate to explain an intervention or serve as a basis for more complex but essential investigations. The literature will initially comprise documents of a general, local, and special type related to the watershed. A knowledge of the geology, pedology, climatology, hydrology, distribution and extent of plant cover, planting of vegetation, and the nature and direct and indirect effects of human activity are often available from maps and monographs as well as from periodic reports published by authorities and organizations.

The literature must also include documents dealing with the ecology and hydrobiology of the particular aquatic medium (ARRIGNON, 1973). These documents generally include fish maps and records. Those dealing with information on hydrology and hydrography relate to the developments in fisheries along the water course or reservoir. They also contain information based on an analysis of problems of characteristic sites as well as certain zoophytological samplings and the results of soundings and fish inventories. In these we eventually find data related to certain interventions: introduction of fish, fish diseases, and pollutions.

In France, legislative and statutory provisions since 1984 in the laws on fishing and management of fish resources have resulted in the creation and implementation of protective programmes and adoption of techniques of investigation in the aquatic medium of a standard type that can be repeated in nature and based on programmes for protection, rehabilitation, management, and improvement of fisheries, mainly by the use of data processing, for simple investigations as well as in cumbersome operations of demographic inventories.

B. ELEMENTARY INVESTIGATIONS

1. ENQUIRIES

Enquiries provide circumstantial information related to unusual changes in characteristics already recorded or even fish facts such as the outbreak of a zootic

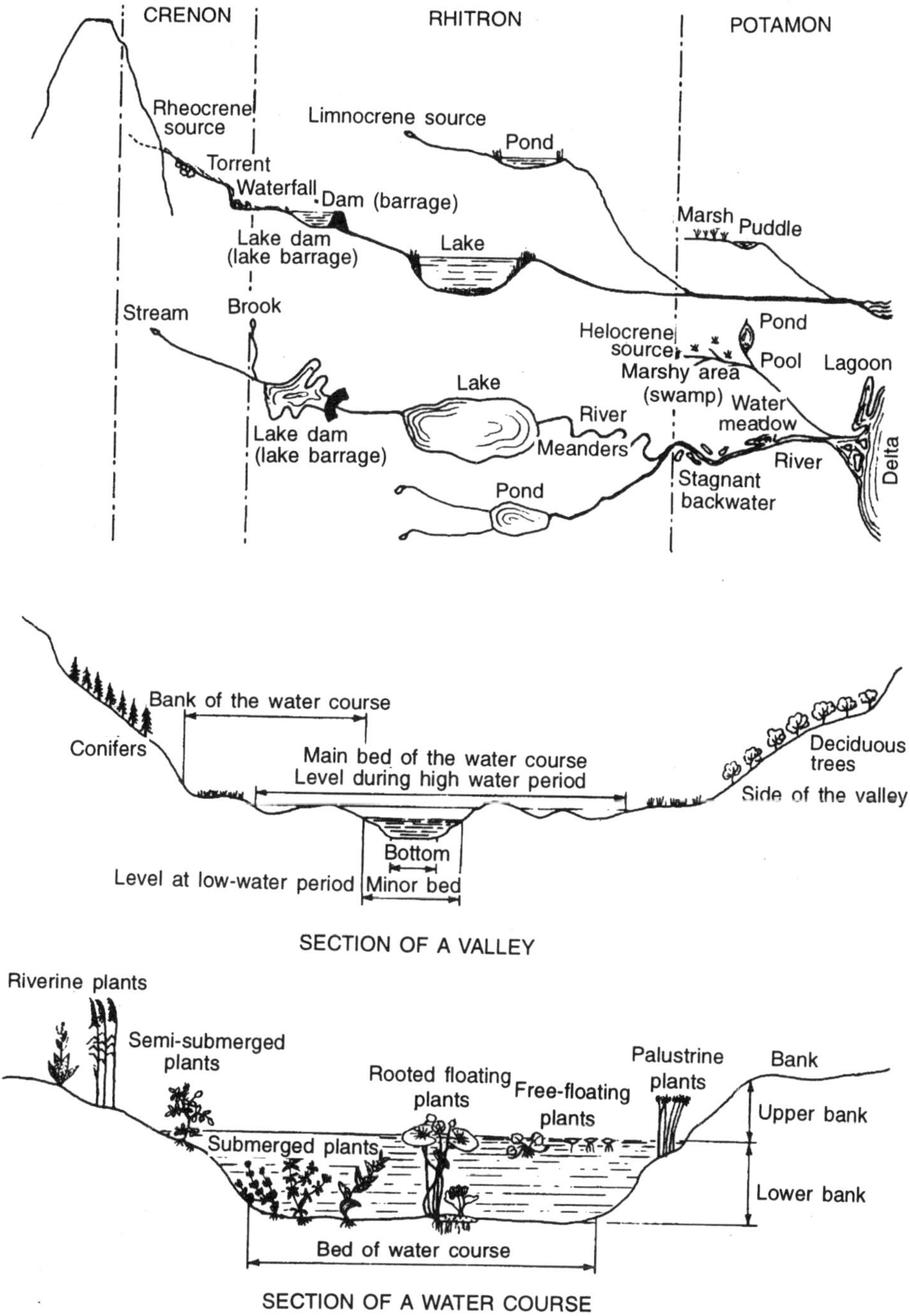

Fig. 117. Principal types of fresh water

Table 14. Usual physicochemical parameters—standard form

Identification: site (code) ____________	(clear) ____________
Operator: ____________	Quality: ____________
Date: ________ Time: ________	Meteo.: ____________

Water	Sediment
Air temp. (°C)	Dry matter (%)
Water temp. (°C)	Org. C (ppm)
pH	Org. N (ppm)
Conduct. (mho/cm)	C/N
Dissolved oxygen (ppm)	
Oxygen (saturation %)	
Oxidizability (ppm)	
DBO (ppm)	
DCO (ppm)	
Alkalinity (ppm)	Alkalinity (ppm)
Chlorine (ppm Cl^-)	P. Organic chlorides
Calcium (ppm Ca^{++})	Calcium (ppm Ca^{++})
Magnesium (ppm Mg^{++})	
Nitrates (ppm NO_3^-)	Nitrates (ppm NO_3^-)
Nitrites (ppm NO_2^-)	Nitrites (ppm NO_2^-)
Ammonia (ppm NH_4^+)	Ammonia (ppm NH_4^+)
Sulphates (ppm SO_4^-)	
Phosph. (ppm PO_4^-)	P. organic phosphorus
Detergents (T73-260–270)	

Table 15. Spatial organization in management of fisheries in France

Area	Proposal	Action
River basin	Commission for the basin	Survey of the basin
Department	General council	Planning of fisheries
Fishing areas	Owner-lessee	Planning for management of fisheries

or parasitic disease such as IHN or a sudden propagation of a new species such as *Silurus* (catfish) in the Saone basin.

In addition to territorial enquiries there can be local enquiries within the framework of investigations or implementations: choice of inventory sites, selection of raising streams, investigation and prevention of unexpected poaching, or an accidental pollution.

These enquiries are valuable because of the current information that they provide and because some situations need rapid and timely solutions.

2. SAMPLING

Samples, sometimes motivated by an enquiry, are extractions from the aquatic medium that provide indications about a specific situation in terms of time and space.

Water samples are taken in a prescribed manner if the objective is to detect pollution; they have a bearing on the ecology if they are taken in order to estimate the quality of a particular water based on the requirements of certain aquatic species with a view to their maintenance, replacement, introduction, or their extensive or intensive culture.

They are based on fifteen parameters and the formulation of a physiochemical balance represented sectorially or graphically.

The sampling may also include the aquatic flora and microfauna in addition to the foregoing, or separately, for example, with a view to following the development of plankton in productive ponds.

Sampling helps in preparing qualitative and often quantitative records of fauna that can be used to determine the biotic index and also that of saprobes by a comparison of the spectra of the encountered species.

Samplings comply with certain rules and standardized means so that their comparative values are more accurate.

Water samples are described on p. 357 and onwards. In lakes they are collected in bottles, with columns of water from selected sites, in a simultaneous measurement of temperature using a device that operates the closing valves, by a metallic message conveyor along the holding cable (Friedinger bottles).

Samples of sediments are collected with core barrels that provide information on their stratification, enabling a hydroecological study, granulometry, and sorting of benthic invertebrates in the upper layers. In deep lakes, if core barrels cannot be

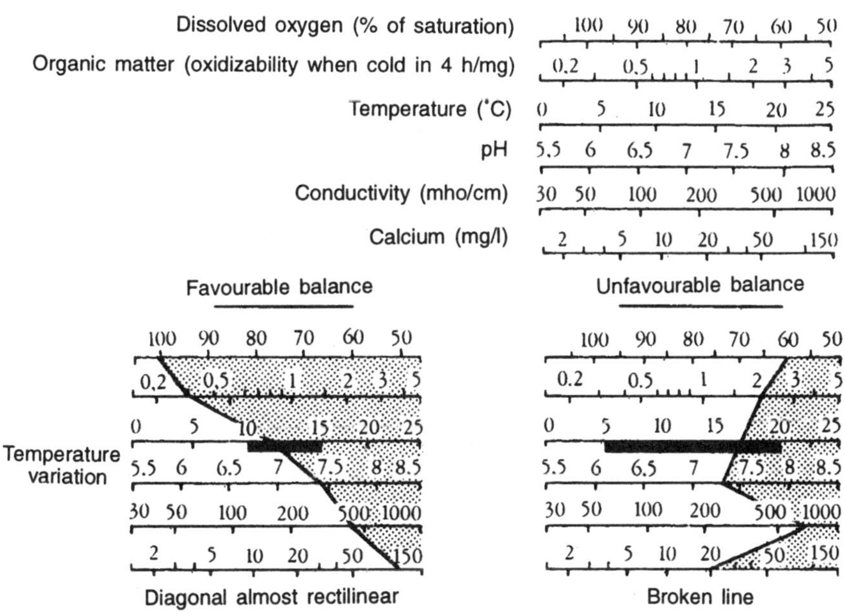

Fig. 118. Graph of the chemical balance in a particular water medium (after CUINAT)

used by divers, a bucket with a flap (the Beckmann's bucket, for example) is used, which, however, does not offer the same advantages.

Aquatic plants are sampled by areas of the same dimensions within a frame; they are examined for species and volume. This examination is completed by samples of the periphyton that are found on branches and leaves.

The bottom is examined vertically to a depth of 10–15 cm using a sampler (Surber sampler) formed of two metallic frames hinged at a right angle. One is placed horizontally at the bottom and demarcates the area to be examined; the other supported vertically acts as the opening of a conical pocket in **bolting** cloth. Placed in the direction of the current, this pocket collects debris and animalcules.

The operator cleans the stones and pebbles, stirs the litter, and triturates the mud within the frame: the products are carried by the current to the bottom of the pocket. A **nozzle** with a tap enables the content to be collected in a flask. This material (benthos) is examined on the spot or in a laboratory after it is fixed in a formalin or alcohol (the same applies to the periphyton).

The water mass is prospected with fairly sophisticated plankton nets depending upon the characteristics of the water body and our objective. These nets are in the form of cones, moved by a handle or towed by a boat at a depth, and for a given distance known as a "run". In view of the small size of these elements, the collected plankton is usually fixed and examined in a laboratory.

Sampling is also an easy method for estimating the health of a fish, its general condition, and its growth after examining the scales: the sampling here is done using rods, nets, bow nets, and electricity, and it provides strictly qualitative results.

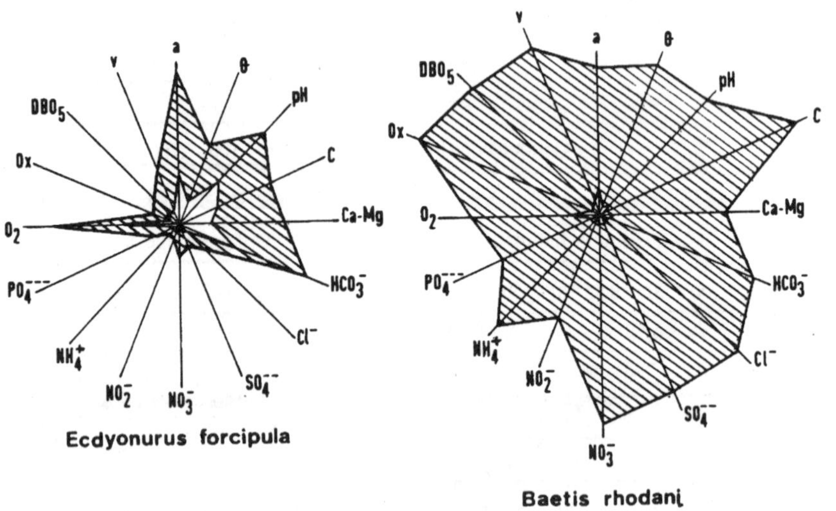

Fig. 119. Ecological spectrum of *Ecdyonorus forcipula* and *Baetis rhodani* in the hydrographic network of the Doubs (after VERNEAUX, 1973)

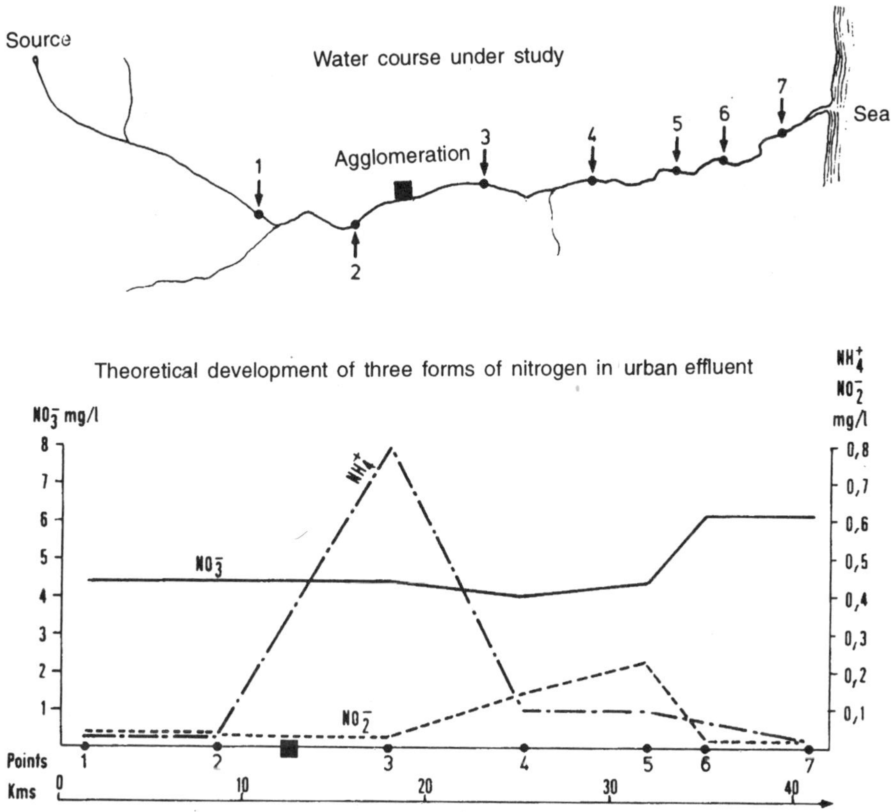

Fig. 120. Parameters in spatial evolution

C. MARKING

1. MATERIALS AND METHODS

Marking (or tagging) involves the identification of animals individually or collectively during the period of time required for the information that we wish to obtain.

Many types of marking are used, mainly for fish. Tattooing, branding, **cold branding,** the ingestion of radioactive markers, and mutilation of some fins enable a collective identification for an average duration of 1–18 months. The use of opercular clips, mandibular or dorsal clips, hydrostatic tags or small pennons on migrators attached to a metal wire or a thread passed through the back of a fish like a stirrup provides an individual long-term identification (1–5 years).

Markings on a large number of individual fish are carried out by manual or automatic injection of microelements of the fish, detectable on their being caught

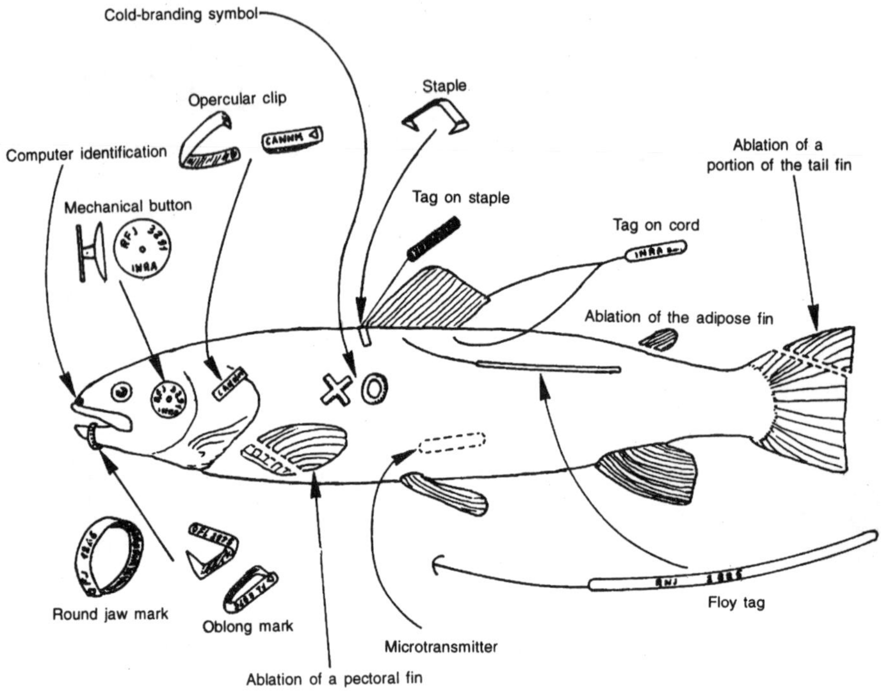

Fig. 121. The position of various types of tags on a fish

again when they pass through an electromagnetic field, suitably linked to a data-processing system with a display, with or without a printer.

Before they are tagged, fish are generally tranquillized with tertiary amyl alcohol, methane tricaine sulphonate (MS 222) or, preferably, with Merck 2-phenoxyethanol liquid in a solution of 3–5 mml/10 l of water for anaesthesia, and 3 mml/100 l of water in an atmosphere of O_2 as a tranquillizer for transportation of the fish (35 kg fish in 200 l water).

They are most often examined, measured, and weighed. The most effective marking procedures are:

– tattooing with a **dermoject**, cold branding with liquid nitrogen,
– placement of dorsal metal clips on sedentary fish, and
– fixation of a dorsal pennon (tag) or nasal micro-codage for migrators.

There are a certain number of markings of sizes that correspond to the subjects to be marked.

Fig. 122. Injection of coded marks in the snout at the rate of 700 units/h, one, standard (1.07×0.25 mm), comprising 262,144 different codes in a binary format, the second, simpler, detectable by X-rays (1.07×0.41 mm) (courtesy Fisheagle Co.)

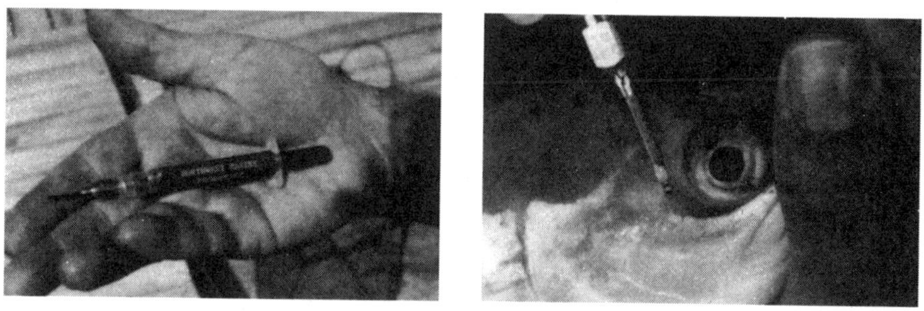

Fig. 123. Implant of coded marks behind the eye in the transparent tissue: 1—manual injector; 2—operation (courtesy Fisheagle Co.)

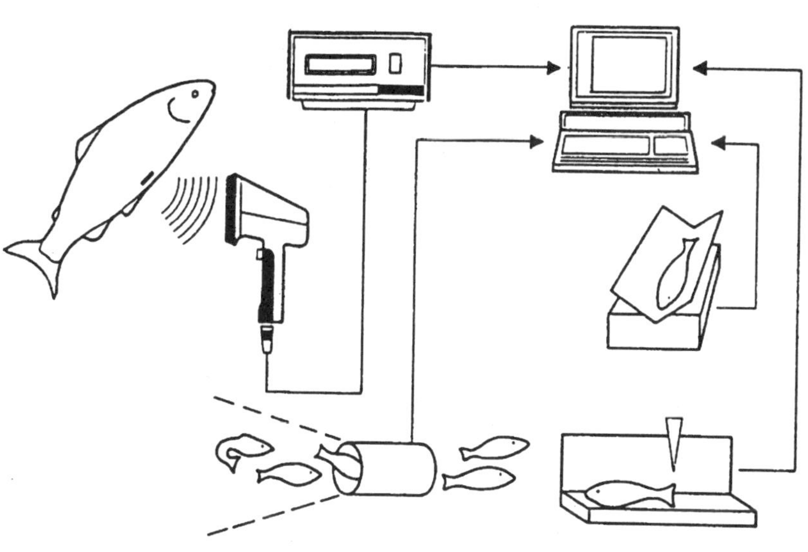

Fig. 124. Detection circuit from the tunnel of a sorting bench and a combination of biometric measurements (length/weight) for identification and data processing (courtesy Fisheagle Co.)

Fig. 125. Electric fishing (J. ARRIGNON)

Fig. 126. Marking a salmon smolt using a surgical needle with a double cord and a tag under the dorsal fin (J. ARRIGNON)

2. ORGANIZATION AND IMPLEMENTATION

A tagging or marking operation, whatever its objective, should be based on a sample of more than 100 individual fish in order to allow for the return of an adequate number. In the case of amphibiotic migrators, in view of the difficulties involved, the sample should be of more than 2000 individuals.

The objective may be limited in time and space: to estimate, for example, the percentage of a lot that was released just before fishing was authorized and will be caught again during the week after rod fishing is permitted.

Or it may be a long-term objective, such as the need to learn, over a period of time, the extent of predation around the coasts of Greenland and the percentage of fish that return to the spawning areas where they were born in a stock of young salmon marked at the time they moved to the sea.

Whatever the case, tagging requires strict organization: indentification of the tags before and during their use, and when the fish return; despatch to all organizations of details and information about the subsequent return of the marked fish; and repeated publicity and incentives to arouse interest among the fishermen concerned.

ARRIGNON (1968) provided information on markings of 30,030 brown trout in the basin of the Seine with a view to studying the behaviour of trout used for restocking, of foreign origin, which afforded no benefit to the water course in which they were released. Of these 2.83% of the marked fish were caught again in the lower region of the Seine after a journey of 560 km in 73 days. Others were caught in the North Sea. As a result the policy for restocking the basin was revised.

The utility of marking, therefore, appears to be considerable because it can lead to immediate measures for protecting or improving aquatic ecosystems under examination.

D. SAMPLING

1. EXAMINATION OF STOMACH CONTENTS

Examination of the stomach contents of a fish provides information that cannot be obtained by direct observation alone about its food habits and the diversity of available food.

Extraction of the stomach contents is carried out after the animal is killed or by a simple stomach wash. *After the fish is killed,* the examination must be conducted as soon as possible since digestion continues post-mortem. The stomach, which begins directly from the back of the mouth, comprises an anterior cardiac portion in which the prey consumed is generally still fresh and a posterior pyloric portion of lesser interest. The stomach contents, collected in a flask containing a 5% solution of formaldehyde, may be examined on the spot or later in the lab.

With the help of a pump (SEABURG, 1957) we can wash out the stomach of a tranquillized fish. The content is forced into a small container, collected, and preserved as indicated above.*

---

*This equipment has been improved upon by P. GAUDIN based on his work on the sculpin or bullhead (P. GAUDIN, 1981, Eco-ethology d'un poisson benthique = le chabot, *Cottus gobio* (Cottidae), thesis).

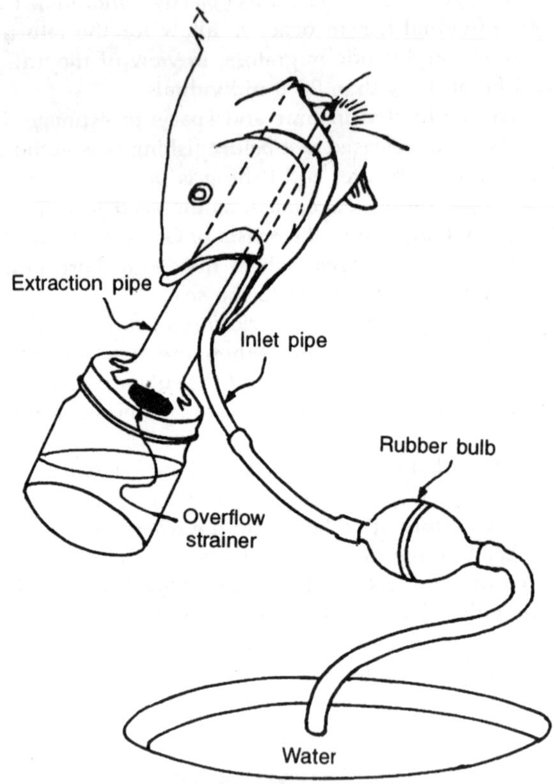

Fig. 127. Stomach pump, after SEABURG (1957)

The results of this technique lead to a qualitative estimate of a meal: it may be within the study of a food cycle, in which case the synthesis should take into account the average number of organisms the fish has ingested, the percentage of each category of organisms in the total volume of food, and other factors.

2. SAMPLING OF SCALES

Sampling of scales often enables scalimetric readings and interpretations that indicate the age and subsequently by retromeasurement, based on the age, the growth curves of fish with all that it may reveal of events that took place during their lives (hypotrophy, disease, heterogeneous growth due to a warm winter, a prolonged summer, a cold winter).

Scalimetric studies are essential for a demographic assessment in order to establish the structure of fish populations.

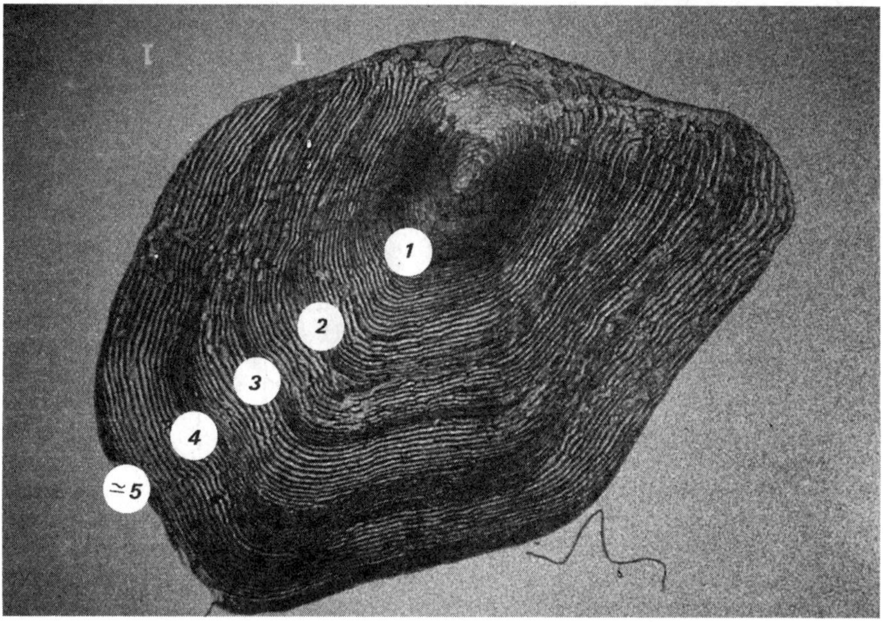

Fig. 128. Counting the annual growth rings on a trout scale

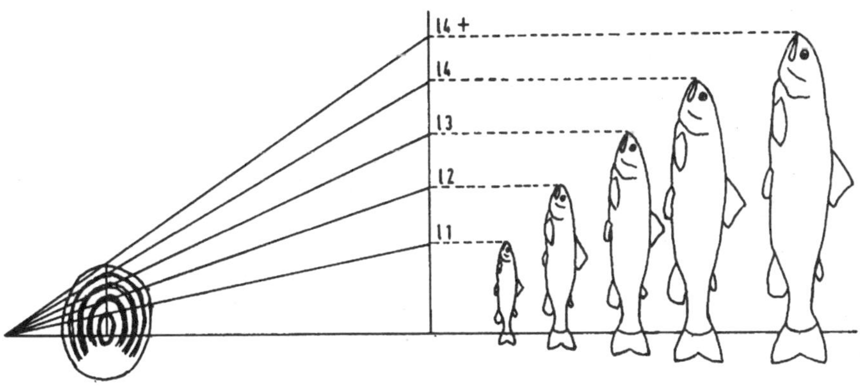

Fig. 129. Backcalculation based on scalimetry

3. OTHER STRUCTURES

Since in some species scales do not provide any worthwhile information, the opercula may be examined in a similar manner (perch) or, if not possible, the otoliths, after preparation and grinding (eel). HOESTLANDT and RUDELLE (1979) carried out

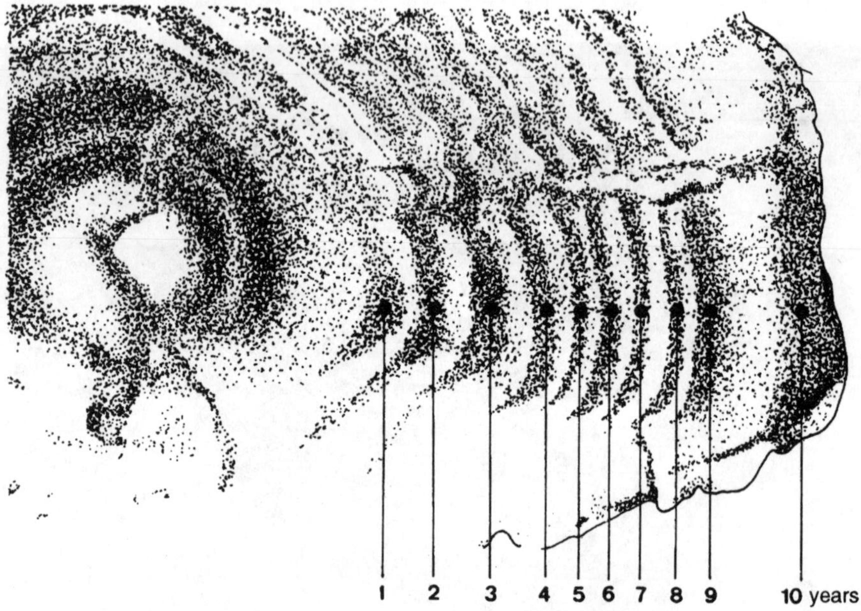

Fig. 130. Counting of annual growth rings on an otolith of an eel (after SIMON, 1975)

densitometric examinations of opercula of the perch using an electronic densitometer. The annual growth rings visible on the opercula can be characterized by densitometric variations that have a significant value.

E. DETECTION

1. DISCRIMINANT ANALYSIS

Discriminant analysis of digital images may be employed for reading scales, not only to estimate age but to discriminate between two populations of the same species of fish based on the characterization of the forms of their scales.

The study implies classical samplings in the aquatic medium, extraction of scales from the same places on each fish, and an analysis of the shape of the scales. An image analysis is obtained using a microscope fitted on a camera, itself linked with an analogue/digital processor. The entire treatment is operated through a microcomputer.

Treatment of the image results in extraction of the contour of the scales given by a code. With a description of shape we may reconstitute the contours. We then enter the coefficients that characterize each individual and make a selection using multiple linear regression; discriminant analysis of the data, for the sampled site, gives the ratios of different populations.

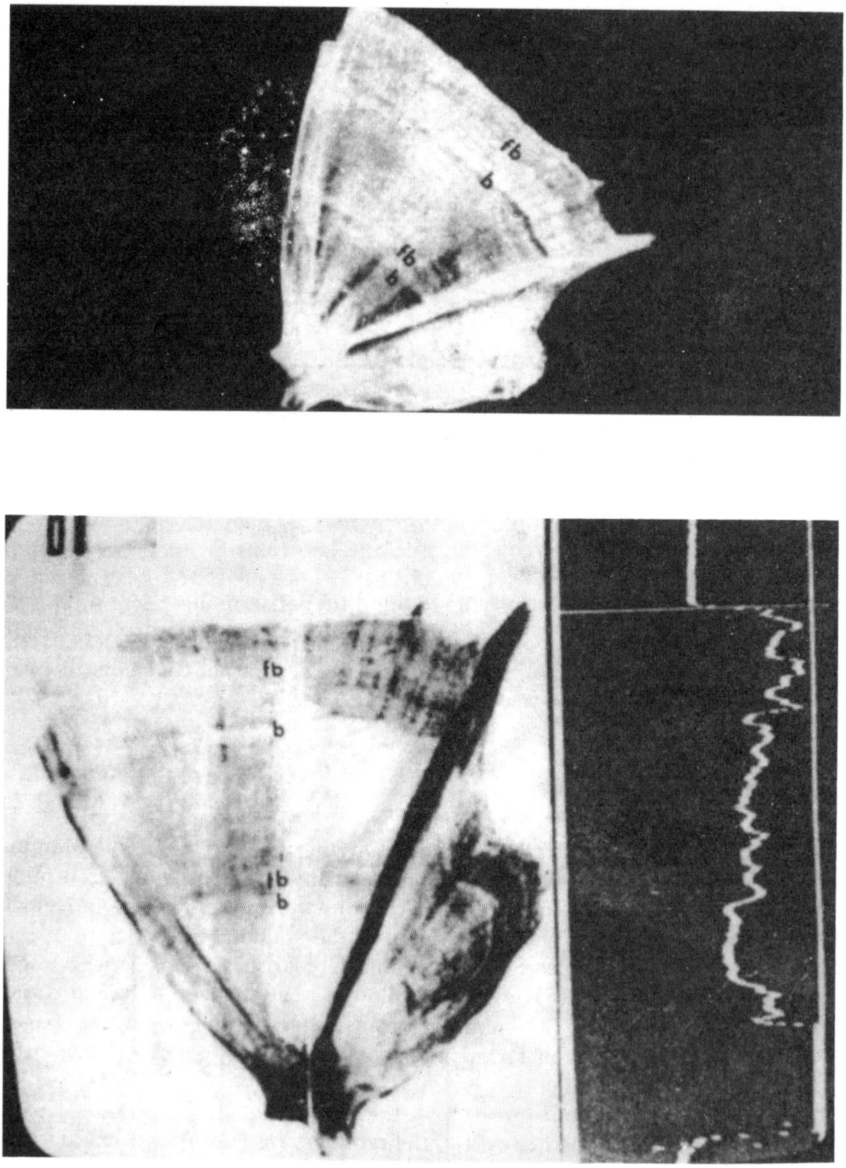

Fig. 131. Operculum of *Perca fluviatilis* after densitometric examination (after H. HOESTLANDT and J. RUDELLE, 1979): Top, left operculum of a 24 cm long perch. Bottom, same operculum on densitometric examination. b = winter ring, fb = false ring

In this way, FRAISSE (1990) studied exchanges in two populations of dace (*Leuciscus leuciscus*) in the Rhone that came from two different areas (Ain and Rhone). The technique adopted has a major advantage over classical biometric measurements in that it is independent of the operator.

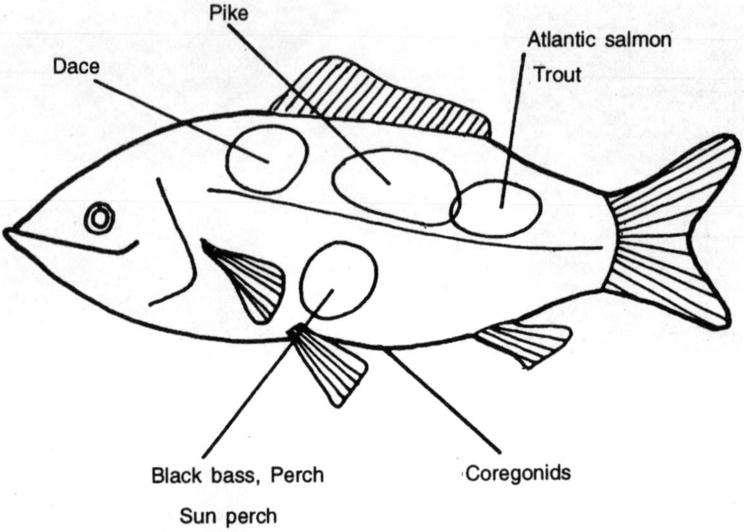

Fig. 132. Areas of scale extraction in different species (after CASSELMANN, 1967; JEARLD, 1983; BAGLINIERE 1985; RICHARD, 1986; CHAMPIGNEULLE, personal communication) (in BAGLINIERE and LE LOUARN, 1987)

2. RADIO TRACKING

Radio tracking is a means of following and studying the path taken by an animal in its natural environment (mammal, bird, reptile, fish. . .). It is based on a transmitter and receiver of Hertz waves. The animal carries the transmitter and the movement is followed by triangulation and recoupment of the emitted signal.

The radio transmitter is inserted in the stomach of a fish. As soon as it is caught, the animal whose movements we wish to follow is anaesthetized and held upside down on a water surface. The miniature transmitter (length 55–75 mm, diam. approximately 16 mm) is then forced into its stomach through two plastic tubes introduced into the oesophagus.

The animal is revived and put back in the water after the transmitter and its antenna have been positioned correctly, the receivers on the ground having been tuned to the signal from the transmitter.

Triangulation is done using two portable radio receivers, each with a directional antenna that receives signals from the transmitter. The maximum strength indicates the direction and goniometric recoupment of the two bearings gives a fairly exact indication of the location of the animal at that particular instant. This technique, known as **radio tracking**, is extremely useful in identifying the direction of movement of migratory fish, their behaviour when they encounter obstacles, and the duration of each stage of movement. Widely adopted in the United States, it is also used in

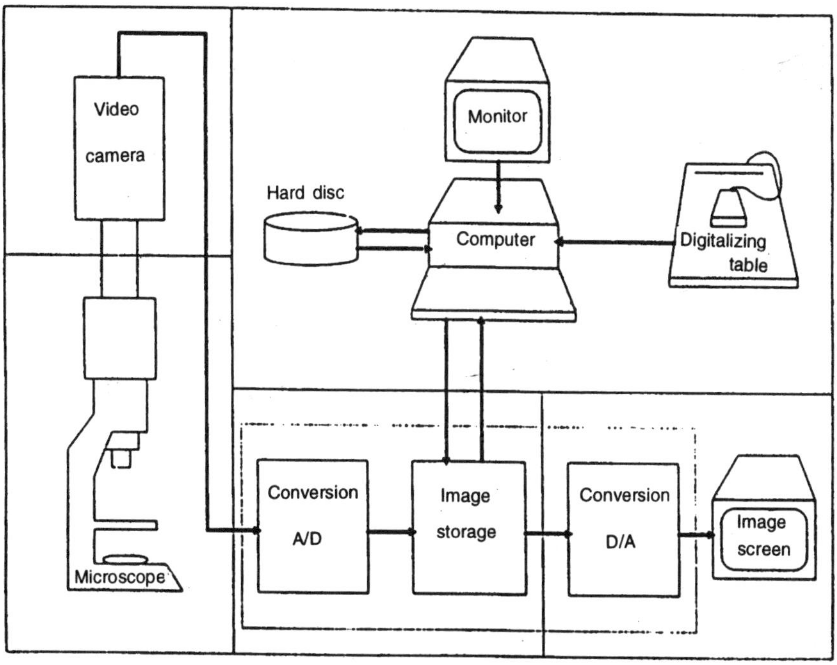

Fig. 133. Equipment for analysis of images after H. de PONTUAL (1988); A, analogue; D, digital

France to study the behaviour of large salmon returning along the axis of the Loire and Allier (BARIL and GUENEAU, 1986).

3. ECHO-SOUNDING

The use of acoustics as a method for studying fish populations is not suitable for water courses and ponds; it may, however, be employed for deep water bodies such as lakes.

There are two methods that are commonly adopted (MARCHAL, 1985). The first of these is based on counting echoes from fish on the return of a sound wave; it is not applicable in the case of a dense concentration. The second method takes into account the intensity of detection, which is proportional to the number of individual fish per unit of volume. It is generally known as **echo-integration**.

The intensity of an echo is also proportional to the size of the fish and we may, in this way obtain an image of the distribution of sizes based on intensities of the echoes. The response depends also on the species, although it has not so far been possible to determine this acoustically even based on the specific shape of the air bladder as an echo reflector (ESCOFFIER and GOUBIER, personal communication, 1978).

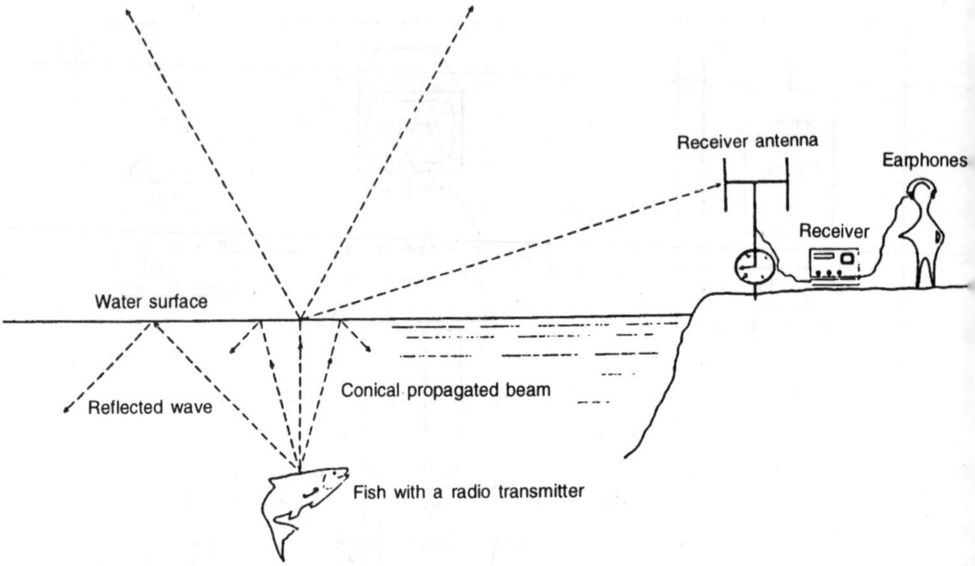

Fig. 134. Principle of radio-tracking

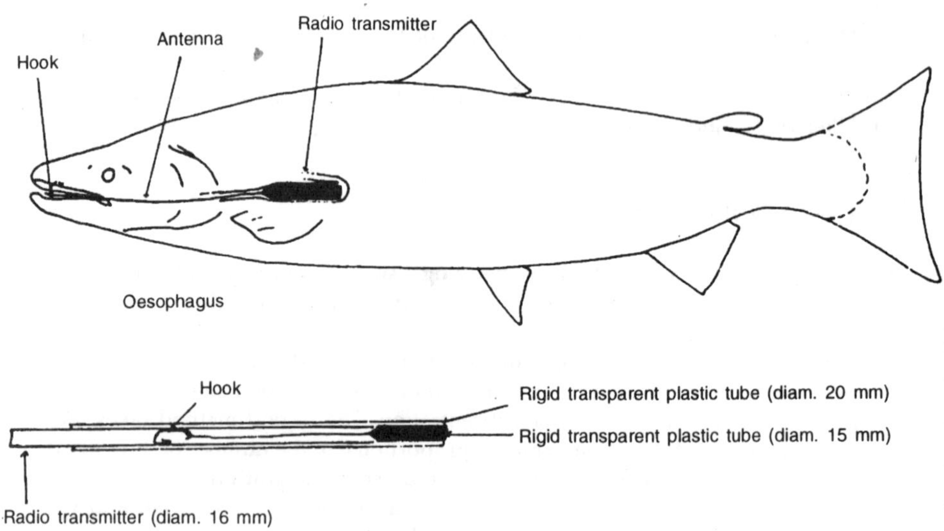

Fig. 135. (above) Insertion of a radio transmitter in an adult salmon; (below) Manner of introducing the radio transmitter.

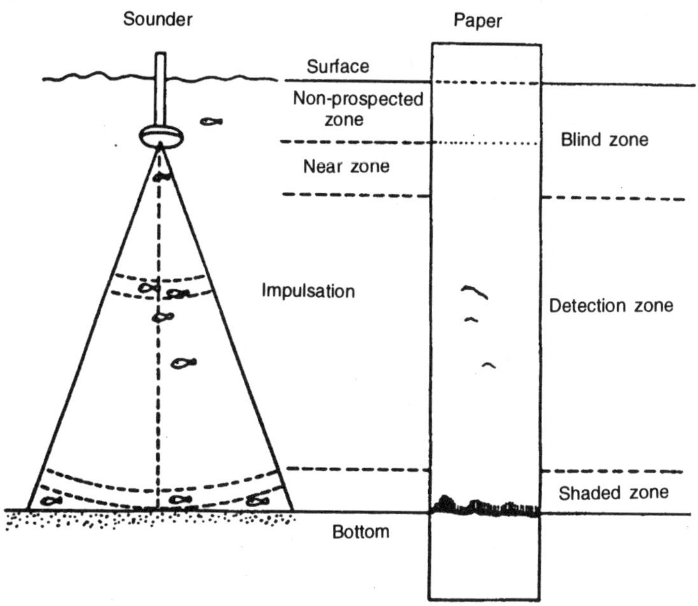

Fig. 136. Diagrammatic representation of a zone detected by a sounder and the corresponding recording on paper. We note a mixing of echoes from the bottom with echoes from two fish that are close together at middle depth and two that are close together at the bottom. The recording on paper corresponds to a series of waves (after MARCHAL, 1985)

In ichthyological studies in lakes echo-sounding is usually employed for studying:

• the spatial distribution of fish, variations in time, movements, relationships with conditions in the medium, behaviour, mode of associations, etc.

• the abundance of different species with a view to its incorporation in a model of management, surveillance, and fishing forecasts.

The data based on a sample, however, must be treated statistically as such (as stated earlier).

F. FISH PRODUCTIVITY

A general and ordinary definition for the term "production" is "activity to produce and what is produced." "Productivity" is defined as a "faculty of producing, the state of what is produced, the measurable relationship between a given production and a single or all implemented factors." Production is capital; productivity is interest on capital.

In piscicultural terms, production is the amount of fish actually produced in a unit of time: in units of weight, sometimes in terms of individual fish when the production is homogeneous, per unit of surface and often per unit of length. Production expressed in units/ha/yr or in kg/km/yr is always accompanied by its values in kg/ha/yr.

Productivity will be the potentiality, the possibility of production: this is what a particular pond or water course may produce, taking into account a known value of the organic and inorganic components.

To clearly establish the notion of productivity as being a potentiality we may, for example, say that given the production of various trophic levels (benthos, periphyton, phyto- and zooplankton, herbivorous fish), in the absence of a production of carnivores, since there are none, the **productivity** in terms of carnivores would be x kg/ha/yr.

Productivity can be calculated in many ways of unequal value but of complementary interest. Some provide theoretical values based mainly on an estimation of several components of the biotype or the biocoenosis, easier to estimate than the actual fish population. Others, based on samples and fisheries inventories and various statistical calculations, quantify the fish biomass. Four of these will be examined, including a theoretical one.

1. THEORETICAL PRODUCTIVITY ACCORDING TO LEGER, HUET AND ARRIGNON (1970)

The method is based on **biogenic capacity**, developed by LEGER (1910). The theoretical productivity, as estimated by this author for alpine rivers, is stated as follows:

$$P = 10B$$

where P is the theoretical productivity of trout in kg/ha, B is the biogenic capacity on a scale of 1 to 10, and 10 is the conversion per hectare of the productivity of a water course 1000 m long with an average width of 1 m.

The biogenic capacity (B) is described as an expression of the nutritive value of the water for fish.

In waters where trout is the dominant species, the main source of food is from endogenous and exogenous invertebrates. Classification as poor or oligotrophic ($1 \leq B \leq 3$) average or mesotrophic ($3 \leq B \leq 7$), and rich or eutrophic waters ($7 \leq B \leq 10$) will be on a quantitative basis after extraction with a bottom sampler (Surber) and examination of aerial inputs depending upon the season and the extent of vegetation around the river.

Several standardized descriptive columns are based on the list given in Table 16.

Determination of the empirical coefficient requires considerable experience because of certain difficulties in estimation such as the following:

- Bottom samplings should provide an average indication of available food in a particular sector; the volume of collected invertebrates may be from 2 to 20 cm^3 per 1/10 m^2, depending upon whether the sampler had prospected a sandy bottom or one of aquatic plants with callitriche and rich in gammarids. It is, therefore, necessary to have a clear idea of the section, the relationship between revetments and pits and between barren regions and those covered with vegetation, the

Table 16. List of observations required for recording biogenic capacity (*B*) (after LEGER, 1910)

Observations	Material used
Temp. of air and water	Thermometer
pH (acidity, alkalinity)	Litmus paper, pH meter
Current velocity	Decameter, plug, chronometer, current meter
Relative no. of revetments and pits per 100 m	Sketch
Average width and depth	Telemeter, limnimeter
Vegetation on banks and exogenous food	Butterfly net
Invertebrate aquatic fauna (at one or several sites depending on homogeneity or heterogeneity of sector)	Bottom sampler prospecting 1/10 m^2 to a depth of 10 cm, tweezers, small brushes, basins, bowls, graduated test tubes
Synthesize the observations on a scale of 1 to 10	

comparative value of marginal zones with their underbanks and aquatic plants and also of the median zone, which is often less productive.

- The collected volume contains invertebrates, which are the usual prey of certain fishes and occasionally of others: in one lot there may exist a remaining number, not expected in normal circumstances.
- The invertebrates in the prey are, themselves, of unequal nutritional value for an equal volume.
- The density of nutritive fauna, at a certain stage, bears an inverse relationship to that of the fish that feed on it. The biogenic capacity, on this account, would be seriously diminished if we confine ourselves only to an estimate of the nutritive fauna.

Listing of biogenic capacity of cyprinid and pike waters is much more complex. LEGER (1945), based on studies by VIVIER and his own studies on the Saone, calculated that though hydrobiological factors are the most important for estimations in trout waters, in the case of cyprinid waters, non-biological aspects must also be taken into account, such as:

a) hydrophysical factors

b) hydrochemical factors (oxygen, pH, pollutants)

c) hydrogeological factors (nature of the bottom areas through which the waters have passed)

d) hydromechanical factors (flow velocity, obstacles)

e) hydromorphological factors (contours and structures of banks, width, depth, sectional profile)

This is what led HUET (1949) to propose the theory of declivity, to dissociate factors (a) and (b) of this list from biogenic capacity, which were to be studied and codifed with other primordial factors and symbolized by (*K*), products of factors (*K*1), (*K*2), (*K*3), (*K*4). The formula therefore is:

$$P = 10 \times B \times K$$

From 1964, a comparative examination at a single site of the theoretical productivity, based on the aforementioned LEGER-HUET formula, and of productivity based on the fish population inventories carried out with the new technique of electric fishing revealed an inadequacy of the formula with regard to the situation in water courses draining the impluvia of early cretaceous formations. The observation, noted in about twenty water courses in Normandy and Picardy, listed according to a strict operational methodology, was extended to suburban water courses in the Ile de France and the industrial regions of the Pas-de-Calais in the north.

The nature of the impluvium led ARRIGNON (1970) to introduce an increasing factor when a water course drained organic waters from a basin with aquatic plants and a reducing factor when it received waters that were polluted to various extents, flowing in from large impermeable urban surfaces. This factor ($K5$) depends on the nature of the impluvium and the type of valley, as explained by HUET.

Theoretical productivity is, therefore, given by the formula

1) $P = 10 \times B \times K$, the productivity in kg/ha/yr

2) $P = L \times B \times K$, the productivity in kg/yr/km of the water course with a width of (L) metres and factor (K) = ($K1$) $\times$ ($K2$) $\times$ ($K3$) $\times$ ($K4$) $\times$ ($K5$).

In spite of its empirical nature depending upon the competence of the recorder, the calculation formula for theoretical productivity, much improved and carefully balanced by the introduction of productivity factors (K), provides a highly approximate value of the productivity indicated by the fish population: the latter also enable it to be verified if required. The recorder is also guided in his efforts by the typological descriptions of water bodies provided by WURTZ (p. 6). The main advantage of this formula is the facility and rapidity of its use for cumbersome and expensive operations in fish inventories.

2. PRODUCTIVITY BASED ON STOCK ACCORDING TO TIMMERMANS (1961)

It is generally accepted that the total population of dominant salmonids is at least equal to or double the animal production.

We may, therefore, state that the productivity in terms of kg/ha/yr is equal to half the existing fish stock, an element that is provided in each sector of the inventory:

$$P_2 = \frac{p + p' + p'' \cdots + p''}{2} + \frac{q}{2}$$

here $p, p', p'' \ldots p''$ represent the weights of trout $x, x', x'' \ldots x''$ years old, in each hectare, and q' the quantity of secondary and predatory species per hectare (with the exception of accompanying species intended for consumption by carnivorous species).

3 PRODUCTIVITY BASED ON POPULATION STRUCTURE

Given the number of individual fish that have reached the age of $x = n$ and the number aged $x' = n'$ weighing, respectively, p and p', the net production during the course of this period $(x-x')$ is, therefore:

$$p = \frac{p + p'}{2} (x - x')$$

According to CUINAT and VIBERT (1963), by adding the periodic productions corresponding to age classes of the existing stock, we obtain the total net production, which, on a per hectare basis of the water body, gives the productivity in kg/ha/yr for a well-defined species, for example, the trout:

$$P_3 = S\left[\frac{p + p'}{2}\right](x - x')$$

4. PRODUCTION ACHIEVED BASED ON THE MODELS OF BEVERTON AND HOLT (1966)

We can calculate the production achieved, in other words, the total weight extracted of fish of an age between that of the first catch *tc* and the maxium age *TM*, using the following equation:

$$Y = F \bullet R \bullet W \Sigma_0^3 \frac{U_n e^{-nk} (T_c - t_0)}{F + M + nK} \quad \text{(MOREAU, 1980)}$$

This is based on the VON BERTALANFFY equation. This author considers growth to be the result of two opposite processes: one (anabolism) proportional to the surface of the organisms (and, therefore, to the square of their length), the other (catabolism) proportional to their weights and therefore to the cube of their length) (VIBERT and LAGLER, 1961).

W_∞, K and t_0 are the parameters of the VON BERTALANFFY equation describing weight gain.

R is the number of the fish having reached the restocking stage t_r.

M is the instantaneous coefficient of natural mortality and F the mortality due to fishing.

With the help of the BEVERTON and HOLT (1966) tables, we may determine

$$Y' = \frac{Y}{RW_\infty}$$

in other words, the production extracted from the medium, relative to this population, if we know the value of R.

It may be noted that the age at the first catch *tc* is always difficult to assess. It depends on the fishing equipment used. It is agreed that the age at the first catch is that at which a fish has a 50% chance of being caught.

It may be suggested that longevity is the age at which only 0.5% of fish of age t_r are still alive (MOREAU, 1980).

The models of yield per introduced fish as given by BEVERTON and HOLT are excellent tools, provided we are able to avoid a frequent uncertainty about the coefficient of total mortality M.

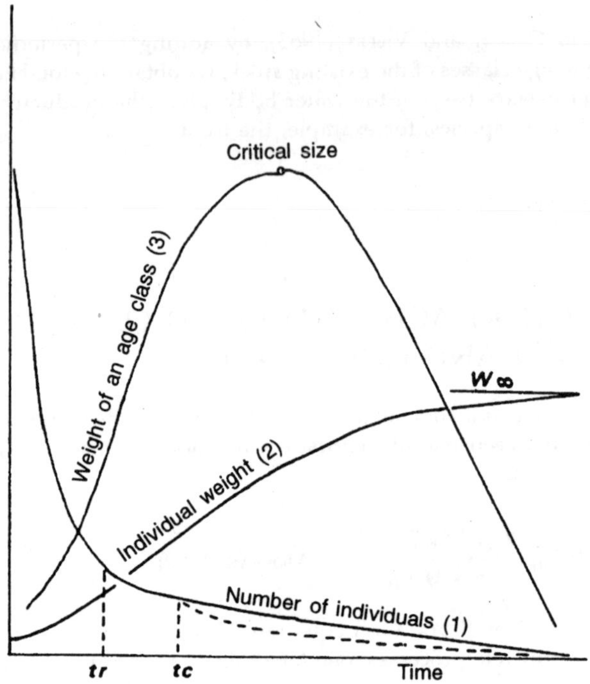

Fig. 137. Changes in numerical and weight characteristics of an age class of fish (after VIBERT and LAGLER, 1961). The value of the ordinates of curve (3) representing the change in time of the maximal weight of a given age class is the result of the product of the value of the ordinates in curve (1) representing the development of the number of individuals of this age class by the value of the ordinates of curve (2) representing the average weight of individuals of this age class

5. PRODUCTIVITY OF TROPICAL WATERS

Independently of the LEGER, HUET and ARRIGNON formula (1970), which deals with water courses containing tropical fish, the productivity of tropical waters, especially lakes and rivers with vast flood zones, has been studied by RYDER, HENDERSON and WELCOME (1974), who have established a *morpho-edaphic index* (MEI) that gives the production based on conductivity, average depth (in the case of lakes), and the surface of flood plains (for water courses). This is explained further in the Appendix.

6. REPRODUCTIVE POTENTIAL

Evaluation of reproductive potential is based on a thesis of CUINAT and VIBERT (1963) according to which "in a hypothesis, corresponding generally to reality, where the mortalities that will intervene till the next reproductive period will be compensated by the total number of individual increases among the descendants, estimating 1000 to be the number of eggs laid and fertilized per kilogram of adult trout (males and females), we can estimate the number of eggs that may be laid during the next season."

This is, obviously, only a simple potential independent of any information about the availability of spawning areas and the suitable conditions of the medium for stocking, after subsequent spawnings.

G. HYDROECOLOGICAL STUDY

An ecological study of a water course is more subtle than that of a water body because of the open nature of the particular aquatic system. Much more strictly than for a water body, it indicates the hydrobiological state of a water course only at the time it is being studied.

This situation involves physicochemical characteristics, the phytozoological components, and piscicultural populations with an estimate of the earlier state and an assessment of the present situation.

An ecological study is a finding based on a situation if it is used as a basis for scientific works and synthetic information techniques. It may also be prolonged by hypothesis of development based on changes in the medium and in concrete—and most frequent—cases, include directives for improvement of fisheries in the aquatic medium.

In cases where we need to be aware of problems related to fast-growing streams, an ecological study is a valuable basic document because of the amount of data it provides and the correlations based on the assessment that flows from it.

1. NATURE OF INVESTIGATION

Hydroecological study of a sector or an entire water course must be based on knowledge obtained from the aforementioned literature as well as various investigations in the aquatic medium providing a knowledge of the many biocoenoses existing in it.

The investigations are based simultaneously on the environment, the support, the hierarchy of the various kinds of biomass, and especially the biomass of fish.

Each investigation forms part of an inventory of the aquatic medium, based on fishing and more often electric fishing and samplings followed by statistical speculators.

For an ecological study of an entire river or a large part of its course (2 to 50 km) it is necessary that we prepare an inventory of the flora and fauna of the most representative stations in its various facies (Fig. 138).

A physical study of the environment, chemical analyses of the support, samplings of the flora and invertebrate fauna, electric fishing of the stock, and a dynamic study of the medium and populations provides this investigation with a certain rigour and enables a serious estimation of the "state" of a particular water course.

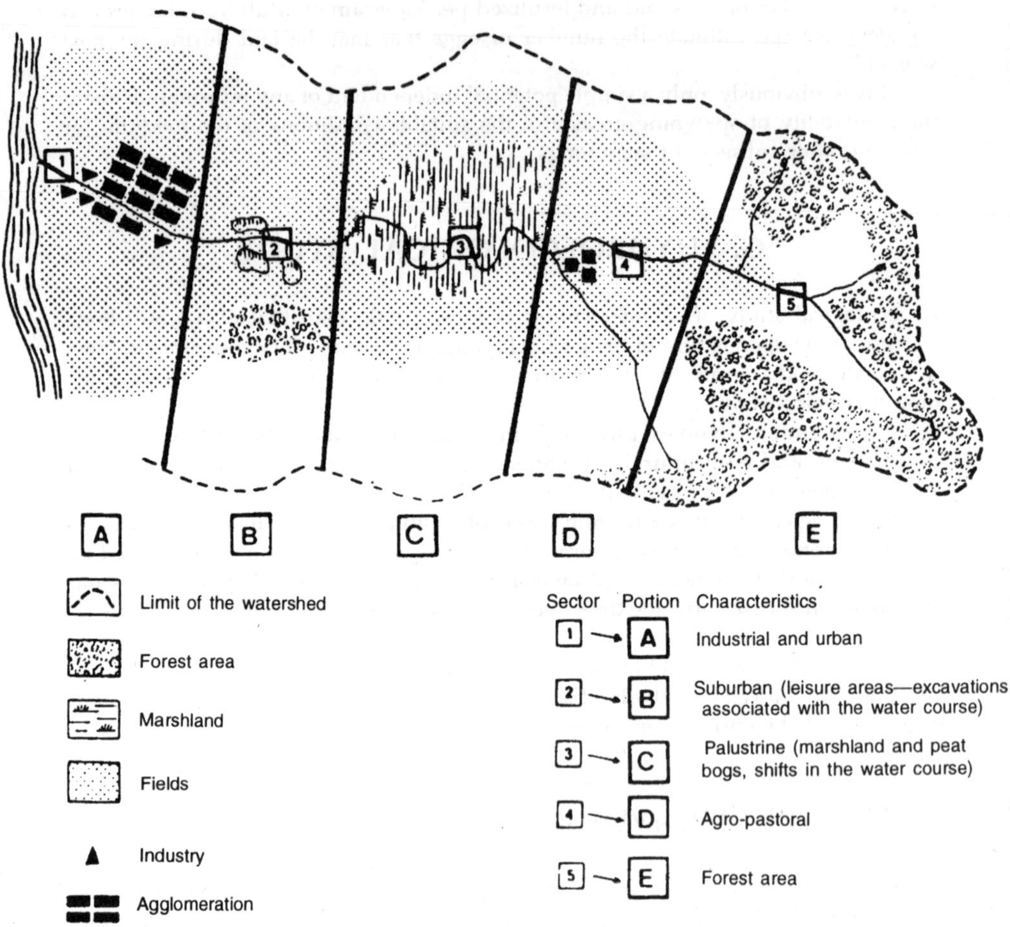

Fig. 138. Section of a watershed in representative sectors

Furthermore, this study may, by providing the biologist with information on the components of the medium (support substratum, higher and lower plants, lower and higher animals), highlight phenomena of an unusual type or otherwise, which have a bearing on the development of this medium that may be favourable or unfavourable.

From this point of view, a study of the particular water course, samples of the aquatic fauna and flora, and chemical analysis of water samples taken from different characteristic points should sometimes be conducted seasonally and before a demographic inventory based on electric fishing, though this may not always be essential. What is needed is an understanding of the problems created by the water

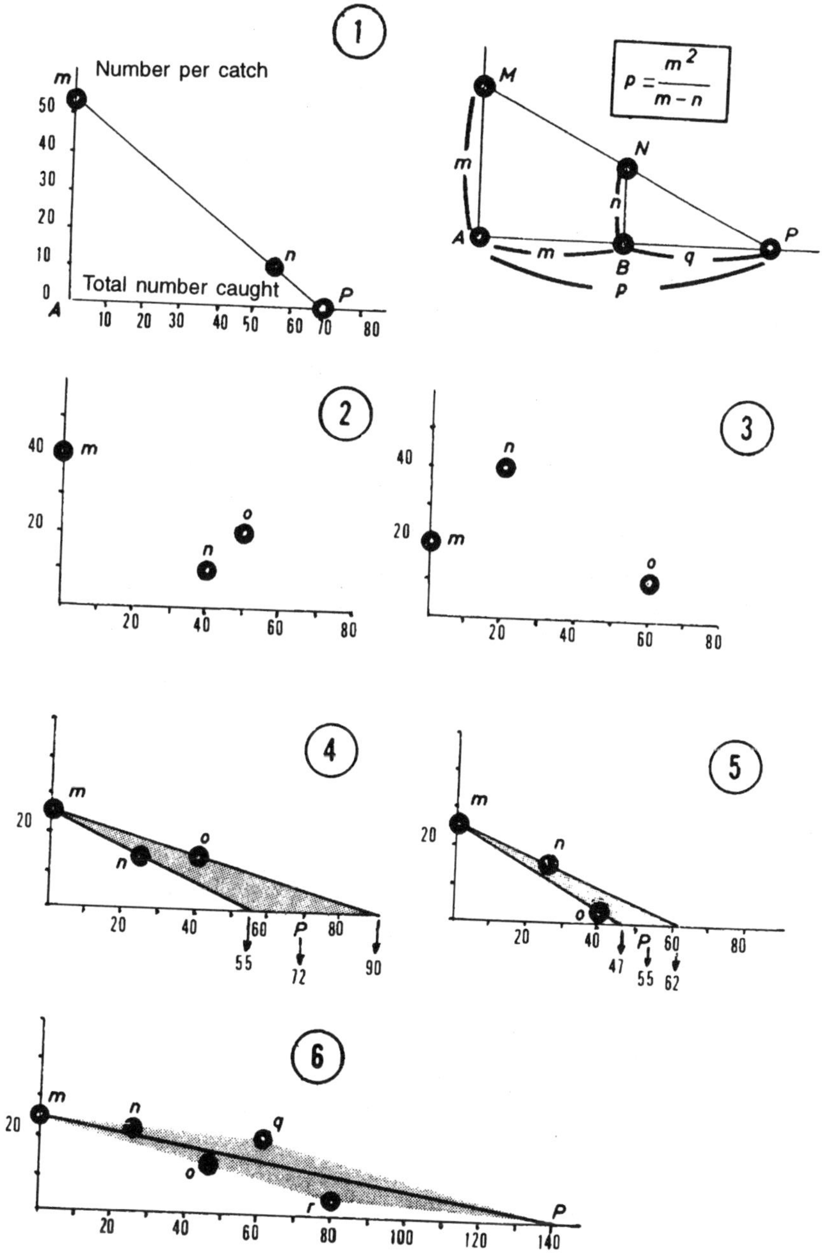

Fig. 139. Regression curve

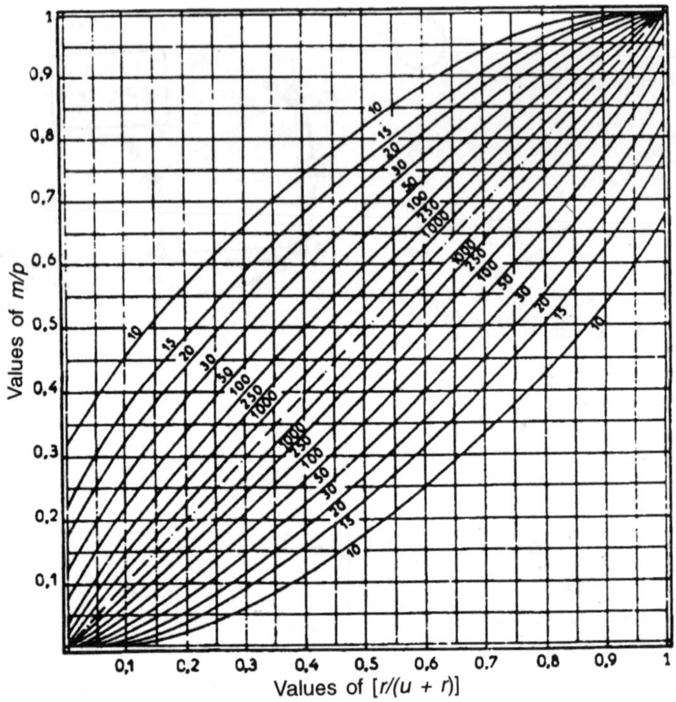

Fig. 140. Clopper and Pearson chart

course, and a selection and hierarchy of the means of investigation necessary to study them.

2. PRINCIPLE OF AN INVENTORY

Reconnaissance of water courses enables a breakup of the fluvial space taking into account criteria such as the gradient, current velocity, section of the valley, hydrogeology, nature of the banks and bottom, apparent extent of degradation, extent of fishing, intervention in the medium (clearing, removal of silt, consolidation of banks, introduction of fish, dumping of material...), which together result in different facies of the water course in so many functional wholes.

In each of these wholes or portions, a working sector should be selected that itself provides an optimal representation of the working portion and should cover the average number of working portions in the sector. This sector of the inventory is the unit on the ground, as it is in a laboratory or a study centre. It may have a fairly long development and be divided into subsectors if working conditions so require.

The most frequently adopted methods of calculation are indicated briefly further on and the calculation explained in the Appendix.

2.1 Petersen Method

In the Petersen method, during the first catch, a maxium number of fish are caught in the sector of the inventory. They are marked and put back in the same sector.

A second catch in the same conditions enables us to recover unmarked fish that had not been caught earlier. The percentage of the latter as compared to the former and the total number caught enables us to determine the most probable number of fish in a particular sector with a calculation of the limits of confidence that should be accorded to this number

$$P = \frac{m\,(u + r)}{r}$$

where

P = the most probable number in the fish population,

m = the number of fish marked during the first catch and put back in the water,

r = the number of marked fish that were caught during the second catch,

u = the number of unmarked fish found in the second catch.

Use of the Clopper and Pearson chart:

On the abscissa is the scale of values of $(r/(u + r))$

On the ordinate is the scale of values of (m/P)

The spindles correspond to the scale of values of $(u + r)$

The chart provides graphically, with a coefficient of certainty of 95%, the limits of confidence relative to the statistical means based on the binomial distribution.

Example: $m = 250$, $r = 100$, $u = 900$, based on the calculation $P = 2500$,

Abscissa = $(r/u + r) = 100/1000 = 0.1$—starting from 0.1 on the axis of the abscissa, let us draw a vertical line upwards till the intersection with the lower and upper spindles marked at 1000 (value of $u - r$).

From these points of intersection, we revert to the right angle on the axis of the ordinates that we cut at two points corresponding approximately to 0.08 and 0.125 as the value of (m/P). Here, since m is equal to 250, the limits of confidence of the mean are 250/0.125 and 250/0.08 or 2000 and 3125. The most probable value, at 95%, of the particular population is between 2000 and 3150 units.

Other calculations may reveal that when the number marked is higher, the interval of confidence is reduced.

2.2 De Lury Method

The De Lury method is based on the following principle: if we undertake successive catches in a single isolated sector without putting back the fish that are caught and if the effort, as well as the fishing conditions, are the same, the number caught will be less in every catch.

The number of fish caught each time is proportional to the number of fish that were in the sector just before that catch.

A third catch is often necessary: the most probable number of fish is obtained by a regression curve.

$$P = \frac{m^2}{m - n}$$

This formula for calculation is based on the results of two successive catches, where

- P = the most probable number in the fish population,
- m = the number of fish caught in the first catch,
- n = the number caught in the second catch,
- o = the number caught in a third catch.

In fact, the difficulty in using the De Lury method after two or even three catches is considerable in view of the rigorous condition that must be complied with. Even when the method can be used, there is a tendency to underestimate the population. It therefore appears necessary to raise to four or even five the number of successive catches to benefit from less draconian statistical conditions.

2.3 Carle and Strub Method

Like the De Lury method, the Carle and Strub method is applicable to successive eliminative catches in an isolated sector. It is useful whenever the probability has not been constant during several catches. The number caught on one occasion may even be higher than that during previous ones; the method addresses the probability of a catch.

This method used as software helps us to rapidly obtain the number of fish, their weight, species by species, of each sex, and even of each size group, if these data are recorded while fishing.

The software is indicated in the Appendix, with an example of inputs and outputs (GERDEAUX, 1987).

3. AMPLITUDE

For it to be worthwhile, an investigation should cover a stretch of at least 2 km. An investigation in a limited period and space leads to extravagant conclusions. This is why it is desirable to cater for investigations at two levels, spatial and temporal.

3.1 Spatial Amplitude

The sectors of the inventory should be selected in representative locations.

a) the first, an upstream sector that will be a reference free from ecological "stress" (for example, above the effect of pollution);

b) the second, a sector subjected to the stress;

c) sectors of observation further downstream, for the ecological effects of the stress and their development;

d) finally, one furthest downstream from the second reference sector (to assess the self-cleaning capacity of the water course, depending upon the nature and the

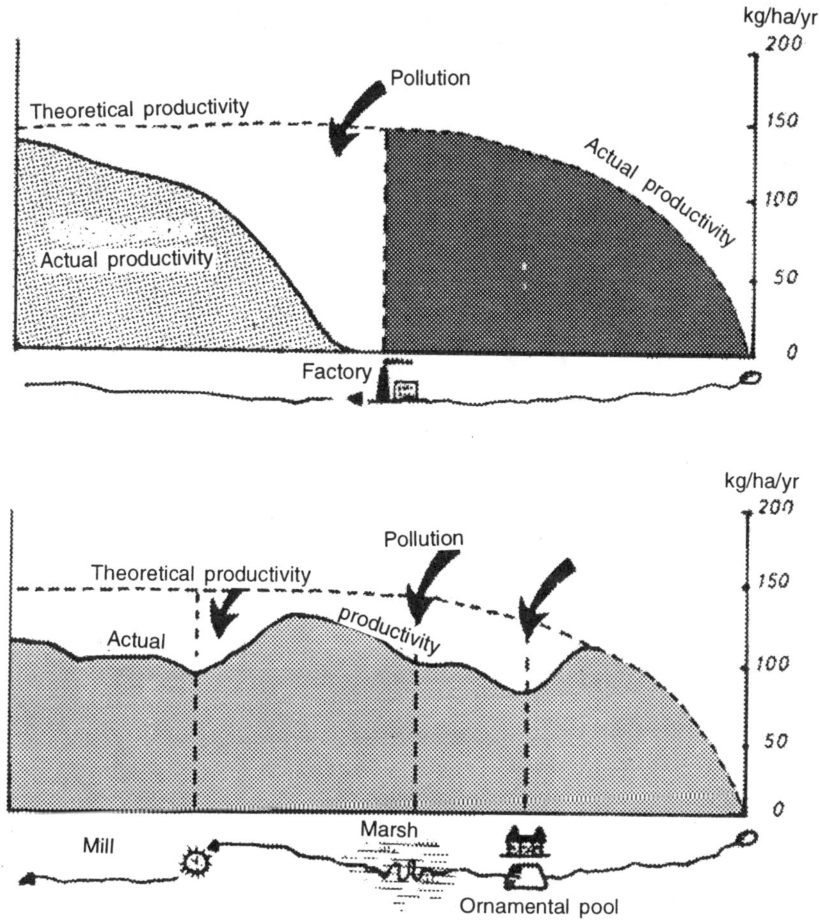

Fig. 141. Piscicultural balance provided by a hydrobiological study
1—of a water course subjected to the effect of a pollutant
2—of a water course affected by a series of pollutions

extent of pollution, for example, and also depending upon the flow, gradient, and other physical chemical and biological characteristics of the water course).

As already stated, for each sector there are somewhat extended corresponding portions of various lengths.

3.2 Temporal Amplitude

a) an initial phase before the anticipated ecological event,
b) a phase during this event (if possible),
c) a phase one month after the event,

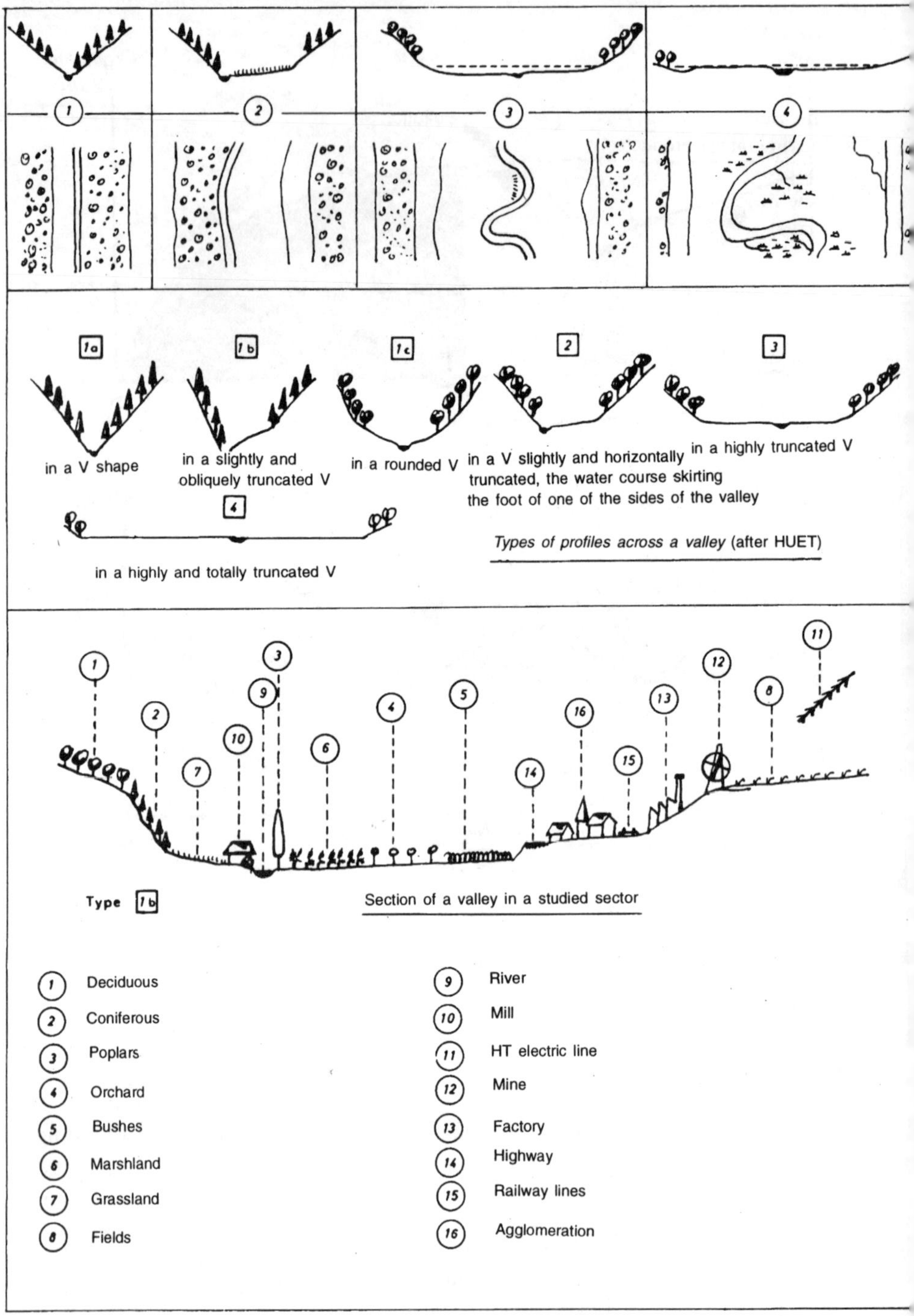

Fig. 142. Section of a valley in a studied sector

d) a phase during the next spring,
e) finally, a phase one or two years after the event.

These different phases enable an assessment of the behaviour of various species of the population in a water course under study and eventually the extent of restocking. Consequently, they provide an estimate of the situation and the directives for improvement that appear to be most desirable.

The likelihood of an increase in the number of operators fishing with electricity in a river restricts the size of water courses for which inventories can be prepared.

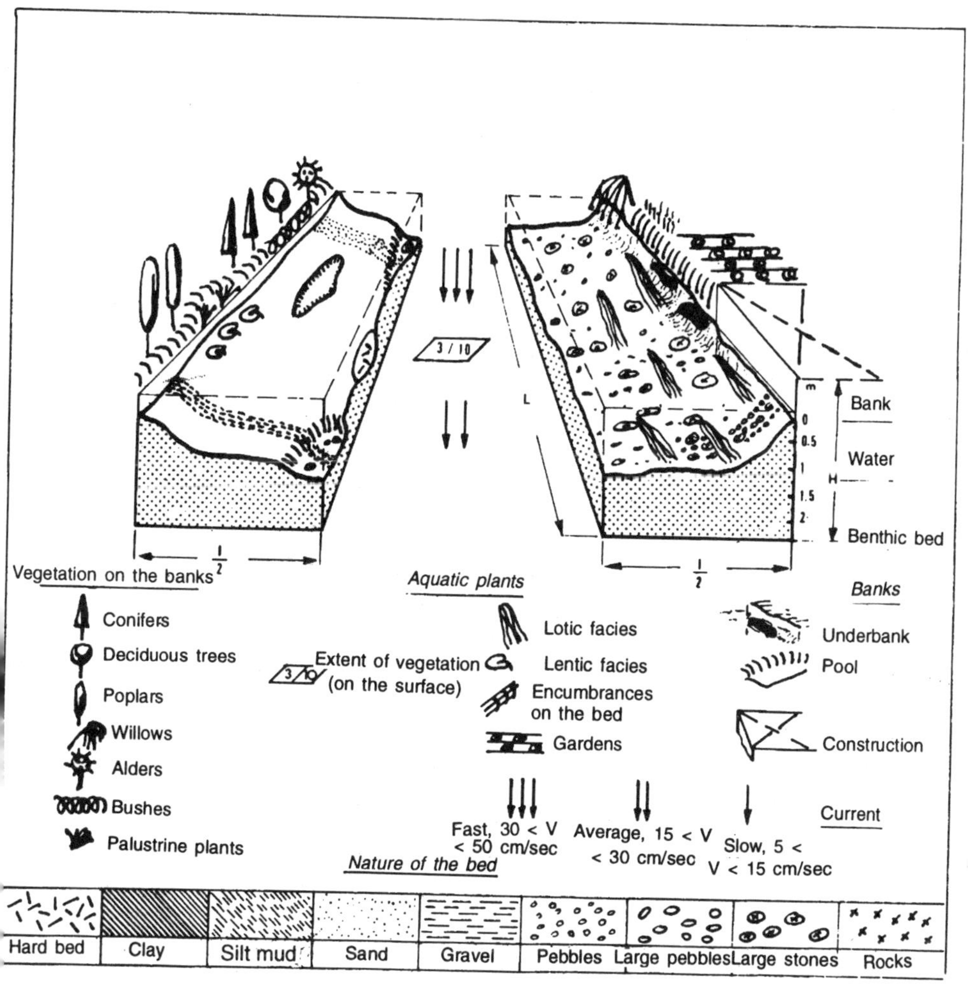

Fig. 143. Expanded view of a river bed in a sector under study

3.3 Database on Aquatic Mediums

In France, public authorities have a data bank on water courses and aquatic mediums intended to create an informative tool to preserve the data collected when developing departmental schemes for fisheries (DSF) (page 166).

This data bank (called "COURSE") has, since 1990, been available for other uses. The software preserves a database useful to anyone interested in water courses and aquatic mediums. The information is organized in four parts:

– A general description of water courses, physical, administrative, physicochemical, and hydrobiological information.

– A detailed description and qualitative evaluation of the DSF, piscicultural and halieutic management of aquatic mediums.

– A description of works on the rivers and use of water courses (e.g., water supply, rejects, dams, microcentral power stations, draining, extraction of granules).

– A follow-up of reports based on fishing policy.

The aim is to make available to local administrative services responsible for managing aquatic mediums a tool for storage, consultation, classification, and easy and rapid sorting of the data needed to complete their work. It is, therefore, a helpful instrument in decision making.

As a manager of the tool, the Departmental Directorate of Agriculture and Forests is responsible for ensuring the basic inputs, ensuring their integrity and coherence, and organizing and coordinating its publicity, use, and dissemination to interested parties. Such management contributes to the participation and logistical support of all concerned at departmental and regional levels.

PART TWO

Fish Breeding

Fish breeders have always aimed to produce fish for the table. For 150 years they have also been producing species required for restocking waters in order to compensate for exploitation by an increasing number of fishermen and, especially, for the last 25 years to supplement a natural production of fish that has been reduced because of degradation in aquatic mediums.

Intensive fish culture provides fish for food or restocking, intended to be caught again almost immediately after their introduction, corresponding to the American "put and take". Extensive fish culture provides fish necessary for a balanced and durable restocking in aquatic ecosystems.

All the intermediate situations between these two types of rearing presently exist in Europe, from improvement of natural spawning conditions, the first stage in improved production, to industrial fish culture, which provides a maximum amount of fish in a minimum time and space with the most economical fish food.

The contribution of all types of fisheries is essential to maintain fish populations in various aquatic mediums, and the nature of the interventions is based on the threats to these populations as well as opportunities associated with the ecological context, in the widest sense.

1 IMPROVEMENT OF NATURAL SPAWNING CONDITIONS

Proper interventions to improve natural spawning conditions are less a matter of breeding techniques than of a measure of common sense requiring a thorough understanding of the biology of the species being bred.

They consist of access of breeding fish to spawning areas, quality and surface of the areas during the reproductive period, incubation, hatching, and resorption of the yolk sac by young fry. They also depend on the quality of the aquatic environment in the spawning areas.

A. ACCESS TO SPAWNING AREAS

Access to spawning areas determines the maintenance of species that have rigorous requirements in the choice of spawning areas: these are spatial, hydraulic, benthic, biochemical, and thermal requirements. Breeders are more often prevented from moving to spawning areas by a physical barrier than by a physiological barrier due, for example, to a pollution zone: the salmon has disappeared from the Rhine more because of the destruction of Swiss spawning areas than because of the effect of pollution from the confluences of the Ruhr and Wupper rivers located on its passage further downstream.

Another example is that of the pike. Marshy water bodies and flood zones linked with water courses are suitable for reproduction of the pike. In February–March, as soon as the water temperature rises above 7°C, breeders move up the streams leading to spawning areas with a large amount of vegetation and covered by a shallow layer of water. They are attracted by the thermal gradient as well as the effluvia that emanate from organic transformations due to flooding (Arrignon, 1972).

Here, they find aquatic plants essential for depositing their eggs, and still waters that are warmed easily by the sun in spring, which generate plankton, the necessary food for fry. At the end of spring the young fish move back to the main bed when the waters subside.

Although not all spawning zones can be protected, at least those must be, which ensure a quantitative and specific population of the water course compatible with its capacity to harbour them and this is essentially dependent on periodic flooding of these zones and their accessibility at the right time for the breeders.

This is why the pike in the lower courses of the Oise river cannot reproduce in the flooded marshes that it used to visit after they were isolated from its inhabitable expansion zone for reasons of sanitation or hydraulic requirements of navigation.

The species has since been maintained more by introduction of pike fry from fisheries than by costly and random introduction of adults from catches in ponds which have neither the morphology nor the hereditary characteristics of fish in streams.

Demarcation of essential spawning areas and regulation of their flooding and access, according to the period of reproduction and the release of fry, have resulted in reasonable solutions at certain sites. Cut-off arms, backwaters, shallow stagnant waters, abandoned meanders, smaller rivers and large water courses are favourable not only for the reproduction of pike but also for Cyprinids, which find ideal conditions for spawning in an aquatic vegetation of the nupharian type. The yield in such zones is extremely high as reported by MAILLY (1967) in the flood zones of the Aisne and Marne rivers. Fifteen catches undertaken between May and July 12, 1965, enabled a check on 16,776 young pike of the year, of large size.

The utility of these zones may be seen from different points of view (or sometimes complementary ones) depending upon whether the objective is to extract surplus breeders to use them in a pike fishery or to extract some of the surplus young pike, when they move to the main water course, to introduce them in deficit mediums.

This implies a free movement of the fish in both directions at times when the water regime varies considerably. Some works may often be necessary in water meadows to avoid a drying up that may result in the death of a large number of young pike: they may require improvement or creation of a network of drains or excavation of pools at the lowest points, from which the fish may be collected by net or by electric fishing.

Sand pits, gravel pits, and peat bogs connected with major water courses provide shelter to fish subjected to certain pollution fronts moving downstream in water courses. Apart from providing banks and shallows with aquatic plants they are also excellent potential spawning areas for populations of lotic ecosystems that are normally subjected to repeated adverse conditions, such as pollution and the disturbance caused by river craft.

Table 17. Sizes in the lot of young pike collected from natural spawning areas

Size in cm	No.	Percentage present
4–6	300	1.78
6–8	2222	13.24
10–12	6162	36.73
12–14	1010	6.02
14–20	6971	41.55
over 25	111	0.66

Improvements in areas for crossing fish also encourage reproduction of salmonids by providing them access to new areas for spawning: for this we reduce natural rocky sills, remove dams that are no longer in use, and construct passes enabling circumvention of obstacles that could not be crossed earlier.

SMART (1965), in MILLS (1971), reported a considerable increase in production in the North Esk river of Scotland after such works were carried out.

B. PROTECTION OF SPAWNING AREAS

Protection of spawning areas is also extremely beneficial. It includes measures that restrict or preclude their degradation by certain hydraulic maintenance practices in water bodies or works in the medium (extraction of aggregates from the bed in salmonid water courses) so that they have, in large measure, the qualities that will induce breeders to use them.

The observations should enable a judicious choice of the best time for maintenance works such as clearing of beds and removal of weeds. Removal of weeds, if not done carefully, may deprive cyprinids of aquatic plants that provide a support for their eggs or destroy those already laid. Clearing may cause clogging in gravel beds before salmonids have spawned or even after and, in the latter case, suffocate and destroy eggs that have been laid.

In large cyprinid-pike water courses, vegetation should be cleared along central longitudinal veins to ensure a maximal flow based on their geometry and not, for example, on the banks that are most favourable for reproduction of cyprinids and perches merely because they are the warmest and most calm. In water bodies, a careful examination of conditions for reproduction leads to a choice of areas to be cleared and this is done by rotation depending upon the period and the sites for spawning. The dates of these operations are then selected.

In salmonid rivers, the time periods and the site for clearing the beds are decided upon in relation to the periods when trout and salmon arrive in these spawning areas. In Normandy, it is not recommended to undertake clearing within a distance of less than 5 km upstream from October to March, which is the time the animals collect together in spawning areas till the emergence of fry (Arrignon, 1973).

In critical situations where a threatened stock has to be protected, electric fishing is carried out near the visited spawning sites in order to remove predators (nose carp, eels, pike, large salmonids) that are likely to destroy the spawn. In Champagne such operations, repeated every five years, have restored the trout stock in the Suippe brook.

C. IMPROVEMENTS IN SPAWNING AREAS

Improvements in spawning areas are ensured by encouraging the growth of certain aquatic plants favourable for the reproduction of cyprinids and pike (e.g., water milfoil), either by clearing to eliminate other less favourable and invasive plants (constituents of the scirpion and phragmition), or by clearing to remove silt and sediments that prevent these plants from taking root (sterile deposits or thiosaprobic sludge), or even by judicious amendments (lime, carbonate of lime).

In salmonid water courses, improvements in gravel beds and their irrigation by a suitable water current with an appropriate depth are carried out using a harrow or a hoe and with well-positioned deflectors (rows of large stones, tree trunks and plants, suitably placed and fixed). Zones that have been improved in this manner are almost immediately chosen by breeders looking for spawning sites.

The requirements of salmonids are particularly rigorous. They must be able to spawn in beds with a specific granulometry (1–8 cm depending on the size of the female); embryonal development continues for 2–3 months, depending on the water

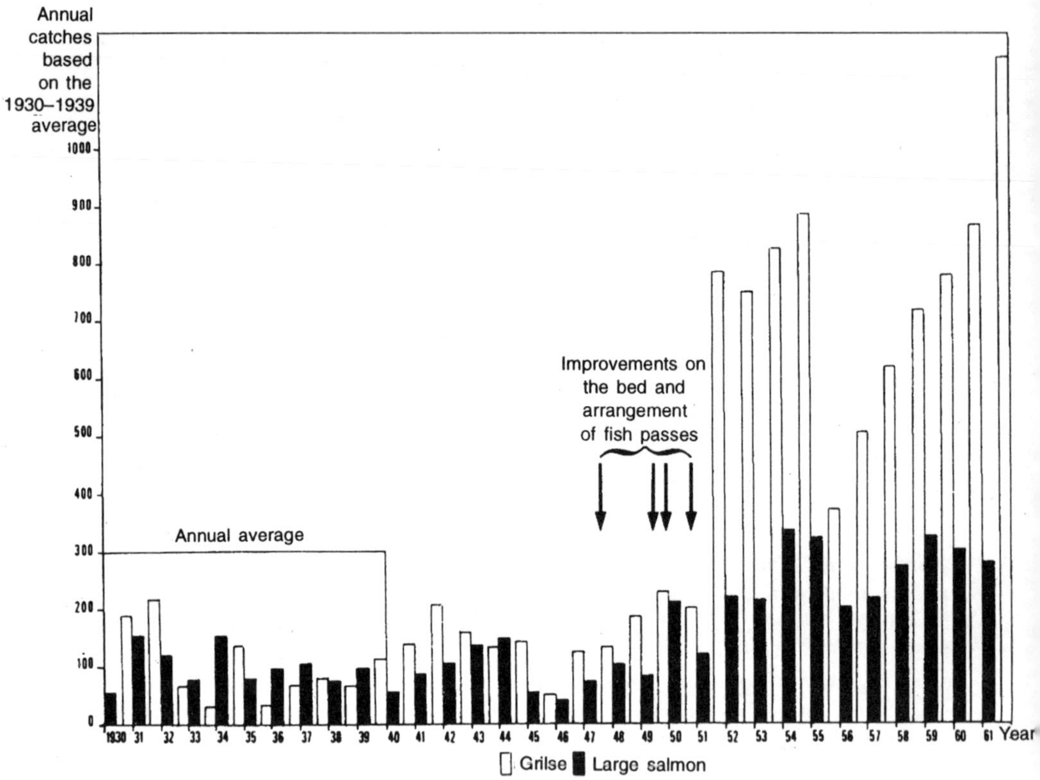

Fig. 144. Salmon catches in the North-Esk-Angus river from 1930 to 1961 (after SMART in MILLS, 1971)

temperature, and during approximately the first two-thirds of this period the eggs must be able to meet their respiratory needs by percolation through the gravel beds. The zones selected by breeders are generally of two types: beds of coarse alluvium deposited during recent high-water periods, and the downstream limit of a pool where the difference in level as compared to the next pool creates an almost vertical current across a permeable bed. The first type is more fragile because of its instability and, more than the second, needs to be improved upon and protected.

D. ARTIFICIAL SPAWNING BEDS

Artificial spawning beds are improvements carried out on the substrate: deposit of gravel or digging of laying channels for salmonid spawning. Because of very different requirements, artificial spawning beds for pike, perch and cyprinids—with the exception of the gudgeon—are formed by natural or artificial plants placed on the substrate, or floating half submerged.

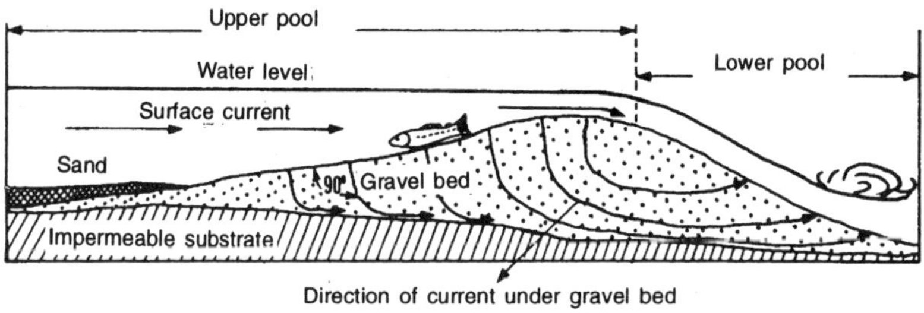

Fig. 145. Section of a trout spawning site showing the relationship between the main water currents and position of the female before nesting (after STUART, 1953)

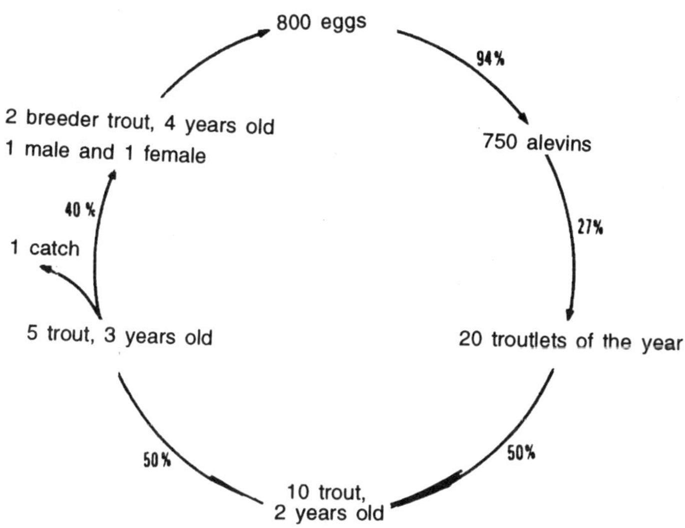

Fig. 146. Simplified diagram showing survival of the spawn of fario trout (female and male) weighing 1 kg

1. PLANTING OF AQUATIC PLANTS

Natural plants are generally placed in pots or in tanks measuring as much as 4 m^2, submerged at a suitable depth in streams and water bodies with a relatively constant level to provide good conditions for the visiting of the spawning beds and incubation of eggs. The spawning beds are prepared in calm, shallow sites, sheltered from wind. They are used to ensure reproduction in virgin water bodies (pools, sand pits, gravel pits) in cyprinid and pike water courses that have been subjected to major reclamation and reprofiling works as well as leakages and locks of canals.

2. FIXED SPAWNING BEDS

Some aquatic mediums are not suitable for natural plants all year round because of the wakes of craft (navigation canals), the nature of the banks, concrete or pile plank (navigation canals and water supply canals), and the content of suspended matter.

We may cater for the reproduction of cyprinids and pike by providing artificial plants fixed to the walls or plants attached temporarily to vertical banks shortly before the reproductive period, at a correct height. Some may also be placed under water at the bottom, at spawning time, depending on the requirements of the species.

These plant beds are brooms of plastic material, or even imitation plants, of a green colour and with branches, obtained from the artificial plant trade. The beds are of artificial turf.

After the reproductive period, the movable plants are retrieved, washed with a water jet, disinfected, and kept in a shady place till the next season. Before they are used again they are dusted and washed.

These spawning beds have been successfully used in many canals in the north of France and the region of Paris (LUCHETTA, 1991, personal communication).

Fig. 147. Artificial spawning beds fixed to a metallic bank (St. Denis canal, Paris, photo by M. CORTADE)

3. FLOATING SPAWNING BEDS

Artificial floating spawning beds are extremely useful in water bodies with a variable water level and in water courses subjected to considerable and repeated disturbance due to navigation; many techniques are adopted depending on the sites and the species.

Spawning beds on a fixed support are designed in the form of panels with a plant substrate required for reproduction of fish. The direction in the horizontal plane is regulated by buoys which also, depending on the water level, ensure that the panels remain vertical. The panels slide along vertical supports fixed to the bank (GILLET, 1989).

In an identical but simpler system, a buoy is placed at a site suitable for spawning (calm, sunny, deep) and, on the anchoring rope, at a suitable height, a strip of geotextile is tied which will provide support especially for eggs of the perch.

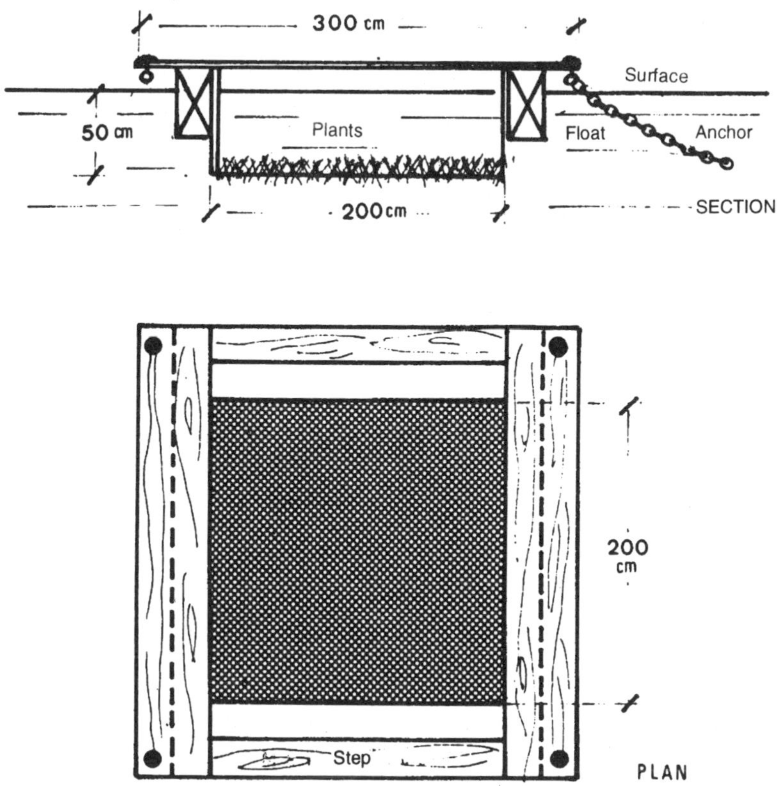

Fig. 148. A free-floating spawning bed for pike and cyprinids (after ARRIGNON, 1976)

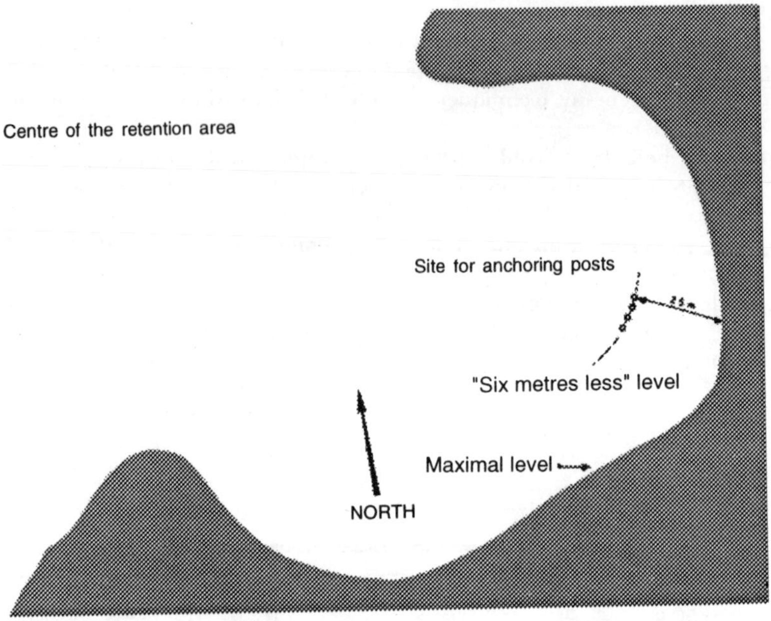

Fig. 149. Position of the anchoring arrangement for artificial floating spawning beds

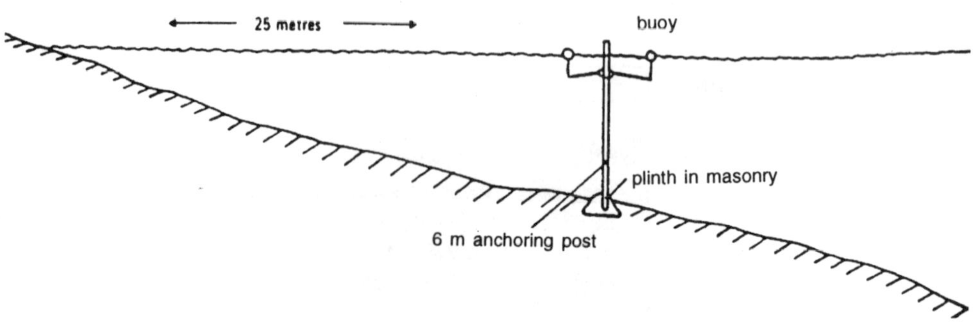

Fig. 150. Anchoring arrangement for a floating spawning bed, sectional view (after GILLET, 1989)

Free-floating spawning beds are made up of expanded polystyrene floats supporting a submerged frame in 50–60 cm of water with natural or artificial plants. The surface of the frame varies from 1 to 5 m^2. The anchoring arrangement of the bed is designed so that the frame can follow the variations in level. They may be moved to sites for restocking where eggs can hatch and fry emerge (ARRIGNON, 1976).

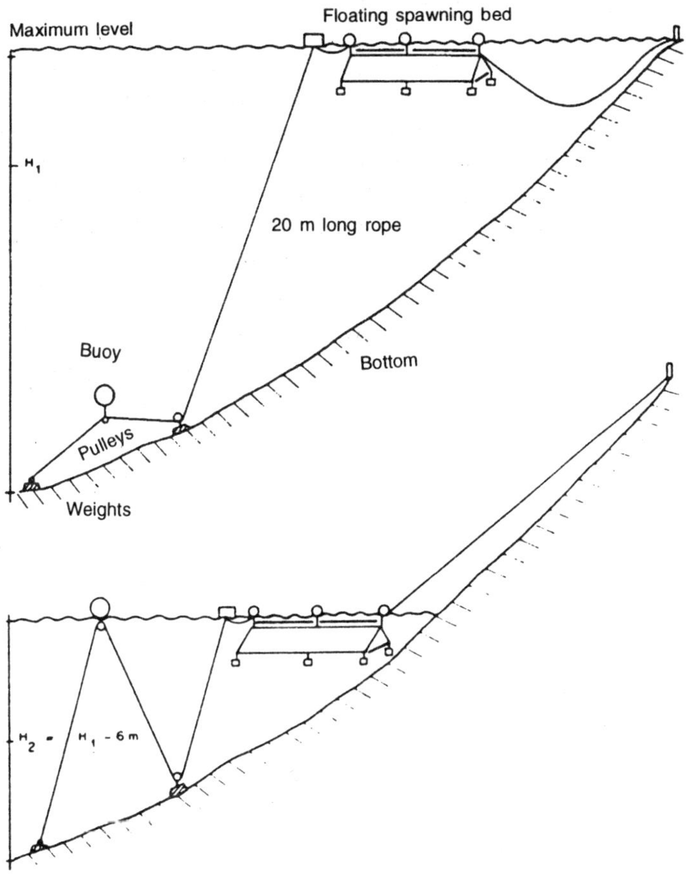

Fig. 151. Anchoring system (after GILLET, 1989)

Table 18. Density and survival rate of pike eggs in the Vouglans lake

Substrate	Density, no./m^2	Survival, % (caudal bud)
Spruce 1986	455	96.3
Enkamat 1986 (plastic)	57	100
Spruce placed on 16.4.87	111	100
Substrates placed 1 month before spawning (17.3.87)*:		
Spruce	1154	92.3
Juniper	742	80.0
Cypress	330	68.4
Enkamat	711	70.6

*Spawning substrate covered with mud.

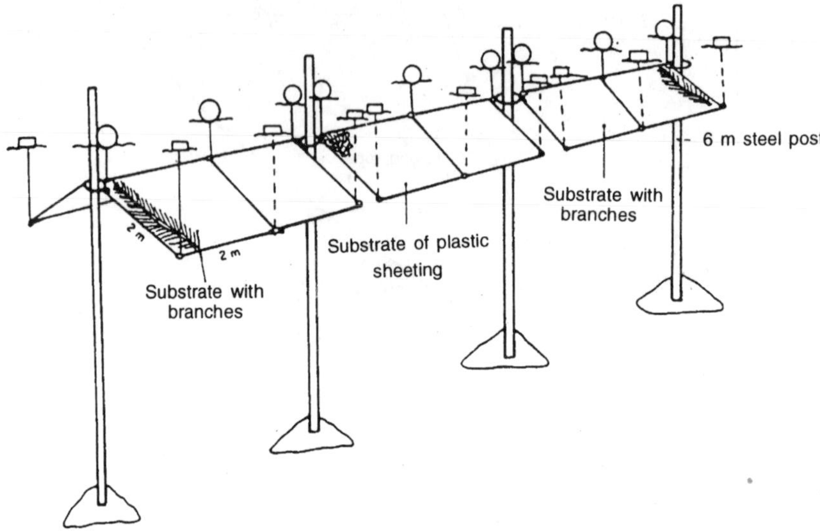

Fig. 152. Assembly and sketch of three artificial floating spawning beds each of 16 sq m. Anchored on steel posts, only the steel bars of the frame of the spawning beds have been shown (after GILLET, 1989)

Table 19. Fertilization (%) and width of perch spawn (mm) in 1986 in various types of artificial spawning beds in Lake Leman. Number of observations in parentheses.

Type of bed	Fertilization (%) at different stages of development				Av.	Width of spawn (mm)
	Blastula	Epiboly	Caudal bud	Eyed ova		
At the bottom: Branches (4 m above)	97.6 (10)	97.14 (7)	96.07 (14)	98.63 (8)	97.18 (39)	50.44 (34)
Grill	97.43 (7)	100.00 (2)	97.43 (7)	99.25 (4)	98.05 (20)	50.58 (12)
Wattle	96.71 (17)	96.60 (5)	96.00 (14)	99.50 (14)	97.28 (50)	46.96 (36)
Floating 4 m below the surface, 8 m from bed: Wattle	97.92 (13)	99.00 (1)	98.50 (8)	98.91 (11)	98.42 (33)	41.91 (23)
Floating 4 m below the surface, 12 m from bed: Wattle	94.75 (4)	91.33 (3)	97.00 (2)	97.50 (2)	94.73 (11)	44.50 (10)

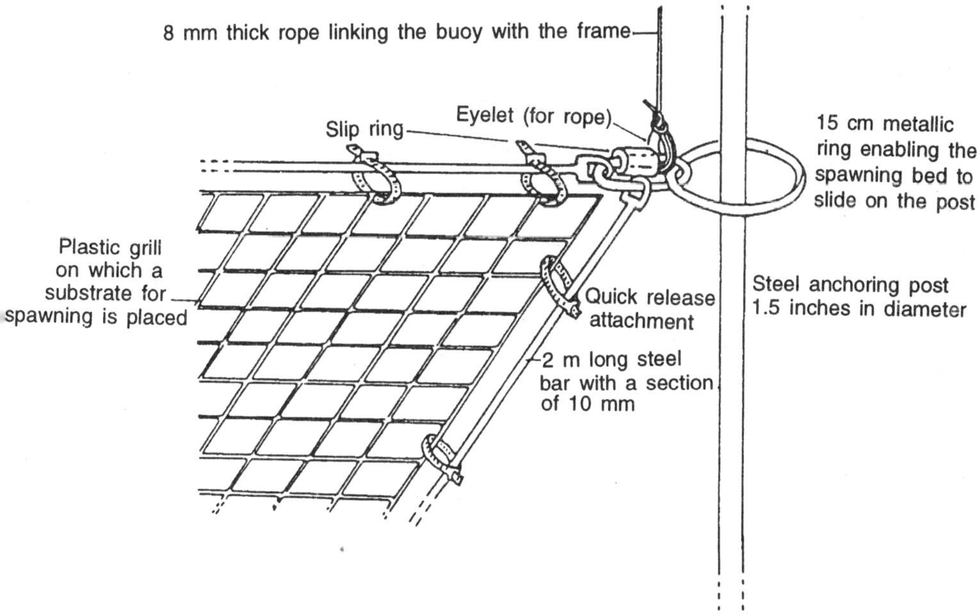

Fig. 153. Detail of the frame of an artificial floating spawning bed (after GILLET, 1989)

Table 20. Density of roach eggs (number per cm^2) in various artificial floating spawning beds in Lake Leman in 1987. All values of the survival rate are between 98 and 100% (after GILLET, 1989).

Type of substrate	Fixed spawning beds		Floating spawning beds	
	9.6.87	12.6.87	9.6.87	12.6.87
Enkamat (plastic)	83	85	43	28
Norway spruce	224	252	137	188
Cypress	412	337	177	315
Juniper	269	284	158	126

4. GRAVEL BEDS FOR SALMONIDS

Salmonid gravel beds are made of round pebbles of suitable size (Fig. 201), placed where the current velocity is about 40 cm/s, in 40–50 cm of water. The thickness of the bed should be 50 cm and the surface area more than 4 m^2. This may be adopted whenever the substrate is suitable for spawning by salmonids and when they are

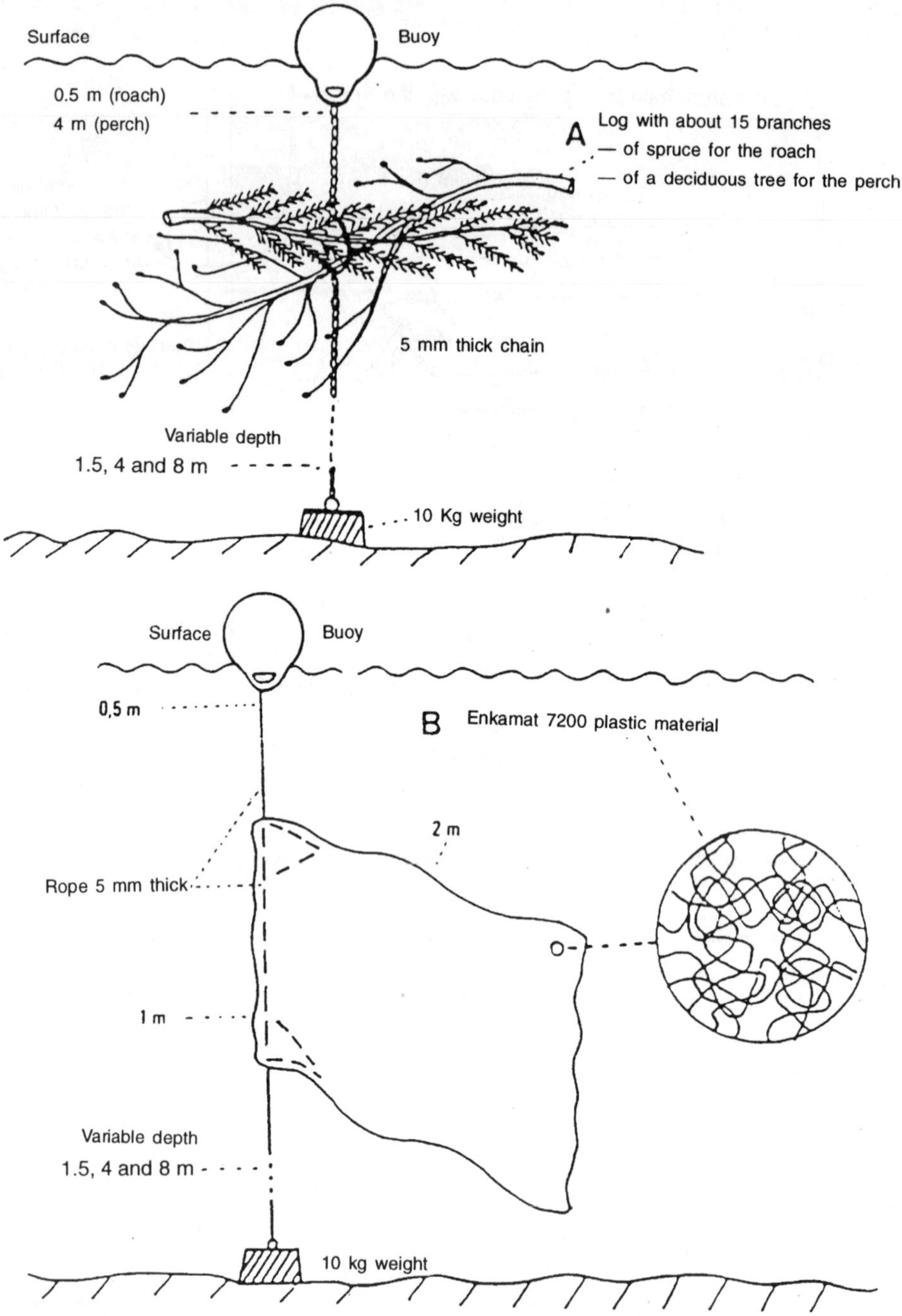

Fig. 154. Diagram of artificial floating spawning beds used for the roach and the perch (after GILLET, 1989)

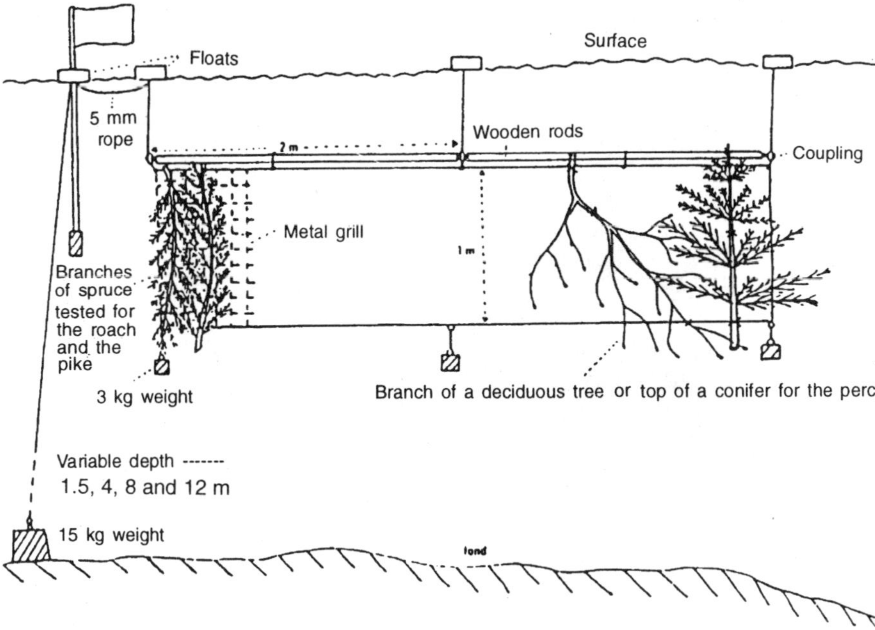

Fig. 155. Artificial floating bed with branches. Experimental model for the roach and the perch in a vertical position. For the roach the device is inclined at 15° with ropes and buoys connected with the lower parts. For trials at 45°or horizontal the length of these ropes is altered (after GILLET, 1989)

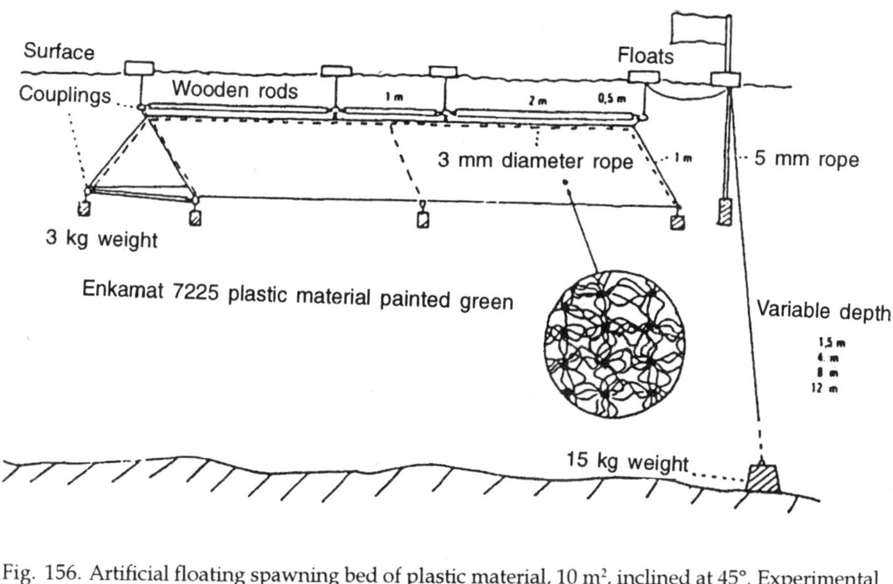

Fig. 156. Artificial floating spawning bed of plastic material, 10 m^2, inclined at 45°. Experimental model for the roach, the tench, the carp and the pike (after GILLET, 1989)

Fig. 157. A spawning channel

unable to spawn further upstream or in the tributaries. The substrate should, however, be fairly firm so that it does not absorb incoming matter: for this reason the bottom of a stream with soft mud or one that is slightly boggy should be avoided.

In 1972, it was observed in the Bresle river (Normandy) that within an hour of completion, such spawning sites were visited by salmon.

CHIMITS (1958) obtained good results in the Landes rivers with a sandy bottom by placing beds of pebbles in them, retained by wooden planks and logs; he also designed grilled gabions open at the top and filled with pebbles, for the same purpose.

One of the important conditions for the future of the emerging fry in these spawning sites is that they can find zones nearby which are suitable for their

Fig. 158. Trap for smolts downstream of a spawning channel

existence, being not very deep, with moderate currents and irregularities that can be used as hunting posts or shelters.

5. SPAWNING CHANNELS

Spawning channels, designed in North America to improve the reproductive potential of both the *Oncorhynchus* on the western slope (Gates Creek and Weaver Creek, in the Fraser river basin) and *Salmo salar* on the east coast (Indian river, in Newfoundland), were intended mainly to protect eggs from the hazards of the nival regime.

Spawning channels provide breeders with a suitable and constant water current, clean beds of gravel of the right size, and safety from the dangers of high and low waters.

It has been estimated that the spawning channel in Gates Creek has increased the survival rate of eggs by a factor of 6 to 10 compared to that in a river (more than 80 fry per 100 eggs against 10–15 in a river). It is 3000 m long and 7 m wide with a water surface of more than 1 ha. The number of fish introduced is one sockeye salmon for every 2 m^2. The flow is 1150 l/s. The water comes from Gates Creek and passes through a decantation basin; this prevents the danger of tannins from floating logs and other material that could stifle the eggs.

2 *IN SITU* HATCHERIES

As explained earlier, some mediums are not suitable for carrying out improvements on substrates. The requirements of several species like the pike-perch (*Sander leucioperca*) are such that their introduction in the form of eggs needs the support of certain expedients which appear, in many respects, to be useful.

The eyed embryo is actually the cheapest item for restocking. Fry produced in the natural way obviously suffer a heavy infantile mortality but when they grow, since they have not been domesticated or handled and since they result from natural selection, their survival rate compares with that of fish in the wild.

The problem that arises is how to submerge eyed ova by arrangements and with appropriate materials, in conditions corresponding to those prevailing in spawning areas: these are incubation boxes and cradles.

Table 21. Comparison of the selling price (in francs) of an adult trout based on the stages of introduction in the natural medium (adapted from RICHARD, 1997)

Stage of introduction	Cost (per 1000)	Survival (%)[1]	Sale price of adult
Embryonated egg[2]	60	0.5	12
Fry with resorbed yolk[2]	90	0.75	12
Swimming fry	260	1.8	14.5
Pre-summerlings[3]	600	1.8	33
Summerlings[3]	2200	2.5	88
Adult (200 g)[3]	8 (per unit)	50	16

[1]Optimal survival rate
[2]Official cost
[3]From fish farms

A. INCUBATION BOXES

Incubation boxes are filled with eyed ova from a fishery and transported to an aquatic medium in such a manner that incubation and hatching occurs in the best possible conditions.

1. VIBERT BOX

The design of the Vibert box was based on the need to have the spawn of a pair of trout or salmon of a weight of about 1 kg. It therefore contains 600–800 salmon eggs or 800–1000 trout eggs.

Fig. 159. Vibert box

It is made of hard, transparent plastic and measures 70 × 63 × 45 mm. On its entire surface it has oblong slits that enable the water current which flows in gravel beds to effectively irrigate the eggs. Their shape and size are such that an egg cannot pass through these slits but the fry, because of their shape, can come out.

Filled with eyed ova of a stock that has generally been certified, the Vibert box is intended to ensure a complete stocking in virgin waters such as those in the Kerguelen islands or where salmonids are unable to move upstream (because of natural sills or dams that cannot be crossed) or to nursery streams.

The immersion sites should have the same characteristics as natural spawning sites. Gravel beds that can be used to bury the boxes are generally abundant in mountain water courses, in foothills, and on plains when the current is alternately fast and slow.

Certain precautions need to be taken before their immersion, such as the removal of predatory fish including mainly eels, nose carp, sculpin, and minnows, as well as an initial clearing of gravel beds that have a tendency to clog.

The boxes should be buried taking into consideration that predatory endobenthic invertebrates do not generally colonize a bottom beyond a depth of 10 cm. We should undertake an early introduction so that the fry emerge before the main activity of predators that may have remained in the water.

According to VIBERT (1975) the immersion techniques must comply with the following general conditions:

1. The selected site must be irrigated by an adequate water current.
2. The box should be buried sufficiently deep so that it is in total darkness.
3. It should not be liable to be covered with silt or sand.

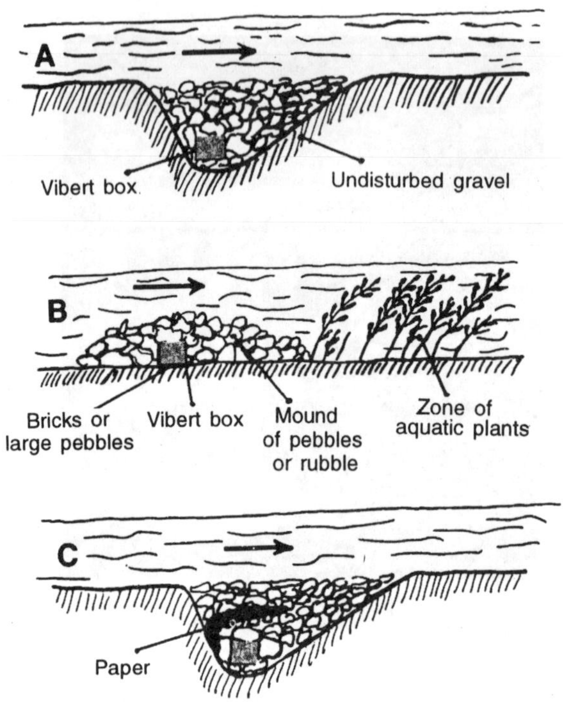

Fig. 160. Placement of a Vibert box
A) in clear water with a fairly fast current
B) in clear water with a fairly slow current
C) in a running stream with turbid water, with a protective paper shield (courtesy the review *La pisciculture français*)

Sections of the river with a rapid current should be avoided. The newly emerged fry will be carried downstream and be subject to predation.

In clear rivers with a slow current, the box must be buried in a mound of gravel, above the level of the bottom. This mound should be near aquatic plants (water cress, callitriche) where fry can find shelter and food.

In turbid and slow-flowing streams, placing the Vibert box demands certain expedients. Apart from the raised level there should be a shield (of tar paper or plastic sheeting) ensuring below it a zone of clean gravel where incubation can continue in the normal course. In such cases it is even better to use floating incubators.

2. CORCHUS BOX

The Corchus box has been designed for restocking pike-perch in water bodies and streams using their eggs, though certain conditions limit this facility.

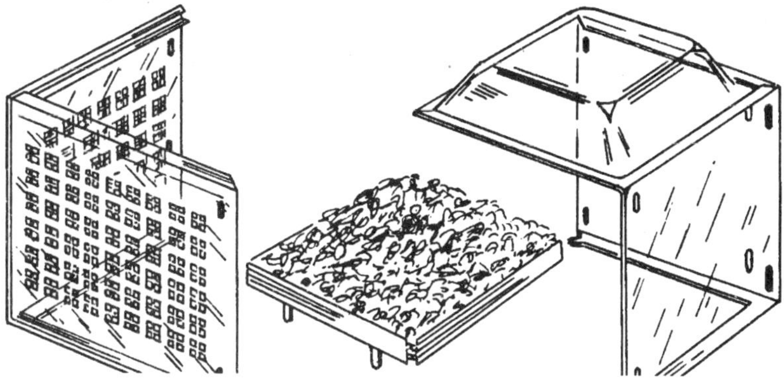

Fig. 161. Sketch of a Corchus box

The pike-perch spawns in calm waters on plants where the male prepares a nest at a depth of about 70 cm. The eggs adhere firmly to the plants.

It is customary in fisheries to replace natural plants with artificial spawning beds, or nests, made of 25 removable trays that hold a fraction of the spawn.

After it has been visited the nest is placed in a tank where it is washed with a spray; it is then dismantled and each tray, of 15 cm square, with fertilized eggs, forms the base of an incubator which, once fitted, is not opened again. After this stage the eggs are protected against most harmful mechanical effects.

The model for ponds is perforated on all four sides so that there is an adequate replacement of the water inside it. A deposit of silt and mud is not likely. The model for running streams is perforated only on two sides: a pair of rings enables us to hook the box to a picket. Due to the effect of the current the incubator faces it with the unperforated corner that resists the water pressure. The eggs are thereby protected inside the box against major turbulences and sedimentation.

The top of the box is closed and dome-shaped. The dome contains the reserve of air essential for newly hatched fry in order to fill their air bladders; in this way they may safely ensure an essential operation that is always difficult under natural conditions.

Immersion of the incubator box requires certain precautions:

1. As soon as it is received, unpack it and keep it in a cool place and quickly carry out the operations preliminary to immersion.

2. Immerse a sufficiently heavy grappling anchor to submerge and hold the box till the eggs have hatched.

3. Measure the water level so that the dome of the box is not less than 40 cm from the surface.

4. Immerse the box carefully and vertically without tilting it so that the air remains in the dome and the fry can fill their air bladders.

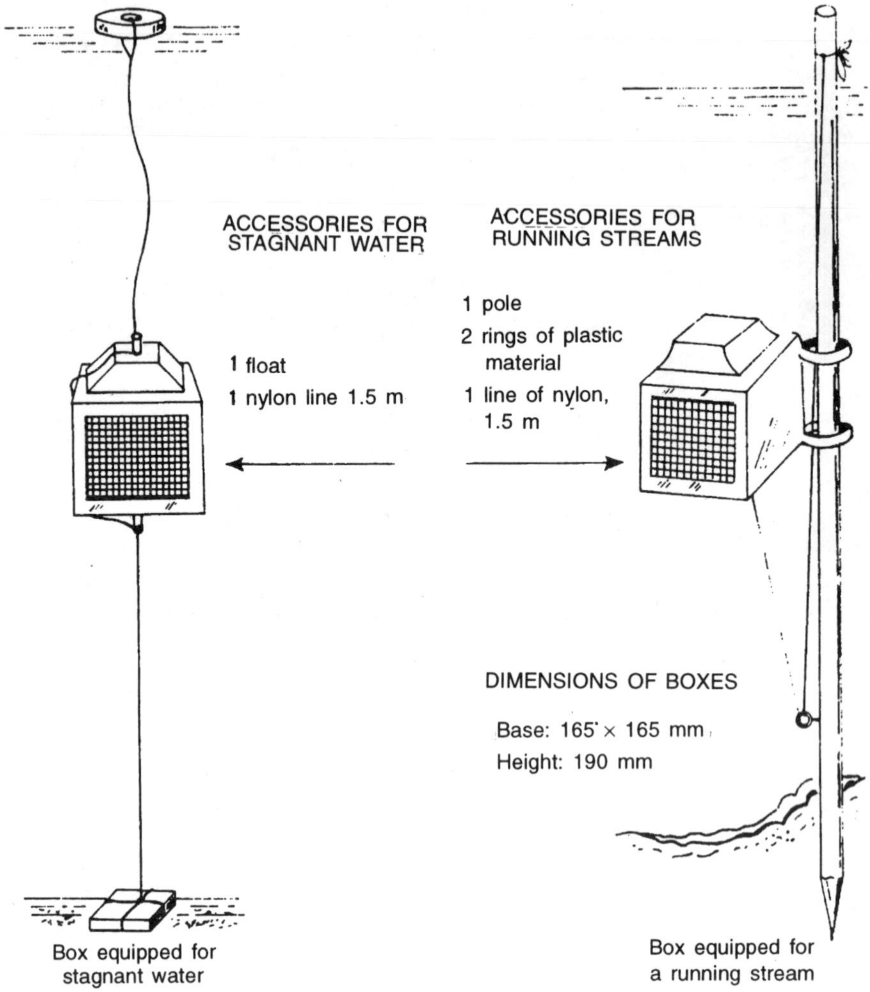

Fig. 162. Immersion of Corchus boxes

Once the box has been immersed, nothing should be touched or moved and the box should be retrieved only after a month regardless of the results during this period.

The survival rate of young pike-perch hatched in a Corchus box is 10% at the end of the first year as against 0.5–1% in natural spawning conditions. A box containing 20,000 eggs corresponds, therefore, to a production of fry equal to that of a pair of pike-perch living in the wild and enables a stocking of about 10 ha of a water body.

Fig. 163. Floating incubator containing young trout fry ready to be introduced into a nursery stream (photo by GOUYSSE)

B. INCUBATOR CRADLES

The common incubators are of two types:

- spawning baskets placed at the bottom of a water course and
- floating incubators

1. SPAWNING BASKET

The spawning basket may be a simple small cage filled with pebbles in which we place Vibert boxes or a basket designed for this purpose to prevent the entry of eels, which feed on large numbers of newly hatched fry. The basket, in the form of parallel pipes, 50 cm long, 25 cm wide and 30 cm high. It has a framework of round iron bars 6–8 mm in diameter, covered with a fine grill except on the upper side, over which a grilled cover is fitted. Two handles welded to each end make it easy to move. In it are placed 4000 eggs of trout or salmon (as many as in four Vibert boxes) within a mass of pebbles of an approximate volume of 35 dm^3.

The Gouysse model is a more elaborate one having, in front and at the back, a compartment that acts as a decanter in a water course where the water level is high and that contains a lot of silt. A deflector hinged on the prow of the incubator directs the current above the heap of pebbles so as to ensure irrigation of the eggs

Fig. 164. Spawning basket and floating incubator. Note, on the upright apparatus, the movable deflector and the decantation corners (photo by GOUYSSE)

comparable with that in natural spawning areas (Fig. 166). Made of non-rusting perforated metal, this model of the same dimensions as the aforementioned one holds the same number of eggs.

Fig. 165. Incubator for fast running streams. The eggs are buried under a mass of gravel (photo by J. ARRIGNON).

2. ARTIFICIAL GRAVEL BED

The artificial gravel bed is in two parts. In the first there is a small heap of gravel placed on a grill with a double bottom. This apparatus ensures an irrigation current that is an ascending rather than a descending one. We put in 10,000–20,000 eggs of eyed trout ova, depending upon the biogenic capacity of the water. Downstream of the gravel heap, there is a fish pond that receives the emerging fry.

The artificial gravel bed is generally used in streams with a gradient that is adequate, without disturbing the banks, to ensure the difference in level between the upstream and downstream portions of the device (50–60 cm). The bottom of the stream is levelled, the gravel bed is placed on the surface, and a dam between one

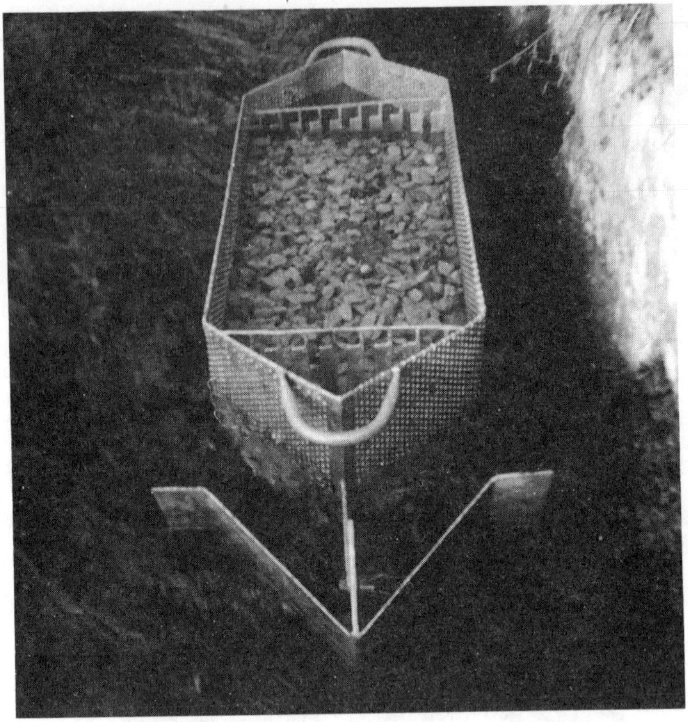

Fig. 166. Spawning basket, filled and submerged; the deflector helps to direct the irrigation current; sediments are collected in the corners. GOUYSSE-type basket (photo by RENARD).

of its walls and the opposite bank ensures the difference in level. Adjustable frontal flush-boards enable regulation of the flow between 30 and 50 l/m depending upon the number of eggs.

If there is a rise in water level, the water, without flooding the gravel bed, passes over the dam, of which the length has to be estimated relative to subsequent high-water periods. A second dam, erected further downstream, keeps the level at 10 cm below the sill so as to ensure that the fish pond remains filled.

Most of the fry migrate to the recovery pond. When all have emerged, the water level is reduced, downstream of the gravel bed; when the outlet trap door is raised a flushing effect eliminates silt accumulated under the grill and removes some of the fry that had been able to come down through the pebbles. The pebbles are cleaned, the trap door is closed, and we can then place a second instalment of eggs that were laid later for hatching in it.

In a temperate maritime climate, the artificial gravel bed may be used thrice in succession during the same season if the initial instalment was of early eggs. The yields of swimming fry vary with the quality of the eggs and the irrigation water from 10% (RENARD, 1971) to 95% (GUYARD).

Fig. 167. A battery of floating incubators (photo by J. ARRIGNON)

Production from the gravel bed is suitable for any external introduction: it is a small fishery unit.

3. FLOATING INCUBATOR

In a floating incubator we place 4000–6000 eggs of salmonids. It is put in a spring or stream or against the bank of a small water course.

The original model, designed by LABBE, is widely used in the northwestern region of France for seeding growth streams. Two boards form the sides of the cradle. The frame, which measures 80 × 20 × 35 cm, looks like a floating fish tank of which the bottom, front, and rear are covered with a fine grill of rust-free metal or plastic. It has a wooden cover.

A greatly improved model has been designed by GOUYSSE. The floating cradle is of metal. Floating is ensured by two lateral ballasts which, depending on the amount of fine sand introduced into them, allow the level of the cradle to be changed depending on the state of development. On each ballast there is an opening through which the four corners of the apparatus can be filled with plates of lead to give it the desired inclination depending upon the current. The traps at the ends ensure a regulation of the flow within the hatchery and the lid may be locked.

In the LABBE incubator, the eyed ova are placed on the grilled bottom and are free in the water, while in the GOUYSSE model 4000 eggs may be introduced within a gravel bed with a variable hatching rate (60–90%). A battery of incubators may also be used that will increase the production of the spring or stream in which they are placed.

Fig. 168a. Artificial gravel bed, without a grill or cover, in use

Fig. 168b. Battery of artificial gravel beds

This small fishery unit is an extremely practical one because its small size enables it to be taken to places where sexually mature breeder trout are not able to find natural gravel beds to bury their eggs. We can, in such cases, carry out artificial fertilization, put the eggs in an incubator, place it suitably, and wait for development of the eggs and fry. Conditions for success depend upon the following:

1. An easily regulated current should pass through the incubator. It should be gentle if the eggs are free and faster if they are buried under gravel.

2. It is advisable to change the direction in which the incubator faces every two or three days so that impurities accumulated on the upstream side are released by the current in the opposite direction.

3. During emergence of the fry, the pebbles are removed carefully (they can be used in a second incubator) and the fry are collected with a fine net, like those used by aquarists.

The final results of restockings carried out through *in situ* hatcheries are even better when the fry have developed in the larval state under gravel and have an appreciable part of the wild heredity from their near ascendants, according to BAMS (1973) and our own observations in the rivers of the Eure department (ARRIGNON, 1974).

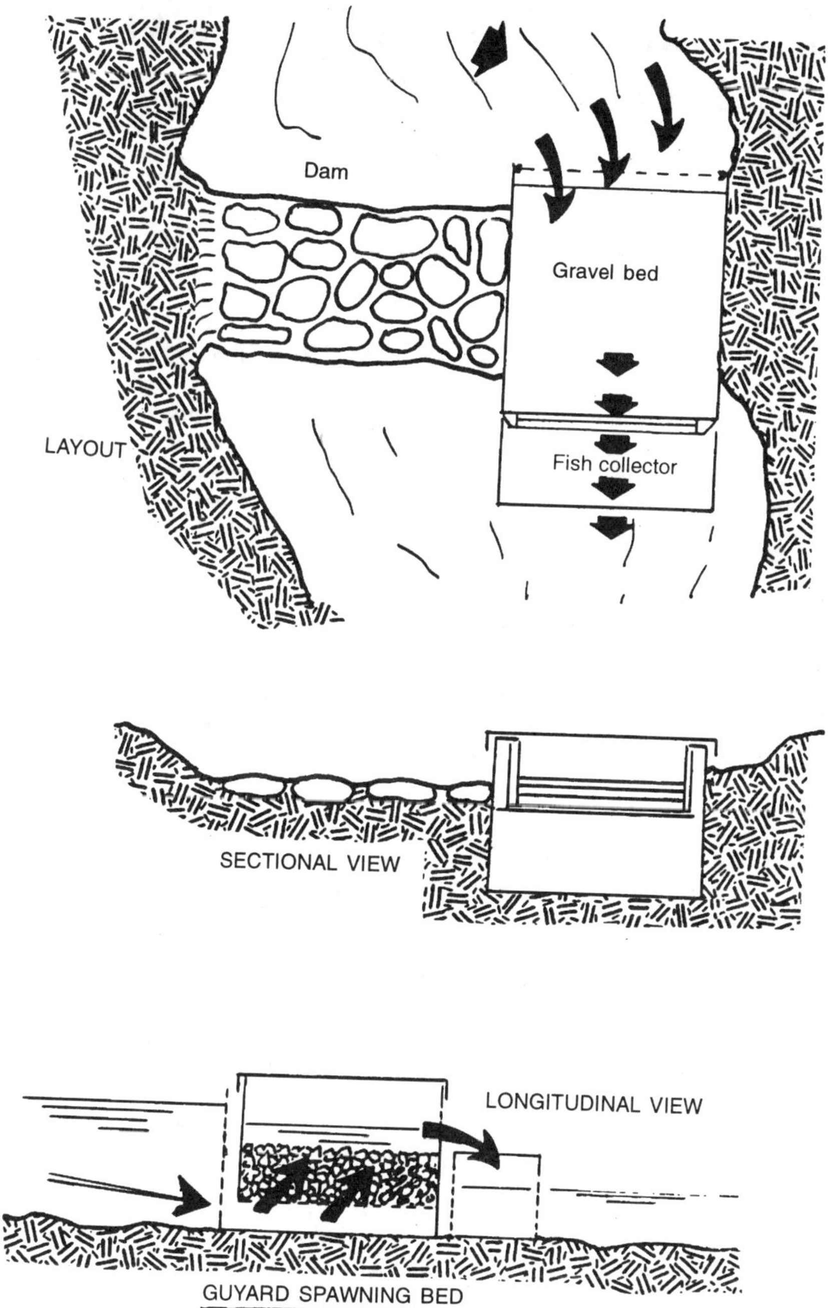

Fig. 169. Artificial gravel bed

3 GROWTH IN A NATURAL MEDIUM

A. HARDINESS OF SPECIES

The adverse conditions in some aquatic mediums for fish at the juvenile stage lead us to avoid any introduction of fry that would not have sufficient opportunity to meet the required stocking in a reasonable period. We therefore find it necessary to use fish that are older, more hardy, and likely to adapt to these mediums. This is even more desirable when restocking with species that are valuable because of their variety or cost.

Assessing the hardiness of species to be introduced, in other words, their ability to resist existing harsh effects in a wild medium to survive, grow, and reproduce in it, helps us to avoid introducing fish that are highly domesticated due to a recent past existence in intensive culture.

According to CUINAT (1971), hardiness depends on:

– genetic factors resulting from the selection,
– effects relative to diseases, transport, and a sudden change in medium, and
– the raising conditions.

Ideal restocking should therefore be based on fish of a selected strain, either indigenous or perfectly adapted to the medium in which they are to be introduced, in a good state of health, having spent the early period of their lives in the best possible natural conditions.

1. NATURAL SELECTION

Natural selection leads to elimination of fish least resistant to harsh conditions in the medium (high-water periods, thermal effects, diseases, predators) before they are able to reproduce. In identical conditions, results will be different, depending on the aptitudes the fish have inherited from their selected parents due to conditions in the medium or human requirements.

According to SKOCHOWSKA (1969) in CUINAT (1971), a downstream migration of 39% has been observed of common trout descended from one to four generations of sea trout, as opposed to 7% in the descendants of river trout.

It was observed (1973) that 27% of adult pike taken from the Seine were caught, again, after their introduction in a similar system of streams, the Oise, as against 3.20% of pike taken from ponds and introduced in equal numbers at the same place and the same time.

Unless we are able to have an adequate number of local young stock, well adapted to the medium, we are led to look for those living in a comparable medium and provide others with the hardiness of their parents by recourse to artificial fertilization.

Nevertheless, though some wild species, like pike and carp, provide products that are easy to raise, this does not apply to others such as the fario trout. In the fario trout, fertilization of a domesticated female by a wild male generally results in products that are easily raised, with most of them having the hardy characteristics of the father, which is what we are looking for.

Removing some male trout from a water course does not greatly affect the reproductive potential of the local stock. The duration of male fertility is such that indigenous females have every chance of being fertilized, even if one-third of the males are removed. In subsequent raising operations the milt of a single wild male can fertilize the ova of several domesticated females.

2. DISEASES AND STRESS

Diseases are often transmitted to an indigenous stock by the introduction of fish, generally adult, for purposes of restocking. Many incidences of this type have been observed in water bodies of northern France as a result of uncontrolled restocking of cyprinids. Latent infections may not appear till after their introduction, mainly during the period of least resistance associated with transplantation in a new medium.

The ensuing mortality a few days after their introduction is also attributable to fatigue caused by transportation. Fish tire more easily than mammals and even more if they are from cold waters: according to CUINAT (1971), the lactic acid in their blood increases by a factor of three to eight after a quarter of an hour of activity. Their recovery period is also much longer (6–12 h).

VIBERT and LAGLER (1961) referred to some death rates (as many as 93%) after introduction attributable to fatigue caused by transportation. ARRIGNON (1964) noted a mortality of at least 72% of adult pike, exhausted by a long period of transportation in an overoxygenated medium and transferred too quickly to the water course at the destination.

The size of restocked fish, the number of handlings, and the care taken in transportation greatly affect the survival rate and the hardiness of those placed in a new medium.

3. BREEDING CONDITIONS

Breeding conditions have an effect on the hardiness of species. Salmonids raised in fisheries with food rations distributed periodically or from time to time do not have the instinct for hunting and protection necessary for their survival in a wild medium and are often dominated by indigenous species.

Observations after repeated markings of a part of the stock in a river in Picardy, the Matz, from 1964 to 1968, revealed that 17% of domesticated adult trout moved downstream within a week of their introduction, and 6.5% moved up to areas immediately surrounding a fishery and remained there. On the other hand no trout of a regional strain raised in a natural medium migrated beyond the limits of the sector studied.

Apart from the utility of incubators under gravel, discussed in the previous chapter, that of raising young salmonids in a natural medium is no doubt considerable if we are more interested in the quality of extensively raised fish rather than their quantity. At the same time, the survival rate of young pike, perch, and cyprinid fry is much better if they have, from the earliest stage, the ability to hide from predators.

Although extensive breeding may not provide yields as high as in intensive breeding, it can nevertheless be improved considerably by certain practices and some improvements in the conditions of shelter and provision of food.

B. BREEDING MEDIUMS

Some mediums are of no interest for fishing as a sport and for natural fish production but may be developed for this purpose, as in the case of larger water courses, by efforts for improvement and good management.

This applies to springs, brooks, channels, and pools as well as marsh meadows and zones subjected to flooding, when they cannot be visited by spawning fish in the natural course.

Some portions of streams, declared as reserves (areas around locks and dams) or temporarily closed to fishing, are also places where fish, kept to grow for a certain period, acquire the desired size without losing their natural qualities.

These various mediums are piscicultural annexes of streams and water bodies that are normally open for fishing purposes and for which problems of restocking and maintenance may arise.

1. SPRINGS

Springs are quite suitable for incubation, hatching of eggs, and young salmonids till three-quarters of the yolk sac has been resorbed, provided the dissolved oxygen content in the water and the pH reading are compatible with the requirements of the species at that stage of its existence.

These requirements, which are of little consequence before the embryo develops in the egg (3–5 mg of dissolved oxygen per litre), increase with its development and hatching of the fry (9 mg/l on hatching). In springs, however, the water that emerges from the ground has not been sufficiently in contact with the air to have acquired the normal oxygen content. Only aquatic plants that provide oxygen can ensure the quantity necessary for breeding purposes. Springs with aquatic plants such as callitriche or cress are therefore suitable for this purpose.

Salmonids can tolerate water with a pH of 6 and, temporarily, of 5.5; they are, however, comfortable only in water with a pH between 6.5 and 8.5. Some springs that emerge from acid peat bogs, because of their very low pH, are unsuitable for incubation of eggs. It is therefore essential to verify the oxygen content and pH at the initial stage.

Resurgent waters are often unsuitable for incubation, as are also springs that bubble at the point of emergence, because of their high carbon dioxide content and nitrogen dissolved under pressure. The excess of these gases is likely to be released in the circulatory system of young fry raised in these mediums and cause a mortal embolism. Because of the difficulty in detecting these excessive contents by methods presently available, it is worthwhile, during an inventory of raising sites, to locate their hydrogeological origin and, if possible, to arrange for a natural, mechanical, or artificial stirring that will release the dissolved gases before irrigating the raising site.

When a stream appears suitable for extensive breeding, floating incubator cradles may be placed in it (Fig. 167) and filled with eyed ova, or otherwise. These cradles will be anchored as far as possible from the site of emergence. If the relief permits, small obstacles, dams of pebbles or logs, may be arranged a few metres upstream of the raising site to help in the release of gases under pressure and the dissolved oxygen content in the water, on contact with the air.

The water current should be regular and adequate to irrigate the eggs and the fry that will be raised till three-quarters of their yolk sac has been resorbed so that they can be introduced, for example, in growth streams. This is, therefore, the first stage in extensive breeding.

2. BREEDING STREAMS

2.1 Nursery

Nursery brooks are selected and improved upon so that eyed ova of salmonids can be hatched and fry raised during a cycle of one year or less in an organized and systematic manner. In these brooks are placed Vibert incubator boxes, spawning trays, floating incubator cradles, or, if the gradient permits, Guyard spawning beds.

Nursery brooks are neither artificially excavated channels nor annexes where intensive breeding is carried out. The young fish are raised without the distribution of food, in a wild medium, assisted by physical and biological improvement in living conditions (removal of encumbrances, provision of hiding places in the bed, and the removal of predators).

2.2 Growth

Growth brooks, larger than nursery brooks, receive not only eggs but swimming fry which, depending upon the capacity of the brook to provide them with shelter and food, are kept to the age of one year or older, till, for example, they reach the legal size at which the species may be caught.

The difference between a nursery and a growth brook is identical to what exists in forestry between the planting of seeds and the transplanting of young plantlets.

a) Prospection

Prospection is often systematic when a group of fishermen aim to find a method for extensive restocking of quality fish to be repeated every year in a number of known

Fig. 170. A typical well-maintained nursery brook. The illumination is varied, but good. The bed is heterogeneous. There are many hiding places (after ARRIGNON, ROUYER and CHANCEREL).

water courses. The number of young trouts to be produced in this way is known and the final choice is only of the brooks that are most favourable for this production.

Nevertheless, prospection is generally occasional, depending on personal relationships with the owners of the brooks. The prospected brooks are not always the ideal types for nursery or growth brooks. They must in such cases be subjected to suitable improvements so that they can be used under the best possible conditions.

b) Choice

The choice of brook involves an overall assessment of the physicochemical characteristics of the water, including the summer temperature, which if too high is extremely harmful for fario trout and salmon.

The average gradient of a nursery brook should be 2–4‰. In a growth brook it should be between 1.5 and 3‰. The flow should be studied at the low- and high-water periods. Brooks that are subjected to sudden rushes of water because of their impluvium should be avoided. Temporary brooks may be used for short breeding cycles (7–8 months). According to ROUYER (1964) they can provide a high yield.

The average section of these brooks is about 0.50 m^2 (1–1.5 m wide and 0.15–0.50 m deep). The length may vary considerably but it is recommended that it should be more than 500 m so that the production is compatible with the effort involved. When the brook section is larger (3 m wide and 1 m deep), the young fish are

Fig. 171. Recovery of troutlets by electric fishing in a nursery brook (after ARRIGNON)

Fig. 172. Troutlet growth channel; bed and banks in a natural state (after ARRIGNON)

difficult to recover. The production capacity is also related more to the surface below and above the water level at the banks than the actual surface of the water body. The banks actually provide shelter as well as endogenous and exogenous food for young trout.

The area around the brooks should be cleared to ensure that there is adequate sunshine for the bed and water plants and that the bed can be traversed easily by operators who recover the fish.

The approaches to the brooks should be easy so that a watch may be kept on natural predators that may soon decimate the young fish (e.g., herons, kingfishers).

According to BURDIN (1967), brooks that flow through orchards where production is intensive should be avoided because of the risk of pollution from plant protection products. The same applies to those near piggeries, dairies, or cider houses. However, a slight organic matter content greatly increases the growth rate of fish being raised (as in brooks passing through rich fertilized grasslands).

c) *Improvements*

Improvements are made on the sites at which the incubator boxes or incubators are placed (pp. 216, 225) and subsequently on the zone where the fry will remain after they emerge; if there are no natural shelters some should be created, e.g., underbanks, stones in a quincunx arrangement or in longitudinal rows, hollow bricks, pieces of wood.

Grilling arrangements meant to prevent intrusion by predatory fish (pike, trout, nose carp) are not very effective except where a watch can be kept over them and they can be easily cleaned and repaired. We may use grills that are vertical or inclined, or those that can be drawn up or turned, which are relatively expensive, or we may simply use existing obstacles (falls, dams) or those created with the consent of the owners of the brooks and that of the regulating authorities. A successive arrangement of large stones can create a series of barriers for predators coming from the downstream side. Generally, in view of their location at the head of the pond, breeding brooks are hardly likely to suffer any danger except an invasion from the downstream side.

A downstream movement of young salmonids is considerable when the numbers introduced are excessive, when the brook is swept by a rush of water, or when the introduced stock is a migratory one. BURDIN (1967) observed that the difference in yield between a grilled stream and an open one was not appreciable if the initial operations to remove predators have been effective and if the stream is isolated from cyprinid and pike brooks or water bodies. SIMONET (1973), in a brook isolated by beds of filtering pebbles, obtained yields similar to those from brooks with standard grills.

The removal of existing fish from a breeding brook considerably affects its yield. This is essential, by electric fishing if necessary and in several stages, immediately before introducing the fry, to ensure there is no vital competition. This is why a purge in November with a view to stocking in March will be ineffective if it is not supplemented by a second purge a day or two before stocking.

d) *Stocking*

The numbers to be stocked are determined on the basis of the hardiness of the strains that have provided the eggs and fry. They depend also on the aforementioned conditions in the medium and finally on the selected breeding cycle, whether it is a short cycle of 6–8 months in temporary brooks or a long cycle of 11 months in permanent brooks (in the 12th month there are purges by electric fishing and subsequent improvements made in the brook before a fresh stock of eggs or fry is introduced).

Various experiments conducted in different hydrographic regions lead to the following recommended scales for stocking:

– 5–30 embryonated eggs per sq m (5000–30,000/km of a brook that is 1 m wide, and 7500–45,000/km of a brook that is 2 m wide). The average figure is 10–15 eggs/sq m.

– 3–20 swimming fry per sq m (3000–20,000/km of a brook that is 1 m wide and 4500–30,000 km of a brook that is 2 m wide). The average figure is 8–10 fry/sq m.

The variations are considerable because of the great difference between the productivity of mountain brooks and that of brooks in plains with aquatic plants.

e) Yield

The yield varies with the numbers introduced, the selected cycle, the hardiness of the stock, and the care taken to introduce and recover the young ones from the breeding brook. Burdin (1967) reported that some very poor yields are due to an untimely introduction in the receiving medium. This medium may be climatically behind the medium of origin; we therefore introduce eggs that are precocious or incubated too fast, providing fry distributed too early in streams, with a biotope that is still one of the winter season, very poor in natural food.

Simonet (1973) described an experiment conducted in a growth brook of the Risle basin during which 2500 fry introduced in June in a stream 408 m long, with 6 fry/linear m, produced 814 troutlets at the end of the following month of October, which was 30%, and he added that the distribution of these troutlets depended on vital space. The smallest and most numerous remained in the upper section with 2.5/linear m (average size 80 mm), and the largest and least numerous in the lower section with 1 fish/linear m (average size 140 mm).

The annual cycle often includes an autumn catch that reduces the number in the brook and provides an opportunity to restock the water courses for which the troutlets are intended, at the best state of their hydrological regime. At the end of the cycle, a second catch collects the remainder and the predators that may have been able to enter the stream during the winter period.

The number recovered varies from 5 to 40% of those initially introduced, with an average of 20%. Some fish from streams with a high-density, slow-growing population may be extracted to be put into underpopulated water courses. These transfers may be based on the entire catch or on a portion of the troutlets of that year; those that remain can therefore grow normally because of the increase in vital space and food available to them. Cuinat (1971) demonstrated the difference in growth that resulted from such transfers.

The pluri-annual cycle is of little utility because of the low recovery percentage, mobilization, and consequent exhaustion of the stream that lead to the production of dwarf fish.

Fario troutlets recovered at 6 months generally measure 60–120 mm and those recovered at 11 months measure 100–180 mm.

Table 22. Introduction of fry (after VIBERT and LAGER)

1. Leger formula (1937): $x = 20\ BW$, where x is the number of troutlets, 6 months old, to be introduced per km of a river, W is the width of the river in metres, and B is the biogenic capacity.

2. Embody table and formula (1927)

Number of troutlets of 3 inches (7.5 cm) to be introduced per mile

Width of river in feet	Quality of pools: Good			Average			Poor		
	Food supply			Food supply			Food supply		
	Good	Average	Poor	Good	Average	Poor	Good	Average	Poor
1	144	117	90	117	90	63	90	63	36
2	288	231	180	231	180	126	180	126	72
3	432	351	270	351	270	189	270	189	108
4	576	468	360	468	360	252	360	252	144
5	720	585	450	585	450	315	450	315	180
6	861	702	540	702	540	378	540	378	216
7	1008	819	630	819	630	441	630	441	252
8	1152	936	720	936	720	504	720	504	288
9	1196	1053	810	1053	810	567	810	567	324
10	1440	1170	900	1170	900	630	900	630	360
11	1584	1287	990	1287	990	693	990	693	396
12	1728	1404	1080	1404	1080	756	1080	756	432
13	1872	1521	1170	1521	1170	819	1170	819	468
14	2016	1638	1260	1638	1260	882	1260	882	504
15	2160	1755	1350	1755	1350	945	1350	945	540
16	2304	1872	1440	1872	1440	1008	1440	1008	576
17	2376	1930	1485	1930	1485	1039	1485	1039	594
18	2448	1989	1530	1989	1530	1071	1530	1071	612
19	2520	2047	1575	2047	1575	1102	1575	1102	630
20	2592	2106	1620	2106	1620	1134	1620	1134	648

Beyond a width of 20 feet use the formula $x = 1/2N_1\ W + 8N_1$, where $\mathbf{N_1}$ is the number of 3 inch troutlets for a width of 1 ft, W is average width, and x is the number to be introduced per mile.

For stocking trout of a size other than 3 inches, use the following conversion factors:

Length, in inches	1	3	4	6	10
Length, in cm	2.5	7.5	10.0	15	25
Factors	12	1	0.75	0.6	0.3

3. RESERVES

3.1 Permanent Reserves

Permanent reserves are created within legally determined limits on water courses with a view to hydraulic protection and safety (in areas around hydraulic works) or to protect fishery zones (sensitive areas, spawning beds).

Table 23. Yield from a nursery stream

Area used (sq m)	Introduced			Recovered			Av. size (mm)	Percentage recovered
	Date	Number		Date	Number			
		Total	per sq m		Total	per sq m		
1600	April	15,000	9	July	2311	1.4	74	15
2800	Feb	13,500	5	June	5147	1.8	85	38

Others are earmarked for purposes of fishing and are established in agreement with the holders of fishing rights.

3.2 Revolving Reserves

There is no specific method of using revolving reserves. They are generally an occasional or permanent refuge for fish forced out of nearby fishing sectors by a shortage of food and by sedentary carnivores that are generally large and very old.

Table 24. Representative table of the yield in a trout-breeding reserve

Area used (sq m)	Introduced				Recovered					
	Number		Size (mm)	Breeding duration	Number		Av. size (mm)	Ind. wt (av, g)	Total wt (kg)	% recov'd
	Total	per sq m			Total	per sq m				
3625	1500	0.41	180	12 mo	976	0.27	260	210	205	65
4000	9000	2.25	80	20 mo	3789	0.95	230	109	415	42
4000	7000	1.75	100	9 mo	3352	0.84	235	124	418	47

The best way of using them is to open them alternately for fishing: a particular section kept in reserve for two years is opened to fishing in the third year. Its use corresponds to reserving a section of the water course of the same size and productivity, not contiguous but at a fair distance so that fish from the old reserve do not immediately enter it. It is desirable that they have the maximum likelihood of being caught so that the management of alternate reserves achieves the main objective: a reasonable catch of classes of unproductive age that are predators on the existing stock. A fishery of this type cannot achieve this unless the sector placed in reserve is of at least 1000 m in smaller water courses (average width 20 m) and 500 m in water courses of average size (average width 50 m).

Breeding reserves are sectors of water courses that not only shelter fish but produce more than in natural conditions. They can be created only in rivers that can be completely fished (by electric fishing or nets) at a particular time during the year. These are salmonid water courses or cyprinid-pike canal reaches, the reserve being

Fig. 173. Recovery of trout in a growth brook (after ARRIGNON)

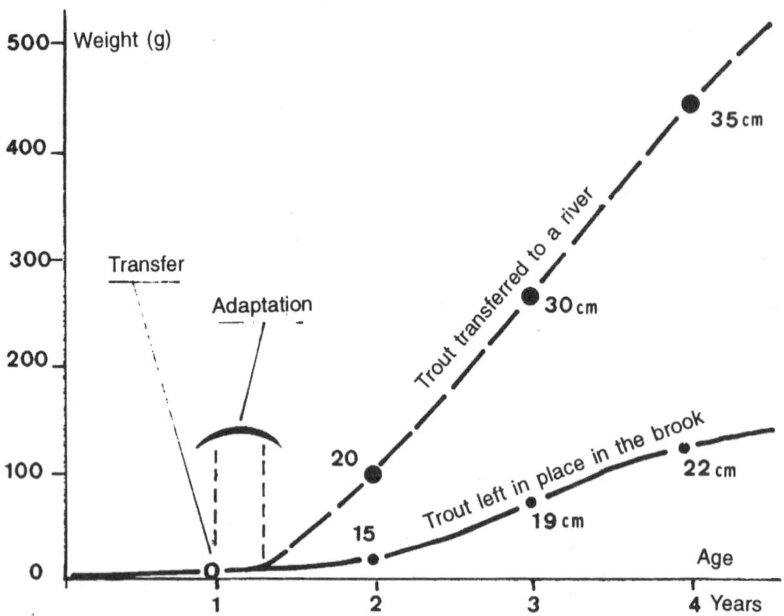

Fig. 174. Weight increase of trout originating from a nursery brook, whether transferred or left in place (after CUINAT, 1971)

therefore limited by two locks and fished when the water level is low, during the "idle period" of the canal.

In salmonid rivers, the reserve is fished at the beginning of spring. All animals of the legal size are removed and distributed in sectors open to fishing. They are replaced with year-old troutlets obtained, for example, from growth brooks. They therefore spend their second year in a more extensive vital space with abundant and varied food.

Stocking is determined in the same way as for growth brooks. The yield and the recovery percentage depend on the numbers introduced, the hydrologic regime of the river, and the presence of predators.

ARRIGNON (1970) indicated that in a tributary of the Oise river in which a part of its course was placed in reserve, the variation in yield was related to the number of fish introduced and their sizes.

4. EXPANSIONS

Marsh meadows that are known to have some utility (p. 199, access to spawning areas) may have an important production potential even if they are not visited by spawning fish.

Provided that a network of channels and pools ends in an obligatory point of passage or in a catching pool from which young pike can be recovered during their downstream migration, marsh meadows may be populated artificially with swimming fry, with 5 fry/sq m of water, if the flood leaves behind tufts of fairly uniformly distributed plants that can shelter young pike.

If in the flood zone there are only short plants, the number to be introduced is calculated from the development of the bank and the areas above water level (crests of slopes, high points), at a scale of 1 fish/linear m.

The yield from a flooded surface is increased considerably if we have earlier ploughed a few rows of which the crests are above water level.

The young fish are collected in the middle of spring (in May north of the Seine) with traps or nets or by electric fishing.

C. IMPROVED EXTENSIVE BREEDING

Improved extensive fisheries are arranged by creating or improving aquatic mediums in which conditions for young fish are rendered better either by encouraging the proliferation of their prey or by having recourse to additional artificial feeding.

1. ARTIFICIAL FEEDING IN A NATURAL MEDIUM

Artificial feeding in a natural medium has been carried out for a long time in fisheries for intensive production of fish for the table: trout, carp, and tench, raised in lakes or ponds.

This feeding with a view to producing young fish for restocking has been undertaken in breeding brooks since food pellets have become available to supplement natural food, which is often limited at the end of the cycle.

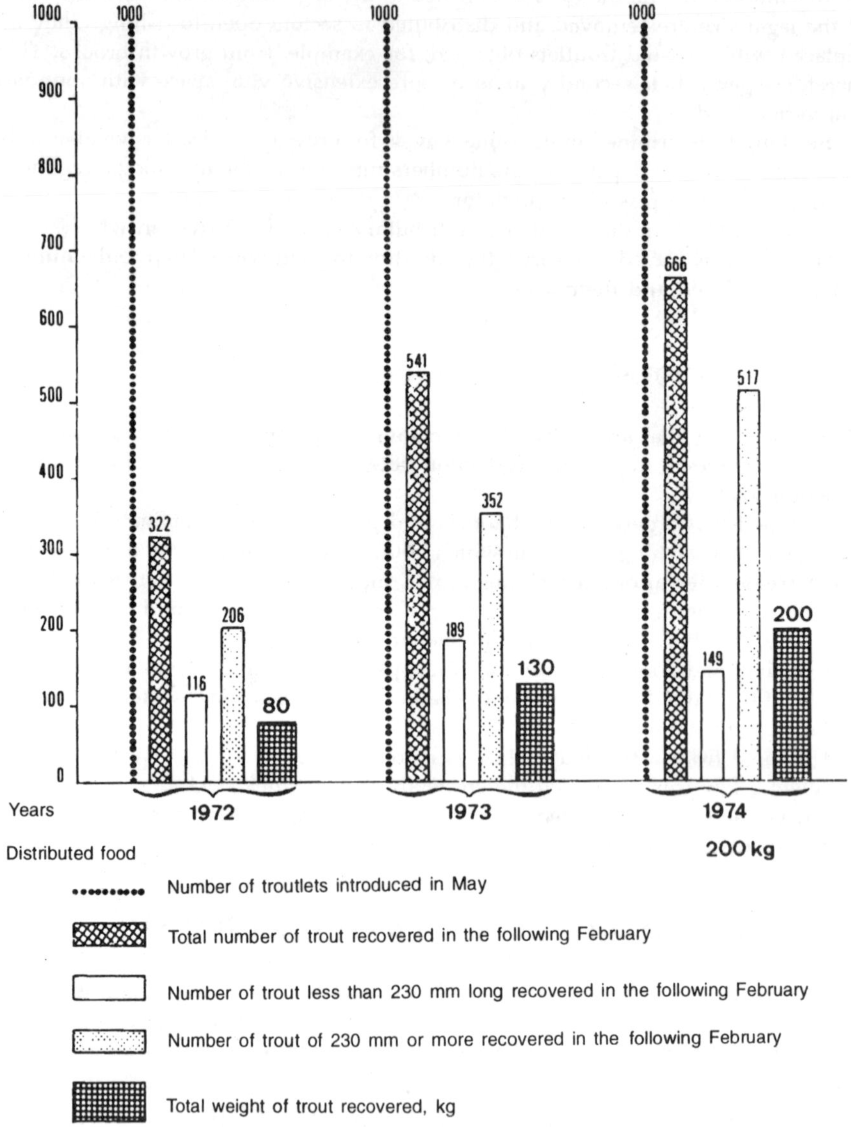

Fig. 175. Histogram representing yields in weight and number of troutlets raised in a brook with provision of artificial food (basin of the Helpe Majeure river in the north)

If carried out modestly, it does not appear in the course of inspection tours of streams to have reduced the hunting instinct of the animals in known examples. In some cases the pellets not consumed immediately by the fish are used by the benthos and therefore indirectly enter the food cycle of the animals being raised.

In a stream of northern France, a tributary of the Helpe Majeure river, we have observed highly improved yields of over 66% at the end of 10 months where 51% of the trout were above the legal catching size, in spite of heavy predation by herons.

In ponds the yield of fario troutlets for purposes or restocking increased by 17% at Tourville (Eure) after automatic distribution of food pellets, although ducks had diverted a considerable quantity of the food (45% of recoveries against 28%, duration of raising 11 months).

2. BREEDING CHANNELS

Breeding channels are artificial streams excavated in generally uncultivated, marshy, low-lying areas in association with drainage works: these are 1–2 m wide and 0.50–0.75 m deep.

Their management, which varies with region and local conditions, is generally the same as for natural breeding brooks. The number introduced varies from 1 to 32 eggs (or alevins with yolk sac) per sq m of water surface. The recovery percentages, from 20 to 80%, are lower when the numbers introduced are large because of an increase in mortality or emigrations due to competition. The average yields are 0.5–2 troutlets/sq m. According to CUINAT (1971) the numbers beyond which there is no increase in yield extend from 7 fry/sq m in the Lyons region (yield of 1.5 troutlets/sq m) to 9 fry in the Drome (yield of 0.9 troutlets/sq m), and 10–12 fry/sq m in Brittany (yield of 1.7 troutlets/sq m). In the Lyons region we conduct two recovery catches, one in summer and the other during the autumn, which considerably increases the annual production.

To the west of the Montagne Noire (Black Mountain), BRUNET (1973) increased the productivity of the breeding channels with young graylings by a flow from a higher channel towards a lower one across a bed planted with cress. The water contained many aquatic invertebrates that provided prey for the young graylings.

Artificial feeding in channels has been attempted in the Herault by DUCRET (in CUINAT, 1971). These channels with concrete walls and gravel beds interspered with canal tiles are traversed by cool hard water cascading at intervals of 8–10 m. Stocking is carried out using a large number of Vibert incubator boxes. An artificial food paste is provided daily on the submerged grills placed at distances of 4–5 m from each other. In 1969 the obtained yields varied from 7 to 30 ten-month-old troutlets per sq m or, in the best case, 300,000 troutlets/ha, weighing 4500 kg.

This is an intensive breeding of troutlets for restocking, which differ from domesticated troutlets in respect of three main characteristics, as highlighted by CUINAT (1971):

—Because of the high current velocity and the various possibilities for finding shelter, the troutlets retain their territorial behaviour (which is lost in overpopulated piscicultural basins with bare walls and beds).

—The lack of health protection measures no doubt results in a natural selection among the stock.

—The manner of feeding, occasional and without a human presence, enables the troutlets to retain a certain wild behaviour.

Curiosity and imitation are such that other carnivores raised extensively in a natural medium with their forage species benefit directly from the supply of artificial food. In a pond in the Laigue Forest (Oise) we have observed young perch feeding when required from a floating feeder, imitating carp and tench that were in the habit of coming to it.

As far as salmonids are concerned, such a fishery is worthwhile only to the extent that the animals produced, even though they do not have characteristics of the wild like those collected from natural streams, are nevertheless significantly hardier than troutlets produced in the fish culture industry.

3. LAKE PASTURING

Lake pasturing involves a massive introduction in a lake medium of young fish that grow well on an unused biomass and produce a biomass that can be used, as well as being profitable, over a period and under given conditions.

It is also intended to make up for deficiencies in natural increases by releasing young fish in a manner controlled and optimized from the technical, biological, and economic points of view.

This implies, initially:

—a knowledge of the existing fish populations,

—improved techniques for managing lake fisheries,

—techniques for obtaining young fish,

—an evaluation of their development after their release in a natural medium.

It necessitates mass production of young quality fish at low cost for purposes of restocking. In alpine lakes, the species and varieties considered for this purpose are the fario trout, the arctic char, and the coregonids. In Lake Leman, summer releases contribute to more than 50% recovery of the arctic char (1988).

4 INDUCED BREEDING

By induced breeding we mean the practice of making improvements that induce fish to reproduce at a particular place, selected so as to produce spawn and fry to enrich deficit mediums or for any other purpose.

A. CYPRINIDS

1. GUDGEON

The gudgeon (*Gobio gobio*) is becoming rarer in French waters (Massif Central and Southwest) probably, according to HOESTLANDT and BRUNET (1974), because of reduction in the zone of the grayling in which it thrived, the silting up of the barbel zone where it is also found, and the withdrawal of waters from dam lakes that are too cold for the species existing downstream. Apart from corrective action to overcome these causes, restocking of the gudgeon is necessary in many streams and water bodies. This is done by catches or when ponds are emptied and, in less frequent cases, by gudgeon from fisheries.

The gudgeon is a sedentary fish with dynamic populations and a high reproductive capacity under favourable biological conditions. It prefers gravel beds. A minimal temperature of 15–17°C is necessary for its reproduction; it does not thrive at temperatures above 25°C. Its normal life span is 4–5 years and it seldom lives for more than 7 years.

According to HOESTLANDT and BRUNET (1974) sexual maturity may be reached during the second summer of the gudgeon, in those measuring 90–100 mm. A female at 1 year plus lays, on an average, 500 eggs, at 2 years plus, 1500 eggs, and at 3 years plus, 4000–5000 eggs. Reproduction is extended in time in the form of successive spawns depending on variations in temperature. The eggs are laid, generally, on a gravel bed to which they adhere. They are white and translucid with an average size of 1.5 mm. Incubation takes 125 degree-days (about 6 days at 20°C). On hatching, the fry measures about 4.5 mm; the yolk sac is resorbed in 80 degree-days.

According to BRUNET (1971), reproduction of the gudgeon is induced by two main factors: the availability of gravel in a basin and an inflow of water with a flow current of 10 l/s for 200 m^2.

In monoculture the number introduced is 0.5–1 reproducing fish (2–3 years old) per sq m of the spawning pond. The resulting production is 10–40 young fish of 0+ (with an individual weight of 1 g) per sq m per year. The selection of older spawners

(3 years or more) yields a more abundant spawn because of a higher fertility (1500–15,000 eggs per female), but the survival rate of the spawners after laying is low (20–30%).

The gudgeon is generally mature at the age of 2 years but a small percentage of the younger fish are capable of reproduction at the end of the first year, which results in an annual production of 350–1000 kg/ha (with *additional* food), combined with an additional stocking of 4–15 young gudgeon per sq m.

In polyculture with other cyprinids (carp, tench, roach), the production of gudgeon is about 100 kg/ha/yr, which is 15–50% of the total production.

There are still some problems in intensive breeding of the species but it is nevertheless considered possible since we can easily plan the **gametogenesis** to produce viable eggs throughout the year by varying the temperature and the photoperiod (8L, 16D) during the **previtellogenesis**. A temperature raised to 15°C is now preferred and a photoperiod of 16L, 8D induces a hastened vitellogenesis and subovular maturity of the females.

Ovulation is then induced by pituitary injection and thermal shock. We use a pituitary extract of carp in a dose of 5–10 mg/kg of fish, in a single injection. About 60% of treated females ovulate 10–18 h after injection, with a yield that varies with the stage of maturation of a fish before treatment.

The larvae of gudgeon (0.5 mg on hatching) fed with a ration comprising 25% of natural food and 75% of dry food have a survival rate of 85–90% after more than 2 months of raising (KESTEMONT, 1990). The young are then placed in basins or introduced into the natural medium.

For purposes of restocking they can be easily transported in polythene bags under oxygen.

2. CARP

The carp (*Cyprinus carpio*) is raised for food rather than for restocking. Nevertheless, a considerable part of young carp is intended for enriching water bodies and the large cyprinid-pike water courses where existing conditions in the medium preclude its reproduction (very low temperature, water level changes). Restocking is carried out using fish caught in ponds, as well as with young carp raised in fisheries.

Being a fish of tropical origin, the carp grows best when the water temperature is regularly between 20 and 28°C. Below 13°C it does not grow well and below 5°C it stops feeding. A carp may reach a size of 800 mm and a weight of 15 kg.

According to HUET (1970), various fish breeding regions have obtained their own ranges of carp, with various types of scales (Bohemian, Galician, Hungarian). There are three main phenotypes corresponding to the various types of scales:

- **The scaled carp**, which is not the wild carp because its index of shape, L/H is approximately 1.
- **The mirror carp**, covered in places on the sides with scales of different size and usually a row on the top of the back.
- **The leather carp**, with a very limited number of scales, located at the base of its fins.

There is a correlation between the scales and some physiological characteristics these are the rate of growth, survival rate, and resistance to diseases. Those fish tha have scales are the hardiest. According to BEUKEMA (1967), wild carp are much more suspicious and difficult to catch than the improved (domestic) carp; this author obtained intermediate values by crossing domesticated carp with wild ones. For purposes of restocking, the desired qualities are mainly hardiness and sporting value rather than scale and shape. In Europe the age of those used for restocking is usually one or two summers.

2.1 Reproduction

Reproduction of the carp is induced not only by a temperature above the favourable threshold (18°C) but also by the presence of plants that are not too short or too tall so that it can deposit its eggs on them.

Till spawning, the fishes that are 5-7 years old are kept in ponds with a water supply at 14 and 16°C in order to avoid premature spawning or delay in sexual maturity.

In an ordinary or excavated spawning basin of 25-100 m^2, with a certain relief of the bottom (Hofer-Dubisch), we place three sets of fish (one set comprises two males and one female). If the temperature remains above 18°C spawning occurs within 24 h of their introduction. The carp spawns on the surface, creating a lot of noise due to the sudden movements necessary to evacuate its eggs. A female lays 100,000-150,000 eggs per kg of its weight. These are transparent and measure 1-1.5 mm in diameter. They are attached to the plant brush of the central tray in the *Dubisch spawning bed* (Fig. 178) and are distributed over the fibres of the brushes—or *kakabans*—placed in the spawning basin in the Indonesian "kakaban method" Five to seven kakabans with 5 sq m of surface area are required per kg of female. At night the kakabans are turned upside down to ensure a uniform distribution of eggs that adhere firmly to plant fibres.

In this case, on the morning after spawning, the brooms are placed in hatching ponds. In Dubisch spawning beds, on the other hand, it is the progenitors that are collected in the surrounding channel to be taken to another basin. This separation is essential to obtain a hatching percentage (50% in the most favourable circumstances): the parents, by digging at the bottom, muddy the water, and the suspended matter may be deposited on the eggs and suffocate them. The activity of the adults in a restricted space may also destroy some of the fry.

The duration of incubation is 100 degree-days (about 5 days at 20°C). After 50 degree-days embryos are formed in the eggs; when they hatch, the alevins measure 5-6 mm. The yolk sac is resorbed 2-3 days after hatching.

One week after hatching, the fry, 9-10 mm in size, are transferred to an initial pond, where they remain for 4-8 weeks. The number introduced is 50,000 young fish/ha. This pond has an area of 2500 sq m to 1 ha and an average depth of 0.50 m. Some cultural practices as well as initial amendments and manuring help to increase the production of plankton necessary for the fry.

When they reach a size of 5-6 cm, the fry are collected and placed in a second fry pond of 2-25 ha area and 1.5-2 m depth. Introduced in July at a rate of 5000-10,000/ha, the young carp remain there till the next spring, at which time they are caught for purposes of restocking deficit aquatic mediums.

At this final stage of breeding, when the fish are 1+, the yield is 25% counted from the stage of the swimming fry. The size of these young carp is 10-12 cm. To

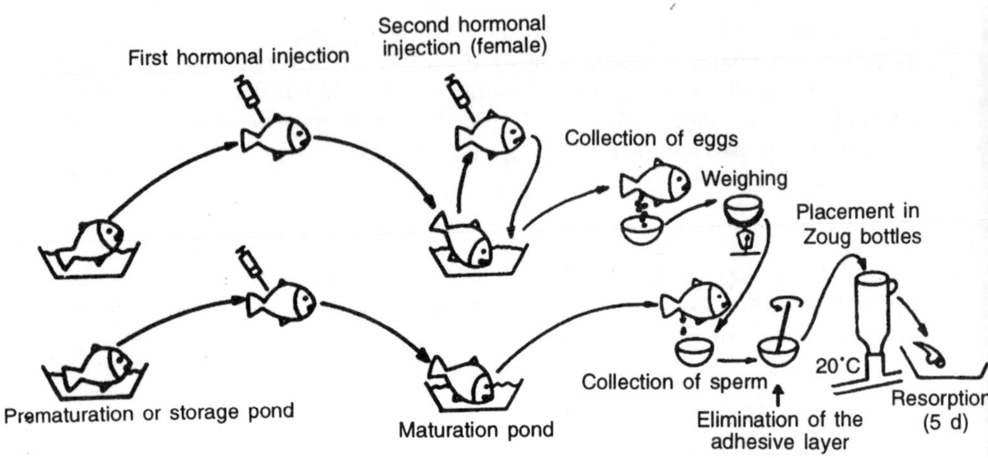

Fig. 176. Pituitary gland extract injection, insemination and incubation (of the carp)

increase the yield from the progenitors there are certain practices that lead to a closer control of reproduction as well as incubation of eggs.

2.2 Hypophysation

Hypophysation involves controlling maturation by injections of pituitary gland (hypophysis).

In the case of carp (Fig. 176) the progenitors are taken from prematuration ponds after a certain number of degree-days and transferred to a hatchery in storage or maturation basins. The temperature is progressively raised to about 20°C (with an increase of 1°C per day). The injection of raw pituitary extract is then given either in the dorsal musculature or in the body cavity. The females are given two injections: the first is 0.3 mg/kg of body weight and the second, after 220 degree-days (11 h later at 20°C), 3–4 mg/kg. For Chinese carp we often base the dose on the circumference of the female (Fig. 177). Ovulation occurs after about 240 degree-hours and, to ensure that the ova are not emitted spontaneously, the genital orifice is stitched at the time of the second injection. The males are given only one injection (1 mg/kg). The average yield is 50%, which means that only half of the females ovulate after treatment (Billard and Marcel, 1980).

2.3 Fertilization

Artificial fertilization is identical in practice to what is done in salmonids, except that the eggs are kept in contact not only with the sperm but also with a solution of carbamide (2 decilitres per litre of eggs). This solution comprises 3 g of carbamide and 4 g of NaCl per litre of water. It helps eliminate the mucus on the eggs, favouring activity of the sperm and extending the duration of this activity.

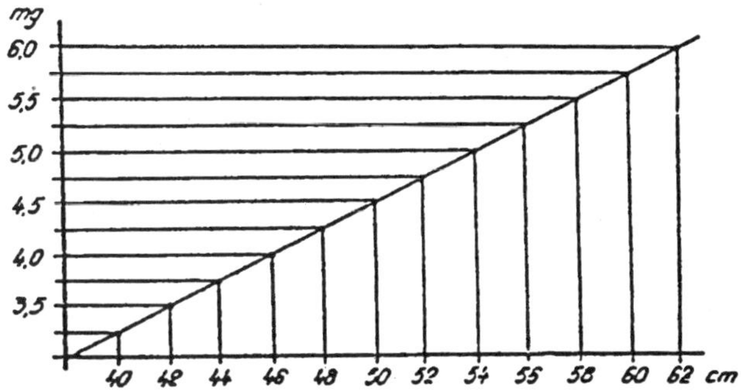

Fig. 177. Chart used in Eastern Europe in the case of chinese carp to determine the dose of pituitary gland extract to be injected, based on the circumference of the female (mg of extract/kg of body weight) (after BILLARD and MARCEL, 1980)

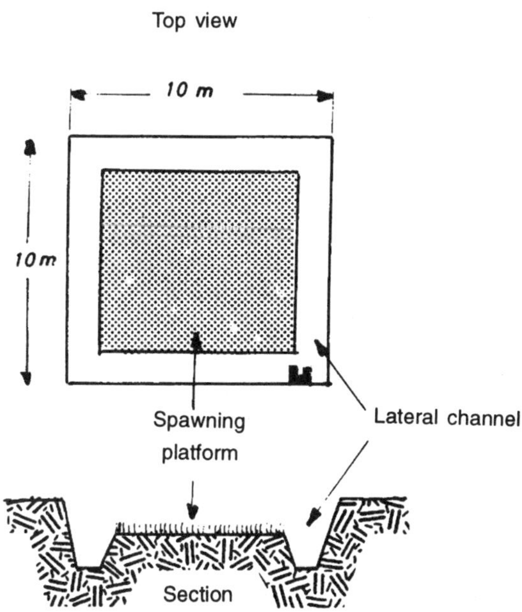

Fig. 178. Dubisch spawning bed

2.4 Incubation

To ensure that incubation in Zoug bottles, similar to that for eggs of the pike, continues favourably without any agglomeration we bathe them in a solution of tannic acid (15 g of tannic acid in 20 l water). The solution is then drained off and the eggs are bathed for about 10 sec. in a solution of tannic acid and then washed thrice in clean water before being put in incubator bottles.

The average survival rate is 30%, from the time of the swimming fry to that of the young carp, two summers old. Pituitary extract is not essential for the carp. Fecundity of females is closely dependent on their physical state (it is considered that 60% of the fish that do not spawn have been injured earlier, especially by the nets used to catch them). Their maturation depends mainly on the temperature limit (18°C) and the photoperiod.

3. ASIAN CARP

Herbivorous Asian carp, though not very widespread in France, play an important role in some piscicultural regions of Europe not only because of their fast growth but also because of their function as biological clearing agents. *Ctenopharyngodon idella*, which is macrophytophagous, and *Hypophthalmichthys molitrix* and *Aristichthys nobilis*, which are microphytophagous, originated from the Amur basin in Central Asia. These are tropical fish. The optimal temperature for their reproduction is 25°C. In Europe the adults spawn from the age of 6 years. Their growth depends closely on the temperature. According to HUET (1970), at the age of 3 years, their weight varies from 250 g (at 16–20°C air temperature in summer) to 1300 g (23–26°C), and 2500 g (24–32°C).

Considering the temperature required for natural reproduction, it is necessary to induce spawning by hypophysation.

The process of hypophysation is the same as described above for carp. The quantity to be injected is determined by measuring the circumference of the fish. According to FERLIN and LEDOUX (1974), for a circumference of 40 cm we inject 3.3 mg of pituitary extract per kg of the female, for one of 50 cm we use 4.5 mg, and for one of 60 cm we use 5.5 mg. Of this quantity, 10% is given 24 h before and 90% 7–12 h before spawning, depending on the water temperature. The genital orifice of the female is not stitched. Males receive an injection of 2 mg/kg 12 h before fertilization.

No solution is used to prepare for fertilization and incubation of the eggs.

Increase in weight in ponds, till we obtain fish for restocking, is ensured as in the case of the carp. The preparation of ponds for fry in Hungary is different in that the zooplankton is eliminated using pesticides before fry are introduced. The water has to be rich in phytoplankton: an additional amount of artificial food (soy paste) is given to the fry in pure breeding. Every species, carnivorous or otherwise, must be eliminated from ponds where the young fish are to be kept; this also applies to whitefish and frogs.

The number to be introduced, when the species is raised in a large pond, is 5–15 fry/sq m. If they are kept earlier in a basin for breeding it may be 50–150 fry/sq m (for a phase of more than a few weeks). The yield in terms of one-summer-old fish is 20–60% of the number of introduced fry, depending upon the quality of the breeding.

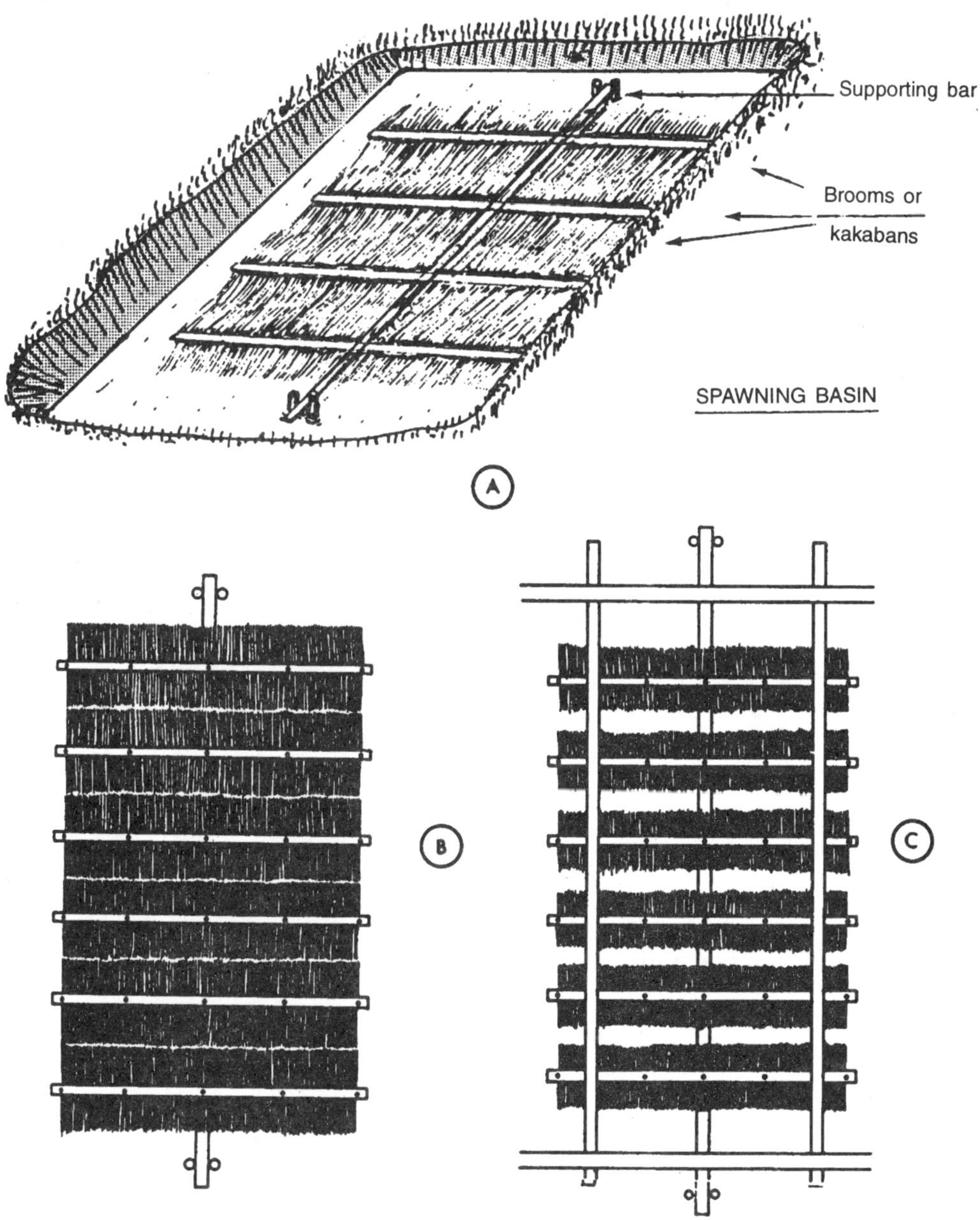

Fig. 179. Kakaban spawning beds (designed by ALIKUNHI, 1966)
A—Overall view; B—Arrangement of kakabans in a spawning basin: dense arrangement to hold the maximum number of eggs; C—Arrangement of kakabans in a hatching pond: loose arrangement, 8–10 cm below the surface to provide more space to the fry and increase photosynthesis (1 kakaban/30–50 m^2).

Fig. 180. Assembling a kakaban in an incubator and hatching box (after VINCKE, CTFT, Madagascar)

B. PERCOMORPHS

1. PERCH (*Perca fluviatilis*)

The perch, abundant and even overabundant in various water bodies where it exists in a dwarf form, is not found in other waters, generally because of a lack of spawning areas, as in navigational canals. Reproducing in spring, a little after the pike, when the water temperature reaches 12°C, the perch affects the raising of pike because its newly hatched fry are a source of live food for young pike immediately after their weaning from plankton. A controlled production of perch is therefore useful in two ways.

Its multiplication creates no problems; it may be ensured by natural reproduction or by artificial fertilization. In view of the need of the perch to reproduce on plant tufts and deposit its eggs on them, the method generally involves placing artificial spawning beds in a medium where there is no vegetation. Artificial spawning beds may be in the form of grilled frames with, for example, tufts of briar or sedge. The perch lays its eggs on these frames, which are then removed to collect the eggs.

Fig. 181. Kakaban covered with eggs (after VINCKE, CTFT, Madagascar)

Perch eggs stick together, forming long, translucent ribbons 6–7 cm wide. Males and females are introduced in equal numbers in the spawning basin. A female 20 cm long lays 200,000–300,000 eggs with a diameter of 2–2.5 mm. The relationship between two variables—the duration of incubation (Y) and the temperature (X)—cannot be expressed in degree-days. We can, however, draw a regression curve based on logarithmic coordinates and obtain the following relationship (HOESTLANDT and DEVIENNE, 1980):

$$\log Y = 1.72 \log X + \log 1039 a X Y^{1.72} = 1039$$

When the female matures, we may also easily carry out artificial fertilization by sprinkling the ribbon, expelled manually from the genital pore, with the milt (generally abundant) of a male. The eggs are incubated in Zoug bottles and shortly before they hatch they are placed in tanks with grills of a fine mesh.

In the breeding cycle of young pike, ribbons of perch eggs are introduced directly in the breeding tanks and the young pike feed on perch fry as soon as they emerge. We do not usually continue raising young perch for restocking purposes after they are a few months old because of the fragility of the species during transfers. It is preferable and less costly to restock the intended mediums with ribbons of fertilized eggs.

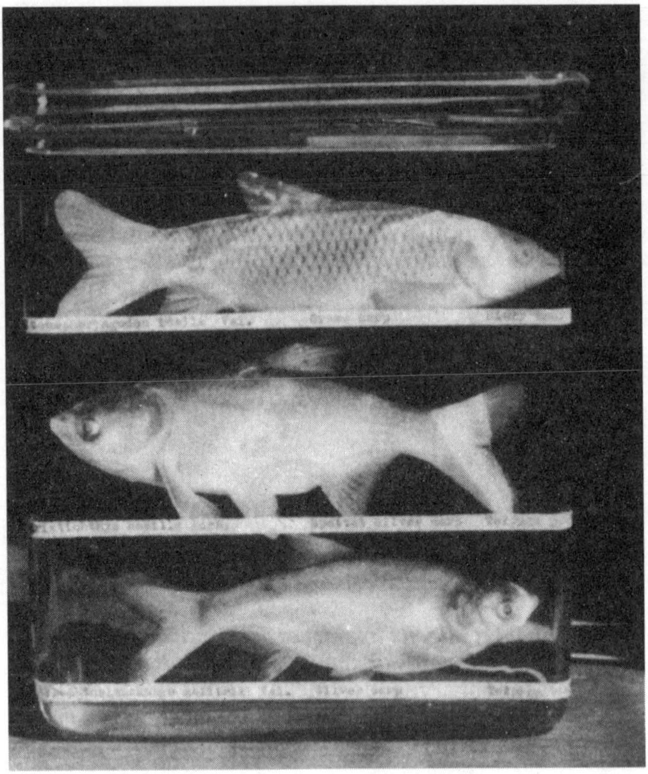

Fig. 182. Chinese carp (after ARRIGNON)

2. PIKE PERCH (*Stizostedion lucioperca*)

The pike perch is now perfectly acclimated in that portion of the French hydrographic network where the ecological conditions are favourable for it, as a result of a systematic effort to introduce it since 1945.

This effort required some improvement in piscicultural practices to produce eggs and fry in sufficient numbers. These practices are based on observation of the natural conditions of reproduction for the species.

The pike perch spawns on plants in still water where the male, in advance, arranges a nest at a depth of more than 70 cm. The sites chosen for depositing its eggs are generally networks of aquatic roots or those covered with short dense plants.

The progenitors reach sexual maturity at the age of 2 years in males and 3 years in females. Egg laying and fertilization occur in the spring, shortly after that of the perch, normally at the end of April and beginning of May, when the temperature of the water remains between 13 and 15°C. The eggs hatch after 110 degree-days.

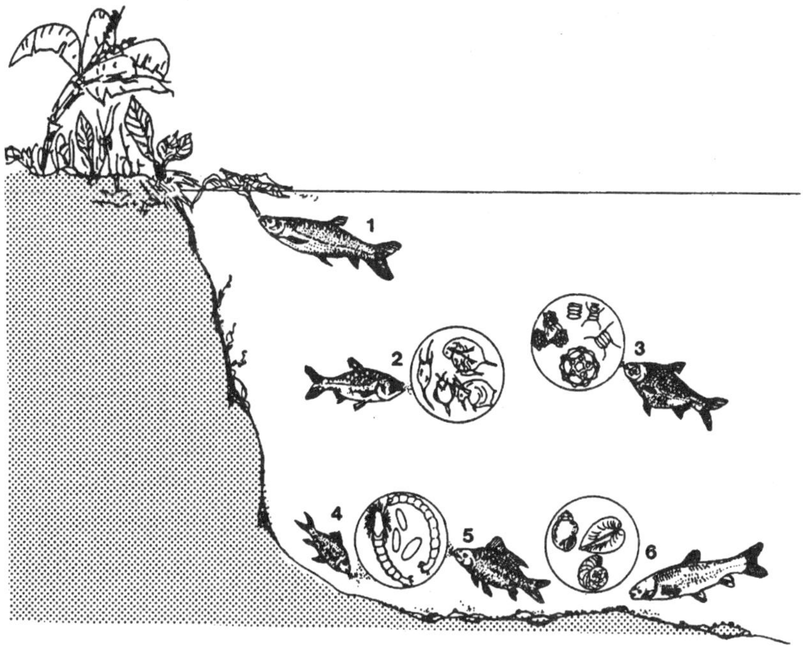

Fig. 183. Habitat and trophic levels of the main species in a combined raising of chinese carp (after BARDACH, RYTHER and McLARNEY, 1972)

1. *Ctenopharyngodon idella:* macrophytophagous at the surface; 2. *Aristichthys nobilis:* zooplanktonophagous at a middle depth; 3. *Hypophthalmichthys molitrix:* phytoplanktonophagous at a middle depth; 4. *Cirrhinus molitorella:* detritivorous, benthic; 5. *Cyprinus carpio*: detritivorous, benthic; 6. *Mylopharyngodon piceus:* malacophagous, benthic.

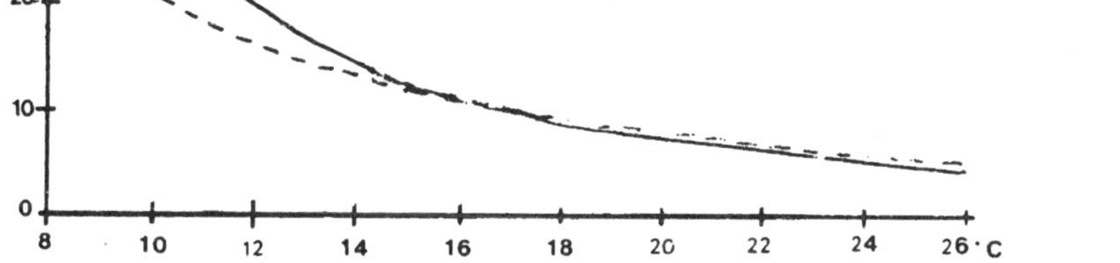

Fig. 184. Relationship between temperature and duration of incubation of the common perch (*Perca fluviatilis*) in V. GOUBIER (1990)

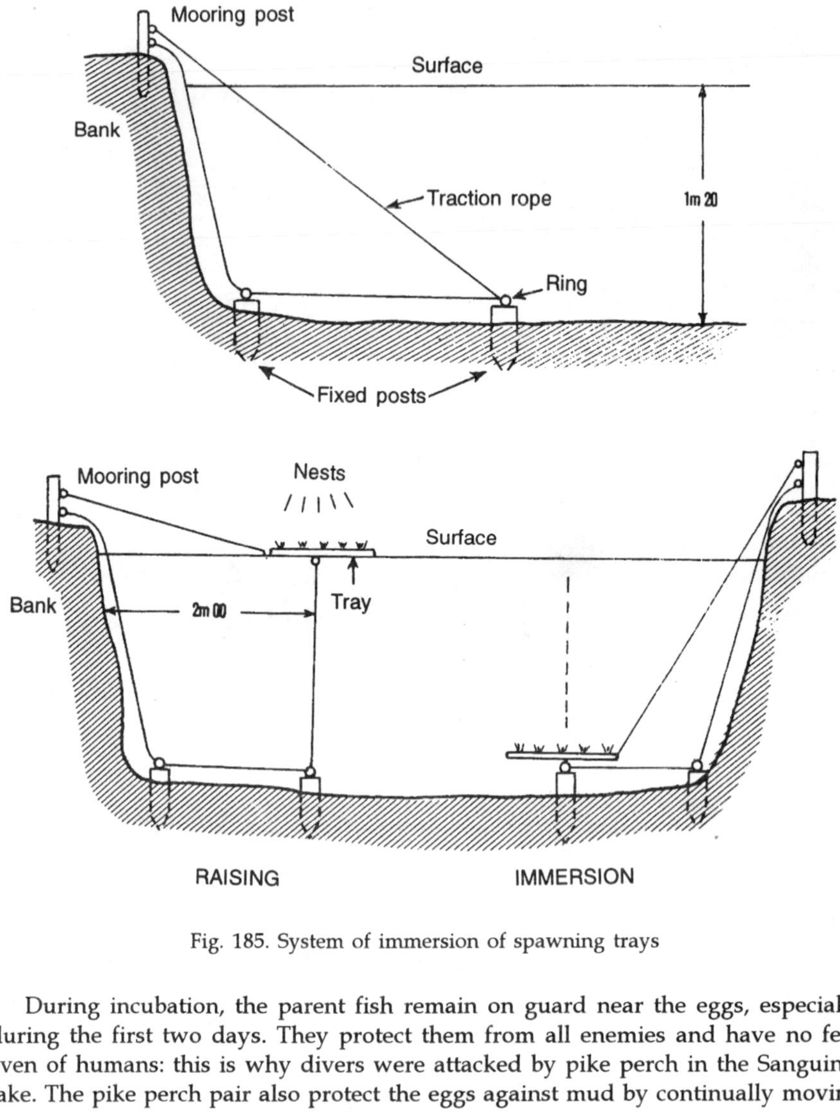

Fig. 185. System of immersion of spawning trays

During incubation, the parent fish remain on guard near the eggs, especially during the first two days. They protect them from all enemies and have no fear even of humans: this is why divers were attacked by pike perch in the Sanguinet lake. The pike perch pair also protect the eggs against mud by continually moving their fins above the nest.

As soon as they emerge, the larvae of the pike perch can swim well as their specific weight is hardly more than that of water because they have an oily yolk sac. The fry hatch with an open air bladder. As soon it is filled with air swallowed at the surface the canal linking the mouth with the bladder closes permanently. Subsequent variations in its volume are ensured by organic changes.

A female lays about 200,000 eggs per kg of its body weight.

Artificial reproduction of the pike perch consists of partly induced reproduction in movable spawning beds where there are no spawning zones in an aquatic medium.

Fig. 186. Spawning ponds. Note the identification posts and traction ropes.

Fig. 187. Checking a spawning tray (after J. ARRIGNON)

Fig. 188. Spawning tray covered with eggs of pike perch (after J. Arrignon)

Spawning basins are provided with well-oxygenated water at a rate of 2–5 l/s. They usually measure 400–500 sq m and are 1.20–1.50 m deep. The more elaborate ones have a device that enables us to avoid handling that may be harmful to the eggs (Fig. 185).

The progenitors are prepared in pairs and placed in spawning basins in October, with one pair per movable spawning basin, together with forage fish (roach, gudgeon, small tench) at a scale of 2 kg per kg of progenitor.

These spawning beds or nests are trays with natural or artificial fibres. They are placed in basins, depending upon the climatic conditions, from mid-April to the beginning of May.

Once placed, they are checked every day. By raising them we note those on which spawning will take place because they have been perfectly cleaned by the progenitors. Once the eggs are laid we replace the nest that was covered with eggs; the next nest may be covered on the following day if the female had not laid all her eggs on the first day.

The visited nest is then broken up, each compartment being used as a base for a Corchus incubator box.

3. BLACK BASS (*Micropterus* sp.)

The black bass with a wide mouth (*Micropterus salmoides*) is the only species presently raised in Europe. The black bass with a small mouth (*Micropterus dolomieu*), introduced in northern France and Belgium, has almost disappeared.

The black bass is found south of the Loire and in ponds in the plains as well as in rivers where the current is slow and vegetation rich. It is often seen in brackish waters. The species prefers waters that are comparatively warm with temperatures as high as 32°C. Below 10°C the animal does not feed. Considered one of the larger freshwater carnivores, it grows very quickly if it has an abundance of forage fish. WURTZ-ARLET (1952) mentions the growth rate in northern France as being 10–50 g in a year, 125–200 g in 2 years, 350–450 g in 3 years, 500–850 g in 4 years, and 750–1200 g in 5 years. This growth is hastened by the temperature of the ambient medium.

The fish are sexually mature at the age of 3 years. The period of sexual activity extends for about 1 month and preparation of the nest begins as soon as the temperature reaches 17–18°C. They reproduce at the end of spring when the water temperature rises above 18°C and remains at this level.

Like all Centrarchids, the male prepares a nest and becomes its attentive owner and vigilant guard. Selected at the bottom where it is hard and clean, with stones or sand, at a depth of 30–40 cm, the nest is about 1 m in diameter depending on the size of the male. At Antsampandrano (Madagascar), we have observed (ARRIGNON, 1953) that the species does not reproduce in muddy ponds with a hard bed and without submerged twigs.

The female lays 5000–10,000 eggs, each about 2 mm in diameter. The incubation is about 180 degree-days. During incubation and after hatching, as long as the fry remain together in a swarm, they are guarded by the male parent. As soon as the gregarious instinct becomes weaker in the young ones (at a size of 12–15 mm), the parental instinct vanishes and a propensity to cannibalism leads the parents to devour their offspring. In fish breeding it is therefore desirable to recover the young before they disperse.

Breeding of black bass is based on the natural summer production intended for restocking. The progenitors are directed towards controlled spawning beds in spawning ponds. The young are raised in a fry pond with the production or provision of live food. Raising is sometimes prolonged and combined with that of the carp in ponds of a larger size (1 or 2 ha) to obtain fish for the table.

In order to induce spawning at selected sites that can be monitored spawning ponds are developed with clayey banks and bottom. Against one of the banks, spawning boxes are arranged side by side. Each box has three sides of 1 m, made of concrete, bricks, or wood. The fourth side is open to the pond. Gravel is placed at the bottom on which the eggs are laid. The optimum surface for such ponds is 1000 sq m per pair of breeding fish.

After spawning, the male guards the eggs as well as the swarm of fry that emerge later. Three weeks after hatching, this swarm should be collected before it is eaten by the male. The aggressive instinct of the male, excited by the exterior, causes it to leave the box. Simultaneously, the open side is closed by inserting a fine grill. The fry are completely isolated in this closed cage and can then be collected and placed in a separate pond.

According to HUET (1970), when very young, the black bass is not exclusively carnivorous. The young ones may be raised intensively, like salmonids, in fish breeding troughs with prepared food (somewhat finely crushed pellets), after an initial provision of live plankton.

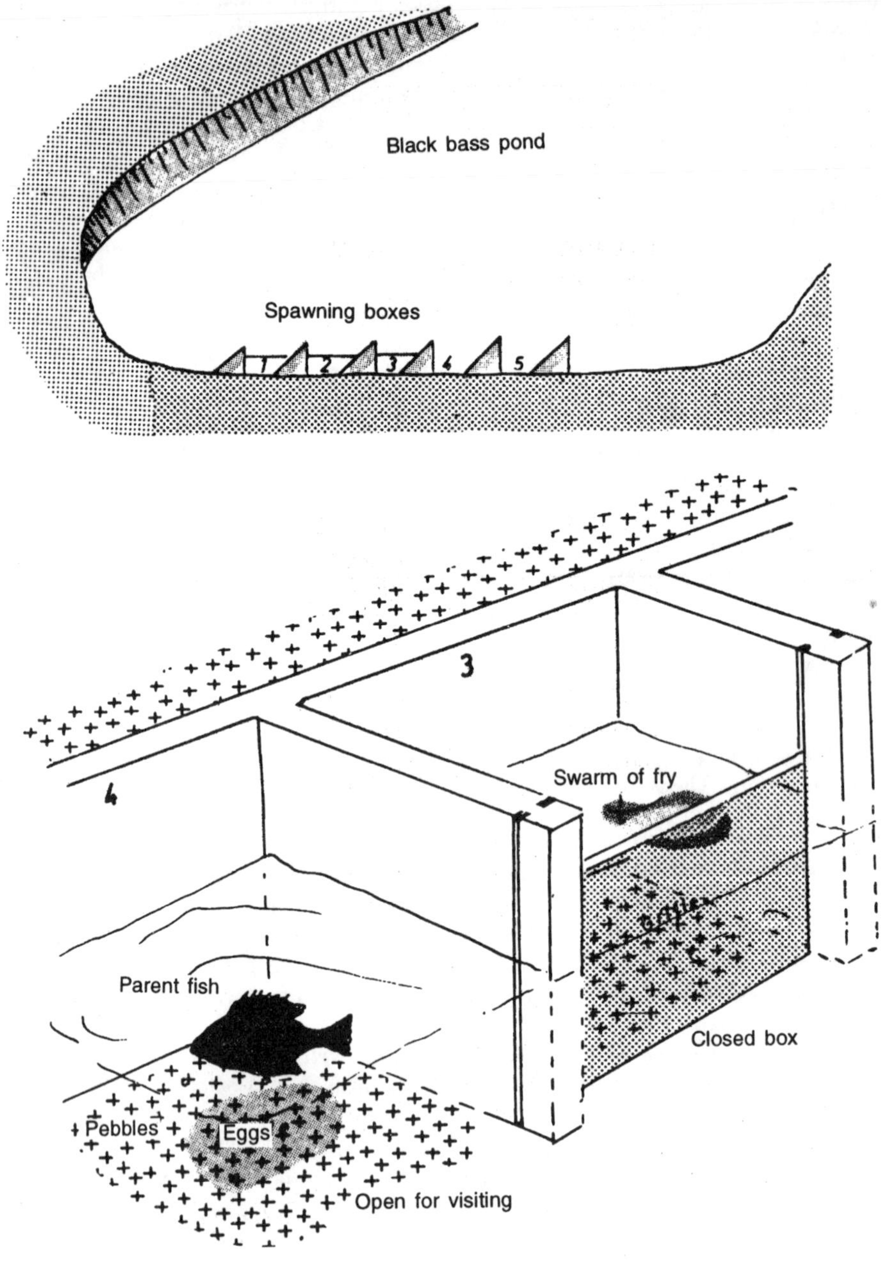

Fig. 189. Black bass pond with spawning boxes

Before the fry are introduced, the pond should be fertilized suitably with a view to obtaining plankton rich in rotifers, cladocerans, and copepods. Young black bass do not generally become ichthyophagous till they are 50 mm in size. If the food is inadequate, cannibalism suddenly ensues. According to ROBBINS and MACCRIMMON (1974), 5–6 kg of forage fish is needed to produce 1 kg of fingerlings.

The number of fingerlings produced in 4–5 months during the summer varies from 7500 to 10,000/ha. The yield is from 25 to 50% (based on the number of fry introduced). During restocking it is important to introduce only 1/10 of the total fish stock, in terms of weight, unless we are producing black bass for consumption, in which case the ratio is 1/2. In such a situation, the following should be introduced (HUET, 1970):

– 150 roach progenitors per ha, which, in July, will provide a large amount of prey for young black bass, or

– in a fertilized medium, 4000 fish, of which 3750 are forage fish and 250 black bass. In a virgin medium, the stock per hectare can be 1000 fish, of which 75 are young black bass.

In this way we can achieve a balanced population that may continue for several years, the black bass acting as a calibrator on all the populations, controlling also that of catfish.

Black bass fry can be easily transported over long distances with the presently available means.

No data are available yet in France on the growth of the black bass under extensive farming conditions. American experiments in warm water indicate that when 20,000 fry were introduced per hectare at an average water temperature of 27°C, the fish, in 100 days, reach a size of 20 cm and a weight of 115 g. These results do not enable us to assess the growth potential in open-air basins.

C. ESOCICULTURE (PIKE BREEDING)

Pike (*Esox lucius*) is bred essentially for purposes of restocking. There are special features relative to catching of spawners, incubation of eggs, and raising of fry. More difficult than salmonid breeding, it is closely dependent on four main factors:

1. Climatic conditions determine and limit production.
2. It is impossible to keep the progenitors in a restricted space, so they must be caught in the natural medium during the precise period of their sexual maturity.
3. The air and water temperatures, thermal variation, and atmospheric pressure affect fertilization, the process of incubation, and the fry.
4. Cannibalism among the fry depends on the water temperature, the habitat, and the quantity and quality of live food.

1. ECOLOGY OF THE SPECIES

The pike, an indigenous European carnivore, prefers stagnant waters and running streams in the ichthyo-ecological zones of barbel, bream, and sometimes grayling; it is also found in brackish water (Flanders, and the marshes of Brittany and Poitiers, for example). It prefers the upper layer of water bodies and streams, which is still and warm in summer. It is easily introduced among aquatic plants, especially phragmition.

It is a predator on all species of fish, except, apparently, the catfish and stickleback. It usually attacks frogs, water rats, and even ducklings, ensuring generally a good balance among the natural fish population where the existing members, as a result of a fairly harsh selection, have a better growth.

The pike feeds on prey that is often undesirable and of little interest to fishermen and transforms it to quality meat. It is, itself, undeniably and justifiably favoured by those who fish for sport. The interest in pike fishing creates a need for restocking.

Because of its voracity, pike should be excluded from salmonid and cyprinid fisheries as well as rivers where salmonids preponderate.

The pike breeds at the end of winter or at the beginning of spring when the water temperature is above 7°C, at the same time as frogs, which, for a pisciculturist, is a valuable chronological indication.

Though generally a sedentary fish, it may sometimes cover a distance of 10 km to find a suitable spawning area, especially when it exists in canals. The reproducing pike arrive in shallow zones with plants that are calm and tend to warm up fast. The eggs are deposited on plant supports; after this the parents have no interest in the offspring.

Females lay eggs at the age of 3 years and often at 2 years. The males mature a year earlier. A female lays eggs weighing as much as one-third of its weight (20,000–25,000 eggs/kg). There may be 50,000–70,000 eggs per litre of emission. The eggs are 2.5–3 mm in diameter, translucid, greenish-red, and sticky; they are often found to be indigestible when consumed.

The incubation period is 120 degree-days; after hatching, resorption of the yolk sac takes 160–180 degree-days. The larva, of a shape different from that of the adult, is 8–9 mm long. On the front part of the head, before the eyes, it has adhesive papillae with which it attaches itself to supports. It suspends itself vertically from a support. Shortly before the complete disappearance of the yolk sac, the fry adopts the normal swimming position. Its attitude and morphology undergo a rapid change. Having acquired the colour and shape of a pike, it possesses a hunting instinct and begins to feed in the natural medium on existing plankton and, when older, feeds on fry of other species of fish. At the age of 1 year, it may often be 400 mm long.

2. CATCHING PROGENITORS

The methods for catching pike in ponds or rivers are organized in different ways.

In a pond supplied with water from a stream, the inlet should be closed and the water diverted through a channel about 10 days before the presumed spawning. Upstream of the inlet we immerse several bags of manure, and downstream we place a trap to catch the fish. As soon as the temperature of the water is higher than 7°C we open the inlet. The percolate containing organic matter from the manure, arriving in the pond, attracts progenitors; they are caught in the traps, which should be inspected every 2 h if a large number of them arrive in a short period.

Sometimes, the fish concentrate at a particular point in a lake or pond, corresponding to a well-exposed spawning bed. They are caught with square dipping nets, light movable traps, or nets spread around the *Scirpeto-Phragmitetum* belt. The pike move about among the reeds where wattlings divert them towards the openings of the traps.

In some cases pike are made to move along obligatory passages towards spawning areas. This is observed in the Jablines (Seine and Marne), and Monampteuil (Aisne). An arrangement is made to catch them in which the cage is lifted at given intervals depending on the intensity of migration.

The spawners are taken to a pike-breeding station in dark transportation tanks ventilated with compressed air in a homeothermal medium. Although males can be kept in storage tanks for about 3 weeks, females cannot be kept for more than 4 or 5 days, to complete their maturation. The temperature of the receiving medium should be slightly higher than the medium from which they were taken. While awaiting release they are kept in large fish tanks (of 4–8 sq m) immersed in a pond with males at one side and females at the other. In cases where the outdoor temperature is lower than that of the medium of origin, we place the spawners, always separated by sexes, in indoor tanks with a suitable water supply.

3. ARTIFICIAL REPRODUCTION

Artificial reproduction of the pike is conducted as for salmonids according to the rules for the dry method.

The females selected for spawning are sexually mature; they weigh 2–8 kg. At this stage, eggs flow from the genital pore by gravity. The males, smaller and younger, have very little milt and it is important to have a large number of them in stock, not downstream but upstream of the fish tank containing the females so that there is no tendency on their part to ejaculate their sperm as a result of sexual excitation. During fertilization the males emit a few drops of milt, which is collected on the tip of a goose feather and mixed with the ova contained in the coelomic liquid. The males are returned to storage tanks after treatment; their spermatogenetic potential is restored fairly quickly and they can be used for a second artificial fertilization operation. It may happen that the number of males is inadequate. In that case we have to kill them, cut them open, and remove their testes, which are ground and mixed, immediately and completely, with the ova in order to fertilize them.

The fertilized eggs can be transported without any danger if the time between fertilization and incubation in bottles is not more than 2 h. This is how the pike fishery at Flevo Lelystad (Netherlands) uses 75–80 kg of eggs emitted and fertilized at places where the progenitors are caught, and sends them to the breeding centre.

Before being incubated the eggs are passed through a bath of iodoform that destroys parasites and viruses around them and, at the same time, removes the layer of adhesive mucus. In Ettenheim (Germany), RIEGGER (1973) used carbamide in the conditions explained (p. 244).

Incubation takes place in bottles traversed by an ascending water current. Zoug bottles contain 6-8 l. Each filled bottle receives an average flow of 4 l/min., regulated so that the mass of eggs is separated and slightly stirred while it remains in the lower two-thirds of the bottle. The temperature of the water is maintained at 9–13°C. Below 9°C the fry emerge tail first from the shell, which results in a high death rate. Above this temperature the fry emerge head first and the mortality is much lower (communication from Huisman, 1975). We also have conical Kannegieter incubator bottles made of a plastic material and these are used for incubating eggs of carp and coregonids. Thirion (1968), during an initial phase of 30 degree-days, kept fertilized eggs on trays in troughs and then put them in Zoug bottles. In his view the survival rate was higher as the eggs were thus protected against a water movement during the most critical period of embryogenesis. This method is closely associated with natural conditions in incubation.

When embryonated eggs appear (30 degree-days) they acquire a dark colour; they become robust and it is possible to evaluate the volume in each bottle as well as the number of live eggs. The flow is stopped, the mass of eggs remains in the lower portion, and the volume is calculated; we use a glass tube 40–50 cm long with an internal diameter of 4 mm, holding it vertically. The open end is closed with the thumb, the tube is withdrawn, and in the total number of eggs we count the wastage. The counted eggs are then put in a graduated test tube that indicates the number of eggs in relation to the volume. In this way it is possible to calculate the numbers that will hatch.

After 70 degree-days, if the pike fishery is required to produce only embryonated eggs, incubation should be discontinued, the dead eggs eliminated, and arrangements made to despatch the lot.

At 110 degree-days we discontinue incubation in bottles and place the eggs that are about to hatch on trays arranged in indoor troughs. We may, however, allow the eggs to hatch in the jug, regulating the flow to the minimum without stopping it. The larvae are put into the trays when 95% of the eggs have hatched. During temperature-controlled raising the eggs are removed as soon as they begin to hatch and introduced in the proportion of 1 litre of eggs for 13 litres of water in a hemispherical container and the water temperature is raised to 15°C. The eggs hatch within 3 hours as opposed to 24 hours. The survival rate is better and is generally between 70 and 90% during incubation. Below 70% it is considered preferable to eliminate the spawn. During hatching the average losses are about 20%.

4. RAISING OF THE YOUNG

Raising of the young begins with the larvae being placed in troughs; it is essential to provide supports for them, for example, plants (cress, callitriche), wooden frames, strips of plastic material floating on the water surface, or semicircular strips of wire netting placed across the troughs to which the fry attach themselves. In the troughs there are tanks with perforated sides in which we introduce 5000 larvae (25,000/sq m). The yolk sac is resorbed in 160–180 degree-days. After 100 degree-days, the larvae become swimming fry. They need to be provided with plankton. This is the stage at which they should be transported for purposes of restocking. During the resorption phase there may be a loss of 10–20%.

The fry are then placed in indoor basins of 4 m^2, made of concrete or synthetic resin, in similar outdoor basins, or in larger ones of 50–400 m^2. In the first of these the number introduced is 5000/m^2 and in the second, 500/m^2. In the first of these, the fry are fed with plankton that is produced and fished out, after which it is strained through a 1 mm mesh during the first 2 days, a 1.7 mm mesh for the next

5 days, and a 2.5 mm mesh till they reach a size of 5 or 6 cm. The size of plankton and temperature control ensure a considerable reduction in cannibalism. The twice-daily distribution is about 250 g/day/1000 fry during the first week.

During this breeding phase the fry are treated with malachite green and a 2 ppm quarternary ammonia solution. The flow is discontinued for 1 h in the basins.

Though the breeding of young fish can be controlled easily in indoor basins of cement, this does not apply to earthern basins. In earthern basins the yield depends on the richness of the habitat in shelters and on the number of predators. The medium will be rich in natural shelters if the bottoms of the ponds, with tall plants, are flooded shortly before the animals are introduced. We may also arrange additional shelters by immersing weighted bundles of hay or frames of wire netting covered with tufts of straw, fern, or briar. The main enemies of pike fry are the larvae of beetles and tadpoles of frogs and toads. The yields, depending on the incidence of these factors, are 2 to 50% under the aforementioned conditions of introduction. While the sizes of the fry are fairly regular in intensive raisings (50–100 mm at the age of 5 weeks), in extensive raisings we observe a certain heterogeneity (ARRIGNON, 1970):

—82% are less than 100 mm,
—13% are between 100 and 130 mm, and

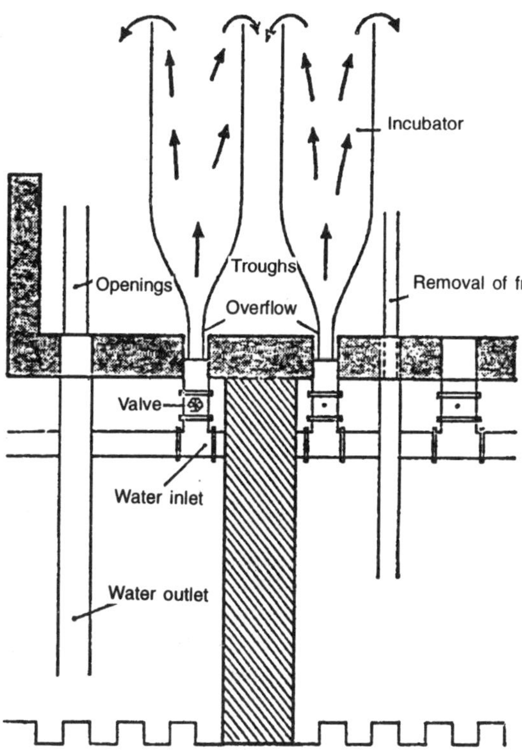

Fig. 190. Principle of Zoug incubators

Fig. 191. Battery of Zoug incubator bottles

Fig. 192. Fry troughs. In the troughs there are supports for young pike fry (after J. ARRIGNON).

Fig. 193. Recovery of plankton, which is put in a funnel and taken to breeding basins

—5% are between 130 and 190 mm.

At the age of 6 weeks, the young pike must be introduced in the intended mediums. To continue this raising in a restricted medium will result in insignificant yields.

The restocking of pike should therefore be conducted in the following three phases:

1. On formation of eyed ova the products are transported in isothermal boxes, at a low temperature, to hatch and grow in another place till the size of a swimming fry or young pike.

2. At the stage of swimming fry, the products are transported in polyethylene bags in an atmosphere of oxygen for purposes of restocking at a rate of 1 fry per metre of the bank or to be kept till they grow to the size of a young pike.

3. At the age of 6 weeks the young pike are transported in tanks with a diffusion of compressed air, or in polyethylene bags in an atmosphere of oxygen, for purposes of restocking at a rate of 1 young pike per 2 or 3 m of the bank, depending on the availability of shelters.

5. IMPROVED NATURAL REPRODUCTION

Improved natural reproduction (INR) of the pike, developed by BRY (1984), examined from the economic point of view by MANELPHE and BRY (1989), and now adopted in many places (DULAC, BRY and NEVEU, 1989), is said to be "improved" because of a protocol: control of the water level, presence of a single female per spawning bed, the absence of predatory fish, and collection of the fry by draining the pond.

Table 25. Results in breeding pools (LEMAIRE, 1981)

Date of laying in water	Date of stocking	Number	Date of emptying	Results
Basin 1 Feb 15	Mar 25	18,000	Apr 20–23	7279 size 45–52 mm 2.6/sq m
Basin 2 Feb 20	Apr 1	36,000	Apr 27–29	15,733 size 45–55 mm 6.2/sq m
Basin 1 Apr 26	Apr 28	35,000 (approx.)	May 21–26	7453 size 40–72 mm 2.7/sq m

Table 26. Results in a natural medium (LUCHETTA and DEHEEGER, 1982)

Station	No. introduced	Caught	Recovery percentage
1	19,000 (in 2 instalments)	1272 in 4 catches	6.6%
2	35,000 (in 2 instalments)	1854 in 3 catches	5.2%
3	34,000 (in 2 instalments)	2139 in 5 catches	6.2%
4	10,000 (at one time)	1685 in 5 catches	16.9%

It is conducted in small ponds that can be drained out (400–3000 sq m), are not very deep, and have many plants that provide a good medium for both natural reproduction and early growth of the pike in extensive conditions. Growth of young pike is ensured by planktonic and benthic invertebrates whose populations develop well during the middle of spring.

The numbers to be introduced in each pond during the middle of February comprise one female (the size of which depends upon the area and richness of the pond) and the two males. We also introduce forage fish (roach, bream, rudd, and tench). The young ones are usually collected in May–June, 70–80 mm in size (2 g) and at a rate of $2/m^2$ of water surface.

The method is simple, based on a low investment (a hatchery is not necessary), and economical in manpower.

D. SALMONIDS

1. BREEDING OF THE ARCTIC CHAR (*salvelinus alpinus* L.)

When breeding the Arctic char we need to take into account that it is the relic of a glacial age and is found in the deep, dark portion of alpine lakes. It is raised exclusively for purposes of restocking.

Table 27. Characteristics of young pike fishery in improved natural reproduction (MANELPHE and BRY, 1988)

Structure of fishery	Small ponds with plants
Area	1500 m^2
No. and wt of reproducers	1 female, 1.75 kg 2 males, 1 kg
Forage fish (kg/kg of reproducers)	0.6 (and later 0.5 kg for winter storage)
No. of days for raising	28–30
Av. no. of young pike collected/sq m	2
Av. wt and size of young pike	2.2–3 g, 6–8 cm
Profitability (francs/ha of land, before taxes)	20,000

Table 28. Production of 9-month-old summerlings in small ponds (June to March, area 240 m^2), effect of introducing young fish of 6–7 g (BRY, 1989)

Introduction (young fish/100 m^2)	7	14	33
Net production, kg/ha	102	75	37
Survival percentage	100	59	24
Individual wt (g)	160	102	79

Fig. 194. Breeding basin for plankton: in the foreground a submerged bag of manure and in the background, a shady area in which there is a concentration of plankton (after J. ARRIGNON)

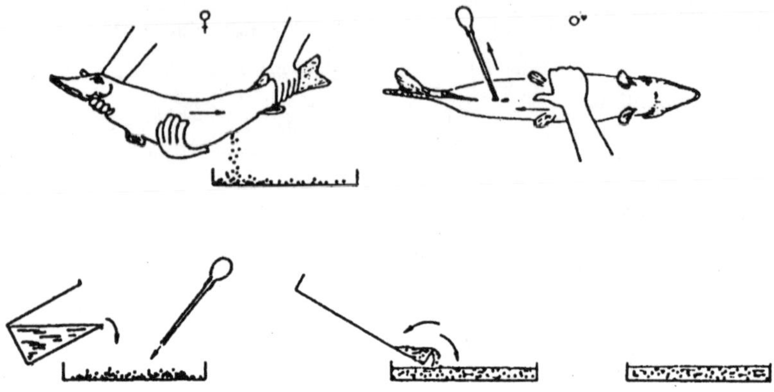

Fig. 195. Artificial insemination of the pike. The eggs are extracted by abdominal massage and collected in a tray. Sperm is drawn out using a pipette or a syringe and poured over the eggs at the same time as the diluent. The entire mass is mixed by decanting and left undisturbed for 10–12 min. before being placed in an incubator (after BILLARD *et al.*, 1976).

LAURENT (1982) indicated that the ideal temperature range for its breeding is between 5 and 7°C. Mortality is observed at 17°C in ponds. In hatcheries, the fry grow rapidly at 12°C but suffer from temperature variations.

The Arctic char requires less oxygen than most of the other salmonids. It can exist permanently in water with no more than 5 ppm of O_2. A flow of 0.3 l/min./kg of fish is adequate and it does not like a current.

Outdoor basins should be provided with opaque covers, otherwise the animal will not feed. The depth should be adequate (150 cm or more) so that the fish, which is a clumsy predator, can catch the pellets before they reach the bottom.

Breeding, in winter, generally involves injections of pituitary extract, so that handling of these fragile animals is reduced. This has the advantage of inducing spawning in 80–90 degree-days and provides fully mature ova which fertilize well and have embryos that have 80–90% survival rate. A female lays 3000 ova per kg of its body weight.

Forty degree-days after an intraperitoneal injection the male produces a large amount of milt with a large number of spermatozoa swimming in a viscous mucus that should be retained.

Incubation is conducted under the same conditions, using the same material as is employed for other salmonids except that the water should be clear and cold (maximum 5°C).

Growth begins best when there is a daily distribution of artificial food and plankton, as soon as the yolk sac is resorbed. The ratio of artificial food and plankton is altered till the ration contains only artificial elements after 5 months of raising, distributed at a rate of 1–2% of the weight of the fish.

Fry and reproducers are very sensitive to diseases affecting other salmonids and effective arrangements for prophylaxis should be ensured.

Table 29. Growth in a controlled and regulated density, and at 8–9°C (after LAURENT, 1982)

Age	Av. length (mm)	Av. wt (g)
0+	94	7.9
1+	164	47
2+	253	185
3+	409	808

2. BREEDING OF THE DANUBE SALMON (*Hucho hucho*)

The Danube salmon is a large salmonid (weighing as much as 50 kg), and it does not migrate. It is a popular fish for sport, and it is capable of controlling excessive populations of cyprinids. It is raised in Central Europe exclusively for purposes of restocking and is of some utility for high-altitude water bodies and large reservoirs in Western Europe.

The natural reproductive period is from mid-April to mid-May. Ovulation in females is synchronized by hormonal stimulation with two injections of pituitary extract of carp given at an interval of 12 h.

According to JATTEAU (1990), ovulation occurs after 150 h, at a temperature of 9°C. The percentage of fertilization is 95% and the survival rate till the independence of the fry is 80%. Sperm is obtained by abdominal massage of the males, which are first tranquillized in view of their large size. Subsequent operations are identical to those carried out on the trout.

The optimal temperature for incubation is between 10 and 12°C and the duration is 23 days at 11°C. The mortality is less than 10% provided that, during this phase, the eggs are not exposed to light. Hatching continues for 6 days.

The optimal temperature for growth is between 16 and 18°C. Weaning is ensured using live zooplankton with 6 meals per day. After 2–3 weeks the ration is supplemented with fish meat, a paste of spleen and liver and curdled milk. We also use artificial foods together with zooplankton. After weaning for 30 days the individual weight of a fry is 0.2 g and the provision of zooplankton in the ration is discontinued.

The distributed pellets are then 0.5–0.8 mm in size; the weight of a fry is 1.1 g. The fry weigh 1.5 g when pellet size is 0.8–1.5 mm. The problem of weaning has been overcome but growth in intensive fisheries has not yet been effectively controlled, which still leaves the raising of Danube salmon in an experimental stage.

3. BREEDING OF THE COMMON GRAYLING (*Thymallus thymallus*)

The common grayling is estimated highly for sport by fly fishermen. It is raised to produce fish for restocking purposes.

Reproducers in storage troughs are fed with pellets designed for trout with a vitamin supplement for 3 days every month (Maisse, 1986). They are highly sensitive to variations in temperature. A temperature drop below 5°C at the time of ovulation will defer it.

During spawning, females are kept together in circular basins of 4 sq m (50 fish/basin). Ova are extracted in the same way as for trout but under anaesthesia. Most ovulations are, however, partial, in which case there should be no further handling and a fresh attempt should be made 3 days later. A female usually lays 10,000 ova per kg of its body weight. The males do not release much sperm and we have to draw out the milt. The sperm may be preserved for 3 days at 2°C in an atmosphere of oxygen.

Artificial fertilization is identical, in this case, to what applies for the trout. The 232 diluent is used in view of the limited emission of sperm. Fertilized eggs increase to twice their original size once they are in water. They are incubated in a single layer with 40,000 eggs/sq m (1.5 l of fertilized eggs). Hatching occurs usually 200 degree-days after fertilization at an optimal temperature of 9°C (6°C $\leq T \leq$ 13°C).

The fry are fed semolina and carefully designed pellets.

4. BREEDING OF THE COREGONIDS

Breeding of coregonids, very similar to that of the pike, is also done mainly for restocking lakes where the different species, both planktonophagous (*Coregonus albula*) and benthophagous (*Coregonus lavaretus*), are required for commercial fishing on a large scale.

Coregonids spawn at the end of autumn and also somewhat earlier depending on the thermal gradients in lakes. They are caught with nets in spawning areas. The age of the reproducers is not less than 3 years. The adult *C. albula* weighs between 50 and 200 g and *C. lavaretus* between 1000 and 3000 g. In the latter species the female lays 10,000–19,000 eggs/kg of body weight or about 30,000/l, each egg measuring 3.1–3.7 mm in diameter. According to Schaeperclaus (1961), *C. albula* lays 2000–10,000 eggs per kg of its weight or 90,000–180,000/l depending on the diameter of the egg, which may be from 1.6 to 2.4 mm.

The reproductive period is a relatively short one (about 10 days); to ensure a successful artificial fertilization, the females must be fully mature and the number of equally mature males should be sufficient, which is often difficult at the end of the season. It is therefore wise to keep males in fish tanks as and when they are caught, as also incompletely mature females.

Artificial fertilization is carried out using the dry method as in the case of the pike. Incubation continues in Zoug bottles for 300–360 degree-days. After 160 degree-days, embryonated eggs are formed. According to Huet (1970), eggs should be incubated in cold water, not exceeding 5°C, so that the fry find an abundance of plankton in the natural medium. This would not be possible for precocious (early) fry resulting from a rapid incubation. Riedel (1974) indicated that a coregonid fry of 20 mm consumes 500 planktonic invertebrates every day, and when it is 30 mm in size it needs twice this amount.

The fry emerge in incubator bottles and, carried by the current, fall into a breeding tank. Resorption of the yolk sac is rapid. It is therefore recommended that they be introduced in the intended medium within 3–5 days after emergence. If we add an average loss of 25% during incubation to a loss of 90% of swimming fry in the receiving medium, we can see that raising should be continued with the provision of live plankton.

The reasons for the low survival rate are many: physical weakness of the fry in view of the harsh conditions in the medium, considerable predation by perch and pike, problems due to transportation, and, especially, temperature variations. The choice of sites of introduction at the limit of the littoral and deep zone, as mentioned by HUET (1970), is certainly important, as well as the care taken during transportation of the fry.

CHAMPIGNEULLE (1990) attempted to produce young ones with dry foods at different densities and at various temperatures. It would appear that during the 4–5 initial weeks of 10°C the raising of coregonid larvae may begin with densities higher than 400 fry/l and survival rate of at least 65%, their feeding being ensured with Tetra Az 30.

A higher temperature (14°C) ensures a much better rate of survival (85–95%) and growth (20–22 mm in 35 days). After this stage, fry raised in tanks reach a size of 30 mm at the end of 2 months with a mortality of less than 3%.

Provision of food and permanent lighting improve the survival rate (by 10%) and growth (59 mg as opposed to 34 mg). Finally, trials conducted with commercially available dry foods have been encouraging. We may now hope to progress from the production of growing fry (14–16 mm) to that of pre-summerlings (40–60 mm), which will probably be more useful for restocking purposes.

5 INTENSIVE FISH CULTURE

Fish culture is said to be "intensive" when, by controlling all the parameters of the breeding medium and the biocycle of the animal being raised, we can produce a maximum number of fish of a given size in a minimum amount of water, space, and time, at a minimum cost and on the basis of a plan initially worked out.

Salmon raising is a typical example of intensive fish culture.

Other works dealing in some detail with intensive trout culture that are part of the agroeconomic sector involving the production of animals for "food" will not be referred to in this chapter except to the extent of salmon rearing, in the strict sense of the term.

Intensive salmon breeding is useful because, apart from measures to protect and improve the habitat, it provides a water course with the largest number of young fish from a given number of eggs.

It is necessary in continental Europe because of the fragility of the existing stocks. More than sedentary fish, migratory salmonids undergo intense and diversified harsh conditions because of the extent of their migrations. The adverse effects resulting from human activity, for example, act at three levels:

—on the high seas, on beds of krill in the Davis Strait, the western coasts of Greenland and Norway, by deep-sea fishing;

—near European coasts and in estuaries in the migration front towards the spawning areas of their birth, by net fishing;

—in fresh waters as far upstream as the spawning areas, first by professional fishermen using nets and then by recreational rod fishing.

According to STODDARD, cited by HENON (1966), although in natural spawning conditions, 30,000 embryonated eggs result in a return of 5 adult salmon, raising 30,000 eggs in a fishery ensures a return of 800 adult fish: the return percentage is thereby greatly increased and enables us to achieve the ecological and piscicultural objective of protecting and rebuilding stocks of migratory salmonids in rivers.

Breeding salmon is more difficult than breeding the common trout but is based closely on methods that have proved successful for trout.

A. ARTIFICIAL REPRODUCTION OF THE TROUT

Artificial reproduction of the trout is of great interest for *in situ* operations on trout that cannot reproduce for reasons mentioned elsewhere. Its adoption is an extremely important factor in intensive rearing of salmonids.

1. SPAWNING

Under natural conditions spawning occurs during winter. It is dependent on the oxygen content in the water, which increases when the temperature decreases. During the first thermocline, at the beginning of autumn, and sometimes earlier, the fish leave their normal habitat and look for spawning areas in cool waters. The males begin to migrate and the first to do so are the youngest ones. During this movement the reproductive organs of the reproducers develop. The animals collect near beds of gravel, often in pairs, awaiting complete maturity. This occurs, depending on climatic conditions, in December and January.

Spawning begins when the reproductive organs are mature. Eggs and milt flow in the current and fertilization occurs. The eggs are lodged in spaces between pebbles where, with a brusque movement of its tail, the female covers them with gravel. It continues to lay until it has released all its eggs. It then allows itself to be carried by the current, together with the male, to a calm zone where it rebuilds its reproductive capacity.

Fertilization should be rapid because a spermatozoon has to enter the ovum through the micropyle and its very small orifice closes because of swelling after it has been in the water for about 4 minutes.

This is an important consideration in the *artificial fertilization process*. For this reason, in preference to the so-called "wet" method, which is based on natural conditions of reproduction subject to climatic factors, we adopt the "dry" method. In undiluted milt, spermatozoa retain their fertility for several days but in water for only 90 seconds.

The ova are expelled manually when the abdomen of the fish is pressed, from the front of the body towards the genital orifice. If the eggs are mature they squirt out under this pressure. The operation is repeated several times till all the eggs are expelled. This is done with two to four females.

The ova are collected in a very dry receptacle and are sprayed with the milt from a male. They are carefully mixed using a feather and left undisturbed for 20–30 minutes. Each egg is covered by a film of coelomic fluid and milt, which renders the spermatozoa more mobile, increases the amplitude of their movements, and prolongs their life. Fertilization takes place, and at the end of the period the eggs are washed in water several times and then placed in incubation trays or introduced in bulk in incubators.

After 4 or 5 days, we examine the females that were kept in storage troughs after spawning; we expel any eggs that may have remained in the genital tract and which, if hardened, could cause sterility in the fish. A female lays 1500–2000 ova per kg of body weight. They are 4–5 mm in diameter and have an orange or amber tint. A male is capable of fertilization several times during the course of a season. Some techniques developed by BILLARD (1975) enable preservation of the sperm of selected fish in a medium with a composition similar to the seminal liquid, which is economical because of the very low dilution of an order of 10^{-3}.

2. INCUBATION

The incubation period is 380–460 degree-days for fario trout eggs and 300–340 degree-days for those of the rainbow trout. The eggs are extremely sensitive to

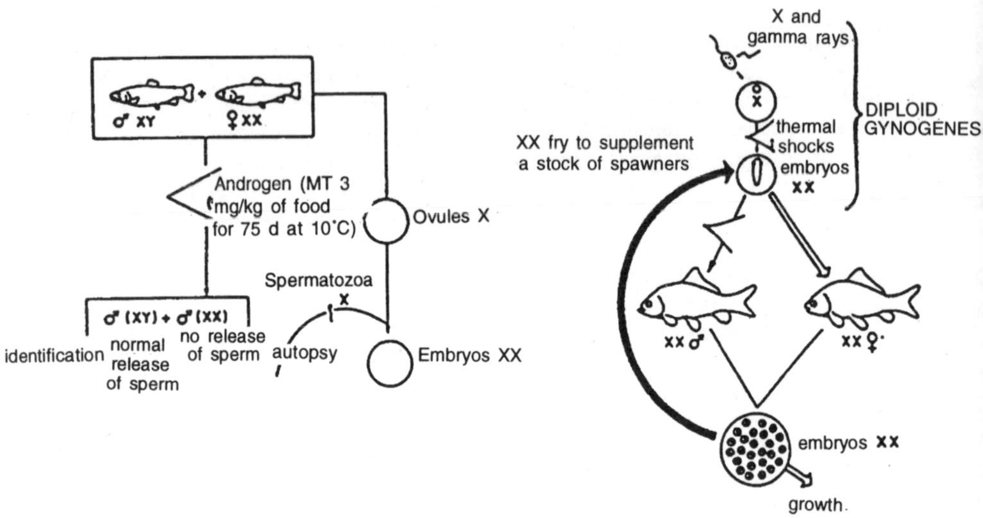

Fig. 196. A monosex female line obtained in salmonids (after KAUSHIK and CHEVASSUS, 1988)

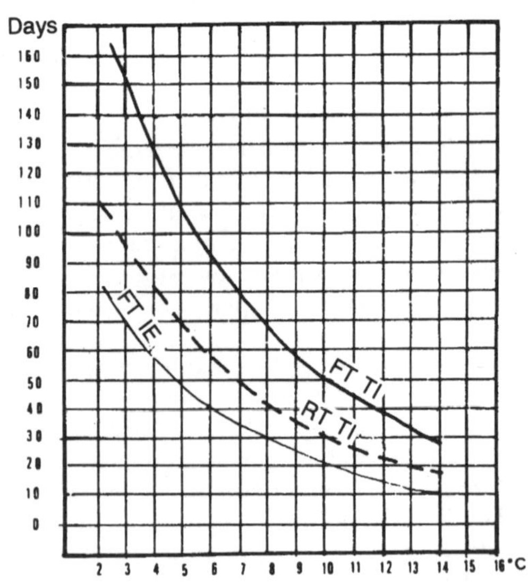

Fig. 197. Duration of incubation depending on the average temperature of the water. TI = total incubation, IE = incubation till the embryonated stage, RT = rainbow trout, FT = fario trout

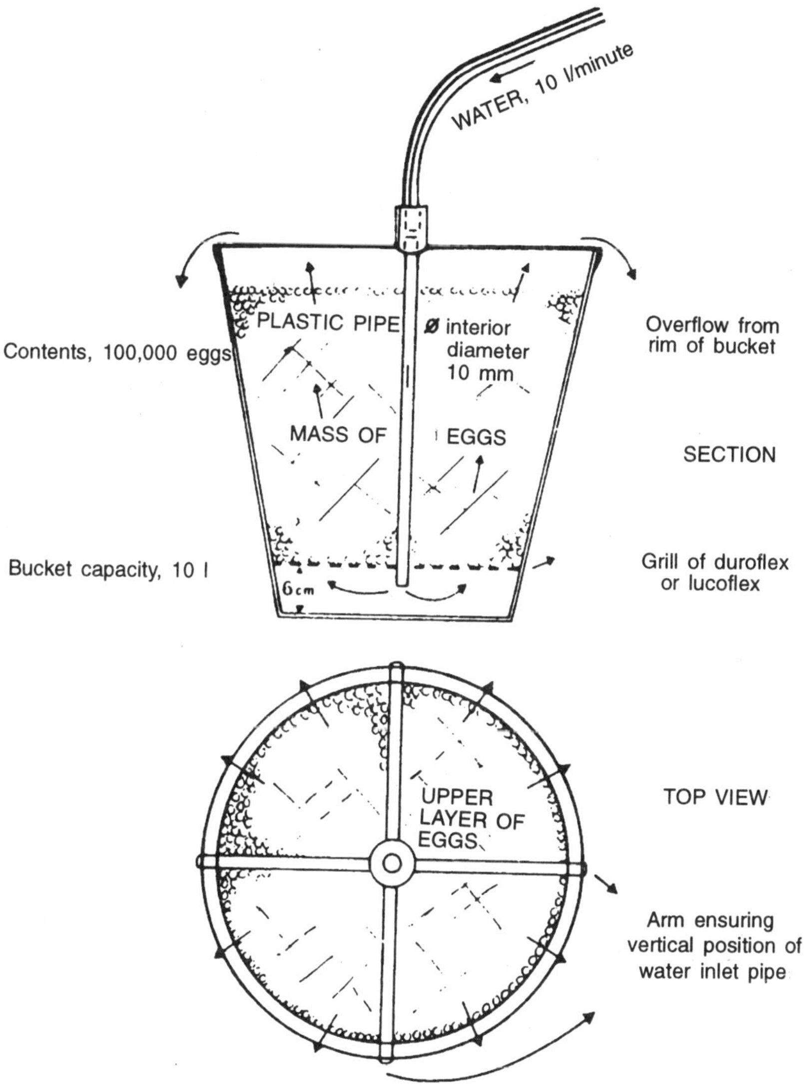

Fig. 198. Incubation in a domestic plastic bucket

shock and rough handling till the stage of embryonation (180–220 degree-days for fario trout and 140–160 degree-days for the rainbow trout). During this second phase, the eggs may be handled, sorted, and transported provided they are kept in a humid atmosphere. When hatching appears to be about to occur, based on a calculation of the degree-days, the eggs are placed in a single layer on trays, if they have been incubated earlier in containers. This is necessary so that the young can emerge easily from the eggs.

During the first phase the eggs do not need much dissolved oxygen. The requirement arises with the appearance of embryonated eggs, when a four-fold flow is essential.

We calculate as follows:

– for 1000 eggs, a flow of 0.5 l/minute.

– for 1000 fry and troutlets, as many litres per minute as the months of age, till the age of 12 months.

– for trout over 12 months old, as many litres per minute as the weight (in kg) of the troutlets being raised.

The temperature for breeding is between 5 and 15°C for the fario trout, and 5 and 18°C for the rainbow trout. Some technical expedients enable us to vary the basic data considerably (e.g., mechanical stirring, recycling).

In fish culture for purposes of restocking, we keep 50,000 eggs/m^2 of water surface, 10,000 month-old fry, 3000 2-month-old fry, and 1500 fry of 3 to 4 months. Some conditions in the medium, as well as certain methods, enable us to increase the average numbers in industrial fisheries by a factor of three or even four (e.g., recirculation of the water, superpositioning of trays, movable troughs in a cascade arrangement).

The products are transported to breeding annexes or to their final destination:

– at the stage of embryonated eggs (eyed ova),

– when fry are 3–4 months old.

3. SUBSEQUENT PHASES IN BREEDING

Subsequent phases in intensive breeding, till we obtain autumn troutlets or troutlets for restocking purposes of a size that can be legally caught, ordinarily continue in fisheries with an annual or perennial cycle when reproducers are raised in them.

Table 30. Relationship between the daily ration, the weight of trout, and water temperature (after SCHAEPERCLAUS)

Temp. (°C)	Wt of the ration (% fish wt)
5	2
7–10	3–5
10–15	5–7
15–18	7–8

Table 31. Relationship over a year between the weight of trout and the average monthly temperatures

March	1%	August	18%
April	4%	September	17%
May	7%	October	14%
June	13%	November	10%
July	16%		

Feeding is often totally suspended in winter.

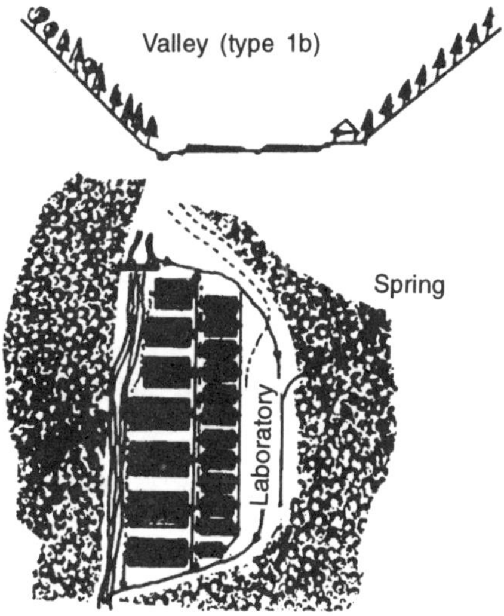

Fig. 199. Layout of a fishery in a valley of type 1b

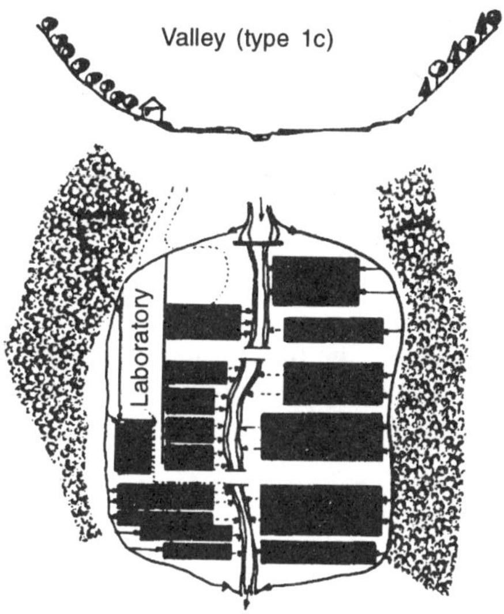

Fig. 200. Layout of a fishery in a valley of type 1c

Fig. 201. Trout eggs placed on trays in fish breeding troughs (after J. Arrignon)

B. REPRODUCTIVE SALMON

The availability of mature reproducers at the right time is limited for three main reasons:

– Reproducers are caught usually during their upstream movement towards spawning areas at the beginning of spring in the case of large salmon and at the beginning of summer in the case of grilse and sea trout, but in both cases much before the spawning period. It is therefore necessary to keep them till sexual maturity, which involves a risk of disease.

–Catching them in spawning areas may be considered when these areas are overvisited and few in number but the use of nets or electricity often results in injuries to the fish, or in females that have already laid their eggs.

–Raising salmon and sea trout in fresh water till an adult age is difficult: the eggs obtained are of poor quality and result in a small percentage of sickly fry.

1. CAPTURE OF PROGENITORS

Progenitors are caught, preferably, in traps set at places where fish have to pass in sites near spawning areas so that mature salmon are caught.

A trap must be checked sometimes every 2 hours, so that the animals do not become excited or injure themselves. They are transported in black plastic bags or

Fig. 202a. Trout fry released in troughs (after J. ARRIGNON)

Fig. 202b. Trout fry released in a trough with habitat (after J. ARRIGNON)

transportation tanks with perfectly smooth walls so that there is no damage to their integument.

If there are injuries, the fish on arrival at the station are given a bath of antibiotics.

They are kept in enclosures such as deep, shady pools. The surface is less important than their depth, the optimum being from 1.20 to 1.50 m. A pool of 9 × 3 × 1.50 m, with a water inlet of 60 l/second, may contain 180 kg of reproducers (40 fish of 4500 g in 40 m^3). The water supply should be from the bottom because supply from a higher level may cause the salmon to leap.

Males and females are kept together till the first female is mature, otherwise the maturity of both sexes will be affected and males will attempt to leap from one basin to another. In any case, it is necessary to cover the enclosure. Since one male can ensure four fertilizations, at weekly intervals, it is unnecessary to have more than one male for two females.

At the beginning of the reproductive period it is recommended that the pool be divided in the following manner:

— upstream: mature and immature males

— downstream: mature and immature females

2: RAISING ADULT FISH IN THE SEA

Raising adults in the sea, which is essentially done to produce salmon for consumption rapidly, in large numbers, and at low cost, also enables us, after selection, to produce progenitors, which are essential for intensive salmon breeding.

The techniques for raising in sea cages also enable us to stock progenitors caught early in the season. Transfer to a marine environment inhibits the development of certain diseases that spread in fresh water; in this way we stock healthy, or apparently healthy, fish till the reproductive period.

Table 32. Methods and procedures for incubating salmonid eggs

Eggs placed in layers	
1) On perforated trays in single layer	– Californian incubator
	– Portable troughs
2) On perforated trays in one or several layers	– Trays placed in troughs for fry
	– Incubation chests with vertical flow
Eggs placed in bulk	
1) In a compartment	– In troughs for fry with a forced horizontal current
	– In troughs for fry with a forced ascending current
2) In a polyethylene container	– In buckets with an ascending current
	– In containers with an ascending current
3) At the embryonated egg stage	– In Vibert incubator boxes
	– In floating incubator cradles

Fig. 203. Water inlet. Double feed: upper pipe with river water, lower pipe with water from a spring (after J. ARRIGNON).

Fig. 204. Combined water outlet with adjustable overflow and safety frontal release

C. FERTILIZATION AND INCUBATION

The procedure for artificial incubation of salmon is identical to that of the trout except for some additional precautions that need to be taken. These are described in the following paragraphs.

Eggs and sperm are collected in a bowl, mixed with a clean feather for 30 seconds, and then covered and left undisturbed for 10 minutes before being mixed again and then washed. If some eggs are covered with blood it is better to remove rather than wash them.

After they have been washed five or six times in succession using clean water, the eggs are left undisturbed in clean water for 30 minutes, during which period their membranes harden. We can then estimate the number by volumetry rather than by gravimetry.

The eggs are placed on trays in vertical batteries or in horizontal breeding troughs; 3 hours after fertilization, they become fragile. Embryonated eggs appear after 200–250 degree-days of incubation: at this stage the eggs are robust and transportable.They are then washed and shaken up in a basin of water, which causes dead eggs to whiten and enables their elimination. It is at this stage that preventive treatments are carried out.

A female grilse lays approximately 3500–5500 ovules; a large female salmon of 5 kg lays 7000–8000. We associate the number of eggs with the size of a fish, rather than its weight, because it remains for a fairly long time in a river without feeding.

Fig. 205. Outdoor layout of a fishery (Rutki, Poland, after J. ARRIGNON)

The water flow needed at this stage is 4.5–5 l/minute. This water should not contain any suspended matter. The temperature can be raised to 10°C when embryonated eggs appear: hatching will then be homogeneous and faster, the mortality will be lower, and we will have fry earlier.

D. HATCHING AND REARING OF FRY

Hatching is observed 450 degree-days after the beginning of incubation. Young fry with yolk sacs must be well nourished and undisturbed.

The colder the water, the higher the survival rate of the fry, as their requirements and activity are reduced. It should be ensured that the pointed end of the yolk sac is not caught in the bottom grills and the animals have some place for shelter, bearing in mind that gravel beds are difficult to clean.

When the yolk sac is almost resorbed, the fry swim at a middle depth looking for food; at this stage the darkness in the hatchery can be progressively eliminated.

The fry are transferred to circular or square tanks of 3–4 m^2 with a water supply of 5 l/minute/1000 fry occupying a surface of 1000 cm^2. The tanks are partly covered and the fry should not be disturbed by external interventions.

Horizontal troughs may continue to be used, depending upon the aforementioned characteristics, by modifying the water inlet and outlet, which should be from the bottom. The zone of influence of the automatic feeder should be in the shade in order to encourage the fry to collect around it.

Fig. 206. Indoor layout of a fishery (Le Paraclet, France, after J. ARRIGNON)

In both these cases, the numbers are reduced after 6 weeks to ensure a density of 600 fry/sq m.

Young migrators are more difficult to feed than young trout. They have some difficulty in swallowing the automatically distributed pellets and are suspicious of static particles that have fallen to the bottom. Pellets should therefore be distributed over a fairly wide space and remain in movement in the current and the space occupied by the fry; if they are caught immediately they are more easily swallowed. Distribution of a very small quantity on a continuous basis is recommended. If that is not possible, food should be provided frequently (10–12 times), preferably at the beginning and end of the afternoon.

During the first week, the feed should be composed of finely minced liver and spleen. A week later this can be supplemented with what we call first-age pellets

Fig. 207. A fishery: aeration by using small obstacles (Hellbourg, Reunion Island, after J. Arrignon)

Fig. 208. A fishery: aeration by projection on a diffusion plate (Rutki, Poland, after J. Arrignon)

Fig. 209. A fishery: outdoor basin with water, pipe operating to ensure aeration of the water by radial dispersion (Slupsk, Poland, after J. ARRIGNON)

in a ratio of 20%, which is increased every week to 40, 60, 80 and 100%. Depending on the composition of the pellets it may sometimes be necessary to continue providing liver to prevent a biotin deficiency. Liver from dead animals should not be used because there is a risk of the young salmon ingesting antibiotics, which are often used to treat sick cattle: this may make it difficult, if not impossible, later to treat fry for diseases at an early stage.

E. RAISING OF SUMMERLINGS

The number of fry is reduced in larger basins where they can adopt a modified territoriality with 5–10 cm between them: on this occasion they are sorted. For the early ones this is done in June and for the later ones in August.

We reduce the numbers to 250/sq m or even 150/sq m in a round or square basin with a depth of 0.30 m. At the end stage, the water supply is increased to 40 l/second/25,000 smolts.

The food supply is in the form of what we call second-age pellets, distributed preferably through automatic feeders with larger amounts at dawn and dusk. In October the young ones have a lesser appetite but feeding is not stopped; between January and the beginning of March a 10% increase in length is possible. It increases in the month prior to the smolt stage.

Fig. 210. A fishery: outdoor basin drained out, bottom and walls with flagstones, and a central drain starting from an inlet pipe (Slupsk, Poland, after J. Arrignon)

Fig. 211. Storage pool for salmon spawners before spawning. Salmon fishery at Cong (Ireland).

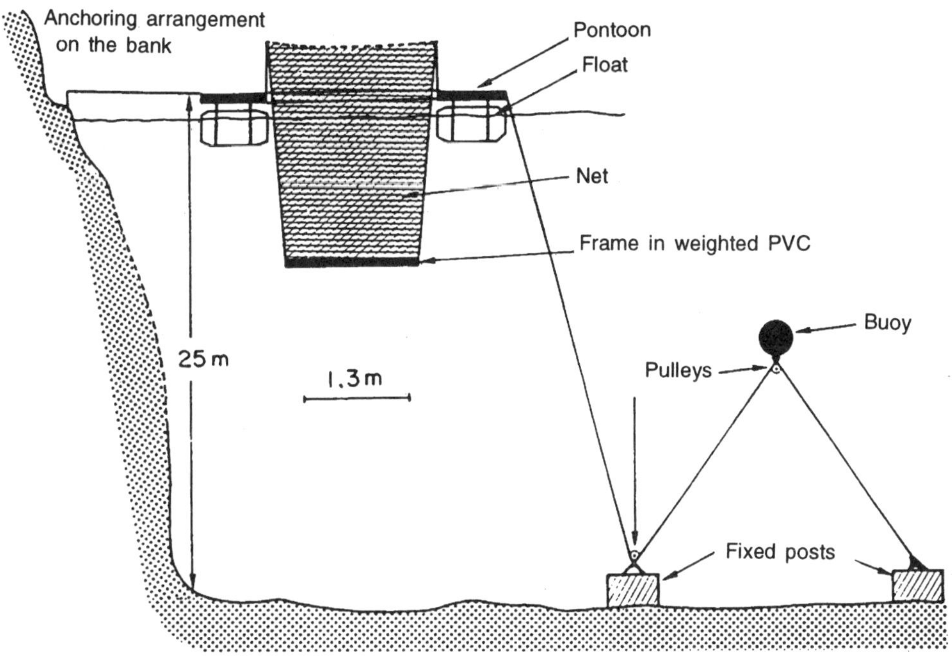

Fig. 212. Anchoring arrangement of the structures for raising in cages (section)

F. GROWTH AND MORTALITY

Piggins (1975) estimated the average survival rate as follows:

from fertilization to the embryonated stage 98%
from the embryonated stage to hatching 97%
from hatching to swimming fry 75%
from swimming fry to summerling 9%
from summerling to young year-old grilse 90%
from young year-old to 2-year-old smolt 85-95%
In other words, the survival rate is 50% of those of the first year.

In normal temperature conditions, it is possible to produce 30% of smolts, 15–16 months old.

A smolt of 15–16 months (1 year +) measures on an average 14.5 cm and weighs 35 g.

A smolt of 27–28 months (2 years +) is usually 18 cm long and weighs 60 g.

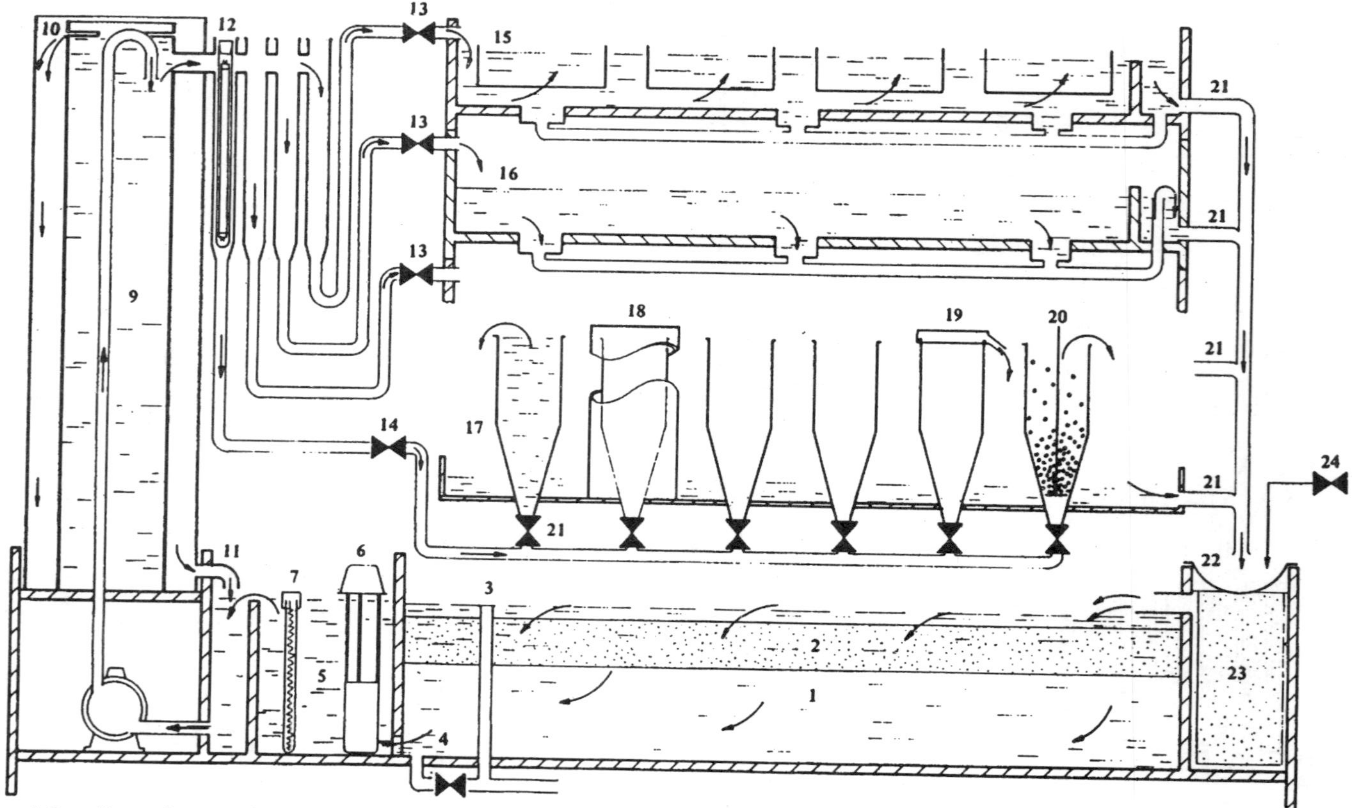

1 Recycling and reserve basin. 2 Bacterial bed. 3 General overflow. 4 Water outlet. 5 Thermal regulation tank. 6 Refrigeration pipe. 7 Heating resistance. 8 Circulation pump. 9 Hydraulic column. 10 Overflow release. 11 Overflow outlet. 12 Feeder with pipes sterilized by UV rays. 13 Inlet tap for incubation chambers. 14 Inlet tap for the row of Zoug bottles. 15 Incubation chamber with incubator cradles (the water circulates from the bottom to the top of the trays). 16 Incubation chamber transformed to a trough for fry (here the water circulates from the top to the bottom through strainers before its evacuation). 17 Row of Zoug bottles. 18 Zoug bottle with a transparent or opaque protective sheath of PVC. 19 Zoug bottle with an overflow spout. 20 Zoug bottle with a movable grill. 21 Outlet for incubation chambers and the row of Zoug bottles. 22 Prefilter grill. 23 Polyethylene foam of the prefilter. 24 Regulator tap (slow and continuous replenishment of water).

Fig. 213. Autonomous module of an integrated hatchery (courtesy *Pisciculture Française*, 1979)

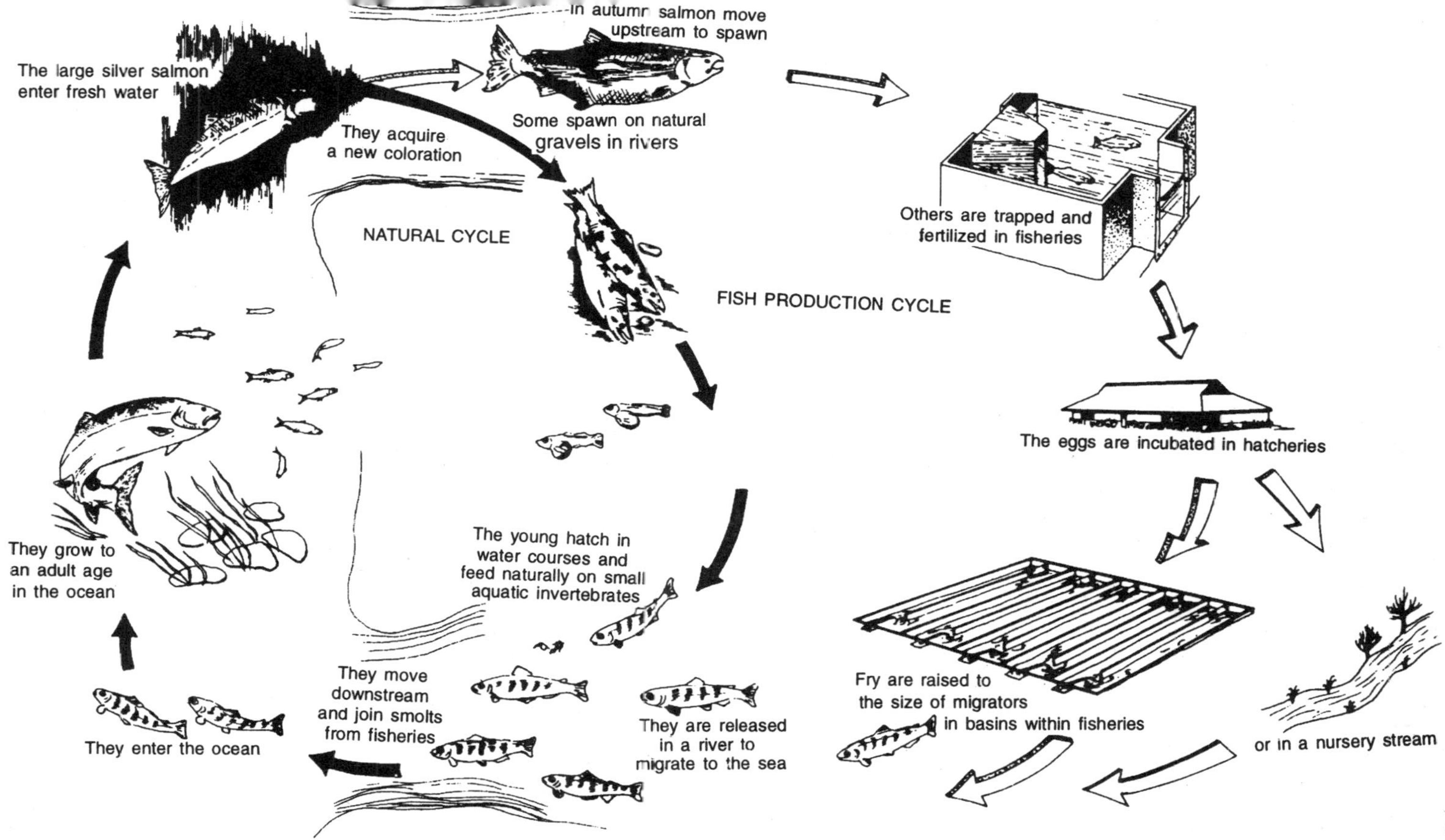

Fig. 214. Natural and artificial cycles of the salmon

G. INTRODUCTION OF SALMON IN THE NATURAL MEDIUM

At the embryonated egg stage, the use of Vibert boxes is recommended.

At the summerling stage, during transportation in plastic bags, the fry should not be exposed directly to sunlight. The temperatures in the bag and the receiving medium should be brought to the same level and mixed progressively. An initial removal of indigenous species in the receiving medium is essential. The optimal density in streams or sectors of rivers is 5-10 fry/m^2. Best results are obtained in summer after initial raising in a fishery.

At the smolt stage, the physiological transformation may extend over 6 weeks, even if the conditions of temperature, the photoperiod, and nutrition are identical. At this stage, young salmon are extremely fragile and they should therefore be released in a basin without a fall at the water inlet, at a rate of 10,000 smolts/25 m^2. They will continue to be fed in this basin, but not so abundantly, so that they become more active.

If they are to be introduced directly in a river, this should be done as far upstream as possible because of the homing instinct. Even though predators can cause damage, this appears to be the best solution.

The number of salmon that originate from smolts in fisheries and are recaptured is 1.4–4.4% in Ireland, 8–10% in Iceland (littoral fisheries), and 25% in Sweden.

Sea ranching in Western Europe is not considered economical and viable because of the limited number of those that return, as a result of a poor survival rate and intensive legal and illegal coastal fishing.

6 BREEDING OF OTHER FISHES

A. RAISING THE CATFISH EUROPEAN WELS (*Silurus glanis*)

Although the *Silurus* is raised, especially in Eastern Europe and particularly in Poland (WICZIEWOLSKI, 1989, personal communication), to restock large rivers, in the West, attempts to raise it have been undertaken exclusively for commercial production in ponds.

Control of its breeding requires a good knowledge of the physical characteristics of fertilization, which is still inadequate, and has led to practices similar to those adopted for the pike and the carp.

Artificial breeding usually involves killing males since massaging their abdominal walls provides a very limited emission of sperm. Used on 3- or 4-year-old fish, the practice is an expensive one as the potential ability of the progenitors could extend over 5–7 years. Inducing the production of sperm by pituitary extracts has been successful only to a limited extent: 1 ml of sperm per kg of body weight (HOLLENBECQ *et al.*, 1988).

The sperm, somewhat poor in spermatozoa, must be carefully managed. A diluent must be used to optimize its fertilization potential. The period of contact with ova emitted by the females, in the presence of a diluent, should not be more than 15 minutes, in which case the fertilization rate is between 50 and 90%.

The eggs are separated using alkalase and incubated in Zoug bottles. Fifty hours after fertilization, organogenesis is at a normal stage and the embryos begin to move (PIONNIER and HEYMANN, 1987). The larvae are put in hatching trays used for incubating trout and pike eggs, the water temperature being maintained between 23 and 25°C. From the second day onwards the larvae can swim and, being lucifugous, move to shaded zones.

According to HEYMANN (in ARRIGNON *et al.*, 1990b), 3 days after hatching the fry are released in troughs (250 × 40 × 15 cm) and fed from a feeder belt. The size of the dry pellets provided is 200–700 μ from the 6th to the 8th day and 700–1750 μ from the 18th to the 26th day, with a preventive treatment of 100 ppm formalin every day. At the end of this stage the survival rate is 60%.

Fry are transferred to larger basins as soon as they weigh 2 g. They are then fed with a semolina of 1.75–2 mm and, after this, with pellets of 2, 3, and finally 4.5 mm. An average individual weight of 1 kg is reached at the end of 10 months at a density of 130 kg/m^3.

PROTEAU and THOLLOT (1988) noted considerable variations in weight (from 85 to 1580 g) after 6 months of raising, due probably to the fact that the reproducers were

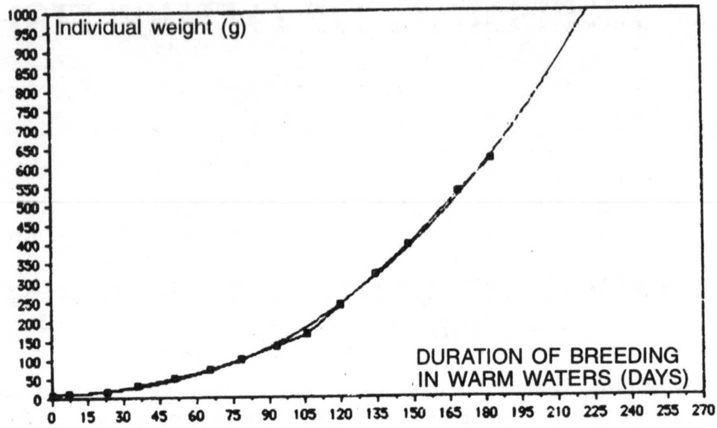

Fig. 215. Average growth of catfishes (after PROTEAU and THOLLOT, 1988)

the progeny of natural unselected populations. The feed conversion rate was of the order of 1.6 and can be improved upon.

A hardy animal, the *Silurus* can be effectively raised in warm waters because the best yield is at a temperature of 25.5°C. It is useful for stocking large freshwater bodies open to fishing for "large" catches.

B. RAISING THE STURGEON (*Acipenser sturio*)

The gradual disappearance of the Atlantic sturgeon, *Acipenser sturio*, from European coasts led to attempts to raise the species with a view to restocking, which met with some initial success. In fact, the stress is now on better management of existing stocks.

Two Siberian freshwater species have been selected for raising: *A. baeri* in France and *A. transmontanus* in Italy, together with a few hybrids, including the "bester" (*A. ruthenus* × *Huso huso*), for commercial production of fish meat and caviar.

The sturgeon does not release its gametes in captivity and has to receive a hormonal injection. We use a pituitary extract of carp, which has proved effective. The best fertilization percentages are obtained 6–16 hours after ovulation begins. According to WILLIOT *et al.* (1989), the percentage of ovulation, in view of the available females, is fairly low (15% on the average). The duration of incubation between fertilization and the first hatchings depends on the temperature.

Raised at 17°C, the larvae are provided artificial feed based on liver and yeast during their first month and, after that, for 3 weeks they are given a commercial feed used for trout fry. The survival rate is approximately 70% and the average weight is 380 mg. The conversion rate is 2 and the specific growth rate is 10% during the first period. During the second period the survival rate is 99%, the conversion rate is 1.2, and the final average weight is 1.5 g (CHARLON and BERGOT, 1989).

The young (50–100 g) are provided the feed usually given to trout at a scale of 1.5% of body weight/day and at a temperature of 17°C. The food pellets given are 1.5 mm in size for 10 to 50 g body weight, 2 mm for 50 to 100 g, 3.2 mm for 100 to 300 g, and 4.5 mm after this, by continuous automatic distribution till 15 g and four times a day after that. The conversion rate increases from 1.6 at a weight of 500 g to 2.5 at a weight of 2000 g with the temperature varying between 14 and 25°C (WILLIOT *et al.*, 1988). A weight of 2 kg is reached at 2 years and the number introduced is of a weight of 20 kg/m^2 (WILLIOT, 1987).

C. RAISING THE EEL (*Anguilla anguilla*)

The reduction in the stock of eels in all the water courses of Western Europe appears to be due to overfishing of its fry, the elver, when it arrives at the coasts and the mouths of Atlantic water courses.

Rules regarding fishing of the species are neither conceived nor followed to ensure a balanced management of the resources. Stop-gap measures for correcting this disturbing situation have been attempted by restocking. Presently, this restocking is carried out only by taking elvers from estuaries to protected zones that were traditionally eel zones.

There are presently no fisheries that produce eels for restocking purposes, though some conduct zootechnical experiments that are limited by a lack of knowledge of certain physiological mechanisms of the species.

The Japanese experience (BILLARD, 1991) is marginal regarding the *A. anguilla*, which is more difficult to raise than the Japanese eel, the *A. japonica*, but it has benefited from the know-how acquired in the rearing of the latter species (production is 40,000 tonnes/year).

Elvers purchased in Europe are raised in small ponds in greenhouses of 10–50 m^2 with 40–70 cm of water at a density of 150–500 g/m^2. They are fed with *Tubifex*.

They grow in an earthern pond. The pond area varies from 60 to 160 m^2, with 60–90 cm depth. The water supply (by pumping) is 25–150 l/minute/pond and the water change varies from 4 to 44 hours. The water is brackish (salinity 12–17 g/l). It is aerated so as to be saturated to the extent of 60–80% with oxygen in a temperature range of 11–27°C.

Stocking is done in July with eels of 30–100 g and varies from 8 to 29/m^2. The feed ration is provided in the form of pellets. The percentage of food is, depending on the size, between 0.48 and 0.81 with a transformation coefficient of 1.02 to 2.03. The eels are collected after 1 year. The yield is 1 kg of body weight in 20–50 cu m of water and the average individual weight of an eel is 140–150 g.

The main problem in the production of the European eel is its inability to withstand the high temperatures used for the Japanese eel in intensive breeding (28–32°C).

D. TROPICAL FISH CULTURE

Tropical fish culture is widespread, productive, and often highly elaborate (especially in Asia). Even though it is not dealt with in the present work it needs to be mentioned for two reasons (ARRIGNON, 1986).

Fig. 216. Feeding elvers with a paste (J. ARRIGNON)

1. The most important, raising of tilapia, has already been adopted for the improvement of several European rivers and water bodies into which warmed water from the cooling circuits of thermal and nuclear power plants is discharged.

2. Tropical fish are now raised in various fisheries and even in combined fisheries, resulting in different approaches to freshwater fishery improvements.

1. TILAPIA CULTURE

The tilapia, the foundation of African aquaculture, is now, with several species endemic in Africa, the basis of freshwater fisheries in the intertropical belt.

Of 3300 listed references, ten species play a primordial role in aquaculture. Six of these practise buccal incubation and are microphytophagous and detritivorous under natural conditions. They are now known by the generic name of *Oreochromis* (earlier called *Sarotherodon*). Four species, of the genus *Tilapia*, do not practise buccal incubation, spawn on substrates, and are rather macrophytophagous. All of them are hardy animals and some can live and reproduce in sea water (*O. mossambicus* and *O. niloticus*) or can be raised in brackish water (*T. heudelotii*). The most useful species, *O. niloticus*, microphagous and omnivorous, often macrophytophagous, is raised in many parts of the world.

Methods of Raising

The prolificity of tilapias has resulted in overpopulation of small individuals in earlier raisings, and several methods have been developed and adopted to improve their production.

a) Mixed or mixed-age-class method

This method is based on the use of different trophic levels in a pond by simultaneous raising of tilapias of all sizes and different species: macrophytophagous, microphytophagous, and omnivorous. In principle, the pond is used to the maximum extent of its productivity.

In practice, there are serious difficulties, especially in the equatorial zone, where the reproductive frequency of tilapias is the highest. On draining the pond we find a large number of small fish below marketable size and a mixture of fry and small adults that eliminates any possibility of selection for restocking purposes.

b) Same-age or separate-age-class method

Fry of the same age are introduced in a pond. They are retained till their first reproductive period. When collecting them, we select adult fish for consumption and put back the fry for a new phase of growth.

All conditions being otherwise equal, the production is less than in the previous method but the percentage of marketable fish (70–100 g) is higher.

c) Method of control by a predatory fish

We can improve the growth rate of the fish by raising tilapias together with a predator. *Hemichromis fasciatus* in a ratio of 1 fish per 12 tilapias (*O. niloticus*) provides good results. *Lates niloticus* is also used, but mainly *Clarias lazera*, which is considered a good fish for consumption.

d) Raising the Monosex Tilapia

In this method fry are selected as soon as we are able to recognize the sexes (20 g). We separate males from females, which have a slower growth rate.

The risks of error in selection depend on the number of fish to be sexed. In practice, the effect of females that may be found among the males (or inversely) is reduced by the introduction of predatory fish, which eliminate any later fry.

e) Raising hybrid tilapias

Hybridization has been attempted to improve the commercial yield in production: *O. hornorium zanzibaricus* (male) crossed with *O. niloticus* (female) provides a progeny of 100% male hybrids. The same applies to *O. mossambicus* (female) crossed with

O. hornorum (male). The male hybrids, in both cases, are fertile, which, in case of a chance intrusion of several females, may create the same problem as mentioned in section 1.4, with the same remedy.

f) Raising of red tilapias ("Rouges")

Crossing *O. niloticus* and *O. mossambicus* results in red hybrids because of albinism. The colour and rapid growth have some attractions in local markets as well as for aquaria. This production is at an experimental stage in Reunion Island.

The most commonly adopted methods in Africa are the methods described in 1.1 and 1.5 for family fisheries, 1.4 for artisanal fisheries, and 1.4, 1.5, and possibly 1.6 for industrial fisheries.

g) Raising tilapias in cages

Cages are the cheapest raising enclosures for lake dams that are fairly calm. Of variable dimensions and adapted to the medium, depending on the depth, the location, and the need to move the units, they are of different volumes depending on the growth stages of the fish (from 20 to 100 m^3).

In cages we raise mainly *O. niloticus* with 125 fish of 20–30 g per cu m, which in 5 months provide a yield of 25–30 kg/m^3, with a weight of 250 g each, and a transformation index of 2.5.

Apart from an infrastructure for raising them in cages we need a regular and large supply of young fry from hatcheries and nurseries attached to the fishery, or from independent units that provide fry to several fisheries, or by fishing organized in time and space to capture the fry needed for the fishery.

The tilapias are provided regularly with fresh and well-balanced artificial feed, costing less than 40% of the overall costs of the fishery. Locally available components should therefore be found for the feed.

2. RAISING CATFISH (*Clarias*)

The *Clarias* offer many advantages, including an extremely varied food regime: detrivorous, zooplanktonophagous, and carnivorous. They effectively and sometimes directly transform fertilizers introduced into the pond and also accept feed pellets.

Their growth is rapid (22–32 cm in a year) and is related to the temperature. Some of these fish can withstand variations and low temperatures as well as a pronounced hypoxia, since they are able in times of distress to use atmospheric oxygen.

Reproduction of the species is easy and rearing is carried out in ponds and basins either with pure populations or in combination with other fish that are part of the trophic level, or as predators for control in tilapia fisheries.

3. ASSOCIATED PRODUCTION

3.1 Rice Field Fish Culture

Fish are introduced in flooded rice fields modified by lateral channels and some sheltering pools, and a water inlet and outlet through which fish cannot pass. The fish, common carp and tilapias, introduced at weights of 20–40 g, are collected at the end of the rice cycle at a weight of 200 g each or later, if the flooded period of the site can be extended.

The yields vary from 300 to 650 kg/ha/year depending on the number of cropping cycles. The favourable effect on the rice yield results in a 5–15% increase in the harvest.

3.2 Association of Pigs and Fish

A piggery is installed at the side of a pond on a sloping bank above the pond in a pen. We usually keep one piglet, 25 young carp of 8–10 g, and 200 tilapias (*O. niloticus*) of 4–5 g per 100 sq m of water surface.

Depending on the altitude and latitude it is possible to have two culture cycles per year with an average yield of 8000 kg/ha/year of pigs on hoof (70 kg) and 8000 kg/ha/year of marketable fish.

3.3 Association of Ducks and Fish

There are two types of installations: at the side of a pond on a dyke, or above the pond in a pen, the latter being cheaper and more judicious.

Fig. 217. Combined raising of pigs and fish; the piggery is above the pond to be fertilized (photo: CHR. NUGENT)

The numbers usually kept are 10–25 three-month-old ducklings, 200 tilapias (*O. niloticus*) or 200 catfish (*C. lazera*) of 4–5 g, and 25 young carp of 8–10 g per 100 m^2 of water surface. We may also include *Heterotis niloticus* at a scale of 25–50 fry/100 m^2 as well as **malacophagous** fish (25 fry/100 m^2) to make the best use of the tropic zones.

It is possible to have three harvests a year if the ducks reach the marketable weight of 1.5 kg in 4 months. The average yield is between 4000 and 6000 kg of ducks/ha/year and 4000 and 4500 kg of fish/ha/year.

We may raise geese with fish under the same technical conditions.

3.4 Association of Hens and Fish

The hens are kept in a pen above the pond. The droppings fall into the water through a grilled floor. The hens, unlike the ducks, have no access to the pond.

The number and types of fish are identical to those mentioned in the preceding paragraphs. In the case of hens we select the most profitable subspecies depending on whether we wish to produce chicken for the table or eggs. We usually keep 10–30 hens/100 sq m. After 4 or 5 months we would have collected about 3500 kg fish/ha and 100,000–125,000 eggs or 2500 kg of chicken. It is possible to have three harvests every year.

Combined and integrated culture in rural development offer a formula for the future with a useful agricultural diversification and economical and judicious hydraulic management: storage of atmospheric water, fish culture in cages, fish culture in rice fields, combined culture in ponds, family fisheries, and use of fishery effluents as fertilizers in market gardening (ARRIGNON, 1986).

7 HEALTH PROBLEMS

The enemies of fish range from virus to fisherman through mosses and fungi, parasitic worms and crustaceans, amphibians and reptiles, birds, and mammals, some attacking spawn and fry, some attacking adults, and others all age groups of fish.

Concentration of fish in a restricted space encourages diseases and predators. Diseases are, however, more to be feared than predation because of the uncertainty about their causes, their effects, and their forms.

Health problems are due to the complexity of three types of factors relative to the medium, the pathogen, and the host under natural conditions.

De Kinkelin, Gerard and Tuffery (1973) have correctly stated that though fish diseases are often fatal, all deaths are not attributable to diseases and it is necessary in an abnormal situation, which is easily recognized, to arrange for a diagnosis of the causes, the effects of which are not clearly indicated.

De Kinkelin *et al.* (1985) explained that a state of disease is revealed by the appearance of abnormalities in behaviour, that is symptoms, and/or in body integrity, such as lesions, that cause a disturbance in the general condition and sometimes death of affected fish. These morbid manifestations are due to physical, chemical, or biological causes acting separately or together. They are activated naturally or induced by man.

A. INVESTIGATION OF CAUSES

1. EXAMINATION OF DISEASED FISH

Examination of diseased fish is based on a series of operations: inquiry, samples of water and fish, obtaining information using a standard method, despatch of fish to a veterinary laboratory, and surveillance of the affected medium (natural medium or a fishery).

Examination of a diseased fish, alive if possible, is carried out by comparison with a normal one. We note any differences in behaviour: locomotion, feeding, respiration. We also note the external appearance, lesions above, below, and on the skin, the existence of parasites, and examine the branchiae (gills).

For an internal examination we open the abdominal cavity and note what appears to be unusual (haemorrhages, parasites); we also examine the contents of the alimentary canal.

Table 33. Diagnosis of the aquatic medium, synthetic presentation of symptoms, measures and analysis (after De Kinkelin *et al.*, 1985) (courtesy INRA)

Measures and analysis \ Symptoms	Sudden death (3)	Nocturnal death (3)	Diurnal death (3)	Insidious and asymptomatic deaths (3)	Disappearance of species (4)	Age pyramid (4)	Poor yield, slow growth (3)	Sterility (3)	Sudden loss of appetite (3)	Respiratory diseases (3)	Nephrocalcinosis (5)	Aeromonosis (3)	Myxobacteriosis (3)	Viruses (5)	Oedema of the umbilical sac (5)	Coagulation of the yolk sac (5)	Dead eggs (5)
Flow (1)	•	•	•	•	•	•	•	•	•	•	•	•	•	•	•	•	•
Temperature	•	•	•	•	•	•	•	•	•	•	•	•	•	•	•	•	•
MES*					•	•	•			•		•	•		•	•	•
Conductivity	•	•	•	•	•	•	•	•	•	•	•	•	•		•	•	•
Salinity (2)	•	•	•	•	•	•	•	•	•	•	•	•	•	•	•	•	•
pH	•	•	•							•	•	•	•				
Hardness							•				•						
Calcium											•						
Alkalinity							•				•						
Chlorides				•								•	•				
Sulphates				•								•	•				
Phosphates			•									•	•				
Air saturation (+)				•	•		•		•	•					•	•	•
Oxygen		•			•		•			•		•	•		•	•	•
CO_2							•				•						
NH_2							•		•	•		•	•		•		
NO_2							•		•			•	•				
BOD**					•	•				•	•	•	•		•		
Oxidizability ($KMNO_4$)					•	•				•		•	•		•		
Biotic indices**					•	•	•										
Algae**			•														
Micropollutants*	•					•		•									
Toxins explained in relation to an investigation	•							•								•	•

*Determinations necessitating stationary laboratory equipment.

**Determinations possible with motorized equipment (laboratory van) but requiring highly trained personnel.

(+) Measures that appear to be undertaken urgently with the corresponding equipment:

(1) For fisheries in running streams

(2) For fisheries in brackish or sea water

(3) Under all conditions

(4) In natural waters

(5) In fisheries

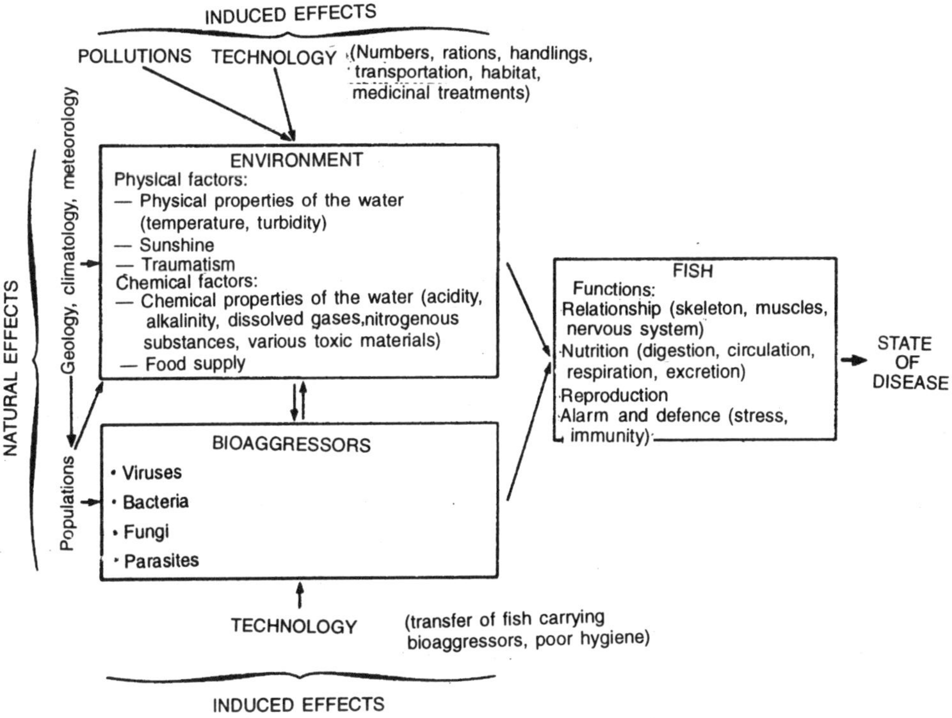

Fig. 218. General etiologic scheme indicating the interactions and effects of causes of disease in fish (after De Kinkelin *et al.*, 1985, courtesy INRA)

2. CAUSES VISIBLE TO THE NAKED EYE

The most apparent causes visible to the naked eye are mycosis due to *Saprolegnia* and *Aphanomyces*, which generally lead to lesions on the surface of the skin as a result of parasitic attacks or handling of fish during sorting or while fishing. Mycosis affects eggs during incubation, and a proliferation of mycelium may endanger others if no treatment is provided.

We may also observe parasitic leeches (*Geometra piscicola*), the opercular theca of *Philometra*, and cysts of *Bucephalus* and *Diplostomum*.

An autopsy may reveal the presence of ligulas in the abdominal cavity: ligulosis due to *Ligula intestinalis* affects all cyprinids. *Cystidicola* are worms that can be seen crawling in the air bladder. In the alimentary canal we may observe *Acanthocephala*, many of which are found in fish that eat gammarids, the intermediate host of these parasites. In the flesh of a fish it is more difficult to identify the yellowish cysts of *Clinostomum*, the adult worm of which is carried by a heron.

Parasitic crustaceans are all subjected to the same treatment: *Argulus* or fish louse, *Lernea, Spyrion* (as much as 40 mm long), *Coligus* (up to 20 mm), and *Ergasilus* (attached to the branchiae).

Ichthyophthiriasis is the only disease caused by identifiable protozoans on the body of a fish (due to the existence of small white spots with a diameter of 0.5–1 mm).

2.1 Diseases Associated with the Ambient Medium

a) Gaseous embolism

This is actually a condition associated with the physicochemical characteristics of the water in which the fish live. It therefore affects all species whose respiratory requirements are heavy: salmonids, the minnow, and the chub. It spreads in the Paris basin, Charente, Alsace, and the basin of the Rhone.

■ **Symptoms**

During resorption of the yolk sac, the fry remains upright, with the head raised; under the jaw there is an air bubble, of the size of a small pellet. **There are no deaths**.

After resorption, a spindle-shaped bubble is seen under the abdomen, where the yolk sac was. The skin is distended, the gills are red, and the opercula are separated. The fry swims on its side. **Abnormal and heavy mortality**.

At the fry stage: the young tend to hide. They have two colorations: one side is light, the other dark. Sometimes the fry are black all over and both eyes are affected. After a few days they are enucleated. **Mortal haemorrhage**.

At the troutlet and trout stages: in a river, the trout are not very active. They are thin and dark in colour. There is a unilateral, often double, exophthalmia. On the opercula there are subepidermal bubbles. The interior of the mouth is filled with large pockets of gas.

Near springs, trout that are apparently healthy are subject to nervous crises. They twist about, calm down, and die. The branchiae are carmine red.

In fish farms we observe the same symptoms, including enucleation of the eye, followed by death. The most affected basins are always those that are upstream.

The disease is observed invariably near deep springs between November and June.

■ **Etiology**

The condition is due to the difficulty in gaseous exchanges between fish and the ambient medium, especially of carbon dioxide and nitrogen dissolved in the water.

The nervous form of the disease, followed by death without the appearance of gas bubbles but with carmine-red branchiae, is due to poisoning by an **excess of** CO_2 dissolved in the water.

The slower form with exophthalmia and enucleation of the eye together with the presence of bubbles under the skin is associated with an **excess of nitrogen** under high pressure.

■ **Explanation**

An excess of carbon dioxide in water is due to bubbling of the water in underground air pockets.

Pumped water and water from artesian wells arrives at a high pressure in the presence of air. It absorbs more gas if the pressure is high. It is then charged not with one volume of O_2 and two volumes of nitrogen but with one volume of O_2 and four volumes of nitrogen. An excessive amount of nitrogen is released in the circulatory system in the form of very small bubbles: this is a gaseous embolism. These bubbles enter the conjunctival tissue under the mouth of the fry, in the umbilical zone of the troutlet, and under the ocular globe of the trout.

■ **Water test**

Resurgent waters are dangerous, as are also waters from bubbling springs at their point of emergence.

Fast-flowing waters from springs, in limestone areas, as well as those forced through pipes need to be examined.

A chemical examination of water may be deceptive because determining inert nitrogen requires a technique that is very advanced. What is useful is a biological test. We introduce a few minnows or a few trout fry in a grilled cage in the water. If the water is bad the fish will die in less than 24 h.

■ **Differential diagnosis**

Since exophthalmia is also a sign of viral haemorrhagic septicaemia (large-eye disease), we need to differentiate as follows:

1. In the virus disease, the exophthalmia is always double and there is distension of the abdomen. In the present condition, the exophthalmia is often simple and the abdomen remains flat.

2. In the virus disease, the exophthalmia is fatal. In the present condition, if the quality of the water improves, there is a cicatrization of the ocular injury and the affected fish survives.

3. The virus disease rarely affects fario trout. The gas bubble affection is observed mainly in fario trout.

■ **Treatment**

Remove the fish to another place. In fisheries keep them in basins as far as possible from the spring.

To treat the water: ensure a flow in the open air for 30 minutes to allow for a release of the gas. If necessary arrange for mechanical degassing or a tortuous circuit of 200–300 m with small obstacles slowing down the water current.

b) Corrosion of the branchiae (Gills)

Corrosion of the branchiae can, evidently, be caused by many chemical products that are likely, as a result of pollution, to be contained in the aquatic medium.

We may mention here three natural excesses that cause such damage:

—hyperacidity of the water (very low pH, for example in water from drains, marshes, and peat bogs).

The early symptoms are a physical indisposition of the fish—irregular swim, leaps out of the water—followed by a change in coloration of the branchiae after a large amount of protective mucus is secreted.

It may be noted that mortality is observed when there is a combination of this acidity, especially with iron.

The remedy is to raise the pH by the introduction of slaked lime or calcium carbonate.

—hyperalkaline water: a naturally alkaline water becomes hyperalkaline when strong sunlight, for example, greatly encourages a proliferation of aquatic flora and, as a result, the consumption of CO_2 by photosynthesis.

The symptoms are the same as the aforementioned ones: ulceration of the opercula, corrosion of the branchiae, and darkening of the skin.

It may be borne in mind that the remedy is to introduce a buffer product, for example calcium carbonate ($CaCO_3$, in other words, chalk).

To summarize, in ichthyo-biogenic water, which is suitable for the normal existence of fish, the pH should be between 6.5 and 8. There will be mortality when the pH is below 5.5 and above 9.

—ferruginous water: in this there is a large amount of sulphurous combinations of iron (for example, FeS_2) that add to an excess of acidity, which causes not only corrosion but also an encumbrance on the branchiae. The "rust" observed in some low-lying marshy areas (for example, smaller valleys of Upper Normandy), may be deposited on the branchiae of fish, thereby limiting the absorption of oxygen at this level and, as a consequence, leading to a risk of asphyxia.

The process is as follows: pyrites or sulphides of iron, FeS_2, are converted to iron sulphate and free sulphuric acid. Ferrous sulphate, which is soluble, may be oxidized and transformed to "rust", which is a hydroxide of iron. This oxidation is rapid in an alkaline medium and slow in an acid medium. Following storms or heavy rushes of water, for example, this oxidation may not take place, because of a shortage of time, before the water reaches the ponds of fisheries and only the branchiae may be affected.

The remedy is, therefore, the same, which is to render the water alkaline and introduce into it slaked lime or calcium carbonate.

It may be noted, particularly, that the harmful effect of rust can occur with an almost neutral pH, 6.5, and an iron content of 2 ppm.

c) *Dropsy of the yolk sac*

Observed in fry of fario trout, rainbow trout, and brook trout.

■ **Symptoms:** Accumulation of liquid in the yolk sac, which acquires a bluish shade (whence its name: blue sac disease). We observe exophthalmia and haemorrhages. The fry are pale and sluggish. The mortality is 50% within 3–4 weeks.

■ **Causes:** Probably a very low oxygen content in the initial fry tanks (hatching), or the effect of a slight pollution, or even excessively rough handling (for example, during transportation of eggs). It may also be due to an excessive number of eggs in relation to the irrigating water flow: the concentration of urea and ammonia, being harmful to fish breeding, causes this dropsy.

■ **There is no treatment**. We can only increase the water flow.

d) *White spot disease*

On eggs of salmonids.

■ **Symptoms:** Appearance of white spots on the eggs and fry with yolk sacs; this is due to coagulation of the yolk.

■ **Causes:** Probably rough handling.

2.2 Lesions

Lesions lead us to consider the existence of some diseases.

According to KINKELIN, GERARD and TUFFERY (1973), a proliferation of whitish spots that look like drops of wax is an indication of "smallpox" of cyprinids. Granulations on the skin that resemble raspberries could be due to virosis, hypertrophic cutaneous fibroma (better known as lymphocystosis), which, in fresh waters, affects the black bass. White cysts on the branchiae and fins lead us to suspect henneguyosis (for example, on the pike).

Changes in skin coloration are mainly due to melanism.

When we observe a dark pigmentation on the caudal peduncle together with symptoms of dizziness, we suspect these to be due to *Myxosoma cerebralis*, especially when fish without the pigmentation and dizziness have bodily defects such as scoliosis or atrophy of the opercula and the lower jawbone. Spots of melanism a few millimetres in diameter are due to an implant of trematode larvae, the adults of which are carried by aquatic birds. Melanosis combined with exophthalmia and a twisted swim, in salmon breeding, lead us to suspect *viral haemorrhagic septicaemia* (VHS), which needs to be investigated in a laboratory conducting virological research.

The greyish-blue effect due to an abundant secretion of mucus draws attention to an irritation that could be caused by external microparasites: *Costia*, *Trichodina*, or *Gyrodactylus*. Ulcers containing blood on the body of a trout could be an indication of furunculosis, which should be confirmed by a laboratory because of the likelihood of these lesions being mistaken for those of VHS. A swelling of the opercula, together with haemorrhages leading to death, may be a branchial infection due to myxobacteria.

When somewhat slender eels are observed in unsorted lots it may be due to an infestation by *Anguillicola crassus*, which was introduced in Europe in the early 1980s when Japanese eels were imported (ASHWORTH and BLANC, 1997). This large nematode, which causes serious lesions in the air bladder, is visible to the naked eye during an internal examination.

2.3 Absence of Apparent Signs

If there are no apparent signs we need to collect some useful information and arrange for an early dispatch of samples.

In the information forms there are important questions to be answered in order to eliminate many hypotheses, including questions about pollution. In France the standard forms have several columns: the address and locality of the medium where these deaths have occurred; details such as the environment, population, fishery, its relationship with the system of which it is a part (other fisheries, association with natural populations); earlier interventions (treatment, restocking, etc.). The problems that confront veterinary laboratories are often complex and their investigations require answers to about fifty questions.

The samples must be despatched quickly to the laboratory and should, if possible, be of animals that are affected *but alive*. The laboratory should be intimated earlier, on the previous day, so that preparatory work can be carried out in time. Dead fish should only be sent if they had been caught while alive. Deep freezing is useful for branchiae and viscera if we are to eventually investigate a poison. Samples of organs are usually sent in small bottles, with a capacity of 50–100 ml, at 0°C in an isothermal container.

PACKING AND DESPATCH OF SAMPLES

■ Live fish

Live fish can, obviously, be sent in tanks designed for transportation with a diffusion of oxygen or in various containers with an aerator (plastic bins, live-bait containers, if they are less than 10 cm long). In all cases, the less the increase in temperature from the initial temperature, the better the chances of survival for fish.

An excellent solution is to place the fish in a plastic bag with water and oxygen. The amount of water required should be such that once the bag is closed and placed on a surface to help in gaseous exchanges with the water, the fish is just covered.

For live fish the best method of despatch is to take them personally to a laboratory. This enables us to provide all additional details that may eventually be required. If that is not possible we must arrange for them to be sent through a rapid transport service that will deliver the samples to the laboratory directly (so that the personnel there do not waste time looking for packages at stations and airports).

■ Dead fish

As in the aforementioned case, it is better to take a sample personally to a laboratory rather than send it. The essential precaution to be taken is that, after cleaning, the dead fish should be kept dry in a plastic bag or in aluminium foil and *refrigerated* by being packed in ice bags.

If the sample is to be sent, the isothermal packing described for live fish is quite suitable. This type of packaging is equally suitable for frozen fish that have to be transported as early as possible. In such cases is it essential to use dry ice to keep the sample frozen.

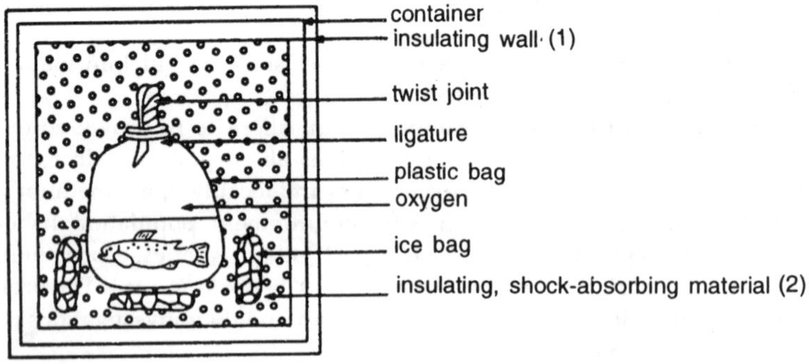

(1) polystyrene
(2) wood or polystyrene shavings, sawdust, newspaper

Fig. 219. Method of packing samples of live fish for despatch by a transportation service

■ **Organs, serums and histological samples**

Place bottles containing samples of organs or serum in an isothermal container surrounded by ice bags. As a precaution keep these bottles in a sealed plastic envelope.

Transport the samples personally or despatch them as is done for fish.

Histological samples do not require refrigeration but the bottles should be carefully packed in a material that will protect them against shock (polystyrene, paper, sawdust). Here again, a plastic envelope around each sample will be helpful.

B. THERAPY

Therapy is intended to destroy pathogens at the level of the animal (treatment) and in the ambient medium (disinfection). It should be adapted to the case under consideration and be undertaken early and in adequate doses based on a certain frequency. The effectiveness of therapy depends both on the manner in which it is applied and on the product itself.

1. TREATMENT

Treatment is administered in somewhat exceptional cases by *injection*. Injections are given intramuscularly under the caudal fin or by the intraperitoneal route on the median line in front of the insertion of the pelvic fins. Administration by the *oral route*, which is the usual one, is preventive in intensive fish breeding. The medicine is prepared by the manufacturer in the form of pellets or it is mixed with fresh food: the dosage is indicated in tables and based on the water temperature, body weight, and other factors.

Medicinal baths are used mainly for treating ectoparasites and branchial infections (GERARD, 1974). This method is effective when fish eggs are the preferred vectors of most contagious diseases, enabling their transmission from the germ-carrying adult reproducer to the fry, quite independent of any contamination by the medium. Only the virus of IPN (infectious pancreatic necrosis), present both on the surface of the egg and inside it, is resistant to this treatment. Eggs are now treated after fertilization or, more generally, when they have been received from another area, at the embryonated stage. We prepare a bath containing a solution of 50 l with a concentration of 50 ppm for 100,000 eggs, which is given only once for 10 minutes. After this bath the eggs are washed three times. The solution after use must never be thrown into basins or breeding channels.

Medicinal baths for young fish may be of short duration (10–15 seconds) or long duration (40–60 minutes). The latter is preferred. Generally, we mix the medicine in water from the basin. The duration of the bath depends upon the water temperature and the concentration of the medicine.

Medicinal baths for salmonids are usually given in water at 10 ± 1°C. In case of warmer water, the baths will be shorter and the fish have to be carefully watched during the operation.

a) Copper sulphate is effective against myxobacteria, algae, fungi, and generally all external microparasites, both as a preventive and as a cure in a concentrated or dilute bath; the dilute bath, using crystals contained in a bag dipped in the water entering a basin or a pond, is the best method because it avoids any handling of fish. The treatment is given as preventive measure every fortnight and as a curative measure at intervals of 24 h between the first two baths, 48 h between the second and the third, and after this at the periodicity recommended for preventive purposes.

b) Malachite green (pure oxalate) is extremely effective against fungi, both as a preventive and as a cure, in a concentrated bath for embryonated eggs or in a dilute bath for fry and adult fish. Treatment is carried out every fortnight, alternately with copper sulphate baths. The curative treatment is given on alternate days till the lesions disappear completely. This treatment is now prohibited by an EEC directive.

c) Formalin is effective against external parasites such as *Costia* and *Trichodina*. It is never used as a disinfectant. For preventive purposes it is combined with other treatments, according to a programme. For curative purposes, it is used at 24 h intervals

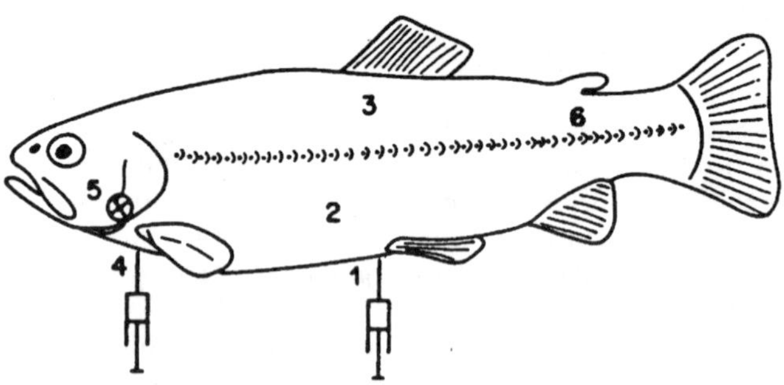

Fig. 220. Points for injection into a fish:
1 and 2, intraperitoneal; 3, intramuscular; 4 and 5, intracardiac; 6, dorsal vessel.

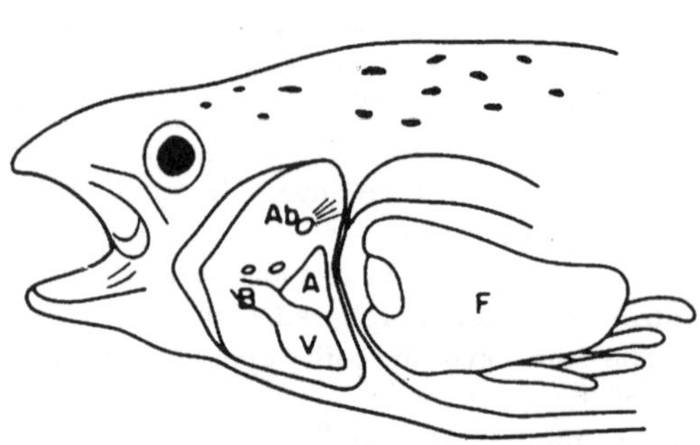

Fig. 221. Anatomical sketch of the cardiac region (by M. DORSON):
A, atrium; V, ventricle; B, bulbus aorticus; Ab, branchial arches; F, liver.

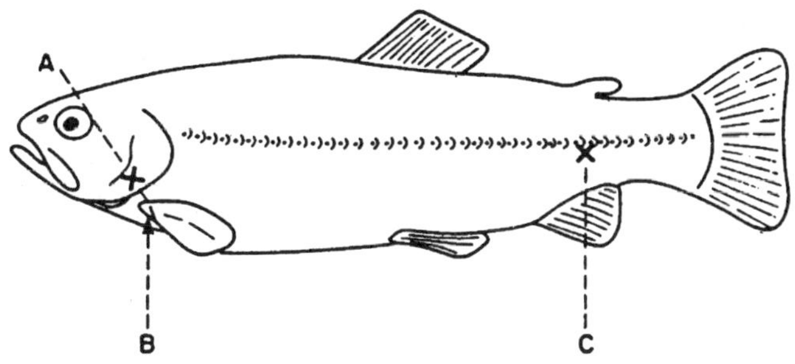

Fig. 222. Tapping points for blood in a fish: A, line along which we tap the atrium and the tapping point (x). B, body level for tapping the ventricle and tapping point (1). C, level for tapping the dorsal vein and extraction point (x) (after DE KINKELIN *et al.*, 1985, courtesy INRA).

for the first three applications, with a 48 h interval before the fourth one, followed by a preventive periodicity.

2. DISINFECTION

Disinfection follows cleaning of the installations in a fishery, the vehicles for transportation of fish, and the tools and clothing used by the handlers.

—*Draining out* basins is effective if done in the summer and for more than a month. Viruses have a low resistance against heat, and ultraviolet rays are an excellent disinfectant. For IPN and furunculosis, this should be followed by an application of lime or soda.

—*Burning* with a flame thrower is equally effective (sides and bottoms of basins).

—*Javel water* (solution of sodium hypochlorite in water) destroys viruses and bacteria. It is used to disinfect basins, instruments other than metal ones, and clothing and shoes that may have been in contact with infected fish or dirty water. A 5% solution is used as a foot bath and for washing and brushing purposes. According to ALMACHER (in DE KINKELIN, GERARD and TUFFERY), the concentration of the disinfectant used is 200 ppm for 1 h or 10 ppm for 24 h. After use, considerable care must be taken to ensure it is not thrown into the receiving medium.

—*Quaternary ammonium*, less caustic than Javel water, is used to disinfect metal items. It has been found effective for treatment of branchial affections of bacterial origin, in a 15 minute bath with 2 ppm of disinfectant. No solution with a content of more than 2 ppm should be released in a river, to avoid killing the fish in it.

—*Iodoform*, at 250 ppm, is an excellent disinfectant.

—*Soda*, used as a disinfectant, should be combined with a moistener so that it penetrates cracks and crevices. It is sprayed along the sides from upstream to downstream, left to dry for 8 days, and then washed with a powerful water jet. The basins are filled and left to be washed over a fortnight.

—*Quicklime* is used to disinfect basins and canals with bottoms of earth, as well as the ponds. We spread it or sometimes introduce into the basins a solution of freshly slaked lime (one part of lime in four parts of water). This may serve two purposes—disinfection and amendment—in which case we leave the lime to act during the dry winter period. In other cases, after a day or two, we let the water in slowly. After a fortnight, we drain out this milky water and replace it with ordinary water. The drained-out water should not be allowed to enter basins or channels where there are fish.

—*Calcium cyanamide* may also be used for both disinfection and fertilization. Disinfection is ensured, especially against *Myxosoma cerebralis*, by spreading it in a dry form, leaving it to act on the soil for a month, followed by a washing out in the case of basins.

C. PREVENTION

Certain measures need to be taken when we observe diseases like mycosis syndrome or *ulcerative dermal necrosis* (UDN), which is known in salmonids living in the natural medium and still destroys many fish in French water courses. It is considered that they are due to restocking of eggs and fry or the proximity of adults that are already carrying the pathogen.

Apart from disinfection of the eggs, we need to adopt measures in respect of reproducers that have been taken from the natural medium or raised in a fishery during the period prior to spawning. As soon as the water temperature falls below 12°C, treatment is provided, alternatively, once a week, using copper sulphate. This treatment is all the more necessary when the skin of the animals has suffered an injury during handling.

Immediately after spawning, the reproducers are treated again with copper sulphate.

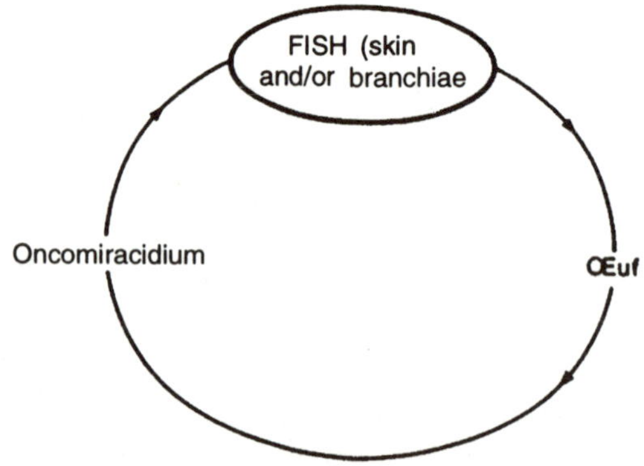

Fig. 223. Life cycle of monogenetic trematodes

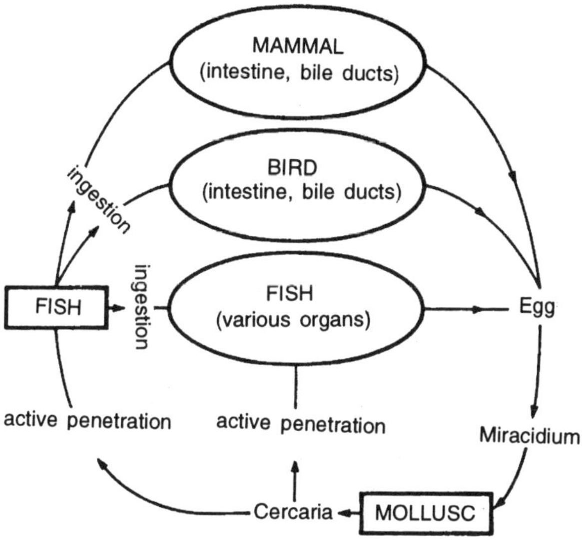

Fig. 224. Life cycle of digenetic trematodes (larval bucephalosis due to *B. polymorphus*)

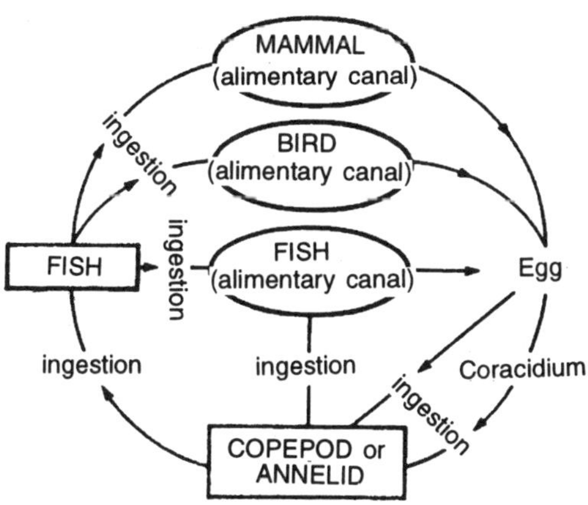

Fig. 225. Life cycle of cestodes

Table 34. Principal causes of disease in freshwater fish (after DE KINKELIN, GERARD and TUFFERY, 1973)

Virus and virosis	Bacteria and bacteriosis	Protozoans	Metazoans
Viruses of salmonids	*Aeromonas salmonicida*	Flagellates	Fungi*
– Viral haemor-	– Furunculosis	*Costia*	*Saprolegna*
rhagic septicaemia	*Aeromonas hydrophila*	– Costiosis	– Saprolegnosis
(VHS)	– Various infections	*Hexamita*	*Branchiomyces*
– Infectious pancreatic		– Hexamitosis	– Branchiomycosis
necrosis (IPN)	*Vibrio*	*Trypanoplasma*	*Ichthyosporidium*
– Infectious haemato-	– Vibriosis	– Trypanoplas-	– Ichthyosporidiosis
poietic necrosis (IHN)		mosis	
	Flexibacter		
Viruses of cyprinids	– Myxobacteriosis	Ciliates	Worms
– Spring viraemia	*Corynebacterium*	*Ichthyophthirius*	Monogenea
of the carp	– Corynebacteriosis	– Ichthyophthiriosis	*Gyrodactylus*
(infectious dropsy)	*Mycobacterium*	*Trichodina*	*Diplozoon*
– "Smallpox" or viral	– Mycobacteriosis	– Trichodinosis	Trematodes
epidermal	(tuberculosis)	*Chidonella*	– Trematodosis
hyperplasia		– Chidonellosis	– *Anguillicola*
	Pasteurella		
Virus of centrar-	– Pasteurellosis		*Diplostomum*
chids (1)	*Streptomyces*	Sporozoans	*Bucephalus*
– Hypertrophic	– Streptomycosis	*Eimeria*	*Clinostomum*
cutaneous	*Streptococcus*	– Coccidiosis	Cestodes
fibroma	– Streptococcosis	*Myxosoma* and	– Cestodosis
Viruses of ictalurids		*Myxobolus*	*Ligula-Trianophorus*
– Haemorrhagic		– Cnidosporidiosis	*Bothriocephalus*
syndrome of the catfish			
			Acanthocephalans
Viruses of the pike			– Acanthocephalosis
– Rhabdovirosis			*Echinorhynchus*
(Haemorrhagic			Leeches
septicaemia in the			*Geometra*
young pike)			Crustaceans
			Argulus
			– Argulosis
			Tracheliastes
			Lernea and *Ergasilus*

(1) Black bass, sun perch.
*Fungi are not metazoans but included as a distinct group in the plant kingdom.

Table 35. Disinfectants and their utilization (after DE KINKELIN *et al.*, 1985, courtesy INRA)

Procedures	Indications	Method of use	Remarks
Physical			
Desiccation Light	All bioaggressors on bottom soil	Dried for 3 mo. at an av. temp. of 18°C	Duration reduced by using a chemical disinfectant
Dry heat	All bioaggressors on cement, stone, iron	Blow lamp, flame thrower	
Moist heat	All bioaggressors in tanks and transport vehicles	Steam at 100°C or more, for 5 min.	
UV rays	Viruses and bacteria in water	50,000 $\mu W/sec/cm^2$	IPN virus resistant
	Spores and Myxosporidia in water	350,000 $\mu W/sec/cm^2$	IPN virus resistant
Chemical			
Acriflavine	Bacteria, water, branchia, eggs	3 mg/l as long as possible	Standard, but spectrum of effectiveness less than that of halogens
Quaternary ammoniums	Viruses, bacteria, hands	1 g/l for 1 min.	IPN virus resistant
	Branchial bacteriosis	2 mg/l for 15 min.	
Calcium (oxide) (d)	All bioaggressors on mud bottoms that have been dried out	0.5 kg/m^2, for 1 week	Refill with water and empty the disinfected basins, maintaining pH < 8.5 in the effluents
Calcium (hypochlorite) (d)	Bacteria and viruses on all surfaces and in water	Solution of 0.01 chlorometrie degrees or	Neutralizable with sodium thiosulphate, see special 30 mg of chlorine/l, leave instructions it to become inactive in a few days
Calcium cyanamide (d)	Spores of Myxosporidia on mud bottom	3000 kg/ha on dry soils, leave in contact for 1 mo.	
Formaldehyde (d)	All bioaggressors, within closed premises	Released from a formogenic substance, generally trioxymethylene. Use as per instructions.	
Iodine (iodoforms)	Bacteria, viruses	> 200 mg/l, a few sec.	See special instructions
	Hands, smooth surfaces	50–100 mg/l, 10 min.	Neutralize before disposal
	Embryonated egg	25 mg/l	Costlier than chlorine
	Gametes during fertilization	25 mg/l* for several hours	

Table 35. (*Contd*)

Procedures	Indications	Method of use	Remarks
Ozone	All bioaggressors, water sterilization	1 mg/l, for 1 min.	Expensive, cannot be used in industrial fisheries
Sodium (hydroxide) (d)	All bioaggressors on resistant supports including cracks and fissures	Mixture: Sodium hydroxide 100 g Teepol 10 g	The most active disinfectant. $Ca(OH)_2$ colours treated surfaces
		Calcium hydroxide 2000 g Water 10 l	and teepol is a surface-active agent.
		Spray 1 litre for every 10 m² and leave it to act for 48 h	Refill with water and check the pH
Sodium (hypochlorit.) (d)	Bacteria and viruses on all surfaces and in water	Based on Javel water. Solution of 0.01 chlorometric degree or 30 mg/l of chlorine. Leave it for a few days till it becomes inactivated or neutralize it with sodium thiosulphate after 3 h.	
	Nets, balers, boots, work clothes, hands	Solution at 0.06 degree, for 20–30 sec. Wash with clean water or neutralize with the thiosulphate.	Same as for calcium hypochlorite

(d) Dangerous. See the precautions laid down in the general instructions.
*The indicated concentrations are those of the active substances.

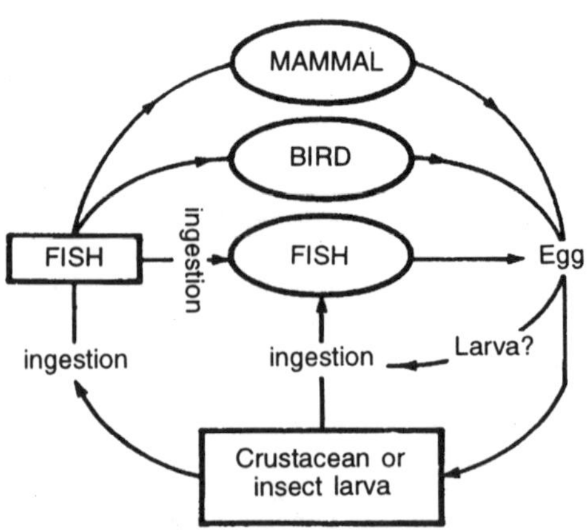

Fig. 226. Life cycle of nemathelminthes (nematodes)

Table 36. Recommended therapies (after DE KINKELIN, GERARD and TUFFERY, 1973)

Medicine	Trade name	Dosage	Dosage acc. to packing	Administration	Indications
Chloramphenicol (now prohibited)		5–10 g/100 kg BW		In the food for 15 d	Bacteriosis
Chlortetracycline	Aureomycin (special BP) Tablets of 100 and 500 mg	13 mg/l water	1 tablet (500) in 40 l water	In a bath	Bacteriosis
Copper (sulphate)		1 g in 10 l water 1 g in 2 l water. A freely selected dose dipped in the water and removed when the fish have left		10–30 min. bath Quick bath	Ectoparasitosis and diseases of the branchiae due to bacteria or parasites
Formalin (30-40% commercial solution of formaldehyde)	Commercial solution	1/4000 at + 10°C	25 g/100 l water	10–15 min. bath	Ectoparasitosis due to micro-parasites
Framycetine with Neomycine	Detrapan (Decaris)	0.25 ml for 300–400 g BW every 48 h		IM injection	Mycoses Bacteriosis
Furazolidone	Furoxone	2.5 g/100 kg BW		In food for 20 d	Bacteriosis (furunculosis)
Malachite green (pure oxalate) (now prohibited)		5 ppm	Make a 1% solution in 70% alcohol and put 2 teaspoons of solution in 20 l water	40–60 min.	Treatment of eggs and fry till resorption
Nifurpurinol P. 7138	Furanace (Dainippon)	1 ppm		30 min. bath	Branchial infection due to myxobacteria
Neomycene with Framycetine	Detrapan (Decaris)	0.25 ml for 300–400 g BW every 48 h		IM injection	Bacteriosis
Oxytetracycline	Terramycine (Pfizer)	3 mg for 300–400 g BW 75 mg/kg BW		IP. injection In food for 10 d	Bacteriosis
Sodium (chloride)	Table salt	10–15 g/litre water 25 g/litre water		20 min. bath 10–15 min. bath	Ectoparasitosis (aquarium fish) Ectoparasitosis
Sulphamerazine		22 g/100 Kg	BW	In food for 14d	Bacteriosis in

Table 36. (*Contd*)

Medicine	Trade name	Dosage	Dosage acc. to packing	Administration	Indications
Sulphathiazine				*In vitro* active against *A. salmonicida*	fry and troutlets
Masoten Dimethyl ester of (2,2,2-trichloro 1-hydroxy-ethyl) acid, 80 g	Masoten distributed by Romeil	0.25 ppm		In ponds without draining out	Ectoparasitosis including leeches

BW = body weight

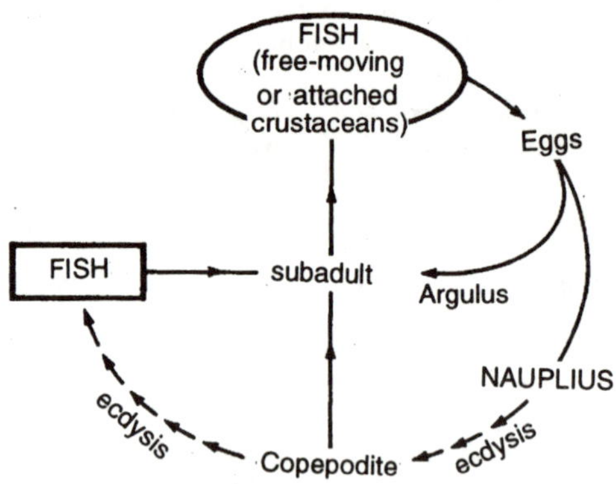

Fig. 227. Life cycle of acanthocephalans

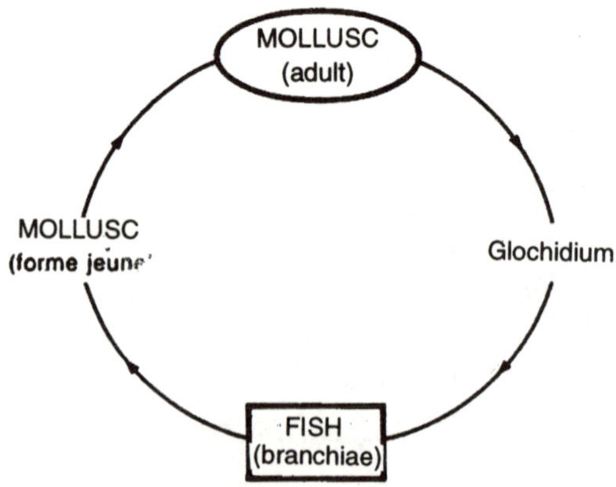

Fig. 228. Life cycle of parasite crustaceans

Table 37. Reproductive stages of parasites (after DE KINKELIN *et al.*, 1985, courtesy INRA)

Parasites	Final host	Aquatic medium	I Intermediate host	II Intermediate host
Sarcomastigophora				
Trypanoplasma spp.	fish**	0	Leech	0
Ichthyobodo (Costa) spp.	fish**, eggs	(free forms)	0	0
Oodinium spp.	fish**	(free forms)	0	0
Apicomplexa				
Eimeria spp.	fish	oocyst	0	0
Microsporidia	fish**	cadavers, spores	0	0
Ciliata				
Ichthyophthirius spp.	fish**	cyst, tomite	0	0
Crytocaryon spp.	fish**	cyst, tomite	0	0
Chilodonella spp.	fish**	(free forms)	0	0
Trichodina spp.	fish**	(free forms)	0	0
Myxosporidia				
Myxosoma cerebralis	fish	cadavers, spores	Tubificidae (annelid)?	0
Ceratomyxa spp.	fish	cadavers, spores	?	0
Myxobolus	fish	cadavers, spores	?	0
Henneguya spp.	fish	cadavers, spores	?	0
Myxidium spp.	fish	cadavers, spores	?	0
Platyhelminthes				
Monogenetic trematodes				
Gyrodactylus spp.	fish**	(free-moving forms)	0	0
Dactylogyrus spp. (free-moving forms)	fish**	oncomiracidium	0	0
Digenetic trematodes[a]				
Diplostomum spathaceum	bird	egg, miracidium	*Lymnaea stagnalis*	fish
Posthodiplostomum spp.	bird	egg, miracidium	gastropod	
Uvulifer spp.	bird	egg, miracidium	*Radix* and *Balba*	
Clinostomum spp.	bird	cercaria	gastropod	fish**
Sanguinicola spp.	fish	miracidium	*Lymnaea* and *Radix*	0
Azygia spp.	fish	egg, miracidium	gastropod	0
Bucephalus polymorphus[b]	*S. luciperca*	egg, miracidium	*Dressena polymorpha*	fish**
Nanophyetus spp.	mammal*	egg, miracidium	gastropod	fish**
Cryptocotyle spp.	mammal, bird	egg, miracidium	gastropod	fish**
Clonorchis sinensis	mammal*	egg, miracidium	*Parafossarulus manchouricus*	fish**
Opisthorchis felineus	mammal	egg, miracidium	*Bithynia leachi*	fish**
Cestodes				
Caryophyllaeus spp.	fish**	egg, coracidium	Tubificid (annelid)	0
Diphyllobothrium spp.	mammal*	egg, coracidium	copepod	fish**
Ligula spp.	bird	egg, coracidium	copepod	fish**
Bothriocephalus spp.	fish	egg, coracidium	copepod	0
B. acheilognathi	fish**	egg, coracidium	copepod	0
Trianophorus spp.	fish**		copepod	fish
Nemathelminthes (nematodes)				
Aphasmidia				
Capillaria spp.	egg			
C. philippinensis	mammal*, bird	eggs	fish	
Dioctophyma renale	mammal*	eggs	*Lumbriculus variegatus*	fish**

*Human infestation possible.

**Stage that may be pathogenic to fish.

[a]Digenetic added to distinguish from monogenetic trematodes—Tech. Ed.

[b]Generic name added—Tech. Ed.

Table 38. Diagnosis of the main diseases of fish (after Paperna, 1980)

CLINICAL OBSERVATIONS \ DISEASES	Stress (cause unknown)	Stress (handling)	Malnutrition	Avitaminosis	Anoxia	Excess gas saturation	Algal toxins	Pesticides (and others)	Lymphocytosis	Epitheliocytosis	Gram bacteria	Septicaemia	Myxobacteriosis	Saprolegnosis	Branchiomycosis	Trichodiniasis
GENERAL																
High mortality rate																
– affecting all species	x	x			x	x	x	x								
– affecting one species										x			x			x
– affecting only fry								x		x						x
Sporadic deaths																
– affecting all species	x	x	x	x												
– affecting one species			x							x	x	x	x	x	x	x
– affecting only fry			x							x						x
– affecting only large fish		x			x							x				
General discomfort				x			x	x								x
Gasping					x		x			x			x		x	x
Apathy	x	x	x	x	x	x				x	x	x	x	x	x	
Loss of weight																x
FORM AND COLOUR OF BODY AND FINS																
Emaciation			x	x						x						
Dropsy	x	x									x	x				
Vertebral deformation				x												
Eroded or frayed fins	x	x	x			x			x				x	x		
Decolouration	x	x		x									x			
Melanism	x	x	x								x					
INTEGUMENTS																
Loss of scales	x	x	x	x							x	x		x		
Eroded scales																
Pearly grey																
Ulcers											x					
Separate haemorrhages											x		x			
Generalised haemorrhages	x	x									x	x	x	x		
Necrosis of the skin									x				x	x		
Excessive secretion of mucus	x	x											x	x		
Small injuries or bites																
White spots (<1 mm)																
Groups of pustules (verts)									x							
White vesicles or nodules									x							
Large nodules or tumours																
Downy formations														x		
Many red nodules																
Dark or iridescent vesicles																
Large yellow vesicles (>2 mm)																
Subcutaneous brown lesions											x		x	x		

Table 38. (*Contd*)

Costiasis	Childonellosis	Glossotella/Scyphidiasis	Epistilis infection	Ichthyophthiriasis	Trypanosomiasis	Coccidiosis and haemogreg.	Myxosporidiosis	Microsporidiosis	Dactylogyrosis	Gynodactylogyrosis	Metacercariifection	Black spot	Clinostomiasis	Nematode infestation	Acanthocephalosis	Nematode larval infestation	Cestode larval infestation	Leech infestation	Ergasilosis	Lernealosis	Argulosis	Isopod infection	Papilloma
x	x			x					x	x													
x	x								x	x													
x	x	x	x	x			x	x	x	x			x					x	x	x	x		
				x					x				x										
x	x	x	x	x							x							x			x		
				x						x	x								x				
										x									x				
x	x	x	x	x							x												
															x	x	x		x	x		x	
													x				x						
																					x		
x	x	x	x								x												
							x																
													x										
		x	x																				
x										x											x	x	
			x							x								x		x	x	x	
x			x							x								x		x	x	x	
x	x									x													
													x								x		x
x	x			x						x													
																	x		x	x	x	x	
				x																			
							x																x
							x																x
																		x		x			
											x	x											
													x										

Table 3. (*Contd*)

CLINICAL OBSERVATIONS \ DISEASES	Stress (cause unknown)	Stress (handling)	Malnutrition	Avitaminosis	Anoxia	Excess gas saturation	Algal toxins	Pesticides (and others)	Lymphocytosis	Epitheliocytosis	Gram bacteria	Septicaemia	Myxobacteriosis	Saprolegnosis	Branchiomycosis	Trichodiniasis
Visible ectoparasites																
Air bubbles between rays						x										
EYES																
Exophthalmia	x	x		x		x					x	x				
Opacity of the cornea	x	x		x							x					x
Opacity of the lens	x			x												
Deformation, blindness			x								x					
White spots																
BRANCHIAE																
Pale											x	x				
White stains													x			
Brownish-white spots															x	
Deformed filaments																
White spot										x						
White nodules																
ANATOMY AND BLOOD																
Abdominal cavity																
– purulent haemorrhagic liquid											x	x				
– clear liquid	x	x														
– peritonitis											x	x				
– white vesicles and nodules																
– yellow nodules																
– vesicles containing red worms																
– dark brown vesicles on intestinal walls																
– white flat worms																
– round red worms																
Viscera																
– hypertrophied kidneys	x	x									x					
– kidneys nodular, grey											x					
– kidneys with white foci																
– spleen hypertrophied, red	x	x														
– spleen hypertrophied, nodular, greyish											x					
– liver, yellow/green			x													
– haemorrhages in the muscles and intestines	x	x									x	x				
Blood																
– anaemia, low erythrocyte count											x	x				

Table 38. (*Contd*)

Costiasis	Childonellosis	Glossotella/Scyphidiasis	Epistilis infection	Ichthyophthiriasis	Trypanosomiasis	Coccidiosis and haemogreg.	Myxosporidiosis	Microsporidiosis	Dactylogyrosis	Gryodactylogyrosis	Metacercarial infection	Black spot	Clinostomiasis	Nematode infestation	Acanthocephalosis	Nematode larval infestation	Cestode larval infestation	Leech infestation	Ergasilosis	Lernealosis	Argulosis	Isopod infection	Papilloma
																		x		x	x	x	
x	x								x														
											x												
				x																			
x					x	x			x	x													
																			x				
											x											x	
				x				x															
							x																
														x	x	x							
						x	x	x			x					x	x						
													x										
														x		x							
											x			x		x							
																	x						
														x		x							
						x	x	x															
						x	x	x															
															x	x							
					x																		

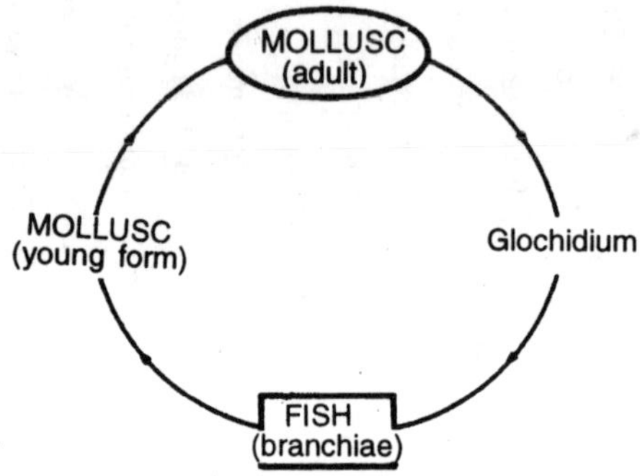

Fig. 229. Life cycle of a glochidium larva (Pelecypoda)

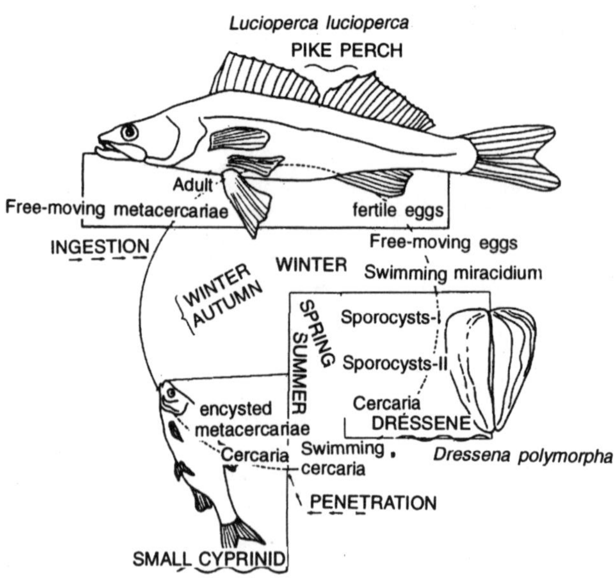

Fig. 230. Life cycle of *Bucephalus polymorphus* (from De Kinkelin *et al.*, 1985, courtesy INRA)

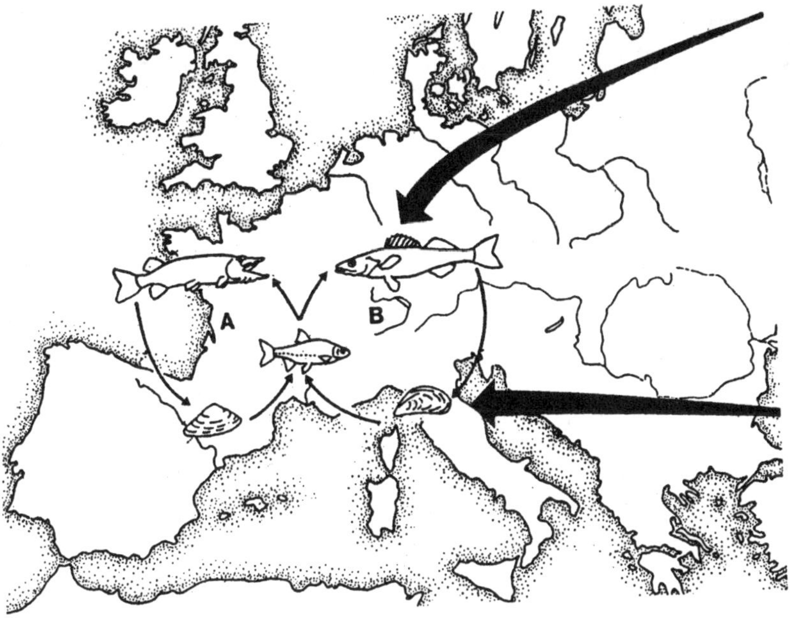

Fig. 231. Life cycles of *Rhipidocotyl illense* (A), an indigenous parasite, and *Bucephalus polymorphus* (B), a parasite introduced in Western Europe. Only the cyprinids, the second intermediate hosts, are common to the cycles of the two trematodes (after LAMBERT, 1997).

Fig. 232. Spread of the striped mussel *Dressena polymorpha* in Europe (after KHALANSKI, 1997)

8 SUITABILITY OF MEDIUMS

A. CLASSIFICATION

1. LOTIC (RUNNING) WATERS

Running waters are *natural* when they are rivers or streams and *artificial* when they are canals.

Lateral canals are parafluvial (e.g., lateral canal of the Oise). Link canals are interfluvial (e.g., canal from the Marne to the Rhine). Some sectors of smaller and larger rivers are canalized. Apart from navigable water courses and canals, rivers that are "suitable for craft", and were earlier of general interest like the former are, in France, part of the *public property of the State*.

Water courses of lesser importance are a part of private property: they are the *private property of the State* when they flow over a bed that belongs to the State (State forest) and *private property* in other cases. The owners of land along water courses are owners of the beds of the water courses but not of the creatures that live in them. Fishing rights, as well as other rights to use the water, are nevertheless indicated in their title deeds.

Depending on their sizes we have *brooks* (average width 0.50 m), *streams* (average width 1 m), *small rivers* (average width 8 m), rivers that can be used for *small craft* (average width 22.50 m), and *navigable rivers* (average width 100 m).

We also classify water courses depending on the substratum over which they flow (chalkstreams, karstic water courses), and depending on their geographic state, often associated with the gradient (water courses on plains, in mountains, torrents, coastal rivers).

2. PONDS

Ponds are classified depending on *their origin* as natural or artificial ponds. Some are the result of an accumulation of water in depressions or in zones where there has been a collapse. They cannot generally be drained out by gravity. Others are a result of human activity. They are excavations, or peat bogs, gravel pits, and sand pits that cannot be drained out, or dam ponds that can be drained, specially designed for fish culture.

We distinguish between ponds fed by springs (emerging from the bed or the banks), by a runoff (ponds in lower hills, storing storm water), or by a water current.

They are also classified according to their *layout*: a dam pond in a valley; a succession of ponds in series when they are fed by gravity, from one to another, or in parallel when they are fed individually by diversion of a water course.

Their *intended use* is extremely varied: ponds for rod fishing, ponds for fishing and production when fishing for sport and commercial purposes are combined, production ponds, and piscicultural annexes (ponds for stocking, storage, spawning, or wintering).

3. LAKES

DUSSART (1966) defined a lake as "any natural or artificial basin containing water and with a life of its own, a certain autonomy."

An extent of water surrounded on all sides, a lake is different from a marsh or a pond because of its thermal characteristics; its waters are stratified and the medium is biologically, physically, and chemically closed.

YOSHIMURA (1936) classified lakes depending on their thermal characteristics. *Tropical lakes* have a high thermal gradient and a temperature that is always above 4°C. *Temperate lakes* (e.g., Lake Geneva, Annecy lake, Bourget lake) have a circulation cycle in spring and a second one in the autumn. The thermal gradient is high. The temperature, above 4°C in summer, falls below this level in winter. *Subpolar lakes* have a low gradient. The thermocline is near the surface. They have two circulation cycles. *Mountain lakes* (in the Alps and the Pyrenees, at a high altitude) are somewhat similar with regard to their thermal characteristics. *Polar lakes* have a short period of thaw and a summer circulation (lakes in upper Scandinavia, Labrador, and Alaska).

DUSSART identified lakes depending on their geological origin. There are tectonic lakes (Lake Baikal, the Saint-Point lake), volcanic vent lakes (Tritriva in Madagascar), crater lakes (Bouchet lake), and dam lakes due to lava flow (Chambon lake). Lakes are also the result of dissolution of some limestone rocks (old lake of Mont-Cenis), dams caused by morains (glacial lakes of Gerardmer and Laffrey), by running waters (Dutch Wielen, along the arms of the lower Rhine), rivers, when they cause a piling up of sediments forming a dam or a reservoir (Thun lake in Switzerland), winds causing a pile-up of sands (lakes in the Landes), or organic activity (coral lagoons).

B. SITUATION

1. PISCICULTURAL VOCATIONS

Waters have different piscicultural utilities, depending on their morphodynamic, phytozoological, and physicochemical characteristics and also on their situation in the French geographical landscape.

These result in various populations of fish that have somewhat characteristic ecological requirements.

In France, legislators have had to determine two piscicultural utilities: category I, based on the existence of a predominant *salmonid* grouping, and category II, based on the existence of a *cyprino-esocid* grouping.

This categorization implies legal constraints designed to ensure a correct use of the French fisheries resources based on regulations that cater, for example, to the protection of species.

The traditional economy of this utilization implies that it ensures only fish productivity without any reduction in the productive capital.

2. PRODUCTIVITY OF OPEN WATERS

In France, the productivity of open waters is much higher than the combined exploitation of professional fisheries and of those who fish for sport in waters of the cyprino-esocid category, but is lower than that caught by amateur fishermen in salmonid waters.

2.1 Salmonid Water Courses

Salmonid water courses are highly productive in mountain regions, which are the starting points of major hydrographic networks. Their productivity is also high in regions of high plateaus, lower thickly wooded hills, and plains of the northern region in the country: the Langres plateau, the region of Caux, the low hills of Armorique, the low hills of Normandy and Artesien, and the plains of Champagne and Picardy.

These may be considered to represent 225,000 km of the French network, in other words:

—150,000 km of brooks with an area of 7500 ha,

—60,000 km of streams with an area of 6000 ha, and

—15,000 km of rivers with an area of 12,000 ha.

Based on population studies conducted by the CEMAGREF (Centre Expérimental du Machinisme Agricole, du Génié Rural, des Eaux et des Forêts), INRA (Institut National de la Recherche Agronomique), and CSP (Conseil Supérieur de la Pêche), the approximate productivity may be estimated as follows:

—Brooks produce about 30 kg/ha/yr (1500 kg/km of their course) or, in all, 525 t/yr (of salmonids).

—Streams have the same productivity, that is, on an overall basis, 420 t/yr.

—Rivers produce about 65 kg/ha/yr (50 kg/km of their course) or, in all, 780 t/yr.

To this we should add a production of migratory fish, sea trout, and salmon, of 170 t/yr.

2.2 Cyprino-esocid Water Courses

In cyprino-esocid water courses there are various proportions of fish of the cyprinid family (chub, roach, rudd, carp, bream, tench, bleak, etc.) and white carnivorous fish (pike, perch, pike-perch, black bass, etc.).

These are found in the lower regions of all hydrographic basins, in a part of the Alsace plain, in many sectors of some large coastal rivers (Somme, the Niort area of the Sevre, Charente), and often in the entire basin of small coastal rivers.

These are the waters of plains and peneplains. It may be assumed that they represent about 48,000 km of the total network, i.e.:

28,000 km of streams with an area of 2800 ha,
6000 km of small rivers covering 4800 ha,
2500 km of slightly larger rivers covering 5600 ha,
8765 km of navigable rivers covering 87,650 ha,
2320 km of canals covering 2550 ha.

Their annual productivity is based mainly on samplings of fish linked with a study of primary and secondary biomasses rather than on a direct approach with demographic inventories of fish. This being the case, these productivities could be approximately as follows:

—Streams produce about 80 kg/ha/yr (8 kg/km of their course) or, in all, 220 t/yr.

—Smaller rivers produce 90 kg/ha/yr or 420 t/yr.

—Slightly larger rivers also produce 90 kg/ha/yr or 505 t/yr.

—Navigable rivers can produce 50 kg/ha/yr or, in all, 4380 t/yr.

—Canals produce 130 t/yr.

For navigable rivers and canals, the productivity has been estimated conservatively, because of many adverse factors to which they are subjected and the difficulty of eliminating them permanently, at least with regard to pollution.

3. PRODUCTIVITY OF CLOSED WATERS

The productivity of closed waters, well known for ponds that can be drained out, is not so well known in the case of lakes and excavated ponds.

3.1 Natural Lakes

The natural lakes are mainly in the Alpine massif: part of Lake Geneva, the Bourget lake, the Annecy lake, to mention only the most important ones. These are highly productive lakes, together with the Grandlieu lake in Lower Brittany.

The somewhat smaller lakes in the same alpine chain massif, the chain of the Pyrenees, the Central Massif, the Vosges, and other less important reliefs are of particular interest to those who fish for sport. They cover an overall area of 50,000 ha with an annual production of about 800 t of fish (16 kg/ha/yr).

3.2 Reservoir Lakes (Artificial Lakes)

The productivity of reservoir lakes is difficult to assess, being apparently modest because of the seasonal fluctuations in their levels that are prejudicial to fish populations. Their present area is 41,000 ha. The oldest of these have been constructed in mountain massifs with a view to produce hydroelectric energy (Eguzon, Tignes). The more recent ones are regulatory reservoirs of very large dimensions and volume (Serre-Poncon, Lusigny on the Seine, and Champaubert on the Marne).

Their production estimated at 400 t/yr based on catches of fish during the 10-year draining out does not take into account what was caught by anglers. According

Fig. 233. French river basins

to DUSSART, WURTZ-ARLET, NISBET, LEFEBVRE and BERTRAND (1956), the Eguzon lake has a probable yield of 68 kg/ha/yr (with 272 ha of water surface). According to ALZINGRE (1975), that of the Val Joly (North) would be about 50 kg/ha/yr (for 450 ha of water surface). P. LIM *et al.* (1990) reported a biomass of 24 kg/ha with 90% of cyprinids in the reservoir at Saints-Peyres (Tarn) with an area of 211 ha located at an altitude of 670 m.

3.3 Ponds

In France there are 120,000 ha of ponds that are productive and to these may be added 30,000 ha that are almost in disuse. Every year 1500 ha of ponds are created (700 ha in the basin of the Seine alone) from excavated areas, gravel beds, and ballast pits formed because of the need for building.

The main traditional regions where there are ponds that produce fish for the trade are the Dombes, Sologne, Brenne, Moselle, Argonne, Forez, Camargue, and the Somme. Their annual production is about 120 kg/ha. If to this we add that from

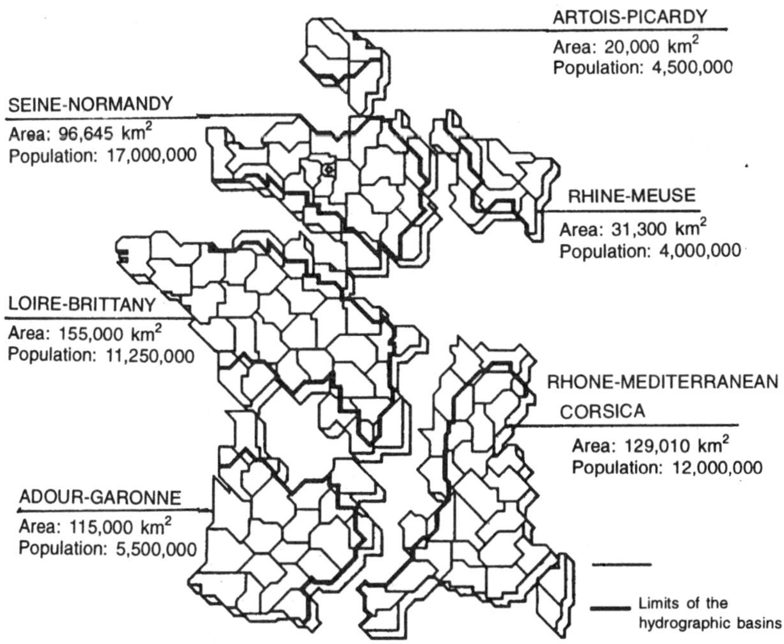

Fig. 234. Basins and water authorities

ponds in excavations, which is not well known, it may be assumed that the production from ponds is about 15,000 t/yr.

C. DEVELOPMENT

1. LOTIC (RUNNING) WATERS

Development in lotic waters is dependent on their quality, productivity, and ability to provide suitable conditions for fish life, all these parameters being interdependent.

The hydrographic network comprising streams and small rivers is certainly the most fragile. With the dispersal of industries it is likely to be affected by pollutants that have already damaged very long sections of larger water courses. It is populated to a major extent by salmonids, which are more severely affected by these harsh conditions than other species.

Though brooks and streams are not of much use for large-scale fishing, they are often excellent spawning zones and may be used as nurseries and growing areas, providing stock for large water courses (pp. 227 and ff). Their productivity may therefore be increased considerably with some minor works and careful management.

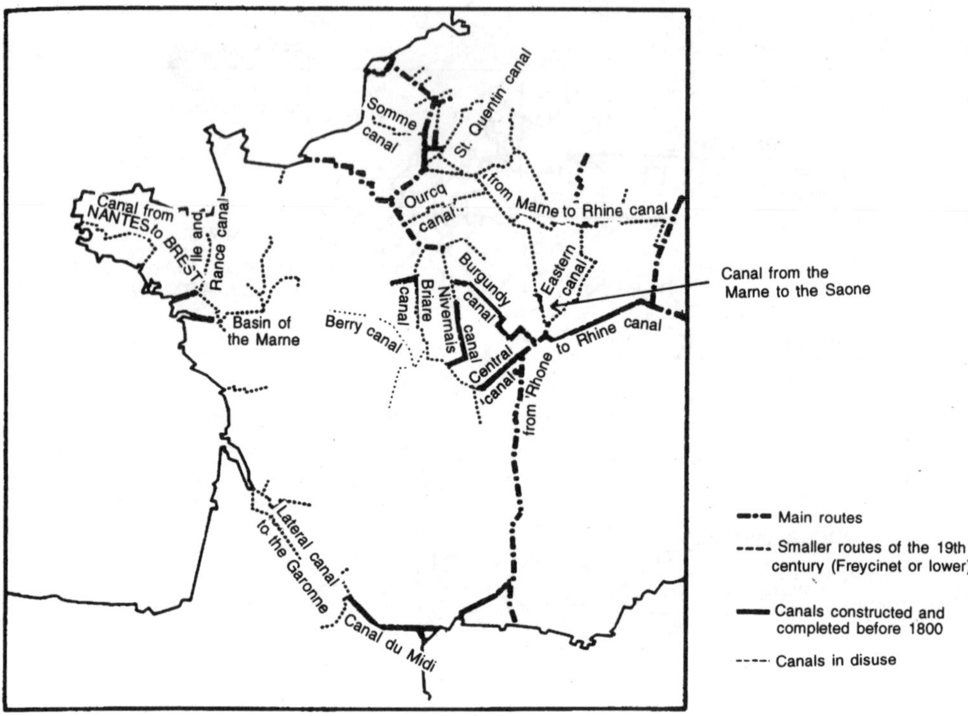

Fig. 235. Navigable route chart (from "Canals and Landscape", Ministry of Urban Affairs)

Small salmonid rivers are generally in a poor state because of a lack of maintenance, pollution that is diffused and difficult to control, and some disorganization in their hydraulic and piscicultural utilization. They cannot be improved unless, all over their basins, judicious and durable measures are taken for their maintenance and protection, and unless a better concept of restocking and a better distribution of the fishing effort is implemented.

Pollution control measures undertaken by industries and urban agglomerations are probably more effective on major cyprino-esocid water courses than on smaller ones because of the greater power of dilution in the former.

Paradoxically, because of their flow, they have been selected for building thermal power plants and a series of these on the same water course may alter its utility without our being in a position to assess the long-term effects. Nevertheless, pollution control measures combined with an improvement in the spawning zones has already resulted in a better situation over some sectors of larger water courses (Old Rhine, Oise, Yonne).

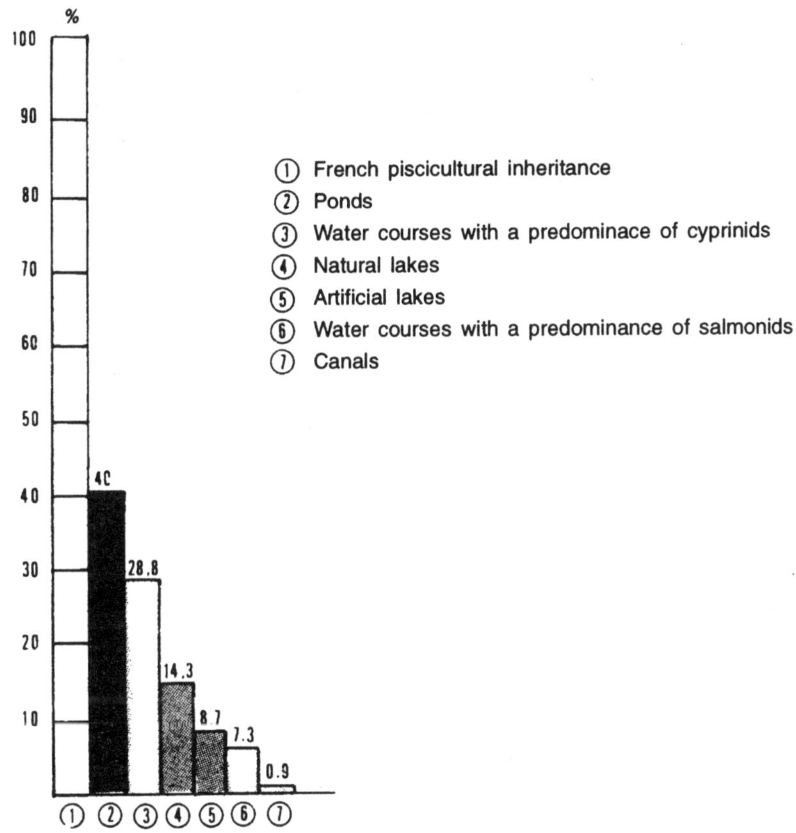

Fig. 236. Extent of the French hydrographic network

2. LENTIC (CLOSED) WATERS

Natural closed waters, after some cleaning efforts that have already shown good results in the Annecy lake, can be improved upon. The type of fishing carried out in them also determines the improvements. Maintaining a good balance between species depends on a judicious extraction of excessive numbers of these species that have considerable resilience as well as the removal of unproductive and predatory ones.

Reservoir lakes have not been designed to encourage fish production but may be provided with equipment for treatments that can ensure considerable increases in production. This may also be increased by rational, systematic, and well-regulated professional and amateur fishing.

Ponds, which are not very productive in France, have a potential that may reach 250 kg/ha/yr, on an average, taking into account necessary improvements in management and control. The same applies to ponds in excavations, the numbers and surface of which is increasing from year to year. As far as ponds, in general, are concerned, it may be assumed that in view of the new direction given to the utilization of water bodies, their production can be increased, easily, from 15,000 to 33,000 t/yr over the existing water surface. Daily amateur fishing, as a sport, actually improves the productivity of ponds more than a yearly harvest of marketable fish; the income that this ensures also justifies the costs involved in amendments and fertilizations.

9 ADVERSE EFFECTS

A. HISTORICAL CHANGES

A hydrographic patrimony is subject to changes in time and space, in respect of quality and also in extent. This development depends on somewhat random intervening factors, such as the following:

Atmospheric precipitations that undergo atypical changes in time: there may be years of severe low-water levels or rainy years with devastating high-water levels.

Changes in impluvium, in other words, the quality of the catchment area. A regional deforestation, in a geopolitical sense, may cause a change in this patrimony. Permanent water courses or lakes may become temporary ones or even dry up.

Modifications in the actual course. As the vector of an element, water, it can be corrected, diverted, or flanked by a lateral channel, canalized, piped, or buried. As a medium of aquatic life, a water body may be disturbed as an ecosystem due to warming, drying up, eutrophication, or pollution.

The superficial patrimony may be increased by new resources such as dam lakes that change the state of the water course from which they are fed; a fast-flowing river may become a series of stagnant water bodies. Newly available resources may be used to extract ground water, resulting in water bodies in excavations and sand pits.

Technical and economic progress catalysed by the effects of major armed conflicts, for several decades, hastened successive changes that have, to a great extent, altered the natural landscape in general and the aquatic patrimony in particular.

Transformation of the rural landscape, with its influence on the nature of the impluvium through consolidation of holdings, changes in the soil cover, and cultural practices, has had serious effects on the network of rivers and streams. Where this impluvium is pastoral or woody, it is absorbent. It stores atmospheric water and returns it gradually, providing a regular regime to water courses on the lower hills, peneplains and plains.

Having become agricultural and open, it is no more absorbent but allows water to run off: atmospheric water flows over the basin during precipitations, carrying a part of the topsoil with it. The vector water courses are not broad or deep enough to absorb the flux, as a result of which we observe flash floods of a disastrous type, blockages and deposits of sediments in the rainy season or during stormy weather. On the other hand, during the dry season, which may not necessarily be in summer, there may be a very limited flow or no flow, inadequate to meet all the types of requirements that have increased at that time.

The solutions are solutions of circumstance. We straighten out a water course in order to increase the flow velocity. We increase the width and the depth and carry out major periodic cleanings. We build storm reservoirs and dams to cater for low-water periods. The water course, itself, may then be unsuitable as a medium for life, and become a **wadi**.

Industrialization of agriculture, which plays a major role in the transformation of rural areas, adds to degradation of the aquatic patrimony in quality and quantity.

Unrestrained increase in productivity causes a disturbance in surface and groundwater resources due to the large amounts of water taken out for purposes of irrigation, which is also increasing because of the requirement for crops that need a lot of water, such as maize. This happens precisely at a time when the surface water resources are at a low level. As a result, ground water is used, causing an alarming and permanent fall in its level and reducing the flow of water courses in chalky regions.

The same industrial crops whose high yields are due to the provision of fertilizers and pesticides have a persistent and cumulative effect on the quality of surface and ground waters, especially in the chalky subsoil of extensive plains, contaminating the resources used for human requirements.

Decentralization of industry, to be expected in view of rural desertification and lower labour costs, has, in rural areas, resulted in degradations, of which water pollution is not the least. These degradations were earlier confined to water courses near towns and industrial areas that are generally larger than the small rural rivers and streams with a low self-cleaning capacity.

The energy policy, which has to cater for a demand that increases geometrically, doubling every 10 years, was directed initially to hydroelectric plants, and later to thermal plants. Subsequently, as a result of successive oil crises, it was, in France more than anywhere else, directed towards nuclear electric production. This policy has resulted in dams and plants of all sizes along water courses and caused changes in their hydraulic and hydrobiological characteristics, with constant risks of pollution in spite of security constraints.

The need to construct buildings and communication routes has resulted in an increasing opening up of gravel pits and sand pits in the alluvial zones of water courses. This exposes the phreatic tables and causes a fall in their level, as well as hydraulic disorders. To increase our aquatic patrimony, steps must be taken to prevent degradations in nearby streams receiving water that is too warm in summer and too cold in winter, upsetting the existing biocoenosis and thereby causing a change in their suitability for fish.

In recent decades, we have also observed a **change in use of water** for industrial, agricultural, and recreational purposes. Logs are not floated down rivers but there has been a change in river craft, from boats pulled from the banks to large motorized barges and extensive convoys.

The towing paths along the banks have fallen into disuse; some small canals have also been abandoned and even filled up. The major rivers are navigated at high speed and the back-wash of river craft degrade the banks, reduce their capacity for fish life, and often endanger light craft and the fishermen on them.

• **Improvements in mechanization** have been made all over the network with increased possibilities of pumping out small amounts of water which, when added up, causes smaller water courses to dry up. The owners of the riverside land no longer clear, remove weeds from, and maintain banks because of lack of manpower, shortage of time and lack of interest: we now use heating oil for warming purposes and not firewood collected from the banks of streams in winter.

The large number of vehicles on the roads has enabled many users to come to water bodies and water courses for leisure and sport of varied types. Rod fishing, hunting for water birds, and canoeing, which are still popular, are now in competition with sailing, surfing, water skiing, rafting, diving, canoe-kayak sailing, and photo safari. This has increased the number of people on the strands of the banks and water bodies, using special types of often costly equipment, involving compromises in their uses which are conflicting. This group of users is also frequently united against harmful effects and degradations described further on.

Aquatic ecosystems therefore suffer harmful effects:

1) in the catchment area, especially on the slopes at the lower end of a valley,
2) on the medium and life support, and
3) on the existing life in the aquatic medium.

B. ADVERSE EFFECTS ON THE CATCHMENT AREA

In the catchment area there are effects on the soil and subsoil as well as changes in the plant cover of the impluvium. Together they affect the hydraulic regime and may even alter the course and configuration of streams and water bodies. The erosion that they bring about causes a hastened sedimentation and silting with a change in the physicochemical characteristics of the water, followed by a change in the biological balances of aquatic mediums and, thereby, in the predominance of certain fish. On a somewhat long-term basis an aquatic ecosystem may be replaced, progressively, by a palustral and later by a forest system. In ponds and lakes, reeds colonize a silted water body and then alders replace the reeds, at least in cold temperate zones.

This is how, in British Columbia, the gold rush at the end of the nineteenth century resulted in a systematic cutting down of the forest on the deposits both to clear them and for making the galleries. The erosion that followed, aggravated by washing of the ore, caused permanent damage to many salmonid water courses in the Rocky Mountains. In this very region building work for the Canadian Northern Railway obstructed the valley of the Fraser, by repeated landslides from 1912 to 1914. The four-year cycle of the blueback (sockeye) salmon (*Oncorhynchus nerka*), which comprised 41 million in 1901, was reduced to 900,000 by 1944. Thereafter it took 22 years to construct the gigantic fish pass at Hell's Gate and for fisheries to rebuild the stock of young salmon upstream. There is now a four-year cycle of 24 million salmon visiting the Fraser.

Of the range of plantations due to human intervention, a wooded impluvium, being compartmentalized, appears to be least unfavourable for hydrobiological balances in a vector water course. MEROT, CARNET, MONTEIX and POIGNAULT (1975) have indicated its role as a buffer during high-water periods in winter against the maximum of the instantaneous flow and the overall runoff. Destruction of wooded sectors to increase the area for cultivation, changes in agricultural practices, and deposits of bushes and uprooted trees on mounds at the lowest points in the water course trigger the aforementioned process and impede the free movement of fish when migrators move upstream to spawning areas.

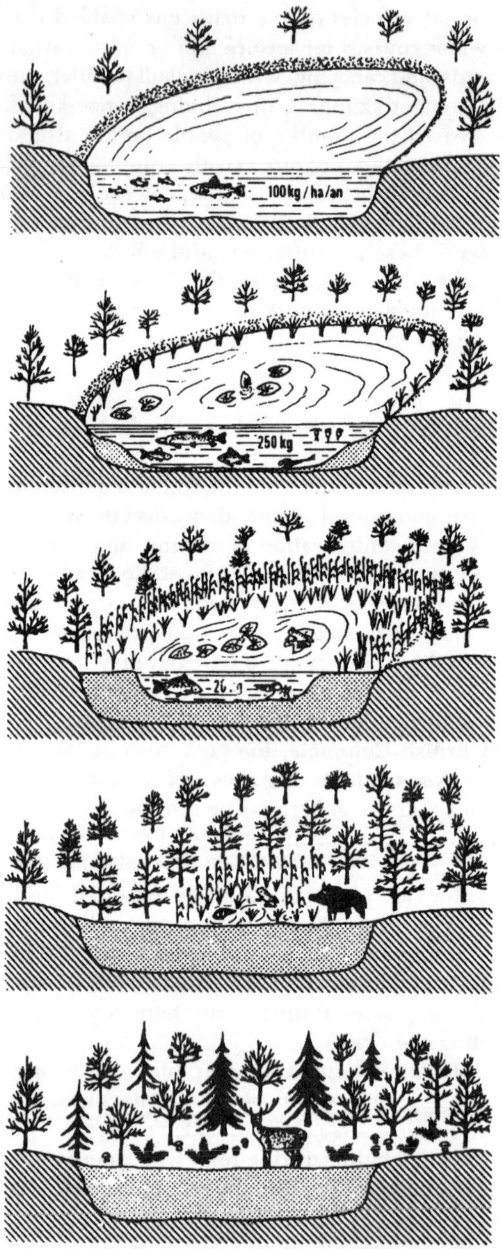

Fig. 237. Transformation of an aquatic ecosystem to a palustral and, later, a forest one

Fig. 238. Valley of the whanganui river (New Zealand) compact forest impluvium (photo: J. ARRIGNON)

In valleys, exploitation of material from the overthrust layer exposes the water table and affects the hydraulic equilibrium between this layer and the water course on the surface. This effect often causes a reduction in the upstream flow of the water course and an increase downstream, which can destroy fisheries and cress farms on the upstream side and fish populations in the lower reaches. The thermal gradient in water bodies that are created in this way, in a direct or indirect relationship with the water course, affects its own gradient and results in the disappearance of the stenothermal biocoenoses and an appearance of euthermal biocoenoses ending in a situation that is less desirable and less acceptable to the users. The washing-out phase of material also causes, albeit temporarily, but with long-term consequences, a mechanical pollution in both mineral and plant spawning areas and may, if the suspended matter content is more than 500 mg/l, result in the death of fish due to asphyxia.

C. ADVERSE EFFECTS ON THE AQUATIC MEDIUM

Effects on the medium often alter its morphodynamic characteristics. This is because of the human need to improve the hydraulic flow of water courses, to utilize the energy potential of the water (dams along water courses and storage dams), to

Fig. 239. Fraser river valley, British Columbia (Canada), degraded forest impluvium (photo: J. ARRIGNON)

improve navigability in a natural or artificial hydrographic network, and to extract and store water for various purposes.

1. DAMS

Dams transform lotic facies to lentic facies: we have lakes with large volumes or which cover vast areas (Serre-Poncon, Lusigny, Champaubert) or a series of reaches on a single water course (Lot). The downstream medium is, to some extent, affected depending on whether the water is restored from the surface or from a depth, or sudden, interrupted, or regular. It is likely to suffer a degradation or, in rare cases, to undergo an improvement.

The effect of the thermal gradient in the surface waters of a lake plays longitudinally the same unbalancing role in the receiving water course as that of excavations does laterally (p. 429). On the other hand, extraction of water from a depth, at a relatively constant temperature, provides receiving rivers with a certain cool homeothermy that may improve their suitability for salmonids, a situation reported by BRUNET (1971) in several water courses of the foothills southwest of the Massif Central.

The method of managing reservoirs may also result in serious damage downstream: a complete draining out or sudden releases can cause serious mechanical and organic pollutions that carry away the existing biocoenoses and sterilize the medium for more than one annual cycle.

The non-existence or poor operation of fish passages may prevent migratory fish from visiting upstream areas.

2. CHANNELLING WATER COURSES

Channelling ensures continuity between a water course and its usual escape zones, such as marshes, water meadows, and cut-off meanders, which are the preferred spawning areas of pike and some cyprinids. The banks are often strengthened by pile planks or stone facings unsuitable for fish except in the case of stone facings that are suitable for American crayfishes. Wakes, caused by the movement of barges, have an adverse effect on the reproduction of fish and degrade banks that are not strengthened. According to ARRIGNON and DEBRUILLE (1970), a navigational channel, because of constant wakes due to the propellers of barges, is not suitable for development of the benthos or for fish. More recently, PORCHER-DECHAR (1975), in a study of the fauna in the river Aisne, established that for an equal water quality in a navigated sector and one in which boats did not ply, the disappearance of the benthic fauna of Trichoptera and helminths is due to disturbances caused by navigation.

Flushing of lock gates is, however, likely to improve the self-cleaning capability of polluted mediums.

3. EXTRACTION OF WATER

Extraction of water from the phreatic table and beds of water courses leads to a drying up that may be temporary or permanent in the upper reaches, especially in early Cretaceous terrain, as has been shown by ARRIGNON and JOANNIS (1972) in France and by DOWNING (1973) and LADLE and WESTLAKE (1975) in England. The solution where water is taken to a storage point or released into a network may, as mentioned by DOWNING (1973), affect the ecology of the fluvial system by reducing the hydraulic and thermal variations of a water course. This, in some cases, is favourable for the maintenance of the original biotope when it is progressively affected by eutrophication.

4. RESTORATION, RESHAPING AND RECTIFICATION

Restoration, reshaping, and rectification of water courses results in a change in their physicochemical characteristics due to a sudden increase in light, an increase in thermal variations, and variations in the O_2 and CO_2 content, because of the proliferation of generative algae that find the light and the shallow water level favourable. The phytological changes are a replacement of submerged aquatic plants by erect plants or beds of filamentous algae.

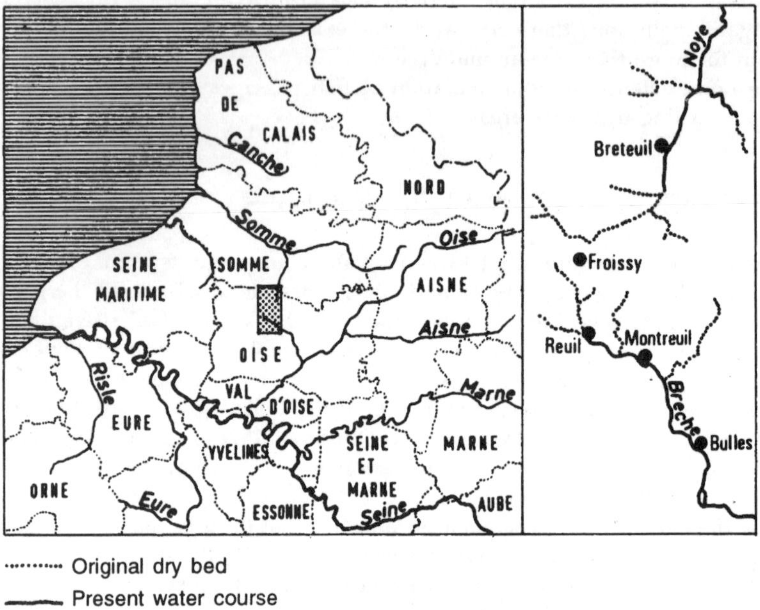

Fig. 240. Drying up of the upper reaches of some water courses in the department of Oise (extract from the piscicultural map of the Oise)

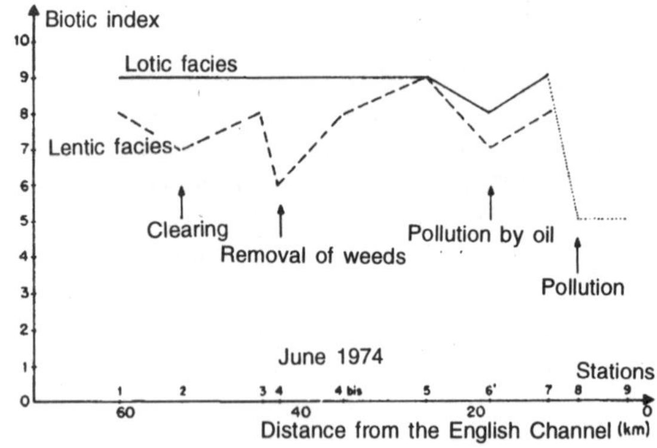

Fig. 241. Effect of interventions on the bed of a water course on the biotic indices (PORCHER and PORCHER-DECHAR, in ARRIGNON, ROUYER and CHANCEREL, 1975)

Changes in the habitat are due to the erosion of underwater slopes at the bank, zones of wakes, still and running waters, the disappearance of submerged aquatic plants, and sterilization of the medium by a radical removal of heaps of silt. Fish are unable to find places for shelter and the water course provides them with hardly anything other than a medium of transit. In addition, salmonid spawning areas are destroyed by the elimination of shallows and gravel beds, those of the pike by the elimination of flooded areas or the means to reach them, and those of cyprinids by the elimination of water plants.

Destruction of the aquatic landscape due to developments in earth-moving equipment, the geometry of high and non-stabilized banks, and the shallowness of the water spoils the environment and its suitability for fishing. The extent and duration of these changes are variable. A study of such situations in Champagne, Picardy, Normandy and Poitou led ARRIGNON, ROUYER and CHANCEREL (1975) to estimate that a river treated in such a manner will revert to an acceptable landscape and hydrobiological state after five years.

5. UNTIMELY MAINTENANCE

Untimely maintenance of water courses and water bodies is harmful and certain consequences of this, which have already been indicated, are aggravated by other factors. Winter clearing upstream of a salmonid spawning ground causes a clogging of gravel beds containing the eggs and suffocates them. Clearing in summer has the same effect on cyprinid spawn. Early clearings destroy many salmonid fry which, after they emerge from gravel beds, seek shelter among aquatic plants.

On the other hand, lack of maintenance causes a slowing down of the current due to obstacles, heaps of debris, silting, fermentation of silt, warming of the water,

Fig. 242. A water course that has not been maintained. The bed is clogged, the current slow with a high sedimentation rate (after J.-J. DEMARS).

and reduced light due to the development of plant overhangs and vaults. The physicochemical characteristics also change, for example, from a lotic to a degraded lentic type. These changes affect aquatic flora and fauna. The flora may disappear because of inadequate light and the phyto- and zooplankton may be replaced by periphyton and benthos; rheophilous species disappear along with stenothermal ones to be replaced by species that are much more ubiquitous. These changes also affect the fish population because some species, such as salmonids, cannot easily adjust to transformations in the medium or are threatened by a degradation in the spawning areas. The situation ends with a change in the predominant species: the trout, for example, may be replaced by the chub, its competitor, a species with fewer requirements but lesser economic utility.

Careless operation of hydraulic works, together with a lack of maintenance, results in damage ranging from the movement of toxic deposits (sulphides) to the drying up of cyprinid and pike spawning areas and, often, of riverside fisheries.

Fig. 243. A water course in a private domain, reshaped and straightened. An aquatic medium with no diversity or shelter for fish. There is nothing on the bottom. Note the obstacle created by channelization (after J. ARRIGNON).

D. POLLUTION

1. DEFINITIONS AND CLASSIFICATION

Water pollution is associated with "discharges, flows, wastes, and direct or indirect deposits of material of all types and, more generally, with anything likely to cause or increase degradation in waters by altering their physical, chemical, biological, or bacteriological characteristics, whether they be surface or underground waters, or sea water within the limits of territorial waters" (France, Definition, Law No. 64-1245 of December 16, 1964, Ch. I, Art I, sec. 6).

"Throwing, discharging or directly or indirectly letting any substances flow into water courses whose effects or reactions have destroyed fish or affected their nutrition, reproduction, or food value, are acts of pollution" (Article L-232.2 of the Rural Code, Law No. 84-512 of June 29, 1984).

1.1 Nature of Pollution

Pollutions of a **physical type**:

—Mechanical pollution (the effects of which have already been described).

—Thermal pollution that, apart from the already described consequences, indirectly increases the toxicity of certain substances (the toxicity of potassium cyanide is increased by a factor of 2 for a temperature increase of 10°C), reduces the resistance of animals and encourages the development of pathogenic agents. SNIESKO (1964), in this way, referred to the disappearance of salmonids from many American rivers due to diseases that have spread because of thermal pollutions.

—Pollutions by radioactive elements, limited because of strict controls in the environment around nuclear installations, the risk being due to wastes from users of radioactive elements such as certain hospitals.

Pollutions of a **chemical type**:

—Pollutions with a large amount of minerals, composed either of non-natural substances of which the toxic effect is immediate or deferred after accumulation in the tissues of living organisms (biocides, heavy metals, detergents), or elements that exist in nature but usually in low concentrations (phosphates, nitrates, etc.).

—Predominantly organic pollution, the only ones that existed before the 20th century, now combined with pollutions of a mineral type in the complex effluents from towns and food industries.

1.2 Manifestation of Pollution

Depending on the manner in which they are manifest, we have:

Acute pollution causing a temporary disturbance in the aquatic medium, due to an accident (leakage from a heating-oil tank), incorrect operation, or a change in fabrication in a factory affecting the efficient functioning of a water-cleaning station.

The effects of acute pollutions are often spectacular and indisputable.

Chronic pollutions, much more dangerous because they are insidious, have a delayed effect, and are difficult to detect and locate. Food chains are partly or totally affected: fish disappear progressively and slowly to a distance of several kilometres downstream of one or several factories with no deaths being observed. An effluent may contain toxic products in amounts that are not immediately mortal for fish and cause their disappearance by destroying other biological elements in the water course in which they are living.

Chronic pollution may suddenly be transformed to serious acute pollution causing many deaths among fish. This can happen in summer when the high temperature

Table 39. Water temperatures causing mortality of 50% (LD 50) in various fish, depending on the initial acclimation temperature. The LD 50 has been obtained for periods of 12 h, 15 h, 24 h, and 1000 min., according to the authors (after N. CHARLON, 1968).

Family and genus	Acclim. temp. (°C)	LD 50	References
Centrarchidae			
Black bass	20°–21°	28°9	LD 50 : 24 h BLACK
(large mouth)	20°	31°8	LD 50 : ? HART
	20°	32°5	LD 50 : ? HART
	25°	37°2	LD 50 : 21 h TREMBLEY
	26°7	37°8–38°9	LD 50 : 18 h TREMBLEY
	27°2	36°7–37°2	LD 50 : 15 h TREMBLEY
	30°1 j.	36°	LD 50 : 24 h HATHAWAY
	30°4 j.	35°2	LD 50 : 24 h HATHAWAY
Sun perch	24°	30°2	LD 50 : 24 h BLACK
	25°–26°	34°5	LD 50 : 12 h BRETT
	30°1 j.	34°2	LD 50 : 24 h HATHAWAY
	30°4 j.	34°3	LD 50 : 24 h HATHAWAY
Cyprinidae			
Common bream	20°	30°2	LD 50 : 1000 mn ALABASTER
Carp	20°	31°–34°	LD 50 : 24 h BLACK
	26°	35°7	LD 50 : 24 h BLACK
Roach	15°	27°3	LD 50 : 1000 mn ALABASTER
		28°5	LD 50 : 1000 mn COCKING
	20°	29°4	LD 50 : 1000 mn ALABASTER
		29°8	LD 50 : 1000 mn COCKING
	25°	31°5	LD 50 : 1000 mn ALABASTER
		31°	LD 50 : 1000 mn COCKING
Gudgeon	15°	27°2	LD 50 : 1000 mn ALABASTER
	20°	28°6	LD 50 : 1000 mn ALABASTER
Rudd	20°	31°2	LD 50 : 1000 mn ALABASTER
Tench	15°	30°2	LD 50 : 1000 mn ALABASTER
	20°	32°	LD 50 : 1000 mn ALABASTER
	25°	33°8	LD 50 : 1000 mn ALABASTER
Percidae			
Pope	15°	28°1	LD 50 : 1000 mn ALABASTER
	20°	30°4	LD 50 : 1000 mn ALABASTER
Perch	15°	28°	LD 50 : 1000 mn ALABASTER
	20°	29°7	LD 50 : 1000 mn ALABASTER
	25°	31°4	LD 50 : 1000 mn ALABASTER
Salmonidae			
Rainbow trout	15°	26°	LD 50 : 1000 mn ALABASTER
		25°9	LD 50 : 1000 mn BISHAI
	20°	26°4	LD 50 : 1000 mn ALABASTER
		26°7	LD 50 : 1000 mn BISHAI
Siluridae			
Freshwater catfish	20°	33°4	LD 50 : 12 h BRETT
	22°6	35°	LD 50 : 12 h BRETT
	26°	35°3	LD 50 : 12 h BRETT
	30°	36°5	LD 50 : 12 h BRETT
	31°2	36°9	LD 50 : 12 h BRETT
	36°	37°5	LD 50 : 12 h BRETT

Table 40. Values of various physiochemical parameters of water considered normal, doubtful, or dangerous for salmonids and cyprinids (based on data provided by different authors)

	SALMONIDS			CYPRINIDS and other families		
Factor	Normal	Doubtful	Dangerous	Normal	Doubtful	Dangerous
Temp. of water sample, °C	< 20	20–22	22+	< 25	25–27	27+
Dissolved oxygen at dawn (50 lux of illumination), mg/l	≥ 8.5	7–8	< 7	≥6	5–6	< 5
Saturation percentage of dissolved oxygen at dawn, %	≥80	50–70	<50	≥70	50–70	< 50
(river) pH (running water)	6–9	< 6 > 9.5	< 5.5 > 9.5	6–9	< 6 > 9.2	< 5.5 > 9.5
Conductivity based on 20'C (river), μS	20–500	500–600	≥ 600	20–500	500–600	≥ 600
Alkalinity in HCO_3, mg/l	weak strong ε -400	-	-	weak strong ε -400	-	-
Calcium, mg/l	weak strong ε 60/200+	-	-	weak strong ε 10/200+		
Sulphates of SO_4 = (river), mg/l	0–50	50–100	> 100	0–50	50–100	> 100
H_2S (river)	-	+	++	-	+	++
(river) Nitrates NO_3, mg/l	weak, 0–10 strong, 11+	-	-	weak, 0–10 strong, 11+		
(river) Nitrites NO_2, mg/l	0-traces ~1/1000	~1/10≥1	0-traces ~1/1000	1	>1	
(river) Ammonia in NH_4, mg/l	0-traces ~1/1000	~1/10	≥1	0-traces ~1/1000	1>1.5, depending on pH	
(river) Oxidizability while cold, in 4 h, mg/l	ε -2	2–5	>5	ε -3	3–6	> 6
Chlorides (Cl) outside the influence of the sea, mg/l	ε -20	20–50	50+	ε -20	20–50	50+

causes a reduction in the dissolved oxygen content in the water while the amount of putrid matter has increased in a river with a reduced flow. Fish are unable to respire and therefore die, often in large numbers, even though industrial and urban discharges may not have increased.

2. LIMITS OF TOLERANCE

Pollutions are characterized by levels of toxicity, beyond which aquatic organisms die. Limited dilutions and minimal mortal amounts nevertheless vary according to many factors, including the duration of exposure, temperature, dissolved oxygen, and carbon dioxide content, the mineral composition of the water, the species, age, and condition of the organisms, and the earlier acclimation period.

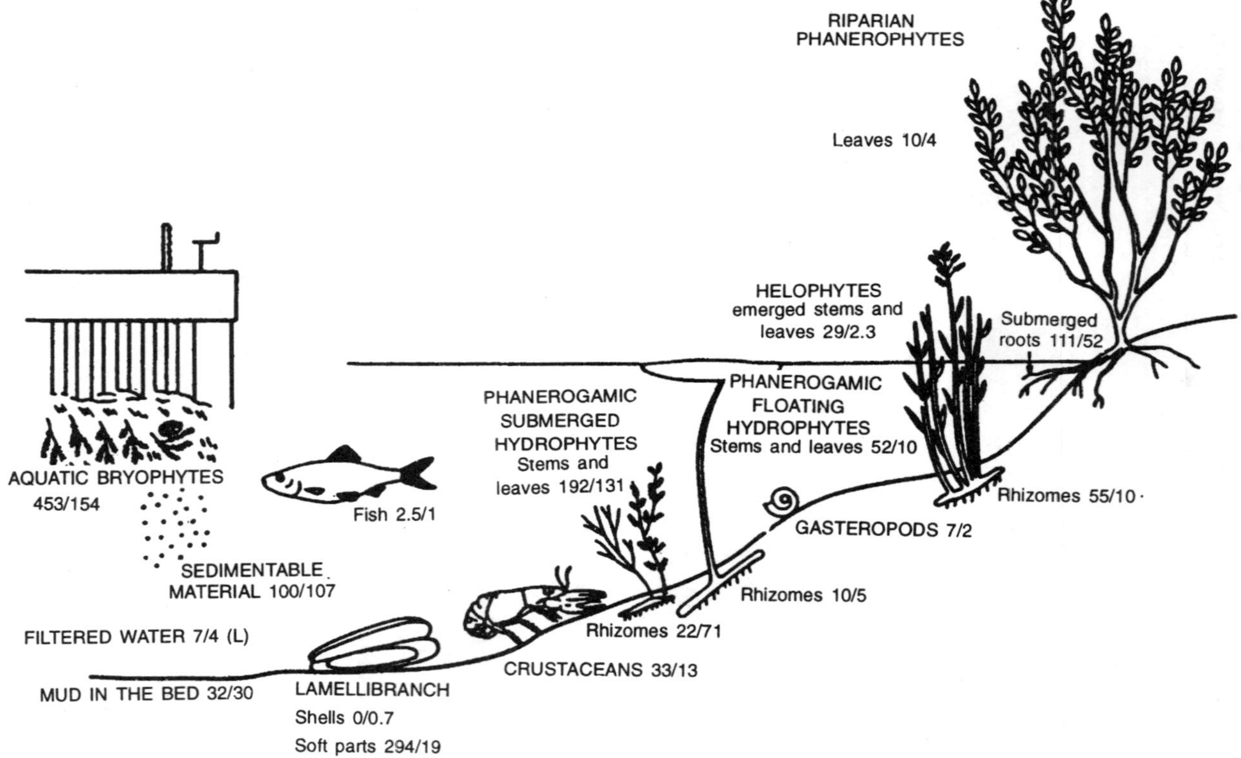

Fig. 244. Average levels of radioactive contamination observed in the main constituents of a fluvial ecosystem. Data relative to the Meuse in September 1971, at 15 km downstream of the Franco-Belgian nuclear centre in the Ardennes. The first figure corresponds to ^{54}Mn and the second to ^{60}Co (pCi/g of dry matter) (Kirchmann *et al.*, 1974, after Descy, 1980)

3. CONCEPT OF AN INHABITANT EQUIVALENT (IEQ)

It has been calculated that each human being, on an average, produces 57 g of organic oxidizable matter (OM) and it is accepted that the emission of the same amount of matter is an *inhabitant equivalent.*

Animals produce amounts of OM that may be less or more than an IEQ, which, in the case of the main European domestic animals, are as follows:

1 pig = 300 OM = 5 IEQ
1 sow with piglets = 450 OM = 8 IEQ
1 young bovine = 576 OM = 10 IEQ
1 milch cow = 1620 OM = 28 IEQ
1 hen = 16 OM = 0.35 IEQ

A knowledge of these correlative values enables us to calculate the organic polluting amounts in a particular region depending on the human and animal populations in it.

J.-L. PELLETIER (1990) provided an interesting example mentioning the effect of human and animal pollutions in the French department of the Armor coasts (Brittany) and the absolute necessity of examining certain developmental scenarios before the start of a programme for improvement in the region.

2,011,400 pigs × 5 IEQ	=	10,057,000 IEQ
188,600 sows with piglets × 8 IEQ	=	1,508,000 IEQ
374,700 bovines × 10 IEQ	=	3,747,000 IEQ
267,000 milch cows × 28 IEQ	=	7,476,000 IEQ
26,696,000 hens × 0.35 IEQ	=	9,343,600 IEQ
548,000 guinea fowl × 0.3 IEQ	=	164,000 IEQ
602,000 ducks × 0.3 IEQ	=	180,600 IEQ
2,676,000 turkeys × 0.3 IEQ	=	802,800 IEQ
Trout fisheries estimated at		600,000 IEQ
Total animals		**33,879,000 IEQ**
Total humans		**538,869 IEQ**

The Armor coasts, a department of 538,869 inhabitants, supports the pollution equivalent of 34.5 million inhabitants.

E. ESTIMATION OF WATER QUALITY

1. SAPROBES

The system of saprobes described by KOLKWITZ, WURTZ, and, later, SLADECEK (1964), studied and improved upon since then by several authors including VAN HOOREN (1975), does not lead to credible conclusions when we refer, qualitatively, to only the indicative species in a given state of quality. In fact, organisms that are genuine indicators are few in number and the absence of a species is no more significant than its presence. It is necessary to take into account the sensitivity of groups of species that are manifest in their order of disappearance during an increase in pollution and even to study the changes that may be seen in their behaviour.

2. QUALITATIVE EVALUATIONS

Since the present system of saprobes has been established, the correlation of certain components of aquatic ecosystems has enabled us, if not to establish laws, at least to work out formulae and indices in order to qualify these ecosystems and include them in zonal groupings and typologies, which help in evaluating the quality of their successive generations in time and space. To this effect, formulae and indices provide estimations that can be applied as part of the various means to prevent degradation in waters, aquacultural mediums, and biocoenoses. The most important of these are described in subsequent paragraphs and their developments are given in the Appendix.

2.1 Toxicity Test on Daphnia

Toxicity tests are conducted on *Daphnia magna* (Strauss) (family of Cladocerans) because of its parthenogenetic reproduction and to have clones with a relatively limited variance. Culturing the species on standard mediums containing unicellular strains (*Chlorella, Scenedesmus*) is also fairly easy.

In respect of **acute toxicity**, the 24 h or 48 h trial is conducted by measuring the concentration of a particular toxic matter that inhibits the movement of 50% of daphnia in a medium (CL 50).

Chronic toxicity is measured by conducting a 21-day test that covers the complete reproductive cycle of the animal. The biotope is a water solution of a standard chemical composition containing the oligo-elements necessary for the development of algae, the main component of the biocoenosis, and *Daphnia magna*, which is the second component. The simplicity of this ecosystem enables an evaluation of the chronic toxicity of active material in pesticides.

A combination and comparison of the two tests enables us to determine the aggressive effect of various toxins (diuron, paraquat, sodium arsenite) in terms of acute and chronic toxicity. Above all, they demonstrate that several indicators are necessary to determine the danger that may be caused by a product. The "daphnia 21d" test is useful because of its low cost, the early information it provides, and the quality of this information (J. Deniel, 1990).

2.2 Toxicity Test on a Fish

The "fish" test that is always conducted on the minnow in a laboratory has been extended in an open and continuous circuit for automatic checks on surface waters by electric means.

The fish introduced is generally the rainbow trout (Zahner, Junke and Besch, 1972; Barbier, 1973). The test is usually conducted downstream of the effluents of factories by observation of trout or roach depending upon the piscicultural category of the water course; the animals are stored in reference cages.

Provision of automatic alarm systems enables continuous surveillance in sectors that are particularly threatened when the water is drawn for treatment by water works for drinking purposes.

Table 41. Representation of saprobes

	Thio-	Poly-	α-Meso-	β-Meso-	Oligo-	Catharo-
Plecoptera						
Perla bipunctata					—	—
Isoperla					—	—
Chloroperla					—	—
Taeniopterix						—
Nemura					—	—
Ephemeroptera						
Rhitrogena						—
Ecdyonurus					—	—
Oligonieuriella					—	—
Epeorus					—	—
Baetis				—	—	—
Ephemerella				—	—	
Large Ephemerans			—	—	—	
Trichoptera						
Goera					—	—
Stenophylax					—	—
Centroptilum					—	—
Notidobia					—	—
Hydropsyche			—	—	—	—
Rhyacophila				—	—	—
Limnophilides				—	—	—
Philopotamus					—	
Phryganae				—	—	
Anabolia				—	—	
Diptera						
Liponeura					—	—
Atherix					—	—
Simullids				—	—	—
Tanytarsus					—	
Tanypus					—	—
Orthocladiines				—	—	
Various chironomids			—	—	—	
Prodiamesa			—	—	—	
Chironomus plumosus and *thumni*		—	—	—		
Stratiomys		—	—	—		
Eristalis	—	—	—			
Odonata						
Aeschnids			—	—	—	
Libellulids			—	—	—	
Agrionides			—	—	—	
Neuroptera						
Sialis		—	—	—	—	
Crustacea						
Various gammarids			—	—	—	—
Carides				—	—	
Asellus		—	—	—		
Holopedium				—	—	
Daphnia pulex			—	—	—	
Daphnia longispina				—	—	
Leptodora					—	

Table 41. Representation of saprobes (*Contd*)

	Thio-	Poly-	α-Meso-	β-Meso-	Oligo-	Catharo-
Turbellaria						
Planaria alpina					—	—
Planaria lugubris					—	—
Planaria torva					—	—
Planaria gonocephala					—	—
Polycelis nigra				—	—	—
Dendrocoelum lacteum				—		
Rotifera						
Notholca longispina					—	
Conochilus volvox					—	
Anurea cochlearis			—	—	—	
Various *Anurea*			—	—		
Various *Brachionus*			—	—	—	
Triarthra			—	—	—	
Pedalion				—	—	
Philodina				—	—	
Callidina				—	—	
Floscularia				—	—	
Asplanchna				—	—	
Proales sordida			—	—	—	
Schizocerca				—	—	
Rotifer vulgaris			—	—		
Rotifer neptunius		—	—			
Rotifer citrinus		—	—			
Diglena biraphis	—	—	—			
Mollusca						
Physa fortinalis				—	—	—
Bythinia tentaculata				—	—	
Neritina				—	—	
Ancyle			—	—	—	—
Radix limosa				—	—	
Lymnaea truncatula				—	—	
Various species of *Lymnaea*				—	—	
Planorbids				—	—	
Paludins				—	—	
Pisidium				—	—	
Sphaerium (Cyclas) corneum			—	—	—	
Freshwater mussel *(Unio)*			—	—		
Dreissensia			—	—		
Margaritana (freshwater pearl oyster)					—	—
Oligochaeta						
Lumbriculus			—	—	—	
Tubifex		—	—	—		
Hirudinea						
Herpobdella		—	—	—	—	
Glossosiphonia			—	—	—	
Hemopis			—	—		
Infusoria						
Ophrydium versatile				—	—	
Colpidium colpoda	—	—	—			
Glaucoma		—	—	—		

Table 41. Representation of saprobes (*Contd*)

Zone	Characteristics	No. of germs per cu cm	No. of coliforms per litre	Oxygen	BOD_5
Catharobic	Clean potable water	< 500	< 20	Saturation	
Oligosaprobic		500–10,000	20–50,000	6–8 mg/l	< 2.5
β-Mesosa-probic	Ammonium compounds transfor-med to nitrates and nitrites	10,000–50,000	50,000–100,000	4 mg/l	< 4
α-Mesosa-probic	Organic matter being transformed to amino acids, ammonia salts and nitrites	50,000–250,000	100,000–1,000,000	2 mg/l	< 7
Polysaprobic	Traces of H_2S	200,000–2,000,000	1 million to 20 million	0.5 mg/l	40
Thiosaprobic	H_2S = 100 mg/l	20 million	10 × 10^9	0	200–700 mg/l

SLADECEK (1963) added a group comprising waters that are antisaprobic because of the presence of toxic substances that kill germs, radiosaprobic because of the presence of radioactive substances—nuclids, cryptosaprobic as a result of the antibiotic effect of a physical factor, such as temperature, mineral matter in suspension (clays), or organic matter (e.g., sludge, coal, oils).

2.3 Global Biological Index (GBI)

The GBI enables an evaluation of the general quality of a water course by analysis of the benthic macrofauna that is considered a synthetic expression of this general quality.

Applied at a site of running water, taken in isolation, the method enables us to determine the global biological quality within a general range. Applied comparatively (for example, upstream and downstream of a discharge of waste), the method enables us to evaluate the effect of disturbance on the receiving medium, within the limits of its sensitivity.

a) Source

The samples of benthic macrofauna (≥ 500 μm) are taken by station according to a sampling system that takes into account the different types of habitat depending upon the nature of the support and the flow velocity.

The taxa that are taken out are identified in order to determine the taxonomic variety of the sample and its faunistic indicator group. Determination of the GBI per station is expressed by a system of points of which the maximal value (20) corresponds to the optimal combinations observed from the nature-variety pair of the benthic macrofauna.

For the GBI, a station is defined as being a sector of a water course where the length is about 10 times the width of the water on the bed when samples are taken.

The index is more significant when it is obtained during an unfavourable period, at a low-water period (minimal flows, maximal temperature), or during a critical period (discharges of water, seasonal activities...).

b) *Sampling*

At a station, sampling of the benthic fauna is based on 8 specimens taken separately from 8 different habitats, each of $1/20$ m^2. Each habitat is characterized by a support-velocity (S-V) pair given among the combinations suggested in the table.

Specimen samples are taken with a sampler (Fig. 245). Each specimen is fixed at the site (10% solution of formaldehyde V/V).

If the available equipment is not sufficiently adapted, because of excessive depth, habitats are selected near the banks. The surface velocities are measured or, if that is not feasible, evaluated at the level of each habitat. The categories of support (S) are looked for in the order of succession given in the table (from 9 to 0). For each category of support, samples are taken in the velocity class that is most frequently associated with the support of a station. The category 0 is not taken into account unless the number of other supports is inadequate.

When a uniform station (e.g., straightened course, silted bed) does not have the 8 different types of supports, the number of samples is made up to 8 by others taken from the dominant support but, if possible, from different velocity classes.

A reference of each sample is entered in spaces of the table at the intersection of the coordinates S and V. The dominant habitat is stressed.

Table 41 gives examples of distribution of samples for the following stations:

a1 to a8: station Rhithron (biotope comprising upper reaches of the river)
b1 to b8: station Potamon (biotope of lower reaches of river, stream)
c1 to c8: recalibrated stretch of the Rhithron
d1 to d8: station of the Crenon (spring-water biotope)

c) *Biological analysis*

List of taxa

The taxonomic unit retained is the family with the exception of several faunal groups (branches or classes) that are poorly represented or of which the identification of taxa is a long and difficult process.

The list (in the Appendix) includes 135 taxa likely to be in the total variety (Σt), of which there are 38 indicators forming the 9 faunistic indicator groups (IG) (the groupings have been made for Odonates, Molluscs, Acheta (non-setose worms), and Triclads.

For France the identifications can be made with the help of a practical guide book suggested by M. TACHET.

The taxa are sorted and identified.

Determination of the global biological index (GBI)

The GBI is established from the analytical table (Table 43), which has on the ordinate the 9 faunistic indicator group (IG) and on the abscissa 12 classes of taxonomic varieties. We successively determine:

—The taxonomic variety of a sample (Σt), equal to the total number of taxa collected, even if represented by a single individual. This number is compared with the classes given in the abscissa of the table.

Table 42. Record of samplings

Surface velocities (l), v (cm/s)	V	v≥150	150>v≥75	75>v≥25	25>v≥5	5>v
Supports	S	2	4	5	3	1
Bryophytes	9		a_1, d_1			
Submerged spermatophytes (aquatic plants)	8			a_2	b_1	c_1
Large mineral sediments (stones, pebbles, shingle), 25–250 mm	7		a_3, b_2		d_2	
Large granulates (gravel), 2.5–25 mm	6		c_2	a_4, b_3		
Large organic elements (litter, branches, roots)	5				a_5, b_4	
Fine sediments ± organic (silt), ≤ 0.1 mm	4					a_6, b_5
Emergent spermatophytes (Heliophytes)	3			c_3		b_6
Natural and artificial surfaces (rocks, stone slabs, soils, walls)	2	a_7, d_3, d_8	c_6, d_5	b_7, c_4, d_6	c_7, d_7	c_8
Fine mineral granulates (sands and silts), < 2.5 mm	1				a_8, b_8, c_5, d_4	
Algae, bacteria and fungi in macroscopic colonies	0					

(l) The limits in velocity classes are given as an indication.

—The faunistic IG taking into account only the indicator taxa represented by at least three individuals in the sample. The IG is determined by following the ordinate in Table 43 from top to bottom (IG 9 to 1) and stopping at the first significant presence ($n \geq 3$ individuals) of a taxon in the list given on the ordinate of the table.

We deduce the GBI in Table 42 from its abscissa (Σt) and its ordinate (IG). For example:

If IG = 8 and Σt = 33 then GBI = 16
If IG = 5 and Σt = 30 then GBI = 13
If IG = 3 and Σt = 14 then GBI = 7

d) *Trial Report*

The trial report for each station should indicate:

—the date
—the precise geographical location (Lambert coordinates)
—the bank(s) studied for a water course with a depth of over 3 m
—the altitude
—the width of the water on the bed where the samples were taken
—the nature of the support and corresponding flow velocity for 8 samples taken at the station—(s-v) pans—indicating the dominant habitat
—the list of taxa taken, specifying their relative abundance
—the taxonomic variety of the sample (Σt)

– the faunistic IG (number in the order of IG)
– the GBI

For preparing a chart of the results, each sector of the water course may, depending on the value of the GBI, be indicated by a colour as shown in the following table:

GBI	≥17	16–13	12–9	8–5	≤4
Colour	blue	green	yellow	orange	red

2.4 Diatomic Indices (DI and DIG)

For assessing the quality of waters this is a promising method when diatoms, brown free-moving or colonial algae, are present from the sources to the estuaries (and beyond), in the cleanest as well as the most highly polluted mediums. Diatoms colonize any substrate, comprise a very large number of species, from the most ubiquist to the most **stenotopic**, with long and short cycles. The variability in their integrative capacity being associated with their perenniality, a proliferation of species of small sizes indicates short-term changes in the medium and, therefore, considerable instability.

Samples are obtained by scraping on a hard surface of 10–20 cm^2 or by squeezing plant material, or both. The diatoms are treated with concentrated oxygenated water to remove organic matter before they are put between a slide and a cover glass for microscopic examination (× 1000).

Countings are carried out on a number of about 400 individuals and converted to percentages of abundance for each recorded species. These percentages are used in computerized calculations of a diatomic index which, for most species, takes into account their sensitivity to organic pollution and their ability to adapt.

Based on calculation of correlations between the values of the diatomic index (DI) and the physicochemical parameters, for an interpretation of the results we may adopt the following six classes of quality (Descy, 1980):

DI ≥ 4.5	:	optimal biological quality, no pollution
DI of 4–4.5	:	subnormal quality (slight imbalance in algal population), slight pollution
DI of 3.5–4	:	greater imbalance, regression of sensitive species, moderate pollution or eutrophication
DI of 3–3.5	:	case somewhat similar to the previous one but the situation is due more to an average pollution level or an accentuated eutrophication
DI of 2–3	:	dominance of resistant species, considerable regression or disappearance of sensitive species (reduced diversity), high level of pollution
DI of 1–2	:	high level of dominance of several resistant species, minimum diversity (disappearance of many species), very high pollution level

Table 43. Value of the GBI depending on the nature and taxonomic variety of the macrobenthos

Total variety Σt		12	11	10	9	8	7	6	5	4	3	2	1
			39	36	33	29	25	21	17	13	9	6	3
Faunistic IG ($n \geq 3$)		≥40											
			37	34	30	26	22	18	14	10	7	4	1
Chloroperlidae *Perlidae* *Perlodidae* *Taeniopterygidae*	9	20	19	18	17	16	15	14	13	12	11	10	9
Capniidae *Brachycentridae* *Odontoceridae* *Philopotamidae*	8	19	18	17	16	15	14	13	12	11	10	9	8
Leuctridae *Glossosomatidae* *Goeridae* *Leptophlebiidae*	7	18	17	16	15	14	13	12	11	10	9	8	7
Nemouridae *Lepidostomatidae* *Sericostomatidae* *Ephemeridae* *Heptageniidae*	6	17	16	15	14	13	12	11	10	9	8	7	6
Hydroptilidae *Limnephilidae* *Rhyacophilidae* *Polymitarcidae* *Potamanthidae*	5	16	15	14	13	12	11	10	9	8	7	6	5
Leptoceridae *Polycentropodidae* *Psychomyidae* *Ephemerellidae*	4	15	14	13	12	11	10	9	8	7	6	5	4
Hydropsychidae *Baetidae* *Caenidae* *Trichlades*	3				11	10	9	8	7	6	5	4	3
Elmidae *Odonata* *Gammaridae* *Molluscs*	2					9	8	7	6	5	4	3	2
Chironomidae *Asellidae* *Acheta* (non-setose worms) *Oligochaeta*	1						7	6	5	4	3	2	1

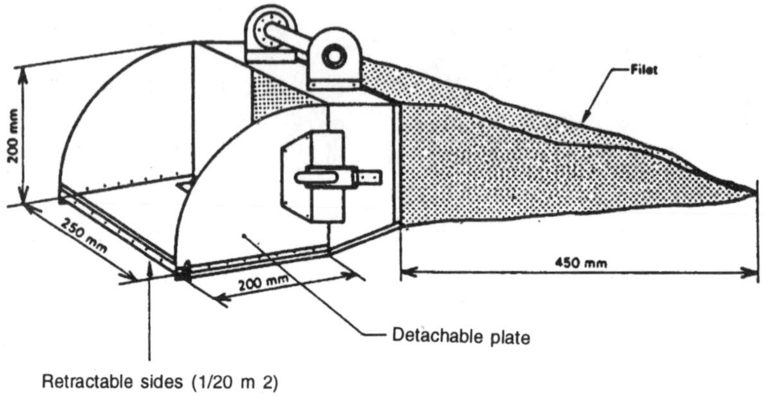

Fig. 245. Sampler—"Surber" position

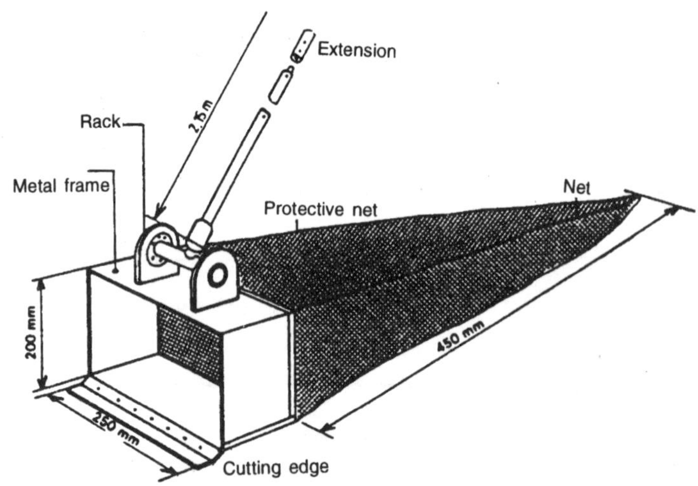

Fig. 246. Sampler—"Shrimping net" position

The utility of this method lies in its feasibility, reliability, rapidity, and simplicity. It nevertheless requires efficient microscopic material and competence (J. PRYGIEL, 1989).

In the basins of the Rhone and the Seine, RUMEAU and COSTE (1988) attempted estimation trials using the genus: the resulting index is called the DIG (diatomic index based on genera). In this way a routine practice helps us to acquire knowledge of the quality of a particular water provided that limiting cases are verified by using species or other indices.

The DI and DIG formulae and the list of diatoms used in the estimations are given in Annexure III together with an example of calculation.

2.5 Method of Microhabitats

This method takes into account, in a detailed manner, the habitat requirements of different fish species at each of their developmental stages. It assumes that other aspects are not limiting ones for the studied populations.

Developed in the United States by Bovee (1982), it has been tried out in some French water courses subjected or potentially subjected to use for hydraulic purposes.

The principle is based on a combination of two types of data:

—a biological type resulting from relationships noted between the existence or the relative density at a given stage of a species of fish and the values of several physical variables that characterize its habitat (water temperature, current velocity, depth and nature of the bed),

—a hydraulic model based on the reconstitution, after several series of measurements on the same water course, of the retained physical variables whatever the flow passing through the sector studied.

We may then, for a portion of a water course and a given flow, award points quantifying the quality of the habitat of the sector studied, taking into consideration the requirements of the particular fish population. It is assumed that a species, at a particular stage of its existence, would prefer a type of habitat that assures the most favourable conditions for its development. This preference is recorded for different morphodynamic parameters that characterize the habitat with the help of points from 1 to 0 depending on the extent to which the conditions are satisfactory.

These values are recorded with the help of **habitat preferenda curves** estimated for each parameter, species, and stage studied.

The water course is divided into homogeneous sectors from the habitat point of view. A study of the hydraulic parameters in each sector enables us, relative to the habitat curves, to award for a particular sector and for each stage of a given species a variable assessment depending on the flow: **the value of the habitat**.

This enables us to suggest a forecast of the effects of any modification in the hydraulic regime of a water course and, especially, based on natural or anthropic seasonal variations (retention or releases from dams) during the most critical periods and stages in the development of a fish population.

It is, however, argued that because of its empirical (award of points) and sketchy nature, which does not, for example, take into account the trophic requirements of the fish, the flow of solid material in water courses, or even their dynamics, the method is best suited for water courses in the hills that are tapped for their hydroelectric potential.

Souchon *et al.* (1989) are, however, of the view that the method could be a tool for explaining the rules for managing water courses provided it is improved upon by using multidimensional analytical techniques.

2.6 Index of Diversity

The index of diversity analyses the structure of an aquatic vertebrate population.

According to ECHAUBARD and NEVEU (1975), this index is even higher by one point when the families in it are represented by a somewhat similar number of individuals.

It is expressed by the formula:

$$D = -\sum_{i}^{i} P_i \log_2 P_i$$

where i is the number of species present and P_i the percentage of the species i.

It can be assumed that an index of diversity greater than 3 indicates a good hydrobiological state. If it is less than 2, there is pollution. The variation between these two values indicates a limiting situation with waters of doubtful quality.

Nevertheless, in water courses that are disturbed mechanically by navigation, dredging, or other improvement works, the use of such methods is not reliable. They are actually based on macro-invertebrates that are unable to find normal conditions for their existence in substrates that are sufficiently stable and it is recommended that our investigations be based on other organisms (especially algae and diatoms).

2.7 Index of Biotic Integrity (IBI)

This American method (J.R. KARR, 1981) based on an index enables multivaried qualification of a water course. The index integrates 12 qualitative and quantitative parameters of a fish population, distributed in three groups: the richness in species, the trophic composition, and the abundance and condition of the fish at a given site.

The conditions at this particular site are then compared with those expected at a similar site where there has been no disturbance. In extreme cases, when it is not possible to locate a site that has not been degraded, the one that has been subjected to the least impact is adopted as a standard.

Each parameter is awarded points on a scale of 5, 3, or 1 depending on whether it is close to or deviates moderately or considerably from the values established at the reference site. The IBI is the sum of these 12 awards and, therefore, varies from 12 to 60 in five qualitative classes:

excellent (58–60)
good (44–58)
fair (40–44)
poor (28–40)
very poor (less than 28)

The IBI has been tried out in several hydrographic regions of the United States and in the basin of the Seine in France (OBERDORFF *et al.*, 1990). Various experiments have demonstrated the utility of such an index as well as the obligation to modify its parameters depending on regional differences in the distribution structure of a fish population. The criteria for this index are given in the Appendix.

F. ORGANIZATION FOR DETECTION (FRANCE)

Pollution may be detected by anyone who observes an anomaly in a water course or a water body, whether it be the emission of a persistent odour, an abnormal colour of the water, or, in more serious cases, the appearance of dead or dying fish on the surface of the water or on the banks.

The matter should be reported immediately to the nearest town hall, police, fishing society, and home of the river guard.

Samples for analysis should be obtained as soon as possible, if not by specialists then at least by official representatives who, in the course of their work, are trained to obtain them (official river guards, police).

Samples merely support a report on the offence, enabling the person who caused the pollution to be prosecuted, but the two operations are not simultaneous and it is always worthwhile to obtain samples as soon as the pollution has been noted: the discharge that has resulted in poisoning a water course may be of short duration and samples taken later on may not enable its detection.

Every sample results in a sampling report, independent of the report on the offence, signed by the persons who obtained it and by witnesses.

1. MODE OF OPERATION

Contact the director of the factory and invite him to be present when samples are taken or to send his representative. If he refuses, record this fact in the sampling report and obtain samples in the presence of two witnesses.

Obtain samples as quickly as possible from four different places:

1. At least 50 m upstream of the point of discharge as indicated further on, at a place where the living conditions of fish appear to be normal.

2. In the effluent at the point of discharge from the outlet channel in the river, that is, the actual point where the residual waters are discharged into the stream, but before they are mixed with it. If the discharge is from an open channel, we take the liquid from it. If it is from a buried pipe, a sample will be obtained by pumping it out. Samples from the effluent will not be taken if they are fermentable unless it is possible to preserve them at a temperature of 5°C.

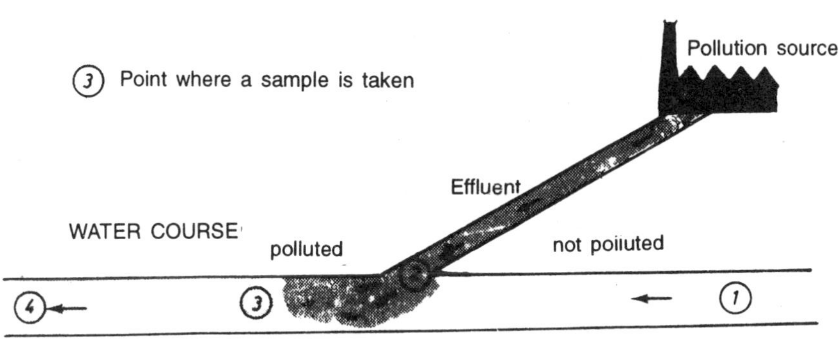

Fig. 247. Taking a water sample

3. From 3 to 50 m downstream of the point of discharge of the outlet channel into the river, in such a manner that the sample corresponds to a mixture of the effluent and river water.

4. From 50 to 100 m downstream from the aforementioned point of discharge in a clearly polluted medium.

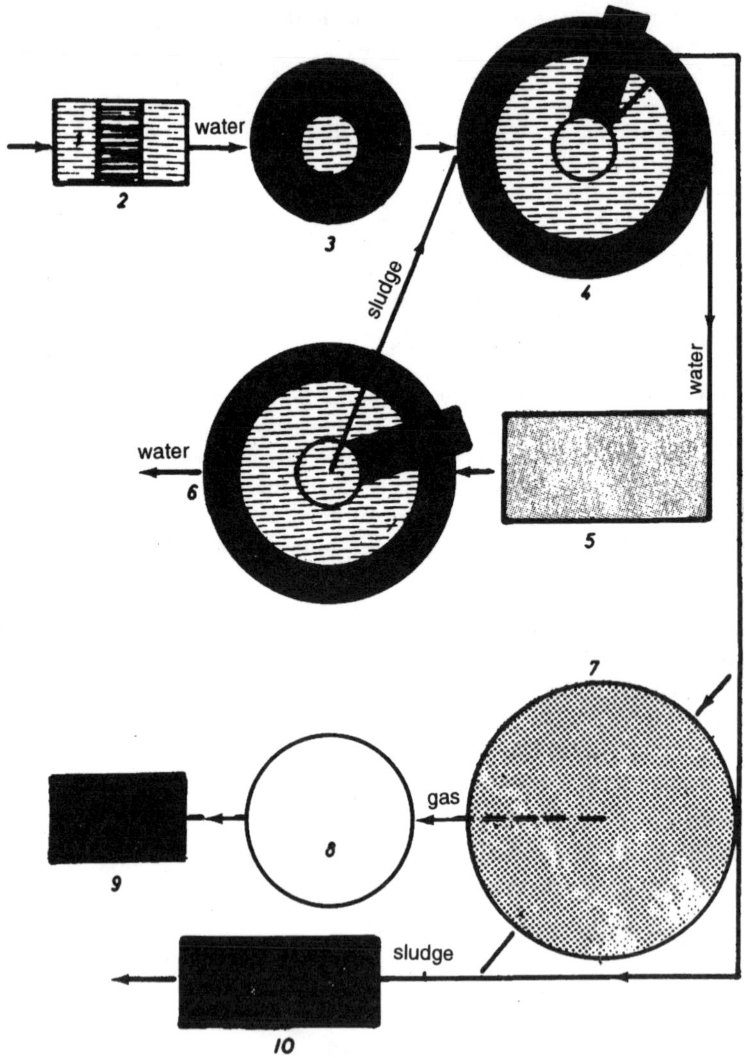

Fig. 248. Normal treatment of waters from urban drains. 1. Raw water. 2. Removal and shredding of trapped matter. 3. Removal of sand and oils. 4. Primary decantation. 5. Biological purification. 6. Treated water. 7. Digester. 8. Gasometer. 9. Central electric and heating plant. 10. Desiccation of sludges followed by incineration.

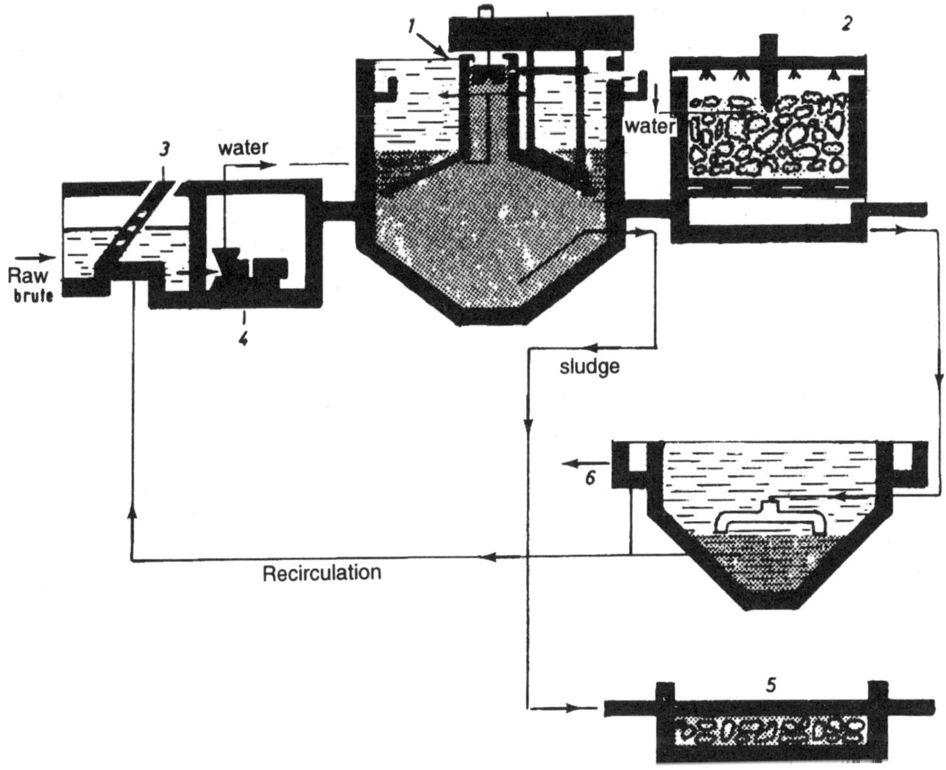

Fig. 249. Diagram of a rural treatment station for waste water. 1. Two-level tank. 2. Bacterial bed. 3. Removal of trapped matter. 4. Pumping. 5. Drying bed. 6. Treated water.

It may be noted that the major effects of pollution are not necessarily immediate, or promptly noted, at the point of discharge from a factory but may be observed at a certain distance downstream as, for example, in a case where the harmful effects of the discharge occur after fermentation.

The four indicated samplings are the normal ones. Their distances and numbers may vary, however, according to circumstances and situations.

If, for example, there are two factories located at a short distance from each other, it will suffice to take samples 50 m upstream of the second factory and at the outlets of the discharge channels of each of them.

There will, therefore, be at least four sampling points. Three samples will be taken from each of them.

The operator will fill three bottles, which he will cap, seal with wax, label, and number as follows: 1, 1A, 1B, 2, 2A, 2B, 3, 3A, 3B, etc.

Fig. 250. Treatment, inlet, removal of trapped matter, removal of oils, and primary decantation (town of La Tranche-sur-mer, Vendee, after J. ARRIGNON)

Fig. 251. Treatment in an aerated shallow pond after primary decantation (town of La Tranche-sur-mer, Vendee, after J. ARRIGNON)

Fig. 252. Treatment: at left, effluent after primary decantation and entry into a shallow pond to be used for fish (town of Munich, after J. ARRIGNON)

Each bottle will have the following information on the label:

Sample no. ....

River ....

Pollution noted on _______ at _______ hours

Sample taken on _______ at _______ hours

Name of the factory ....

Town ....

Name of the place ....

Temperature of water when samples were taken ....

Approximate flow of water at the place where samples were taken ....

Report on sampling

A report will be written immediately indicating the persons present, dates, and places. It will be signed by the person who took the samples, the manager of the factory or his representative, or by the two witnesses. It will be registered.

The manager of the factory will be given samples 1, 2, 3, and 4. If he refuses to accept them, they will be forwarded along with samples 1A, 2A, 3A, and 4A and handed over at the record office of the county court against a receipt.

Fig. 253. Treatment: general view of the piscicultural shallow-pond complex of 233 ha, producing 150 t/year (town of Munich, after J. ARRIGNON)

Samples 1B, 2B, 3B, and 4B will be despatched for analysis, urgently, to a specialized approved laboratory.

At the same time a letter will be forwarded confirming the despatch. This letter will contain the details given on the labels of the bottles and also the following additional information:

1. Name, location, and nature of the offending factory, the products it manufactures, the products it uses, and the products it discharges into the river, if possible.

2. The main fish species living in the river upstream of the discharge, species of fish that were found dead with an approximate indication of the percentages of each of them.

3. Average width of the affected water course, current velocity (fast, moderate, slow), average depth, nature of the bed (sandy, silted, rocky, pebbly), and the type of terrain (chalky or granite).

4. Effects of pollution on the aquatic vegetation from the point of view of its use in households, or its agricultural utility (suitable or unsuitable for cattle).

5. Other discharges upstream of the affected region, if any, and the approximate distance and nature, if possible.

It will also be necessary to:

6. Specify the odour and appearance of samples when taken, since these characteristics may change during the period of transportation for analysis.

7. Attach a sketch of the places where the samples were taken, which should be sufficiently clear and explicit, indicating the river, the outlet channel, the factory, the decantation tanks, if any, the places from where samples 1, 2, 3, and 4 were taken, and the distances between them.

The reporting official must inform the director of the local Department of Agriculture and Forests, who has competent jurisdiction, by sending him a copy of the reports on the offence and the samples along with a copy of the sketch.

2. INSTRUCTION AND FOLLOW-UP

Offences based on reports are recorded. To remain valid till indictment, they must be written and signed by two officials or two river watchers authorized by the administration. No proof should be admitted against the content of these reports unless there is a legal reason for challenging one of the signatories.

The findings should relate to the sampling operations but the police officials should also mention all useful findings concerning the appearance of the river, the colour and the odour of the water, the aquatic fauna, the vegetation and condition of the banks, and, if necessary, the appearance of the river bed at the place from which samples were drawn and upstream and downstream of it.

It is recommended that samples be taken, in the prescribed manner, in all cases. Nevertheless, some findings often provide proof of the offence, for example, when there is a blockage on the bed of a river as a result of physical pollution.

In all cases where fish have died after a particular discharge in a running stream or if there has been an adverse effect on their nutrition, reproduction, or food value, it is recommended that a report be made. In cases of accident, there may not be any penal action but the findings will enable those who have suffered a loss to receive an indemnity.

Further action on the reports may result in several possible outcomes: rejection, abandonment, settlement, or prosecution.

2.1 Rejection

Reports that are radically of little value are rejected: for example, if the facts do not reveal any offence, if the report has been prepared by committing an illegality such as violation of domicile, or if it has been prepared outside the limits of the district in which the police official had jurisdiction.

The decision to reject a report is taken by the Director of the local Department of Agriculture and Forests.

2.2 Abandonment

The Director may abandon certain valid reports indicating offences or contraventions that do not appear serious enough to be sent for trial, when the offence is not clearly established or when the culpability of the alleged offender is not clearly established.

He will send, with comments indicating the reason for this decision, reports that have been considered for abandonment or rejection to the Public Prosecutor, who will consider whether further legal action should be taken on them.

2.3 Settlement

Settlements related to offences covered by Article L-232.2 of the Rural Code are exclusively within the competence of the minister in charge of fishing.

Proposals for settlement are accompanied by the following documents:

—the report;

—the report on analysis of the samples; and

—the opinion of the Inspector from the Crime Branch or, if not available, proof that it has been requested.

The amount of the proposed fine takes into account all circumstances in which the offence has been committed as well as the care taken by the person who caused the pollution to remedy the situation.

In cases of accidental pollution, we need to make a distinction between those that have been caused by unforeseeable events and those that could have been prevented if all necessary precautions had been taken.

No penal action can, therefore, be taken against the owner of a truck that had met with an accident and whose load had fallen into a river, destroying some of the fish. On the other hand, such action may be taken against a person responsible for pollution if there is a breach in a poorly maintained channel above a river or in the case of a discharge from a badly maintained dyke or decantation basin near a water body.

Whatever the cause of the event that has destroyed fish, this must be recorded in the report; if no penal action can be taken, the recorded findings will when necessary help those who have suffered losses to be compensated.

It may happen that a report does not contain enough information to determine, with full knowledge, what action should be taken on it. Some additional information may be necessary, which can be provided only by the police.

In such cases, the Director of Agriculture and Forests of the department will need to refer the matter to an examining magistrate through the Public Prosecutor's Office.

He will request the Public Prosecutor to return the case file to him after examination so that he may forward suitable suggestions to the minister to enable him to exercise his authority in the matter of a settlement.

To consider a settlement the following two conditions must be fulfilled:

a) carrying out works necessary to stop the pollution or, if these are major works, an undertaking to complete them within a specific period and a beginning to this effect.

b) suitable compensation to all those who suffered losses due to the pollution.

During the examination of the report, the administration should inform all interested parties, especially those owners or tenants who have fishing rights, whether they use rods or nets, or organized groups of fishermen, so that these parties may claim compensation.

Permission for a settlement depends on suitable indemnities to those who have suffered losses due to the pollution provided, however, that their claims are not exaggerated. When a plaintiff is unable to obtain compensation within a laid-down period, his demand should be examined to ensure that it is reasonable.

2.4 Prosecution

If the administration decides to prosecute an offender, the case is initiated by the Director of the local Department of Agriculture and Forests. Unless special permission has been granted, the Directorate of Agriculture and Forests of the department must oppose any postponements in the case and take no judicial initiative that may delay the proceedings. If the alleged offender is discharged, the absence of a challenge or an approach to the Court of Appeal amounts, in practice, to a withdrawal of the case. Only the administration can authorize renunciation of such a recourse.

When a case comes up in appeal, the representative of the administration must present his written or oral arguments at a hearing. Only these are valid for consideration of the facts by the Court of Appeal.

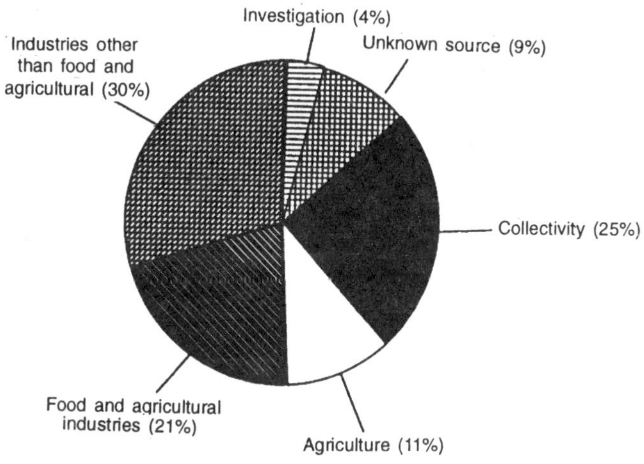

Fig. 254. Sectors of activity that cause accidental pollutions (source: CEMAGREF—National Centre for Agricultural Machinery and Rural Engineering in Waters and Forests, 1989)

Table 44. Table of invertebrates as indicators of saprobes in the estimation of salmonid water

Unfavourable indicators	Limiting indicators	Favourable indicators
Diptera:	Ephemeroptera:	Trichoptera:
Chironomus plumosus	*Baetis*	*Goera stenophylax*
Stratiomys	*Hydropsyche*	*Phryganea notidobia*
Crustaceans:	Diptera:	Diptera:
Asella	various Chironomes	*Simulium*
Molluscs:	*Sialis*	Turbellaria:
Sphaertium cornuum	*Holopedium*	*Planaria torva*
Dressenia	*Dendrocoelum lacteum*	*Planaria gonocephala*
		Polycelis nigra
Oligochaete worms:	*Ancylus*	Molluscs:
Tubifex	*Lumbriculus*	*Radix limosa*
Hirudinea:	Hirudinea:	
Herpobdella	*Glossosiphonia*	

Note: The limiting indicators intervene one way or another depending upon the extent of saprobes. The list given above is only an extract from the list of indicators established by WURTZ.

Table 45. General estimation of the quality of water courses, values limiting quality classes

Quality classes Parameters	1A	1A/1B	1B	1B/2	2	2/3	3	3/HC	HC
DBO_5 raw water, mg O_2/l		3		5		10		25	
DCO raw water, mg O_2/l		20		25		40		80	
MES, mg/l				25		70		150	
NH_4^+, mg/l		0.1		0.5		2		8	
NO_2^-, mg/l		0.1		0.3		1		2	
NO_3^-, mg/l						50		100	
N Kjeldahl, mg/l		1		2		3			
SO_4, mg/l						250			
Cl, mg/l		100		200		400		1000	
Oxidizability:									
$KMnO_4$, mg/l (1)		3		5		8			
Dissolved O_2, mg/l		7		5		3		1	
O_2 saturation		90		70		50			
Chlorophyll, mg/m^3		10		60		120		300	
Average biotic index (2)	≥9		7–8		5–6		3–4		1–2
Global biotic index (GBI)	≥16		13–15		9–12		6–8		≤5
Index of pollution (3)									
Variation between observed biotic index and reference index	0–1		2–3		4–5		6–7		≥8
P total, mg/l		0.1		0.25		0.5		2.5	
PO_4^-, mg/l		0.2		0.5		1		5	

(1) This parameter is not taken into account directly to determine the quality of water course.
(2) The mean biotic index is the average between the biotic index in a lotic facies and the biotic index in a lentic facies.
(3) The reference index is the biotic index observed in a water course comparable with the one under examination but in the absence of any pollution.

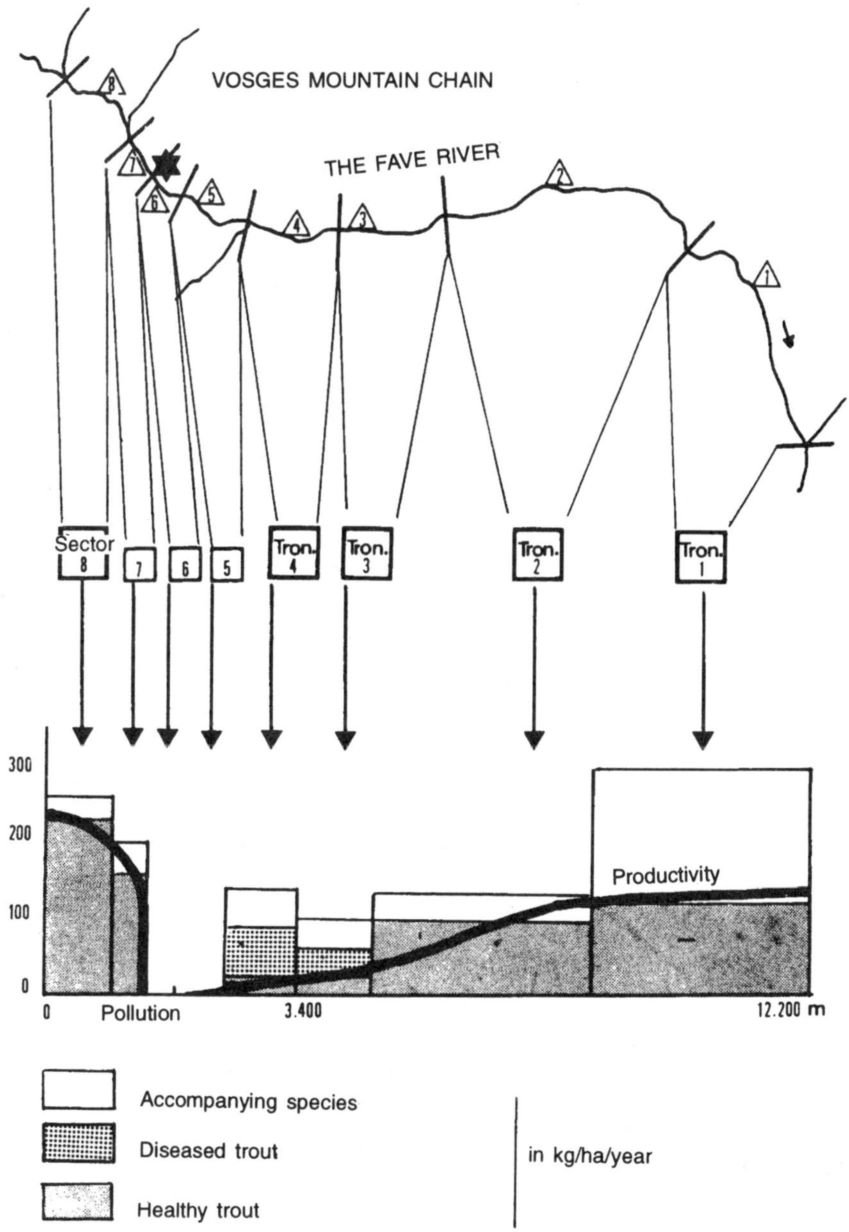

Fig. 255. Hydrobiological study of a river using a demographic fish inventory that has been accepted as a precedent for detecting a pollution and its effects (J. ARRIGNON, 1965, "Etude Hydrobiologique de la Fave," Doc. CSP)

Table 46. General table of the limits of reserved classes

		General water quality					Salinity F				
		1A	1B	2	3	4	S^0	S^1	S^2	S^3	S^4
Total Coliform	N/100 ml										
Fecal Coliform	N/100 ml										
Fecal Streptoc.	N/100 ml										
Water Salmonella											
Temp. of water	°C	≤20	20–22	22–25	25–30	>30					
pH		8.5–8.6			5.5–8.6	≤5.5ou ≥9.5					
Conductivity	µS/cm						0–400	400–750	750–1500	1500–3000	>3000
M.E.S.T. later on	mg/l	≤30			31–70	>70					
BOD_5 day	mg/l	≤3	3–5	5–10	10–25	>25					
COD	mg/l	≤20	20–25	26–40	40–80	>80					
Oxyd. (cold 4 h)	mg/l	≤3	3–5	5–8	>8						
Nitrogen Kjeldhal	mg/l										
Dissolved oxygen	mg/l	≥7	5–7	3–5	<3						
Saturation	%	≥90	70–90	50–70	<50						
Hardness	°F						≤15	15–30	30–50	50–100	>100
NH_4^+	mg/l	≤0.1	0.1–0.5	0.5–2	2–8	>8					
Cl^-	mg/l						≤100	100–200	200–400	400–1000	>1000
SO_4^-	mg/l										
NO_2^-	mg/l										
NO_3^-	mg/l	<44			44–100	>100					
	mg/l										
PO_4^-	mg/l										
NH_3	mg/l										
Fluorine	mg/l	≤1.5	>1.5								
Total iron	mg/l	≤0.5	0.5–1	1–1.5	>1.5						
Manganese	mg/l	≤0.10	0.1–0.25	0.25–0.5							
Arsenic	mg/l	≤0.06		0.06–0.1	>0.1						
Cadmium	mg/l	≤0.006			>0.006						
Total chromium	mg/l	≤0.06			>0.06						
Copper	mg/l	≤0.04		>0.04							
Mercury	mg/l	≤0.001			>0.001						
Lead	mg/l	≤0.06			>0.06						
Selenium	mg/l	≤0.01			>0.01						
Zinc	mg/l	≤0.3	0.3–1	>1							
Cyanide	mg/l	≤0.06			>0.06						
Anionic detergents	mg/l										
Phenolic compounds	mg/l	≤0.001		0.001–0.05	0.05–0.5	>0.5					
Extra substances of chlorine	mg/l	≤0.2	0.2–0.5	0.5–1	>1						
Total pesticides	mg/l										
Reference index-biotic index		≤1	1–3	3–5	5–7	>1					

Note: The European norms expressed in P_2O_5 have been converted to PO_4 with the following formula:

$$PO_4 \text{ content} = \text{Content of } P_2O_5 \times \frac{95}{142} \times \frac{62}{31}$$

Production of potable water						Bathing areas		Fish life			
A[1]		A[2]		A[3]				Salmonid waters		Cyprinid waters	
Guides	Imperatives	G	I	G	I	Guides	Imperatives	Guides	Imperatives	G	I
≤50		50–5000		8000–80000		≤500	≤10000				
≤20		20–2000		2000–20000		≤100	≤2000				
≤20		20–1000		1000–10000		≤100					
abs.		abs.				abs.	abs.				
≤22	≤25								≤21.5		≤28
5.5–8.5		5.5–9					6–9		6–9		6–9
≤1000											
≤26								≤26		≤26	
≤3		3–5		5–7				≤3		≤5	
≤1		1–2		2–3							
								50% ≥ 9et 100% ≥ 7	50% ≥ 8	50% ≥ 8et 100% ≥ 6	50% ≥ 7
≥70		50–70		30–50		≥ 80	≤120				
≤0.05	≤0.5	0.05–1	0.5–1.5	1–2	1.5–4			≤0.04	≤1	≤0.2	≤1
≤200											
≤150	≤250										
								≤0.01		≤0.03	
≤25	≤50	25–50									
≤0.54		0.54–0.94									
								≤0.005	≤0.025	≤0.005	≤0.025
≤0.7	≤1.5	0.7–1.7	>1.5								
≤0.06		0.06–0.1		0.1–1							
≤0.01	≤0.06			0.01–0.06	0.06–0.1						
≤0.001	≤0.006										
≤0.06											
≤0.02	≤0.06	0.02–0.06	>0.06	0.06–1				≤0.04		≤0.04	
≤0.0006	≤0.001										
≤0.06											
≤0.01											
≤0.5	≤3	0.5–1	3–5						≤0.3		≤1
≤0.06											
≤0.2				0.2–0.5		≤0.3					
0	≤0.001	≤0.001	0.001–0.006	0.001–0.01	0.006–0.1	≤0.006	≤0.06				
≤0.1		0.1–0.2		0.2–0.5							
	≤1000		1000–2500		2500–5000						

The parameters that are the object of the norms in the absence of recorded measurements in the pollution inventory have not been used again.

PART THREE

Management of Aquatic Mediums

There are many aspects to managing aquatic ecosystems. These depend on whether the developments are meant to bring back to certain surroundings earlier qualities that have been lost because of lack of proper and regular maintenance, to help in remodelling other surroundings in tune with newly arisen, urgent objectives, or to deal with new or artificial surroundings or those surroundings created for human needs.

Any management plan should at the same time keep in mind the great variety of objectives. For example, sometimes the economy of water is determined more by industrial consumption than by human consumption; quality criteria differ greatly, based on the type of consumption.

The hydrographic situation in France is very different from what it was barely five centuries ago. The industrial age has had rapid and spectacular effects. In addition, the total changes that have taken place in the French landscape during the past few centuries, although slower and more remote, cannot be ignored. The clearing of the forest cover that was spread over the country during the middle ages has completely transformed the nature, potential, and even the ecological vocation of the rivers.

However, it cannot be said with certainty whether the medieval condition of rivers was better than what it was at the end of the 19th century, as far as fish culture is concerned. If we consider the productivity of rivers and ponds having primarily, if not totally, a forest basin, we will realize that it is lesser than in waters fed by a pastoral basin and much lesser than in waters having bocage or grazier basins (Arrignon, 1967). Observations made in British Columbia show that decomposition of vegetable matter results in the ageing of the undergrowth of virgin forest, causing severe organic pollution, which in turn lowers fish production from the existing stock. A similar situation was noticed in French water bodies a few centuries ago. It is possible that their productivity peaked at the end of the 19th century and thereafter, a state of generalized decomposed organic debris seems to have set in the waters, at least in those cases where the waters have not been more directly affected by pollution.

Thus the choice before us is to develop fish surroundings. Very few measures will be able to restore the old situation. Many of them have to correspond to new needs and aspirations and at the same time respect certain rules of fish ecology, which have already been mentioned.

1 PHYSICAL MANAGEMENT

Physical management includes the development of the inorganic constituents of the aquatic medium, its surroundings, and its capacity of external as well as internal reception, quality of the organic constituents, and thereby the entire ecosystem. A wrong physical development of the ecosystem can even lead to the disappearance of the ecosystem existing as an aquatic medium and, in many cases, irreversibly reduce its productivity.

The very unsteady state of balance of the natural surroundings is dependent on proving a comprehensive and regular maintenance and to achieve this, one has to keep in mind economic realities and ecological rules.

A. MAINTENANCE OF THE AQUATIC MEDIUMS

1. MAINTENANCE OF THE SURROUNDINGS

Maintenance of the surroundings involves development and maintenance of approaches that could save anglers the trouble of going through the approaches of other anglers and thus disturbing them. It is important to keep the gates, steps, and turnstiles in good condition, as these provide access to the fishing route or help people to pass along the route without having to open the gates, which in turn could prove harmful to livestock. The maintenance of access routes and fishing routes checks anglers from wandering into pastures during hay-time. Access for animals has to be focussed on well-determined, developed, and well-maintained points. The approach to the drinking trough should be paved with broken brick so that the ground is not trampled into mud while animals drink. Access to vehicles should be limited to well-located and spacious parkings, away from sunlight, where non-anglers can be accommodated with basic facilities, such as benches, rough tables, and well-designed rubbish bins that are regularly emptied.

For access to the fishing stations one should keep in mind certain special cases such as handicapped anglers. A handicapped angler should be able to move easily from the parking lot to the fishing point, and horizontal approaches should be provided. The fishing station itself should be planned so that the angler can easily work from a wheelchair. The station can consist of a plane, square area measuring 120 cm on each side. The sides are protected from the water's edge by a wall-like construction which blocks the front wheels of the chair and by a 40 cm high guard rail.

There are many possibilities for the layout of the sites and the extent of facilities that may be planned for the fishing area (ROLLAND, 1987).

If the surroundings are impenetrable, then we can start with the opening up of the plant cover. The river bed should be exposed to daylight. There is often a very close link between an inextricable vegetation and blockage of the bed. The use of chain saw and clearing equipment will provide the fastest solution. On the plains, two workers can clear a 2.5 m wide and 500 m long river border in one day. The job is carried out in the same way along a stretch of smooth water. The debris is generally burnt except for trunks and branches, since these can be used for repairing the banks.

Depending on the direction of water flow and the sun's rays, it is convenient to leave one bank uncleared or covered with vegetation so that it nurtures insects, a favourite prey for the fish. It is often advisable to operate through clear spaces, following the water flow and its meanders.

In the case of ponds, it is better to let the trees remain overhanging and some stumps buried here and there, as these will help sustain large carnivores.

Once the surroundings are cleared, it will be necessary to use a hoist, capstan or tractor straightaway to remove branches, trunks, and other debris that block the bed. All this is either burnt or disposed of.

Maintenance of embankments calls for refilling the top and sides as soon as these are eroded or hollowed by flood during bad weather conditions. Refilling should preserve the slopes that existed previously and should also be followed by new turfing. The small shrubs and bushes resulting from wind- and water-borne seeds have to be removed. The visible parts of the structure—monk pillar, spillway, ski jump, water inlet, and various canals—have to be repaired. In the same way, the invisible parts, pipes and manholes, must be examined, in case there is abnormal water discharge.

Leaks are repaired and, depending on the extent of damage, are sealed with free mud, or with a mixture of fine mud and clay, or with fine mud sifted and mixed with colloidal clay (benotnyl or benotnite). These materials are poured out with the help of a shovel or wheelbarrow at the base and top of the slope. They are pulled by the water current and consequently seal the leakages.

Repair should also be carried out on the major openings of pond embankments that are not in use. The openings are sometimes covered by thick vegetation, which has to be got rid of. It is cut off and the resulting matter consisting of fallen earth and cut vegetable roots has to be removed. Finally, we come in contact with the ground to be used. This has to be taken up, got more or less ready, before the new material necessary for filling in the openings is poured out and compacted. The junctions have to be carefully supervised. In spite of all the care given, there is always an element of uncertainty about such repair work.

2. CLEARING

According to the terms used in French law, clearing, often called "recalibration" when it applies to water courses, should aim at restoring to the water courses "their original depths and borders." The objective should be the same as in the case of lakes and rivers: to remove roots of vegetation, sediments that raise the level of

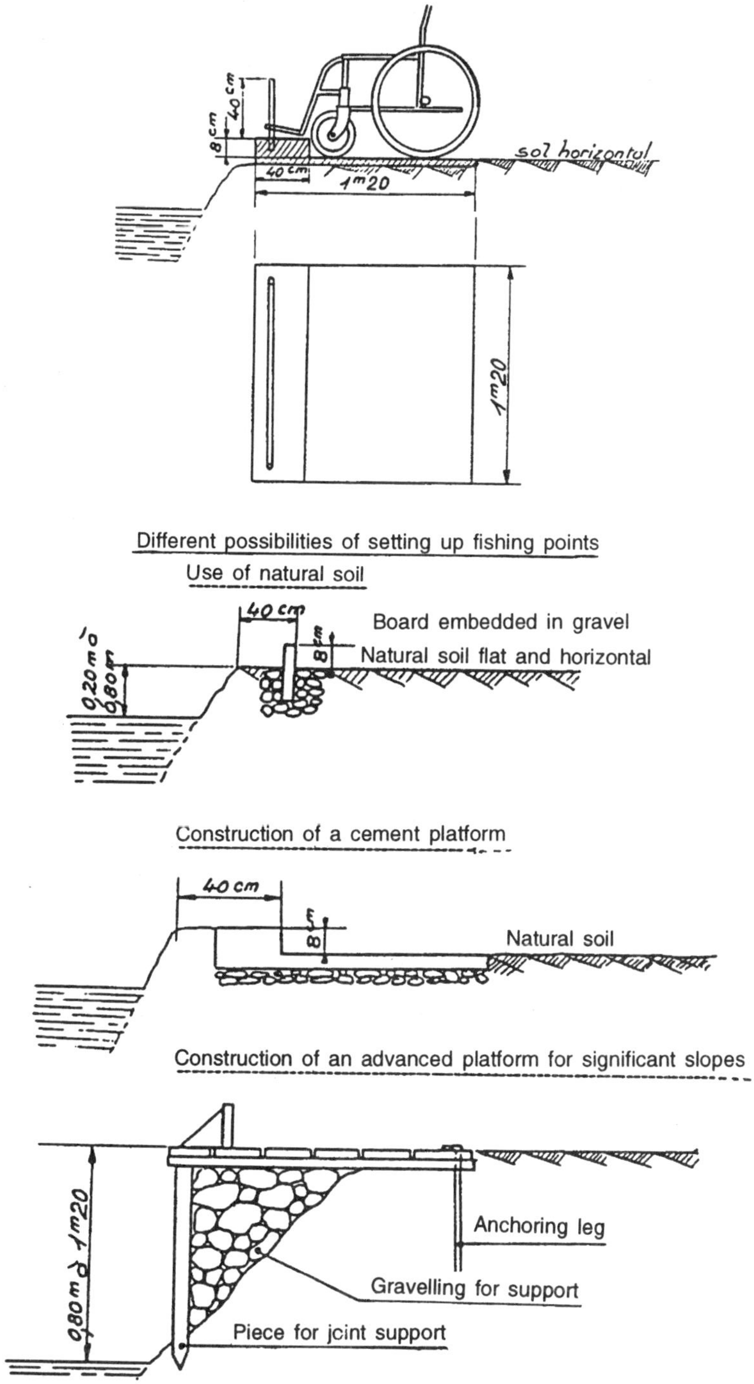

Fig. 256. Development of stations for handicapped anglers (ROLLAND, 1987)

Fig. 257. Repairing a dam

water, and also black sludge, an indicator of bad conditions. The grey sludge, which generates major biological exchanges for the microfauna, has to be left in place, except when it blocks the pan and drainage canals.

It is very much in practice to use a rake, a flexible instrument, which can help to guide the clearing based on the requirements of the habitat. For example, some small plants are left in place and only the blocked loops and bends are cleared.

2.1 Self-clearing

In the case of a constantly large bed with damaged and unsteady banks, self-clearing with the help of deflectors or submerged needles is carried out, so as to reduce its width. Setting up of panels, at places suitable for correction and acceleration of the water current, helps in removing the median layer of sludge, pulling it, and directing it towards the banks. If the current is not strong, this sludge gets deposited and mineralized to form a new and small wall-like structure. The miniature wall can be fortified with the help of a protective pad by setting up fascines and by planting perennial plants with strong roots (*Carex*). Starting from the upper reaches, self-clearing is done in the downstream direction, and the panels are sometimes moved and used again close to one another.

2.2 Digestion of the Sludge

Digestion of the sludge with use of coccolithic pulverulent calcium carbonate has been demonstrated by SAWYER (1965) in England and by GAGNIARD (1965) in France. A pulverulent chalk introduced in a water course filled with sludge makes the organic part of the sludge disappear. The water current then transports the finest mineral particles downstream, and coarse sand and gravel are left in place. This digestion is sometimes impeded by the action of aquatic vegetation. ROFES (1974) shows that the action of chalk is mainly attributed to the presence of Ca^{++} ions which, after passing through the solution, bring about a flocculation of colloids and reduce cohesion of the sludge. As a result, the critical speed or erosion is reduced to 40%, which in turn favours movement of the sludge downstream.

Three to five tonnes of calcium carbonate are used per hectare or per km of water course having a width of 10 m. Sacks of carbonate, tied together in a line, are sunk into the river to be treated and form a barrier. The sacks are pierced with a fork. The current rushing through the holes pushes the chalk out. The chalk gets mixed with the sludge and acts on it. Once in two days, the action is completed by manual movement of the magma remaining in the bags.

Before carrying out any treatment, it is advisable to pay special attention to the calcium content of water and also to the masses of vegetation generating carbonic acid at night. An excess of soluble carbonates leads to the formation of nodules, which in turn will form an unsteady bed and later on this bed becomes concretized and thus unfavourable to any animal or plant life.

The action of calcium carbonate in lakes and rivers brings about only a small reduction in the sludge volume, which gets almost completely redeposited in the same area. However, it modifies the texture and structure of the bed and favours the growth of aquatic plants (Leon pond, Landes; Wingles pond, North).

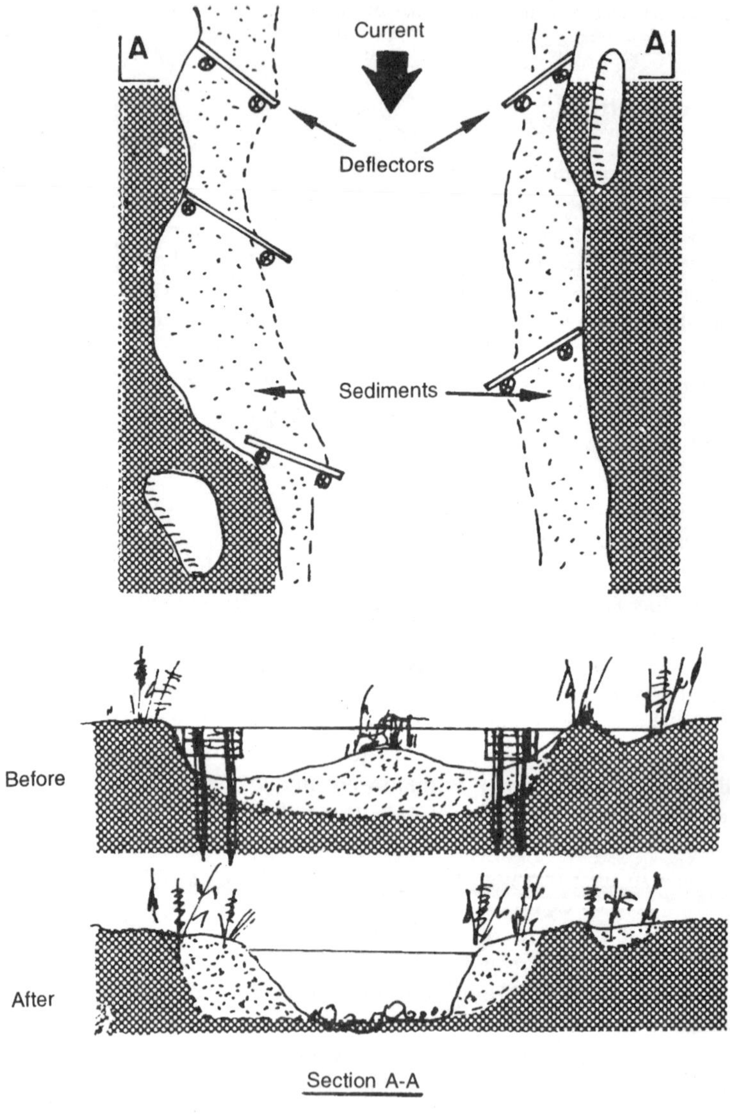

Fig. 258. Self-clearing

2.3 Suction Dredging

Suction dredging is carried out with the help of equipments of varying sizes. The portable equipment highlighted by BIVER (1968) helps in carrying out work with

Fig. 259. Diversification of the facies with a rise in beam (after J. ARRIGNON)

Fig. 260. Self-clearing with the help of deflector panels (note the downstream landing of each panel) (after J. ARRIGNON)

Fig. 261. Clearing with the help of a vacuum dredger

Fig. 262. Pond clearing with the help of a bucket mounted on a shaft. Wingle ponds (Pas de Calais) (after Cl. LEMAIRE).

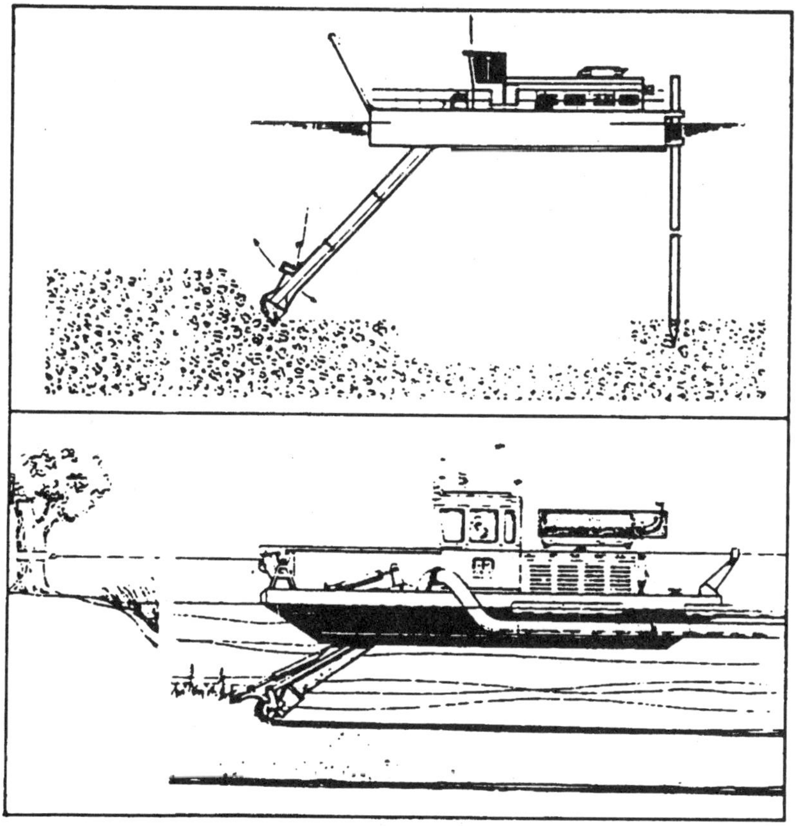

Fig. 263. Clearing a pond: two types of heavy equipment (Anonymous, 1985)

flexibility, keeping in view the habitat. The mixture of water and sludge is released up to 100 m from the site, on to a receiving area, consisting of undergrowth or marsh. However, it is impossible to clear if the depth of the bed exceeds 1 m, which is as far as the operators working in fishing pants in water can reach. This light equipment is often suitable for clearing small streams, rivulets, and diversions that are to be transformed for the purpose of raising small pike and trout.

2.4 Other Methods

The largest equipment includes a wide range of bulldozers with wide tracks, dump trucks, and small and big dredgers. Their use should match the nature and extent of clearing to be carried out. They are difficult to operate and risk devastating the surroundings and destroying the natural geometry of lakes and rivers.

Fig. 264. Fish culture: deflectors in front of water points (Slupsk, Poland, after J. ARRIGNON)

Clearing is usually done in winter, at a time when aquatic vegetation is less spread out in the area. However, it has to be suspended in the salmonid spawning zones up to the emergence of fry.

In the clearing of a water course, one has to start from the upper reaches and move downstream. The operation can be done the other way around only if clearing the upper reaches may release the sources and thus cause flooding downstream.

3. REMOVAL OF WEEDS

The first and foremost aim of using the scythe is to reduce to an acceptable level the surface occupied by the aquatic vegetation in a water course so that there is an adequate water flow, free circulation of fish, and, at the same time, sufficient shade. The second aim is to prevent the slow but steady rise of the river or lake bed by the accumulation of roots, particularly at the banks.

3.1 Mechanical Removal

Clearing carried out during the period of plant growth (from July to the end of August) deprives rhizomes of respiration of leaves. By autumn, they do not have the reserves made available to them till then by photosynthesis. Their regrowth is

Fig. 265. Fish culture: weeding conveyor belt in front of a water point with backside ejection (Augerolles, Puy de Dome, after J. ARRIGNON)

thus in great danger. If this is carried out for three years in succession, mechanical clearing brings about an almost complete destruction of rush. A 30 cm reduction in depth, along with the destruction of the bushes, for example, will correspond to a sludge volume of 1 cu m from 3 sq m of surface. It is easy to do the per hectare calculation since the banks are generally 6–8 m wide. Preventing sludge formation on the pond by regular clearing of weeds is always more economical than clearing.

Effective elimination of aquatic herbs has to be carried out by repeatedly breaking their vital cycle of flowering and fruit bearing. For example, if elimination of water chestnut (*Trapa natans*) is delayed, then it will disperse and colonize quickly. The fruit of this plant continues to grow even when the stem is cut off. Early use of scythes is thus necessary (in June–July), from the beginning and as many times as needed to eliminate the fruit.

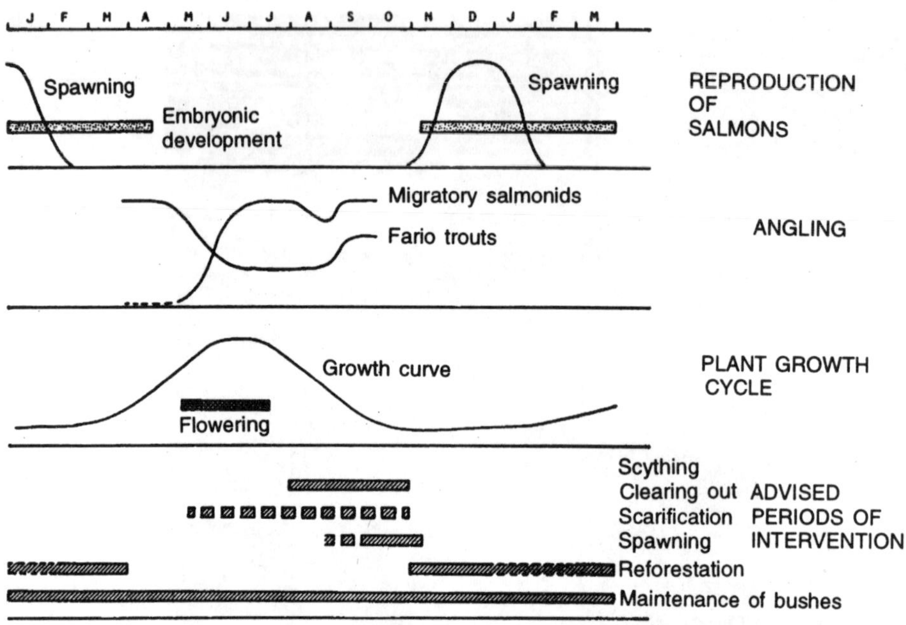

Fig. 266. Calendar of optimum intervention periods in salmon-bearing calcareous rivers of Western Europe (after EUZENAT and FOURNEL, 1987)

Certain steps have to be taken during fish reproduction. Depending on the location of the spawning place, scythes should be used on longitudinal tracks, either in the middle of the river or along any of the banks.

The less complicated the use of the equipment in question, the easier it is to check the spread of vegetation in a planned way. Manual cutting of weeds requires a scythe with a long handle, with a "chatelaine" made up of a dozen cutting blades joined to one another. This scythe has to be pulled along the bed on each bank. The mechanical clearing of weeds requires a number of equipments, ranging from a *scythe block* to vertical and horizontal bars, which can adapt themselves to any landing, on *scything boats* conceived for this purpose. In the same way, there are *amphibious scythes* that enable us to bring down flooded banks and *scything rakes* (ARRIGNON and JUSTINE, 1975), which can remove soft vegetation and cut debris and deposit them on the bank.

3.2 Chemical Removal

Removal of weeds by chemical means presents certain advantages—it saves time, it requires less skilled labour, and its effects last longer—but on the whole it is dangerous when the long-term effect of compounds used on the aquatic fauna are taken into consideration.

Potassium chlorate used at a rate of 500 kg/ha on beds helps burn up the dry vegetation. *Copper sulphate* destroys unicellular algae. *Auxins*, used in spring, dry up plants (2,4D-2,4,5,T-2,4,5.T.P), but the 2,4D, used in normal dosages, kills fish in 96 hours.

The *fatty allogenous acid compounds*, which include Dalapon, TCA, and Basinex, have an effect on foliage. Plants are poisoned and stop growing. They are thus harmful to all plants that appear. The *substituted urea* acts after clearing, even before plants appear. Application is most interesting in canals (C.M.V.—Monuron, Diuron, Telwac). *Triazine* is absorbed by the roots. Leaves dry up, there is very little regrowth the following year, and the effect is lasting. There is practically no toxicity for fish and their nutritive milieu. Triazines do not remain in water forever; they are inactivated as soon as they come in contact with the ground. Generally, Gramoxone and Reglone along with Radoxone are used to destroy mono- and dicotyledonous perennial plants, chloroxone is used to destroy water lilies, and sylvoxone to get rid of bushes having a woody or semi-woody vegetation (bramble).

Application by pulverization is done from the bank and from a landing, through slits, in such a way as to allow a shelter for the fish. The treated waters have to be stagnant. Early treatment in May has to be completed later on with weaker doses. Use of chemicals such as triazines is effective for about three years.

3.3 Biological Removal

Biological removal can be done with the help of fish like the asiatic carp (page 246 ff) and ordinary carps, which stop the development of vegetation by burrowing themselves in the sludge and breeches, and thus can uproot plants from the bed. Similarly, ducks efficiently control duckweed and myriophylloid algae (Vigneux and Vigneux-Quentin, 1975). The coypu is also an excellent removal agent; it consumes vegetation and does not have the damaging burrowing habits of the muskrat.

4. MEASURES AGAINST MUSKRAT

Similarly, measures must be taken against muskrat (*Ondatra zibethica*) (page 89) as part of the maintenance of the aquatic medium because it causes serious problems to the environment.

4.1 Use of Toxic Gases

Use of toxic gases should be discouraged because they are far from efficient; they get dissolved in water and are detected by the animal, which leaves the area before toxic action can set in. Hydrogen phosphide is not soluble, but it can be used only by trained and experienced persons because the active gas is highly toxic. In Germany, cartridges are used. These, when consumed, release gas and vapour, which force the rats away from the area and into traps laid at the entrances of the area.

Table 47. Herbicides suggested for control of aquatic vegetation (after Thirappan Bhukaswan, 1980)

1. Algae

Algicides	Fatal dose	Name of algae	References
Algaecidex	1.0 ppmw (a) ($CuSO_4$)	Phytoplankton	Hiltibran, 1970
Atrazine	0.2 ppmw	Filamentous algae	Hiltibran, 1970
Copper sulphate	0.3–0.5 ppm (soft water) 1.0 ppm (hard water)	Blue-green and green algae	Surber, 1961
Cutrine	1.0 ppmw ($CuSO_4$)	Filamentous algae phytoplankton	Hiltibran, 1970
Dichlobenil	4.5 Kh ha	*Chara vulgaris*	Van Busschbach and Elings, 1967
	1.0 ppm	*Vaucheria*	Jennings, 1967
Diquat	1.0 ppm	*Cladophora*	Hiltibran, 1970
Diuron	1.1 kg/ha	Filamentous algae	Bugenberg de Jong, 1967
	0.1 ppm	Filamentous algae	Bugenberg de Jong, 1967
Pennsalt TD-47		Diatoms	Funk and Gaufin, 1965
Pennsalt TD-188		Green algae, diatoms	Funk and Gaufin, 1965
Pennsalt TD-191		Green algae, diatoms	Funk and Gaufin, 1965
Paraquat	0.5–1.0 ppm	Phytoplankton	Silvo, 1967
Simazine	0.2–0.4 ppmw	Filamentous algae phytoplankton	Hiltibran, 1970

ppmw = parts par million by weight

2. Floating plants

Herbicides	Fatal dose	Name of plant	References
2,4-D acetamide (20% act. ingr.)	11.2 kg/ha	Bulrushes	Surber, 1961
2,4-D, amine	0.5%	Water ryacinth sagittarius, *Sparganium* *Pontederia cordata*	
2,4-D, ester	0.5%	*Typha, lotus,* bulrushes, water lettuce, water lily sagittarius *Alternanthera philoxeroides* *Pontederia cordata* Soft reeds *Sparganium*	
2,4-D, in granules	112.3 kg/ha	Watershield	
2,4-D iso-ester	5.6 kg/ha	*Typha*	
2, 4, 5-T	1.000 ppmw	water hyacinth, *Pistia* *Spirodela ipomea*	Misra and Das, 1969
Amitrole	11.2 kg/ha	*Typha*	Surber, 1961
Amitrole formulation	2.3 kg/ha	Water hyacinth	Gallagher, 1962
Dalapon	11.2–22.4 kg/ha	*Typha*	Surber, 1961
Dichlobenil	1.0 ppm	*Phragmites communis*	Van Busschbach and Elings, 1967
Diquat	0.5 ppmw	*Hydrilla verticillata*	Mackenzie and Hal, 1967
	1.0 ppm	*Callitriche stagnalis*	Surber, 1961
Endothal	0.24 kg/l	*Lemna* sp. (duckweed)	Bennett, 1970

Table 47. (*Contd*)

2. Floating plants (Contd)

Herbicides	Fatal dose	Name of plant	References
Diuron	0.6–1.1 kg/ha	*Chara, Nymphea*	
	2.0 ppmw	*Hydrilla verticillata*	Blackburn and Weldon, 1970
Silvex	9 kg/ha	*Alternanthera philoxeroides*	
	3.4 kg/ha	Bulrushes	Surber, 1961

3. Submerged plants

Herbicides	Fatal dose	Name of plant	References
2,2-D ester (20% granules)	22.5–45 kg/ha	*Myriophyllum spicatum*	Smith and Hall, 1967
Copper sulphate	112.3 kg/ha	*Elodea densa*	Ware, 1966
	0.5–1.0 ppm	Most submerged plants	Newman, 1967
	1.0 ppm	*Elodea canadensis* *Elodea densa* *Ceratophyllum demersum* *Potomogeton* spp. *Hydrocharis morsus ranae*	
	8.5 l/ha	Aquatic milfoil	Jenning, 1967
Diuron	0.6–1.1 kg/ha	*Najas* *Ceratophyllum demersum* *Justicia americana*	Sewell, 1970
	2.3 kg/ha	As above + Lotus and pond plants	Dalrymple, 1971
	3.4 kg/ha	As above + crisped pond plants bulrushes *Persicaria*	
	4.6 kg/ha	As above	
Endothal (in granules)	0.5 ppm	*Potamogeton diversifolius*	Surber, 1961
	1.0 ppm	*Potamogeton pusilus*	
	5.0 ppm	*Potamogeton americanus* *Potamogeton foliosus*	
Hydrothol	3.0 ppm	*Najas guadalupensis*	Surber, 1961
Hydrothol 191 (in granules)	2.5 ppmw	*Elodea* spp.	Ware, 1966
Paraquat	0.5–1.0 ppm	Most submerged vegetation *Elodea canadensis*	Newman and Silvo, 1967
Silvex	0.5 ppm	White water lily	Younger, 1958
	1.0 ppm	Yellow water lily	
	2.0 ppm	Water plantain Aquatic milfoil	
Simazine	11.2 kg/ha	*Potamogeton diversifolius*	Younger, 1958 Surber, 1961
Salium arseniate	2.5–4.0 ppm	Most submerged plants	Surber, 1961

4.2 Use of Microbes

The use of microbes such as *Salmonella,* known in France as "Pasteur virus", has limited potential against muskrats living in colonies. This being the case, we cannot hope to obtain an explosive epizootic disease as with myxomatosis. It helps to use the Pasteur virus baits by calculating the number of baits required for the animals. The biology of the muskrat is a major obstacle in using this method; the animal is very eclectic in looking for its food and consumes bait only accidentally.

4.3 Use of Poisons

According to GIBAN (1960), anticoagulants such as chlorophacinon at 0.015% and coumafene at 0.070% are to be used. Carrots, beetroots, or apples are used as bait, depending on the region. These are cut into big pieces with the help of a root-cutter and mixed with the raticide, which is in the form of an oily concentrate. Mixing is done with an agricultural mixer or a cement mixer. As a general rule, poisoned baits are placed on tracks along bushes through which the animals pass, in the aquatic vegetation, in open burrows, and in holes during winter. The muskrat covers a sufficiently large area and many baiting points are to be located in the path of the animal. It is better to renew the baits till consumption is stopped; the rat has to ingest the toxic substance many times. Moreover, we are never sure if the quantity of bait deposited in each area is enough for the number of rats that frequent the area. It is not advisable to carry out this treatment in February–March and in September–October, when there is a big shift in their population. It is better to wait for the population to stabilize before laying the poison bait. This method of destruction is very efficient if carried out in an organized and systematic manner on large land areas (marshes). Even if the danger of poisoning is practically nil in the case of humans, ruminants, and fish, it is nevertheless considerable for pigs, dogs, and cats and also for other rodents such as hare and rabbits.

4.4 Trapping

Traps are set in winter on tracks and paths and are of many types, such as traps with jaws or with hoop nets. The more accessible the burrows and holes, the easier it is to trap the animal. Long periods of frost act favourably since they allow easy access to holes.

Trapping is a relatively slow and expensive process and requires specialized personnel. In order to keep up the results obtained in the regions treated with poison, trapping seems to be an option better adapted and more certain than the poisonous baits, especially because it brings about a permanent control of the main channels of reinfestation.

Destruction of the muskrat can never be carried out on a small scale if we desire a long-lasting effect. Animals killed are replaced in a fairly short span of time by animals coming from other areas, irrespective of the means used to destroy them.

B. CLASSIFICATION OF PONDS

Table 48. Classification of ponds

1. According to origin	
Natural ponds	**Artificial ponds**
Resulting from water accumulation in land depressions (morainal)	Resulting from human activity excavations peat bogs gravel } generally do not get emptied sand
crumbling areas (mining)	barrier ponds, specially built for fish culture
Generally, they cannot be emptied	Emptied by various means
2. According to feed	
through sources (from bottom or banks)	
through streams (hill ponds, storm and rain water storages)	
through water current	
3. According to arrangement	
valley barrier ponds	
succession ponds —in series (fed by gravity, some by other means) —in parallel (individually fed by derivation from a river)	
4. According to purpose	
Angling ponds	
Fishing and production ponds (fishing as sports and business combines)	
Production ponds	
Fish culture annexes	
Replenishing ponds	
Storage ponds	
Spawning ponds	
Winter ponds (for carps)	

C. CREATION OF ARTIFICIAL MEDIUMS

1. EXCAVATED PONDS

Excavated ponds are made with two distinct objectives:

—leisure time water sports practised in groups or alone (in local ponds and lakes present in country houses) and

—extraction of materials needed for construction and public works (marl pits, sand pits, clay quarries, gravel quarries, ballast holes).

The two objectives are sometimes interlinked with the sale of materials covering the expenses incurred in digging a pond.

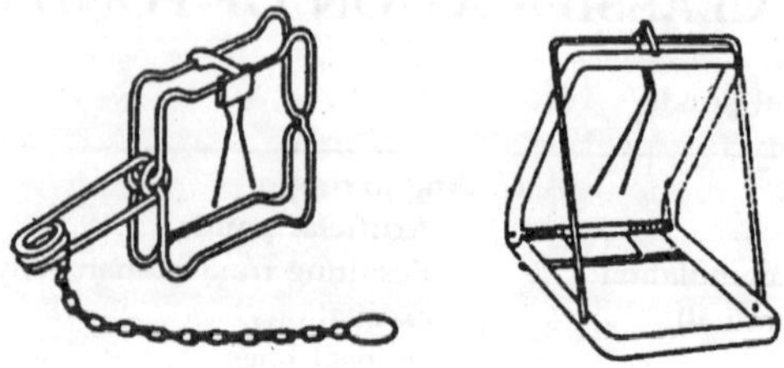

Fig. 267. Trapping of muskrat and coypu with the X-shaped trap or the "prayerbook" trap

However, the second objective need not preclude the first, because the excavation of wetlands, quarries, or ballast holes can be executed in such a way that their future in relation to the aquatic surroundings, fish culture, or recreation is satisfactory.

Natural and ecological factors must be studied to define zones where excavation of quarries will not seriously damage the natural environment on the one hand and the aquatic and fish culture environment on the other hand.

If we have the prospective production of the site in mind, the nature of materials to be exploited has to be planned at a very early stage, so that the deposit ultimately becomes a quality recreative resource.

The following steps are essential in making the excavated site a good fishing pond:

– The staking of the excavation has to have a certain shape.
– The digging has to be carried out according to a particular relief.
– The reuse of excavated soil has to be planned.

1.1 Layout

The layout has to bring about the best possible development of banks said to be good fishing areas for many reasons:

– A uniform surface area of pond results in the longest and most productive banks. The banks serve as shelters for the fish and also provide them living food such as insects and molluscs.

Fig. 268. Trapper and his collection of traps

Fig. 269. "Prayerbook" trap held in a casting

Fig. 270. Scything boat. Note the horizontal and vertical bars. The boat is propelled by the paddle wheels. The fish culture complex at Milicz (Silesie, Poland, after J. ARRIGNON).

Fig. 271. Old scything boat. The cutting apparatus is raised (after J. ARRIGNON).

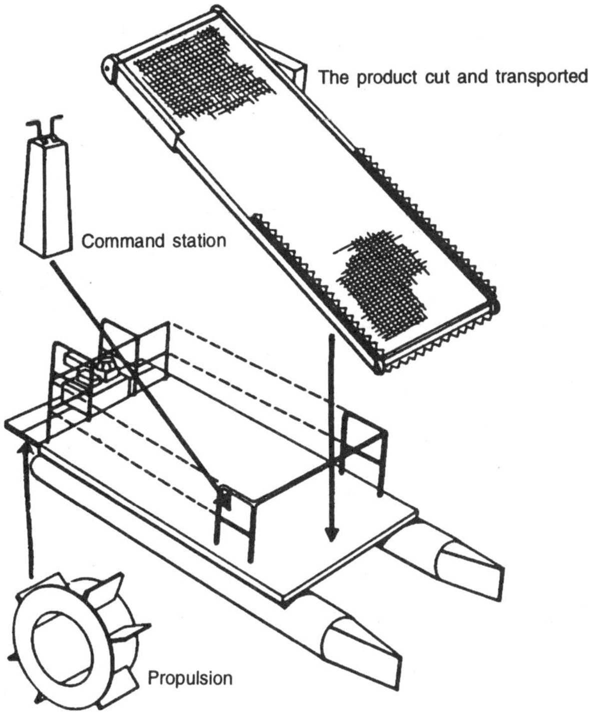

Fig. 272. Portable scythe. The support is similar to the catamaran type, propelled by two independent paddle wheels. The scythe consists of a loading ramp provided with a frontal cutting bar and two lateral bars flanking a conveyor belt that deposits the cut products on a bridge or in a container. The tracks are 120 cm wide and 150 cm deep.

—A uniform surface stretch of pond with long banks can accommodate the maximum number of anglers, whose fishing will cover a bigger area, and can enable a much larger annual fish production.

—A contoured layout breaks the uniformity of the landscape and adds to its charm.

The layout should allow for some areas protected from wind and provide good sunlight or good shade (if there are to be plantations), thus being favourable for fishes, anglers, and strollers.

Frequently, alluvial lands have two layers:

—a layer of arable land, the open land, and

—a layer of usable materials.

1.2 Excavation

Excavation can be carried out in two phases:

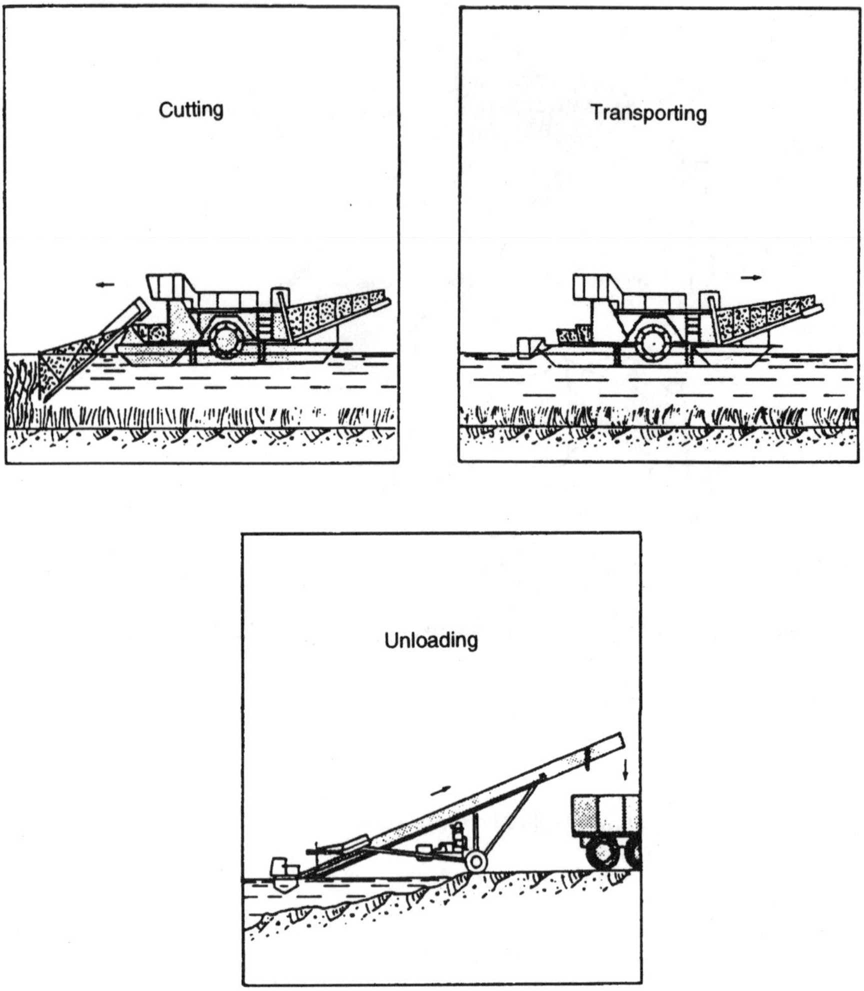

Fig. 273. Scything: phases of work in a scything boat (Anonymous, 1985)

a) One can start by digging out the soil rich in humus, forming a more or less regular heap, which is then removed. At this stage, the banks are generally irregular and the excavation is deep. The bottom of the pond, made up of infertile soil, is not favourable for fish. The height and slope of the banks are similarly unfavourable and even dangerous for fishermen.

b) We can partly rectify this by pushing arable soil towards the banks of the ponds. In time, an aquatic vegetation will form easily and rapidly on the sides, depending on the fertility of the soil. With anglers passing to and fro frequently, steps are formed, more easily on loose soil than on hard stony soil.

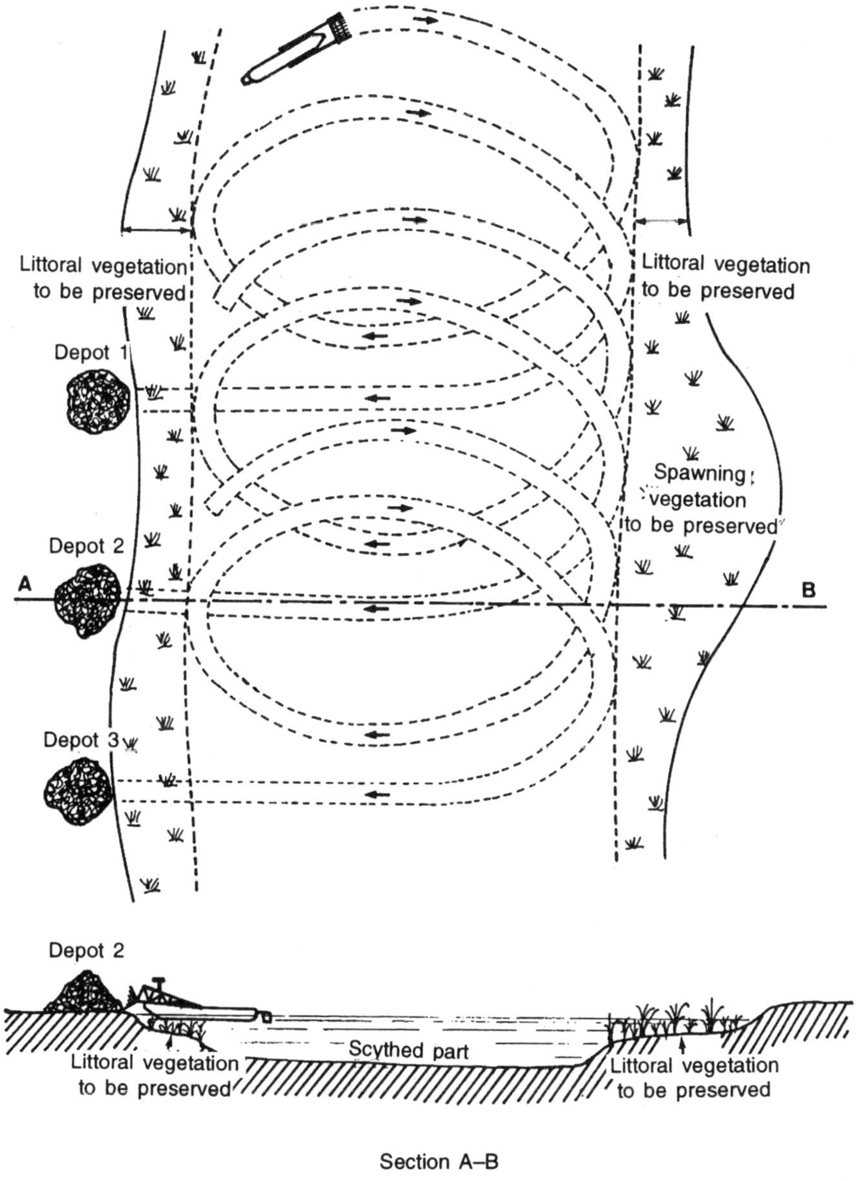

Fig. 274. Schematic diagram of the progression of a scything rake during removal of soft excess aquatic plants.

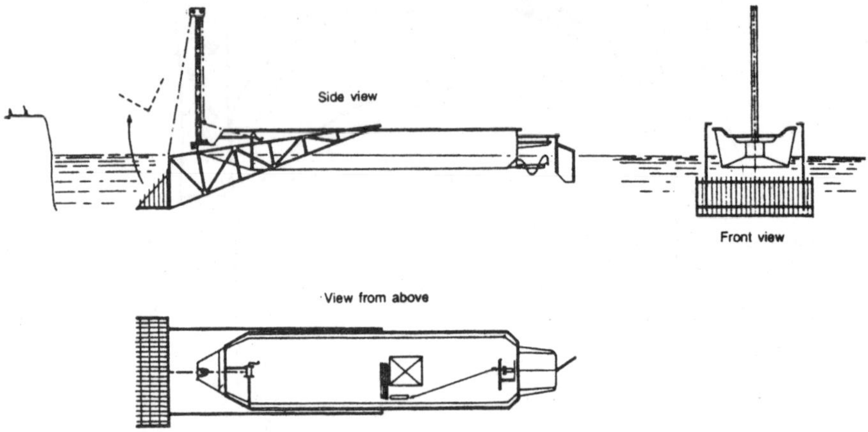

Fig. 275a. Diagram of the working of a rake that can be raised

Fig. 275b. Clearing rake in operation. Note the quantity of soft plant material collected (after J. Arrignon)

Fig. 276. Chemical scything using Reglone aspersion

Fig. 277. Chemical scything, View of the same treated area, 6 months after (after J. ARRIGNON)

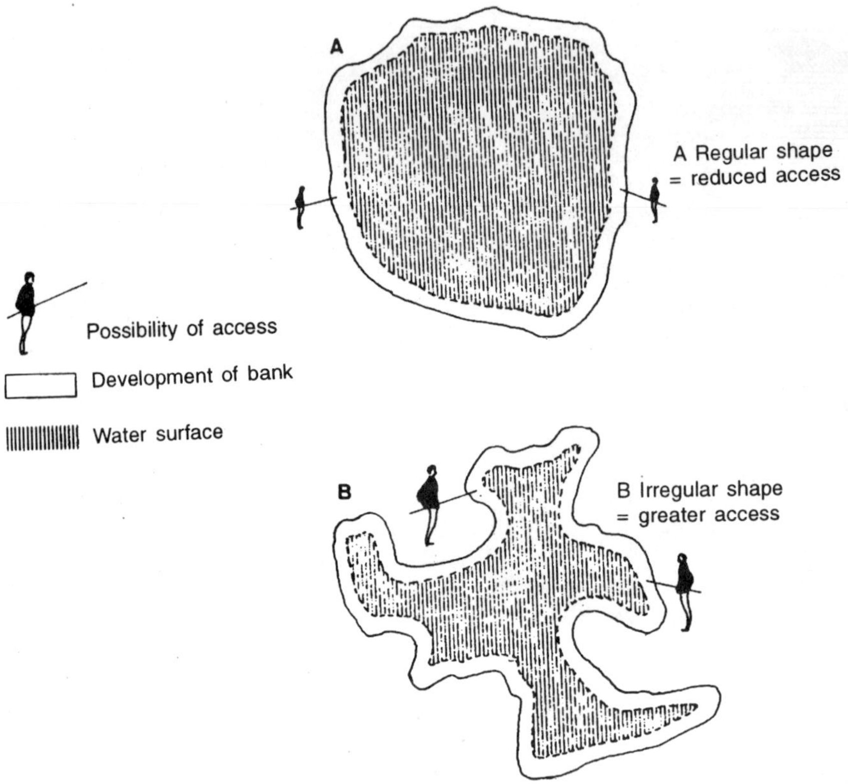

Fig. 278. Importance of the layout of a lake

Special case

When a limited area is being shaped, the optimum method is the following:

—First we determine the site of the future water stretch. The thickness of the arable layer of soil can be studied, from which its volume can be deduced.

—The soil is then extracted from around the pond in the shape of a ring and then pushed towards the centre.

The width of the extracted strip depends on the depth of the pond and the amount of arable soil.

Materials are then extracted from this ring.

—The extracted ring is filled up with the arable soil deposited on the central plateau. Materials are then extracted from this central plateau.

The ring of fertile soil is suitable for vegetation as well as for fish. It makes up the banks of the future pond.

—We can then go ahead with correcting the inclination of the banks, by providing a fishing platform.

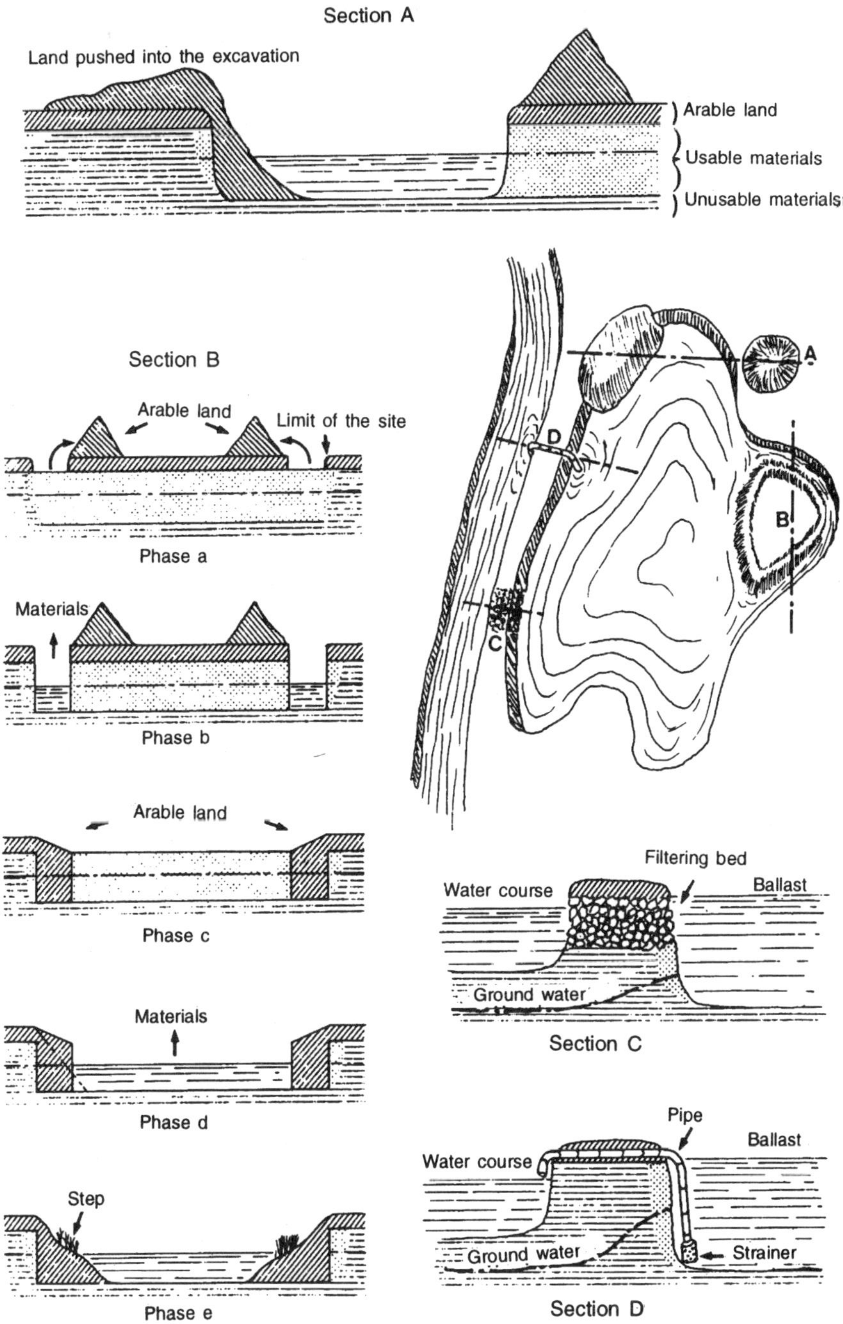

Fig. 279. Phases of exploitation and development of a ballast for later development of fish culture

Fishes require only 1–1.5 m of water and so deep ponds are not best suited for them. Water birds look for their prey at the bottom and so require even less water. It will be best to plan for certain shallow areas.

It is also desirable to plan for a plateau at a depth of less than 0.50 m in the middle of the pond. It will constitute a spawning ground for fish, far removed and protected from anglers and strollers.

1.3 Development of the Surroundings

a) Drainage of over-full ponds

An aquifer is sometimes used nowadays to connect an over-full pond with a nearby river with the aim of draining the pond.

• Control of the bottom. In order to limit any unfortunate effect that this supply may have on the aquatic surroundings of the river, it is better to provide for a method of draining out the water from the bottom and not simply from the surface. This should particularly be done if the pond is very close to a river rich in salmon. The water at the bottom always has a moderate temperature, irrespective of season (9–13°C). The pond can be drained with the help of a siphon whose lower mouth is provided with a strainer.

• Filtering bed. This is a hydraulic joint generally installed to ensure the flow of water between a pond and a river and sometimes between two ponds. Its purpose is to block any movement of fish between the two connected systems without interfering with the necessary flow of water. It must allow an average water flow of 10 l/sec/sq m and prevent the movement of very small fish up to a distance of about 5 m.

For the conditions mentioned above, a filtering bed made up of gravel with a of maximum size 10 cm (passing through a ring of 10 in a grading scale) can completely prevent the movement of very small fish.

It is usually agreed that the normal supply to a cyprinid pond is 1 l/sec.ha without taking to account the evaporation. The section of a filtering bed made up of a heap of gravel up to size 10 should be equal to five times the section of the corresponding free canalization, for a speed of 1 cm/sec of the water current.

Permeability can be calculated from the Darcy law:

$$q = k \times s \, \frac{h - l}{l} \ (\mathrm{l/\,sec/\,sq\ m})$$

where l is the length of the filtering bed, s its section, h the water pressure (initial flow), k the coefficient of permeability. The section is determined by taking into account the average outflow.

The filtering bed is set up on the shallowest point at the bottom of the aquatic system. It can be set up on a hole dug on free land or on a canal with cemented walls. In the latter case, handling is easier, especially when the water has sediments that necessitate periodical renewal of the filtering materials.

b) Plantations

Plantations are normally part of landscaping, but here they have to be treated as constituents of the landscape and the aquatic medium.

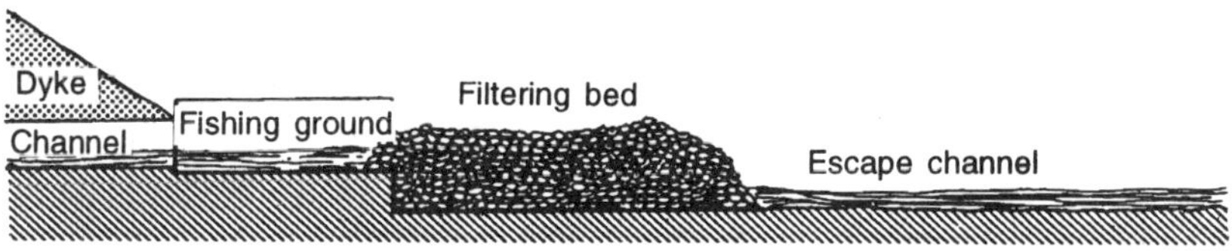

Fig. 280. Evacuation with filtering bed

It is advisable to plant only deciduous tree species (alder and willow) on the banks so as to prevent a very heavy organic supply in the autumn.

Beyond 5 m, other species of deciduous trees such as poplar and ash can be planted.

Twenty metres from the bank, coniferous trees can be planted without causing any damage to the aquatic medium.

The shallowest areas can be planted with species present in the neighbouring ponds and known to be useful in the fish culture environment (e.g., myriophylloid algae; potamots, favourable for the egg laying of cyprinids, perch, and pike; and starworts—Callitriche—and *Ranunculus*, oxygen suppliers, where the temperature allows the introduction of rainbow trout).

The plants or cuttings can be put in directly or embedded in heavy turf.

The aquatic vegetation is controlled by using scything boats rather than aquatic weed killers, whose long-term effects can be noted particularly in areas where water movement is slow or absent and where there is danger of micropollutants in water and sludge.

2. RESERVOIR PONDS

Reservoir ponds and lakes that were once used for fish production are sometimes later used as storm reservoirs, irrigation reservoirs, water reserves for town supply, hydro-energy sources, leisure, and open air spots.

Here, we will only study the establishment of ponds without entering into the details of the requirements and characteristics of barrage lakes, which are beyond the scope of this work.

2.1 Setting Up

Reservoir ponds meant for fish production were earlier set up on marshy lands that were unfit for any other use. But now the variety of their uses, some of which are highly lucrative, has put an end to this practice.

Study of the topographic characteristics should start with the contours across the valley to be blocked. A preliminary levelling is always done and followed by covering that helps in calculating the slopes of the supply and draining canals, the

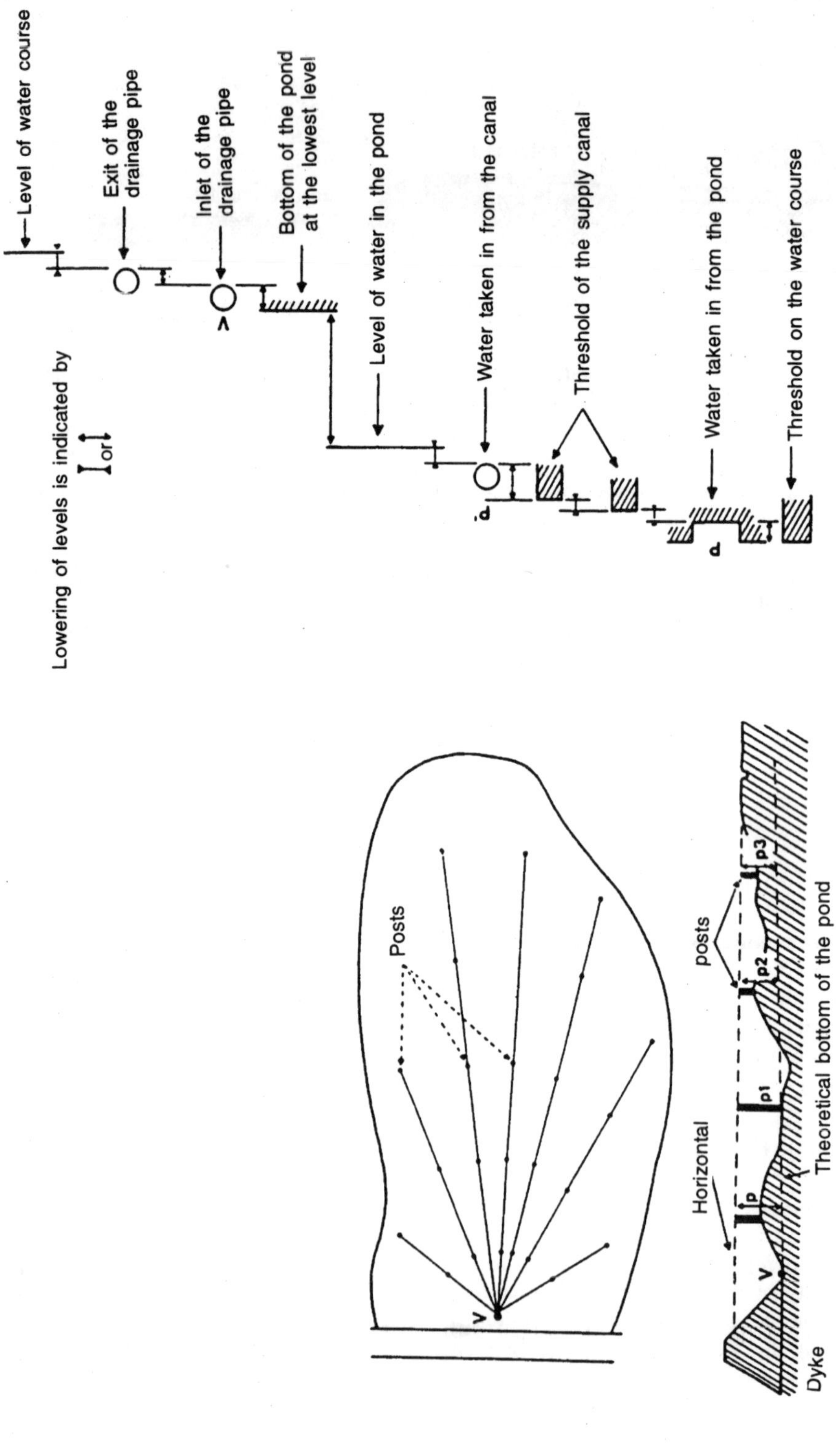

Fig. 281. Marking and layout of the site of a pond (after HUBERT, 1990)

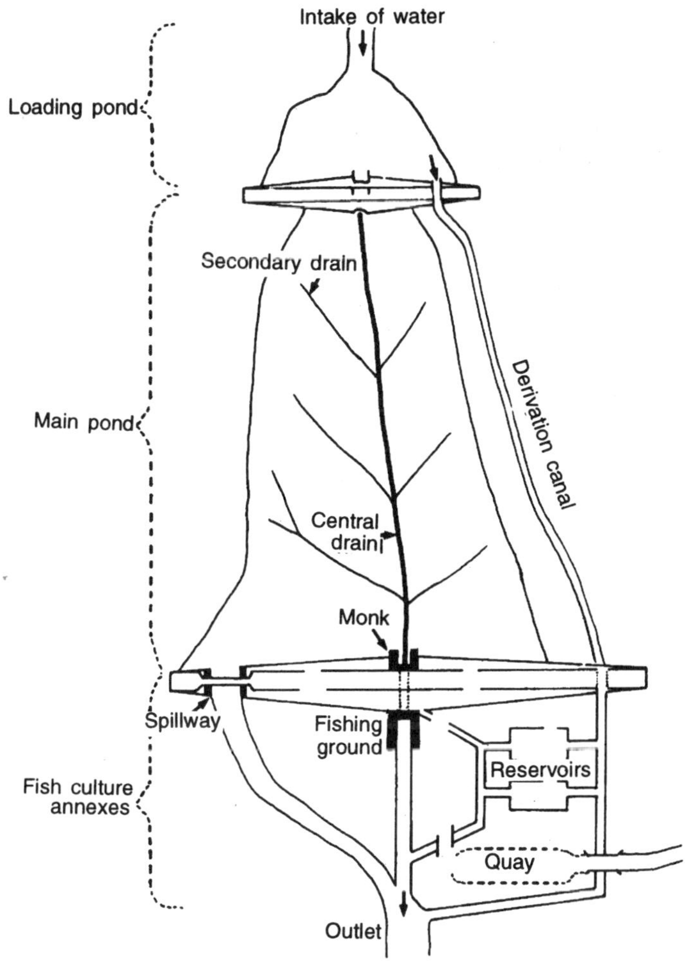

Fig. 282. General set-up of a pond and its annexes

permitted depth of the pond, and the stability of the soil. This plays an important role in calculating the cost.

The base of the embankment has to be suitably located between the nearest escarpments, keeping in mind the maximum area submerged.

The location of the pond in relation to abundant and good quality water resources constitutes an equally important requirement, linked to the former. Water supply should cover losses due to evaporation and infiltration. It should ensure renewed supply even at low water level. Nowadays, the trend is to allow a minimal flow of 3–5 l/sec.ha to compensate losses, to which it is advisable to add the flow necessary for renewing water according to the requirements of different species of fish.

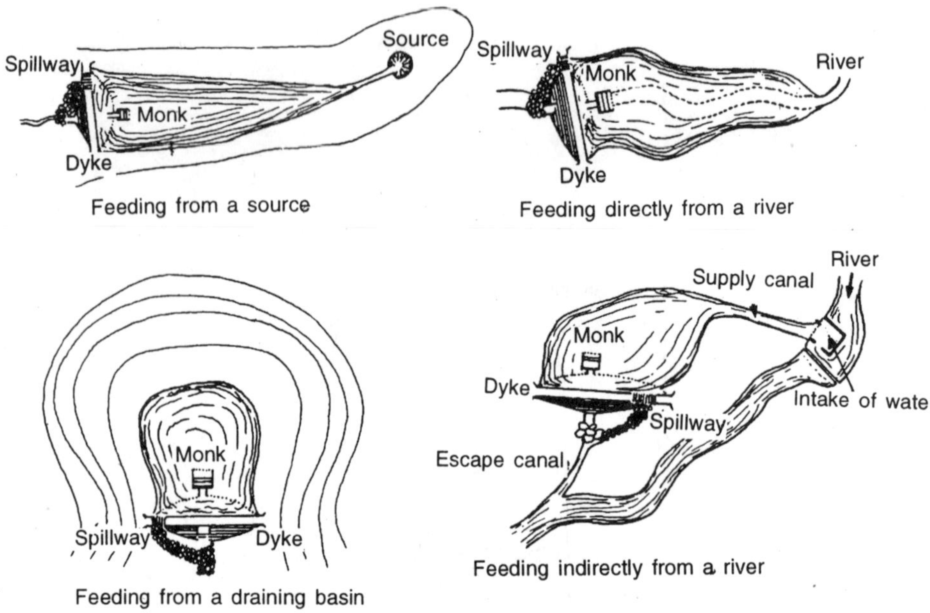

Fig. 283. Supplying water to the pond

Special studies are to be recommended every time the chosen site is affected or will be affected by regional or local phenomena (e.g., meteorology of the Rhone valley with its evaporation phenomena, geology of the karstic regions with their phenomena of loss and reappearance).

2.2 Dyke

a) Site

Reservoir ponds require excavation works for constructing a reservoir dyke. Very often, the soil from the site of the future pond is used and this improves its properties by expanding its surface area and by regularizing its useful depth.

The bottom of the pond has to be drained by a network of channels or draining channels arranged in a herringbone pattern and converging in a central drain that enables complete and easy drying. The channels should have an average width of 0.50 m. The sides are inclined at 2/3. The slope of the main channel is 1‰, and that of the secondary channels is 5‰. The latter are spaced out at 10 m on compact soil and 50 m on light soils. When the pond is dried, the channels are cleared.

b) Construction

The embankment, which is the main part of a reservoir pond, has two essential qualities. (1) It should be solid and impermeable; a badly constructed embankment

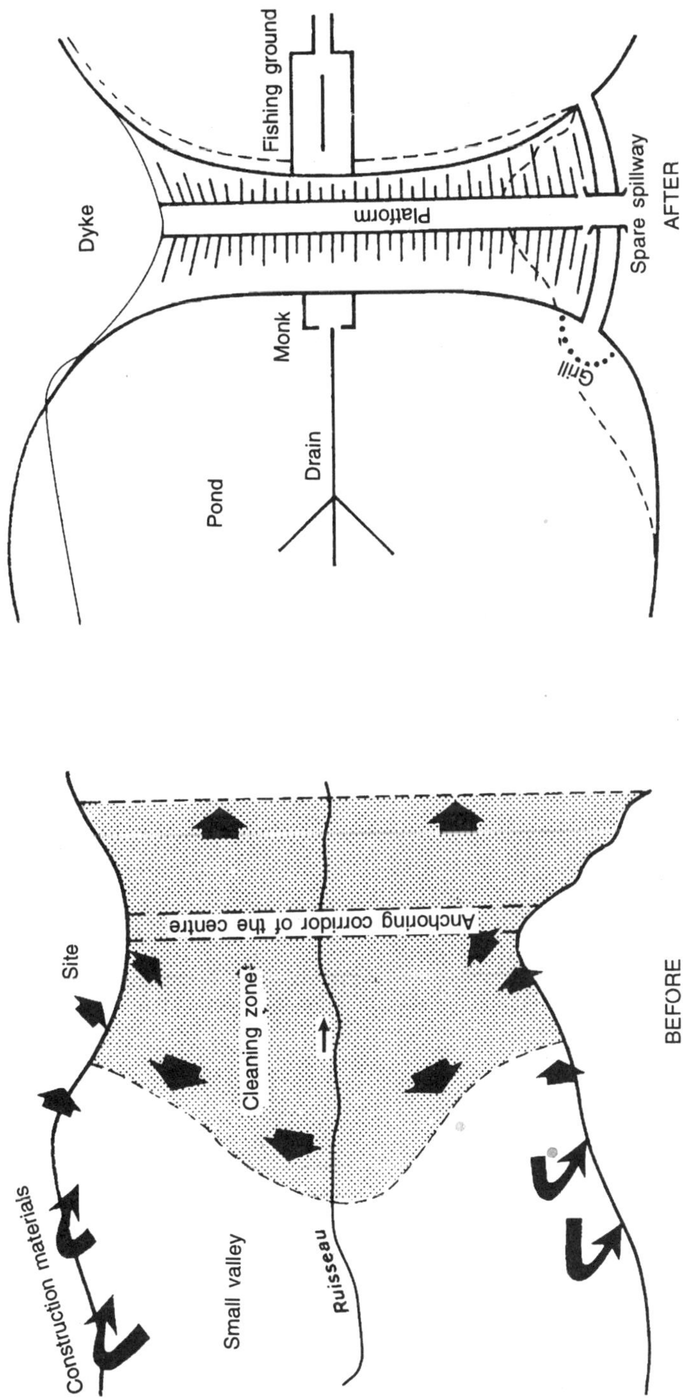

Fig. 234. Dyke of the pond: set-up

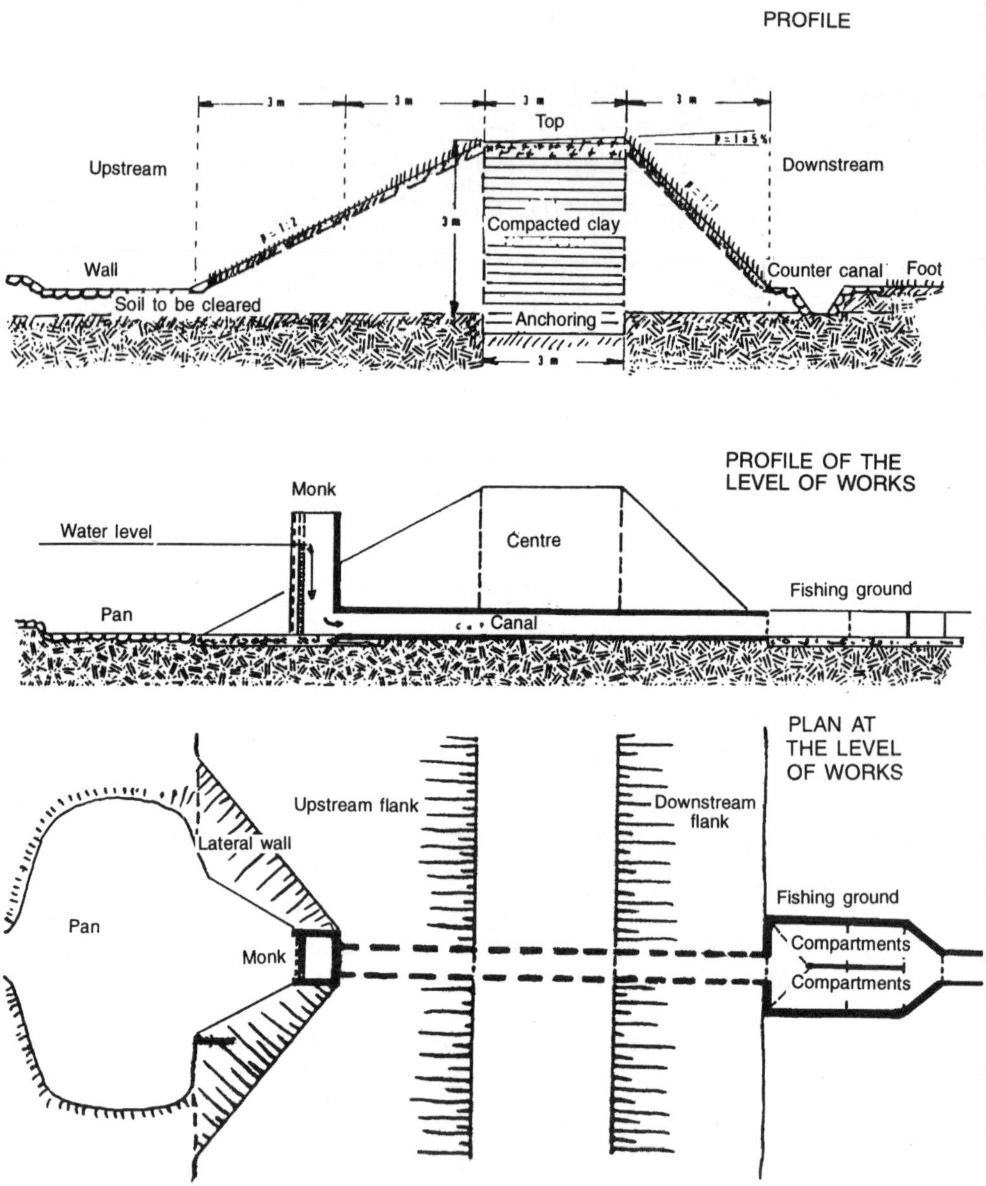

Fig. 285. Dyke and drainage works

cannot be repaired. (2) It has to be seated on a well-cleaned, impermeable soil. The constituents of the soil have to be homogeneous. If not, they have to be thoroughly mixed (clay and fine sand, in general) and arranged in successive phases so as to form a solid, compressed soil. The layers are generally 20 cm thick.

Protection from the muskrat can be planned when the embankment is raised and consists of:

—A waterproof concrete veil in the dyke constructed at a level normally accessible to the animal (from the top down to 0.50 m below the normal water level).

—A waterproof, rotproof veil in rigid polyvinyl chloride sheets placed on a trench, to form a barrier against rodents.

—Chicken wire netting plastered against the banks of the dike at the same height and then covered by the finishing soil.

The properties of the dike depend on its size and the nature of materials used. In relatively modest reservoirs, going by their area and height (5 ha and 5 m), the width of the dike on top should be equal to its height, which should be 0.50 m more than the maximum level of water in the pond. The slope of the embankment downstream should measure 45° and that of the embankment upstream 60°. The roof of the dike should be sloped towards the pond so that the running and gully-forming waters do not have an adverse effect on the embankment downstream. It should be covered by turf or stones if it is a servicing route.

There should be no stone, root, or turf in the body of the dike. There should also be no planting done since the penetration of roots creates an area of low resistance and causes the running water to spread out in different directions.

Space should be left for a monk during the construction of a dike, unless there is a reason to install the evacuation channel earlier. In the latter case, it is advisable to load the channel with 2.5 times its diameter of soil before the earth-moving machines are operated.

It is sometimes necessary to protect the freshly turned soil lying upstream from the splashing water. Normally, a supporting wall made of stones, grouted or not grouted, is built. Similarly, sedges (*Carex stricta*) can be planted as they produce humps, round mounds called clods, or even "peat" and their thick roots absorb the shock of the waves.

The *stone facing or revetment* is, however, indispensable to the surroundings of the floodgate or the monk, as it serves as a protection against landfalls. It leans on the right and left walls of the construction. Downstream and along the embankment, counter-canals 30–40 cm deep and wide are constructed. They are meant to collect the water passing out from the lower part of the dike and direct it towards the emptying canals.

Waterproof veils are planned for all future dikes on land not only to put an end to the danger caused by muskrats but also to stop water leakage.

Such a veil could be a wall starting from the bottom and leaning on the upstream slope of the embankment. A bituminous coating is put on the wall to make it fully waterproof. The wall is generally 15–20 cm thick and the coating 5–10 mm outside the joints.

Waterproof veils can also be made with polyvinyl layers or other plastic materials placed on the upstream embankment with double hem joints. This is sometimes pressed by a clamp joint to make it fully watertight. It is advisable to place the layer on fine sand and cover it with mud or turf to prevent tearing of nets or boats when they are taken out of water.

The bottom of ponds constructed on very porous soil rich in alluvium can be covered with such layers.

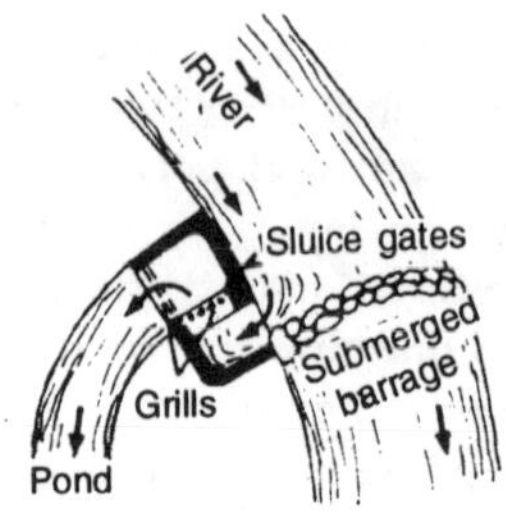

Fig. 286. Feeding water from a river

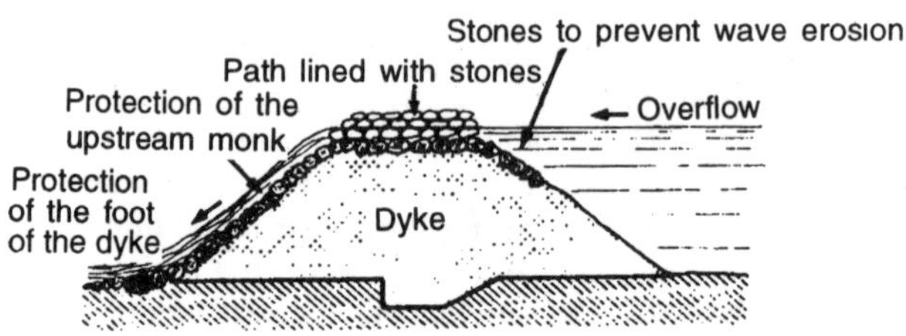

Fig. 287. Spillway for overflow

An angle of the embankment (joining angle at the position of the retaining wall) can be dug out in such a way that the inclination is reduced to an approach ramp at the bank. The ramp is specially useful when fishing with nets and when the fish is hauled at the end of fishing towards firm ground.

The bottom of the ponds as well as the site of the dike can be protected with a new range of products, known as **geotextiles**, widely used in public works. These materials can be used for drainage, filtration, separation, reinforcement, protection, and erosion control, especially for the banks.

The geotextile, placed at the bottom of the pond, assumes the role of a separator and filter between natural non-coherent soil and the mass of water or body of the dike if it is placed on the top of the dike.

In both cases, it is necessary to know the granulometry of the soil in contact with the geotextiles, and it is advisable to stitch the strips together and fix them on top of the bank by burying in at least a 40 × 40 cm trench that can then be filled and compressed. Dry gauze can be used to prevent formation of folds or pockets.

In the first case, the geotextile should be covered with at least a 50 cm layer of sand if it is planned that the pond should be prospected at the foot during draining off. In the second case, excavation is done as shown earlier.

Geotextiles made with synthetic fibres are preferred as they do not run the risk of ageing in the expected working conditions. They should be stored in the shade, away from ultraviolet rays (BERNHARD and LECLERCQ, 1990).

Fig. 288. Development of banks (after J. ARRIGNON)

Vegetation: The layers protecting the slopes outside water are generally covered by 20–30 cm of arable soil. It is planted with a hardy turf consisting of fescue grass, foxtail grass, and meadow grass at 250 kg/ha.

Small shrubs and trees can be planted close to the ponds (but not on the embankment). These plants are chosen because they have harmless leaves and solid roots: willow, alder, birch, dogwood, and later poplar are grown at a distance of at least 10 m from the water's edge.

Heavy protection: In concrete pavement, tiles are placed side by side or overlapping in a geometric or honeycombed pattern. A pavement can be perfectly integrated in a relief but it may slip in case of steep slope and soil creep.

There are a wide range of pavements and the final choice depends on the cost of operation and the aesthetics involved.

2.3 Civil Engineering Works in Fish Culture

a) *Sluice and siphons*

Earlier, metallic sluice with ball and chain, safety valves, or valves in the shape of a hinge cap were used. The first two were easy to close but had the disadvantage of including a pipe that caused a loss of 20–30 cm of the total inclination of the canal, this inclination being significant on a flat surface. The sluice provided with a hinge cap-like valve does not have this disadvantage. It has a similar diameter

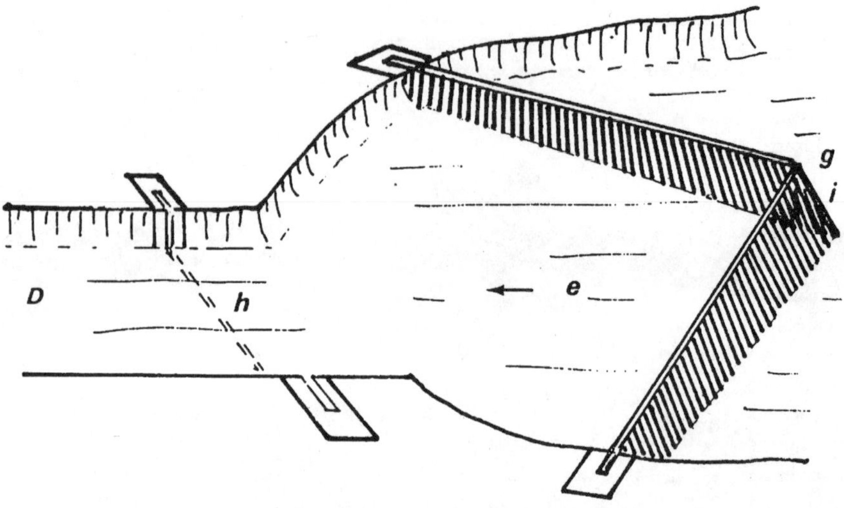

Fig. 289. Spillway and grill (after J. ARRIGNON)

and a better flow than others. However, the surfaces to be blocked must be thoroughly cleaned before they are placed against each other. The pond can never be waterproof without being thoroughly cleaned.

The use of siphons has considerably increased after plastic tubes became popular. Siphons are provided with two sluice gates at the lower portion, one upstream and one downstream, and an opening on the upper side. The main advantage of the system is that it is situated outside the embankment. The main disadvantage is that it can be used only in small ponds (2–3 ha) that are relatively shallow (2–3 m) and do not collect much silt. It is often advantageous to keep it under pressure by draining out water from the bottom. This way there is less risk of its getting over-full. However, a semicircular grill has to be fixed at the mouth to stop the inflow of large quantities of solid matter.

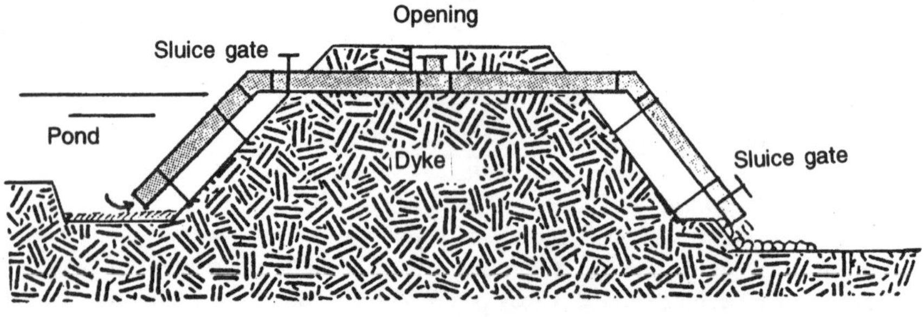

Fig. 290. Drainage of a pond with the help of a siphon

b) Monks and sluice gates

Draining-out monks are much older than sluice gates. Fish breeding in ponds was an activity practised almost exclusively by religious groups in the 14th and 15th centuries, whence the name "monks." These parts were made of wood or even freestone, and it is possible to find well-preserved vestiges in certain pasture valleys where fish culture was once practised.

Draining-out monks perform two important functions in a pond: (1) They help to drain off all water and gradually dry it out up to the landings, which is necessary to recover fish in good condition. (2) When the pond is full, they help to regulate the water level and thus prevent escape of fish.

The water is drained either at the surface or at the bottom. This double capability is indispensable because it enables evacuation of water from the bottom, which is very cold, lacking in oxygen, and filled with elements harmful to aquatic fauna. On the contrary, in ponds with trout, evacuation of water from the surface reduces the risk of heating the water, which is contrary to the requirements of the species.

■ Conception

The monk should be placed a little in front of the upper part of the embankment in such a way that the lower half of its front side is buried in the embankment. If planned carefully, the monk column can be placed exactly in front of the embankment and made approachable only through a movable bridge.

Monks can be constructed in bond-stone, brick, concrete, or wood. The prefabrication technique of monks has been well established in major fish breeding countries (Netherlands, Madagascar, Ivory Coast). This technique has brought to the market equipments that can be handled and installed easily and that are affordably priced.

The draining apparatus that makes up the monk can be schematically dismantled (Fig. 291 (1) and (2)) as follows:

—A distributing bedplate (or foundation) on which the column is fixed or attached with the help of an iron framework.

—A column with a rectangular section, open on the upstream side, provided with a mouth at the base and grooves on the lateral sides.

—An evacuation tube joined at the mouth upstream and downstream after passing through the dike, at the fishing ground or the draining canal.

—The adjusters found on the upstream side of the column, which, depending on their number, help in adjusting the depth of the water. Compressed clay ensures waterproofing in between the adjusters.

—An iron grate placed on the adjuster on the upper side during surface draining or level with the bottom during bottom draining.

The monk can be easily operated if certain details are taken care of during construction. U-shaped fixtures placed in the grooves help in handling the iron grates and the adjuster. Two holes can be pierced in each adjuster at half point in the wood and tenons of a metallic lever can be introduced so that the adjusters can be pulled out without difficulty (Fig. 292).

A sluice gate-shovel operated by a rope and steering wheel is sometimes placed on the draining column of large ponds. It replaces the wooden adjusters and helps in regulating the flow, especially at the time of complete draining and of slowing down the rate of water flow to keep it at the pressures suitable to fish.

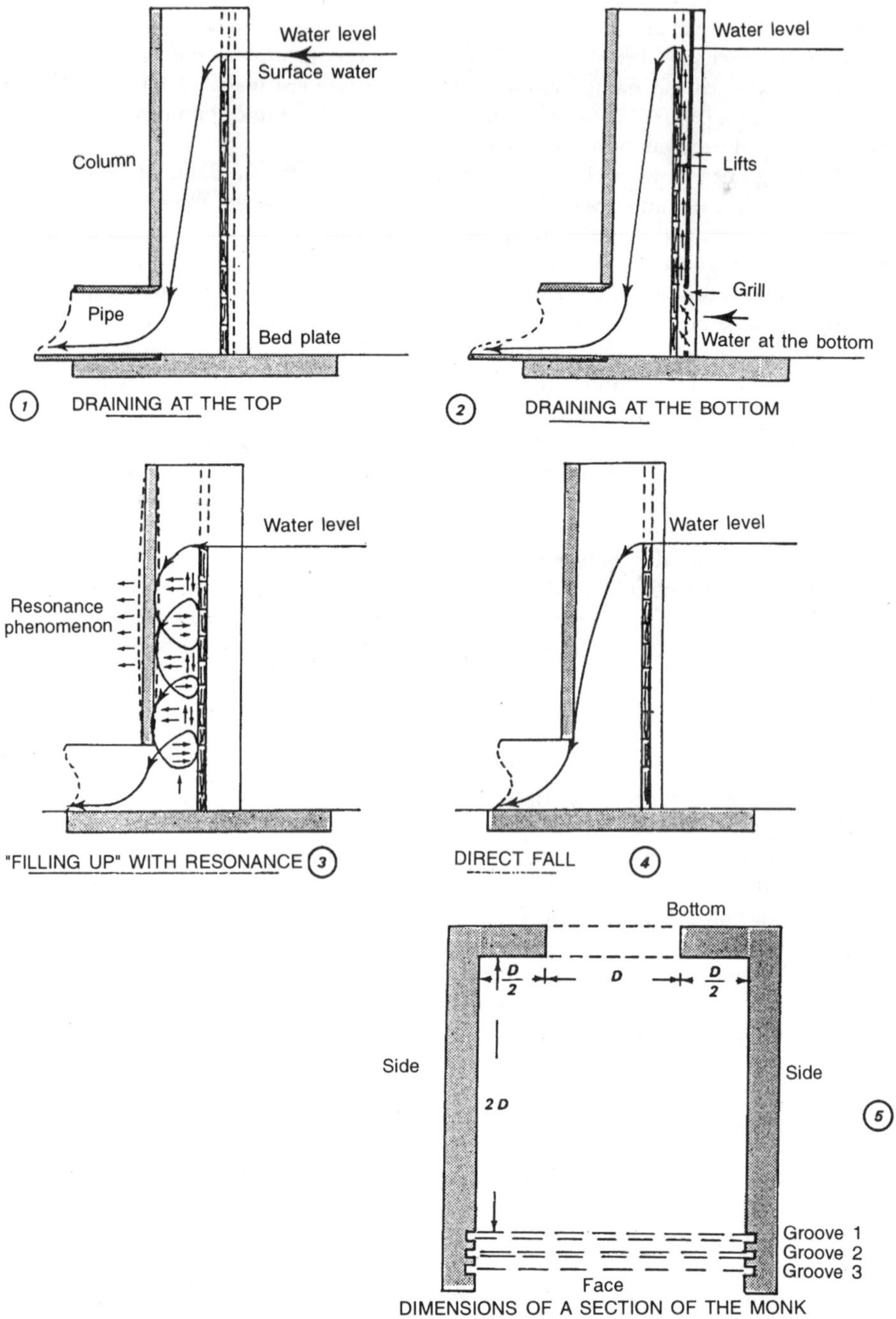

Fig. 291. Draining-out monk

■ Calculation of the section of the column

During evacuation of the surface waters, the discharging strip moves on the adjuster on top and falls on the monk column. Water is evacuated by the pipe passing under the dyke.

If the adjusters are very close to the front of the monk, the discharging strip hits this side and moves more slowly. This produces a series of volutes that in turn causes compression and relaxation of air caught and released in each volute (Fig. 291 (3) and (4)).

This latter action produces resonance vibrations that ultimately cause fissures in the walls of the monk and infiltrations in the body of the dike, which have undesirable consequences.

The section shown in Fig. 291 (5) gives a very simple method of calculating the section of monks normally used in fish culture so that "filling" can be avoided in columns less than 4 m high.

In these constructions, the draining channel is made of sandstone, concrete, or PVC pipes having a diameter of 20–30 cm.

If the pond has to be dried out thoroughly, the draining pipe should be 20–30 cm below the lowest point of the pond.

The draining channel should rest on firm ground or a compressed mound or, better still, on a concrete one. It seems to be a good idea to place the pipe on a metallic section as this forms an absolutely inflexible cradle.

To prevent theft, the monk can be designed with a cover having a padlock, thus making access to the adjusters impossible.

c) *Water supply point*

All ponds should be provided with a water supply point if they do not have their own spring nearby. This supply point is joined to a point that collects water from streams and connected upstream at the reservoir embankment on a diversion canal.

The supply point should satisfy three conditions:

– provide a regular and controlled flow to the pond,

– prevent the movement of fish from upstream to the pond,

– prevent the fish from escaping from the pond and moving upstream.

The best water supply point has a horizontal, submerged grate and a device for regulating the flow. This device consists of a vertical sluice gate that can be raised and regulated by notches or successive holes. It could also be a partition device provided with two vertical grooves facing each other. An opening is provided under the lower board or between two boards and the desired flow of water into the pond can be regulated through this opening.

This device is constructed at the end of an open air feeder canal rather than at the end of a buried pipe. It is therefore necessary to have complete control of the debris that may accumulate. Sometimes, it is useful to make a decantation canal above the water supply point.

d) *Diversion canal and spillway*

Diversion canals should be constructed for the pond whenever the contour of the land allows it. When ponds are built on one or both banks of a water course, the bed of the water course becomes an evacuator and, as the case may be, one or two canals on the side of the valley supply water to the ponds.

The diversion canal or canals are dug on firm soil and not on retrieved soil. The top of the canal should be above the highest level of the ponds.

The spillway evacuates water brought in by storm or floods. It plays the role of a standby spillway, while the normal spillway is the monk. Given its special role it should never be built in the middle of the dyke on soil but laterally, dug in natural terrain.

The crest of the spillway can be at a different level if the sliding channels constructed on the two end walls enable one or many beams to be inserted. The escape canal is made of concrete, stone, or mud, depending on the seriousness of the risk of undermining. It is sometimes good to plan a ski jumps fall over the escape canal.

The section of the spillway should be calculated in such a way that the highest level of water gets stabilized during floods and heavy rises in the water level at 20 cm from the top at the upstream part of the dyke.

A grill is placed on top of the construction to prevent fish from escaping. It is in the form of a semicircle or a corner so as to increase the area of flow and to block floating bodies.

When the pond is considered a fish breeding enclosure as described by the French fishing law, the distance between the bars in the grill should be 10 mm. Otherwise, it is not fixed but generally varies between 10 and 20 mm.

2.4 Annexes

a) Fishing grounds

The fishing ground is a cement or concrete basin to which the drainage pipe of the pond leads. When the monk opens, water and fish enter the fishing grounds, which is built in such a way that fish can be easily caught and handled.

Its area, volume, and compartmentation depend on the functional importance of the pond and the species of fish being raised there. As a general rule, a pond with an area of 1–5 ha is provided with a 6–12 sq m area of fishing ground having a depth of 1 m.

The fishing ground is divided into compartments by grooves. Depending on the need, adjusters and grates are placed on the grooves and these regulate the height of water and keep back the fish during draining. The bottom is sometimes provided with an inclined grating device that enables quick retrieval of big fish.

A fishing ground must receive clean water from a pond, a basin, or a water source, so that the animals obtained at the end of fishing are free of sludge around their gills.

The fishing ground is sometimes made complete with a *pan* located upstream, very close to the monk. It consists of a fishing zone on firm ground where net fishing can be done. This system is used when the topography of the region or the accessory land structure does not favour the construction of a fishing ground below the dyke. It is also used in the case of bigger ponds having a higher population of fish that has to be reduced before moving into the downstream fishing ground.

The fishing ground should be laid out so that one can easily move around its entire circumference. The sifting area, containing the tables that sort out the catch, is located very close to it.

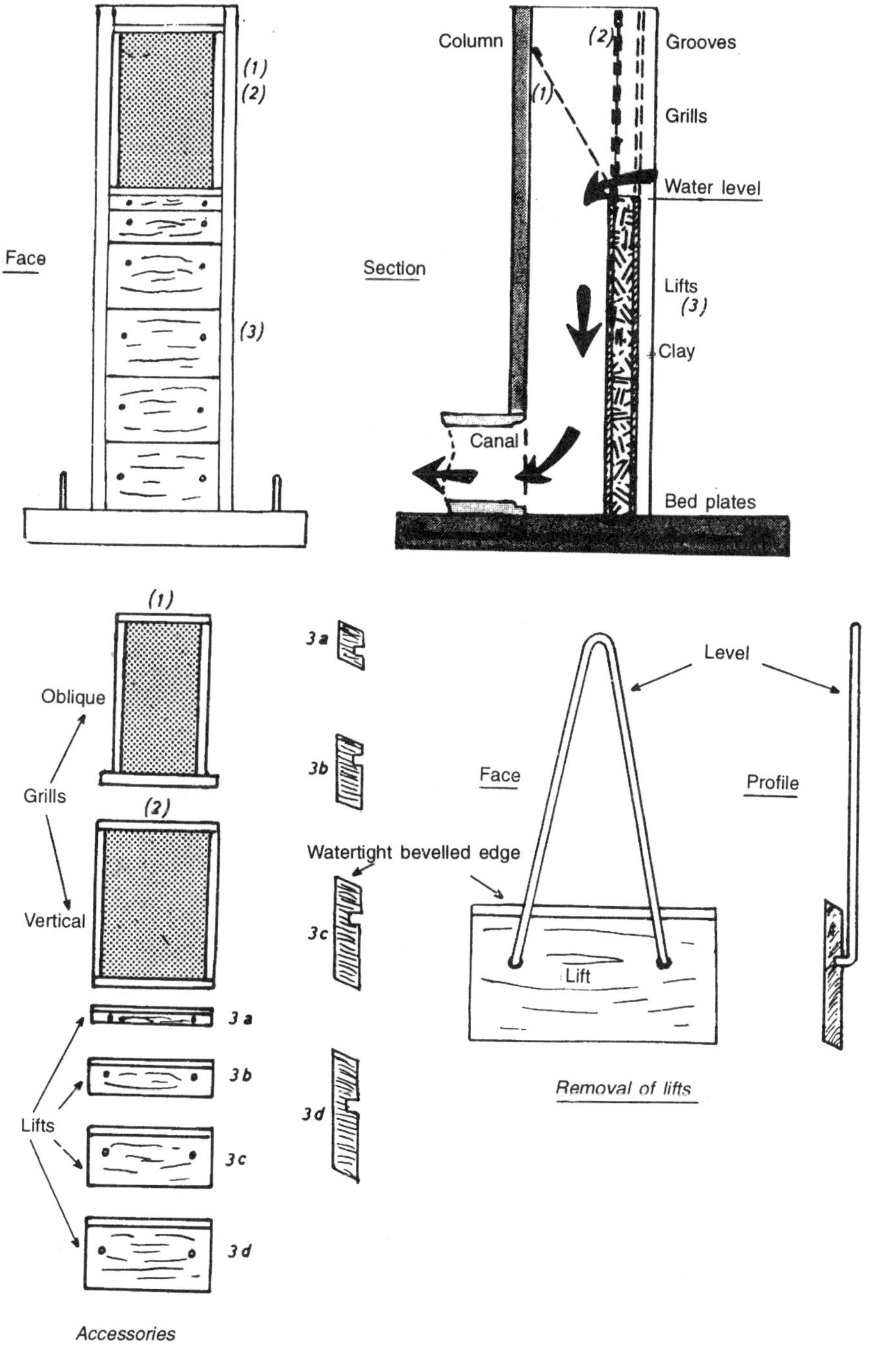

Fig. 292. Prefabricated monk and accessories

Fig. 293. Developments: fishing ground of a lake-reservoir (Champaubert, Aube, after J. Arrignon)

b) *Special basins*

Sustaining basins are close to the fishing ground. They are meant for sustaining fish sorted out according to size and species, till they are channeled out to the various receiving points.

The sustaining basins are supplied with clean water so that the fish, which lived till then in sludgy waters, can get used to clean water.

The area of basins varies from 50 to 500 sq m and sometimes even more. They are generally constructed on soil and the banks are covered with turf rather than concrete, which, because of high density stocking, would damage the tegument of the sheltered fish.

Fig. 294. Pond provided with a single surface spillway, Ambatofotsy, Madagascar (after J. ARRIGNON)

Close to the sustaining basins and servicing area a platform is set up for loading tanks on trucks, at a slightly lower level. They can thus be loaded at the quay.

At the end of the pond or system of ponds, a small *replenishing pond* is to be constructed whenever possible to provide a regular supply of water to the main pond. This reserve collects the fresh water brought by storms and feeds a diversion canal, which in turn feeds the fishing grounds and the sustaining basins with clean water. Finally, the replenishing pond enables us to quickly charge a considerable area of the main pond with water and immediately introduce the initial lot of fish.

Wintering ponds are specially meant for carps. Spread over a few hundred square metres, these ponds have very steep banks and are quite deep (up to 5 m). Various devices are used to aerate water when these ponds are frozen, such as bottom fluting, stakes, or ropes, which enable us to lower the water level by keeping back the ice and form a cushion of air necessary for the survival of fish in winter.

Spawning ponds, which are built close to the production ponds and are sometimes even linked to them, have a special form and shape depending on the species for which they are meant. Dubisch spawning grounds are squarish and have a central plateau with a brush of vegetation and lateral channels for receiving the reproductive fish. They measure about 100 sq m, like the kakaban spawning grounds. The spawning grounds measure about 200 or 300 sq m depending on the number of couples we want to introduce. The black bass spawning grounds often form an integral part of the production ponds. The breeding enclaves of pikes, measuring

Fig. 295. Pond provided with two drainage monks, Manjakandriana, Madagascar (after J. ARRIGNON)

200–500 sq m, are made along the warmest bank of the production pond receiving maximum sunlight. The enclaves are also linked to the latter through sliding channels. The gudgeon spawning grounds are 50 sq m basins made on sloping land, leading to the monk.

3. RESERVOIR LAKES

Reservoir lakes can be laid out so as to protect and increase the development of fish breeding and also encourage fishing.

3.1 Fixed Stretches of Water

It is desirable to set up dams for lakes and one or several fixed stretches of water in the most remote corners. These form an integral part of lakes during high water periods but remain full during low water periods or artificial reductions in water level.

These stretches of water, which are generally shallow, are made by setting up a barrier of pile-planks. Some of them, sunk more deeply near the banks, are always full.

Fig. 296. Excavation of a dyke after construction of an outlet (after J. ARRIGNON)

Fig. 297. A prefabricated double monk (after J. ARRIGNON)

Fig. 298. Placing a prefabricated monk with two columns in a dyke that has already been constructed, Ambatofotsy, Madagascar (after J. ARRIGNON)

A fixed stretch of water plays three main roles: hydraulic, piscicultural, and halieutic.

On the hydraulic front, it serves as a compensation and sedimentation basin for the main lake.

On the piscicultural front, it serves as the main spawning ground and reservoir for the lake. Fish from the lake as from the river or feeding stream can reproduce here without any risk other than that of predation. During high water periods, there is a normal reduction in their population within the entire region.

On the halieutic front, as it is always or almost always at the same level, it makes a choice site for angling, whereas the banks of the main water body may be unsuitable for fishing because of marling and can be made suitable only with the help of special devices.

3.2 Fishing Channels

Fishing channels, created in the most shallow regions of the lake and especially within the fixed water stretches, facilitate fishing where the summer proliferation of aquatic vegetation and the layers of algae along the border make it almost completely unfit for fishing.

A fishing channel is dug at a distance of 1 or 2 m from the bank, along the contour reserved for fishing. It is 4–5 m wide and 1.5 m deep.

3.3 Fishing Pontoon

The fishing pontoon is often a prolongation of the jetty or short lateral fishing platforms.

At the time the lake is established, the areas open to fishing are chosen according to the protection and management of the hydraulic and hydroelectric devices. They are also chosen in accordance with the hydrobiological conditions, exposure, and access to angling. Sometimes these areas are naturally insufficiently developed and need to be improved by artificial means.

The use of earth-moving machines can help to fill some escarpments, with certain promontories giving access to the existing fishing areas during low water periods. Marling does not result in useful prospecting. It is also useful to extend the promontories at the front and at the sides with the help of fixed and floating pontoons. The former are connected to the latter and suitably fastened, and thus follow the fluctuations in water level.

Fig. 299. Wintering pond for carps. Note the protection furrows, and on banks after haymaking, the small sticks. Fish culture complex in Milicz, Silesie, Poland (after J. ARRIGNON).

Fig. 300. A pond of 20,000 sq m with an area for drying nets. Experimental fish culture station in Zabienec, Poland (after J. ARRIGNON).

The pontoons have to be fixed according to the prevailing winds, other water sports, and the general aesthetics of the site.

3.4 Floating Spawning Grounds

The floating spawning ground is best used in the case of a lake barrage having variable levels of water and where the water stretches are not fixed. This is the only means of providing the cyprinids and pikes a natural future and seems to be a better idea than restocking the lake with fish, whatever be their quality.

3.5 Compensation Basins

The compensation basin, even apart from its strictly hydraulic aspect, is indispensable to the hydrobiological layout. Placed at the downstream end of the barrage, it serves as a sluice gate during violent floods. It carries the water to the tributaries with a speed that can be regulated and regularized depending on the frequency and gravity of the flood forecast. Moreover, it serves as a decantation basin and protects the river from warping due to spawning or else from becoming completely choked with silt.

3.6 Draining

Reservoir lakes run the risk of collecting somewhat heavy sediments depending on the impluvium relief of their draining basin. The movement of the sediments brings about partial or total floods and draining that have some effect on the hydroecological successions found downstream.

These water movements should take into account the various modes of sedimentation that bring about different consequences.

Very coarse material (I) gets collected like a delta in the form of a plateau at the end of the reservoir. The fine material (II) settles uniformly and interrupts the movement of the water. Finally, density currents produced occasionally, particularly on the sides of the aforementioned plateau, account for a third type of deposit (III). These are in effect underwater avalanches that bring large deposits very close to the barrage (Anonymous, 1988c).

Sediments of type I are inaccessible for fishing because of draining at the bottom. The fine sediments (II) are deposited in a predictable way but the deposits made by density currents have to be evaluated before draining the bottom each time, to find out their size and location. Some of the deposits are concentrated in front of the sluice gate at the bottom and they can even block its lifting mechanism. A sudden gush can cause fine clay to surge forward, causing mechanical and chemical pollution simultaneously downstream.

Thus, drainage of barrage lakes has to be preceded by a geographical, quantitative, and qualitative study of the sediments and also a study of the impact, which will determine the conditions under which work can be executed.

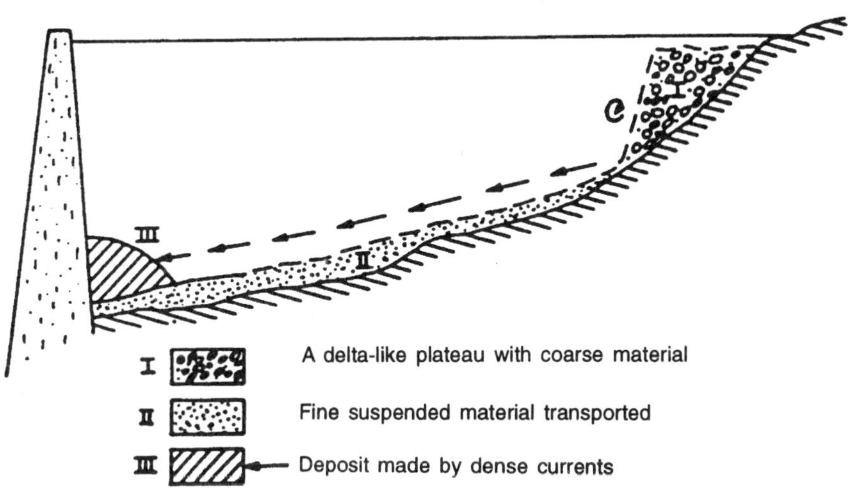

Fig. 301. Types of sedimentation in reservoirs

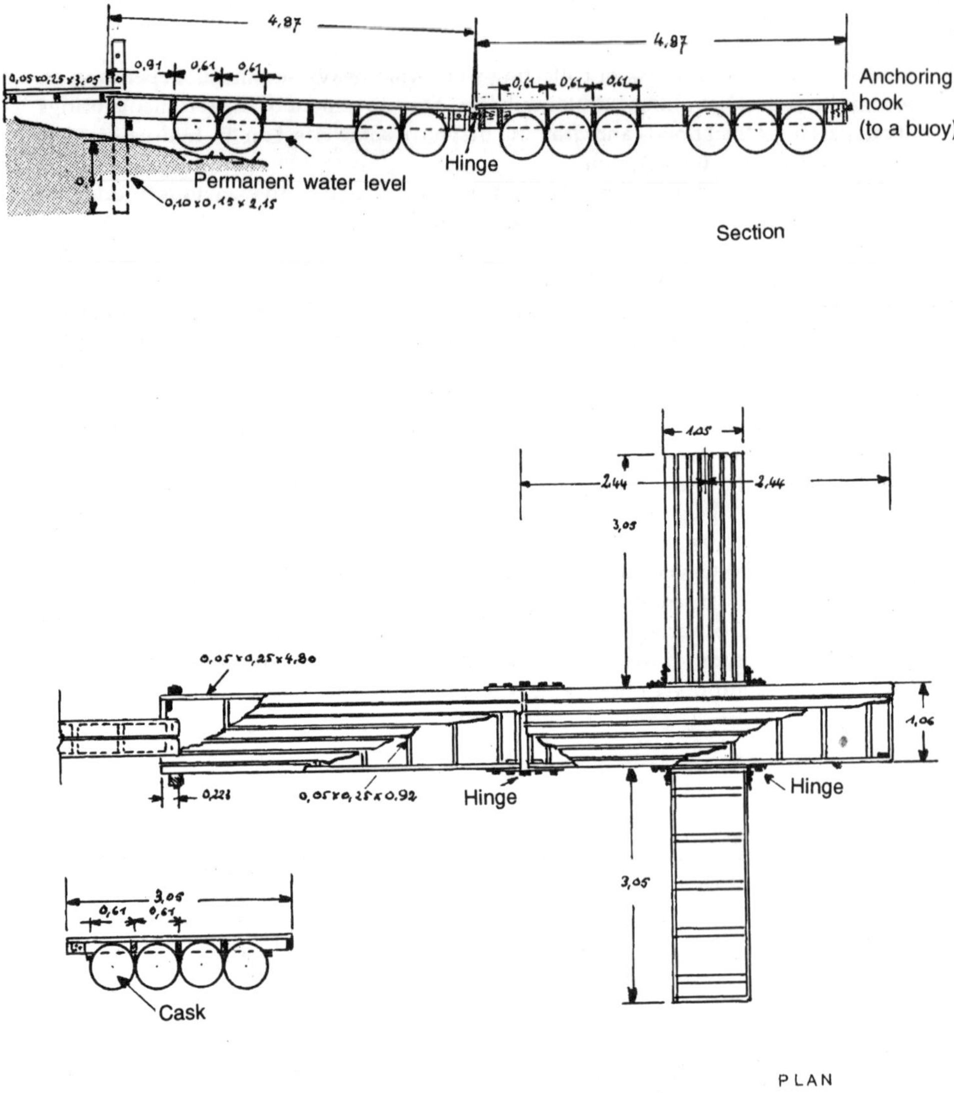

Fig. 302. Floating pontoon

D. CORRECTION OF WATER COURSES

1. GENERAL OBJECTIVES

The general objectives of correction works include: to prevent floods, erosion, landslides, shifting of beds, and destruction to waterfronts; to ensure water flow in agricultural or urban drains; and to facilitate the regrouping of lands and setting up of certain road infrastructures and urban and industrial superstructures.

The demands made by fish culture are very often similar to the demands of nature and landscape protection and it is advisable to keep this in mind while planning projects.

Fish ecology requirements include water flows and natural beds, presence of a number of shelters in the bed and at the foot of steep banks, alternation in the strong current and deep water (wet) sections, and free movement of fish, particularly the migrating varieties. The depth of water at the low water point should be above 30 cm and the speed of current less than 1.5 m/sec at average flow. Finally, it will be helpful to retain or plant some bushes consisting of various plants suited to local conditions, at a little distance from the banks.

2. CORRECTION OF STREAMS

The general rule while planning the layout is to preserve the natural flow of water as far as possible. In case the flow has to be changed, long rectilinear stretches have to be avoided and limited to 200 m in case of plain streams. The position of the water course in a **thalweg** provides good drainage to the lands and a better flow of the low-water point, which is often a determining factor in the conservation of species and in fishing.

During the preliminary study, it is better to determine whether to increase the flow capacity by constructing lateral dykes, thus leaving the bed in its natural state, or to do it by increasing the depth of the bed.

2.1 Changes in the Profile

In case the natural profile has to be changed, it is necessary to examine how the new profile can be adapted to the requirements of fish ecology. In order to conserve a suitable strip of water at the low-water point, the excess meanders, if any, can be cut out, by one arm serving exclusively to evacuate the rise in water levels. This will reduce the increase in the flow of the main water and the possibility of flow in the thin strip of water.

Similarly, a channel of low waters can be made in the normal bed and this forms a small bed. The sides of the large bed serve as a fishing step in the normal period (Fig. 315).

2.2 Protection of Banks

Banks with loose soil are protected by devices such as **tunage**, hedging, and wooden or metal pile planks. These devices offer no advantages for fish culture, for which rocks are more advantageous, reinforced if possible by willow cuttings planted in the joints. The niches encourage the formation of counter currents and resting places for fish away from deep waters and are useful in fishing. In the overthrusting zones, it is better to plan for rock formations rather than conditioned stones filled with mud, which are also not favourable for fishing. Concrete walls or lateral pavings with a smooth surface are used to increase the water flow. Their base can be protected by rock formations, which can also offer shelter for fish. Along the tunages and wooden pile-planks, it is better to set up shelter for fish, as long as the planks do not run the risk of getting silted up. In Switzerland, in the canton of Zurich, the number of shelters is calculated according to the following empirical values:

— In fishing zones having a population of 0.5 trout/m^2, 1 m of artificial underbank, 0.3 m wide, offers shelter to about 5 trout.

— In reserve zones having a population of 1 trout/m^2, 1 m of underbank offers shelter to about 15 trout.

The upper part of the banks can be well protected with small shrubs and turf. According to the Swiss Federal Office of Roads and Dykes (1968), banks can withstand a dragging force of 8–10 kg/m^2 if they are planted with willows and 4–5 kg/m^2 if covered with turf. While planning the dimensions of the flow profile of the streams, one should keep in mind the fact that willows can reduce the section. In a water course with a narrow bed, the short shrubs should occupy only the upper part of the bank above the level of the fastest flowing waters. If not, they reduce to a great extent the profile of flow and encourage alluviation.

2.3 Protection of the Bed

Protection of the bed implies a width determined by the rules of the technique so as to obtain a regular and stable longitudinal profile. When it becomes necessary to fight erosion by laying a terraced bed, rubble thresholds with a mat of rocks downstream can be constructed to protect the bed from being undermined. Similarly, thresholds in concrete can be built and the top of spillways reinforced against wear and tear caused by the alluvium. These thresholds should not be more than 70 cm high so as to allow fish migration. Moreover, in order to protect fish, the upstream edge of the threshold should be rounded and the top should be counter-inclined.

3. CORRECTION OF TORRENTS

The correction of torrents aims at maintaining the bottom in its natural bed as far as possible. In case it is able to withstand the driving force, it is necessary to protect it from the effects of erosion.

The bottom of torrential streams can be equipped with wooden, rubble, or concrete thresholds. The shock-absorbing basin that naturally forms downstream by undermining is, as a general rule, sufficient for fish, especially if the shores are protected by rock formations and thus offer more shelter for fish. When the torrent lashes down, the artificial basins are rapidly filled up by alluvium and become non-functional.

Sometimes steps made of wood, stone blocks, or concrete are constructed with a big shock-absorbing basin at least 50 cm deep. The steps on the vertical downstream side should not be more than 70 cm high so that fish can move up easily.

It is only in special cases that the bottom needs to be paved or cemented, when the site is limited or when the slope is not sufficient, to ensure that alluvium is carried along or to prevent the growth of aquatic plants.

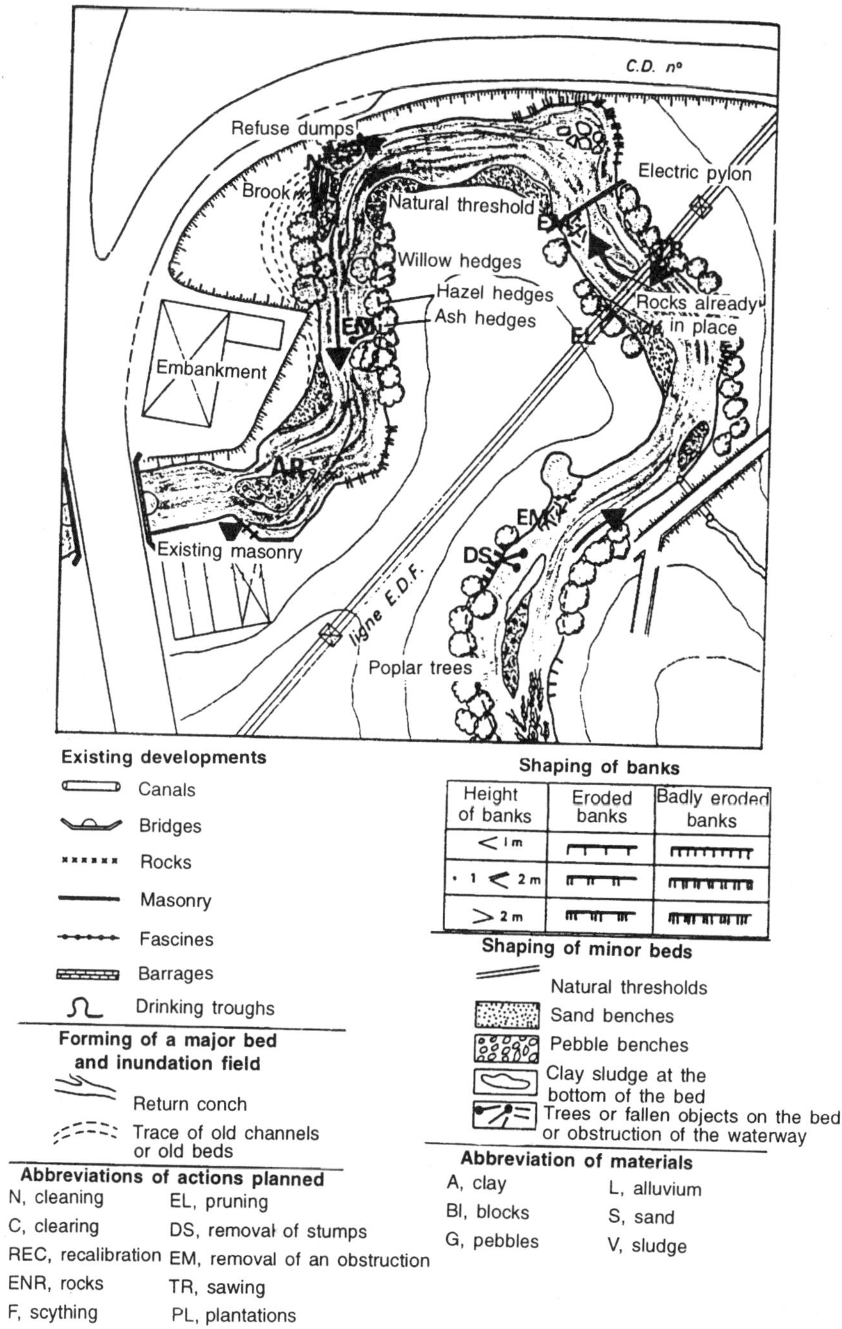

Fig. 303. Development: 1. Observation of the situation (Anonymous, 1985)

Generally, banks are maintained by a combination of protection techniques. The compiling of data will help in planning a maintenance programme in which the different types of protections planned are defined, as shown in the following diagrams.

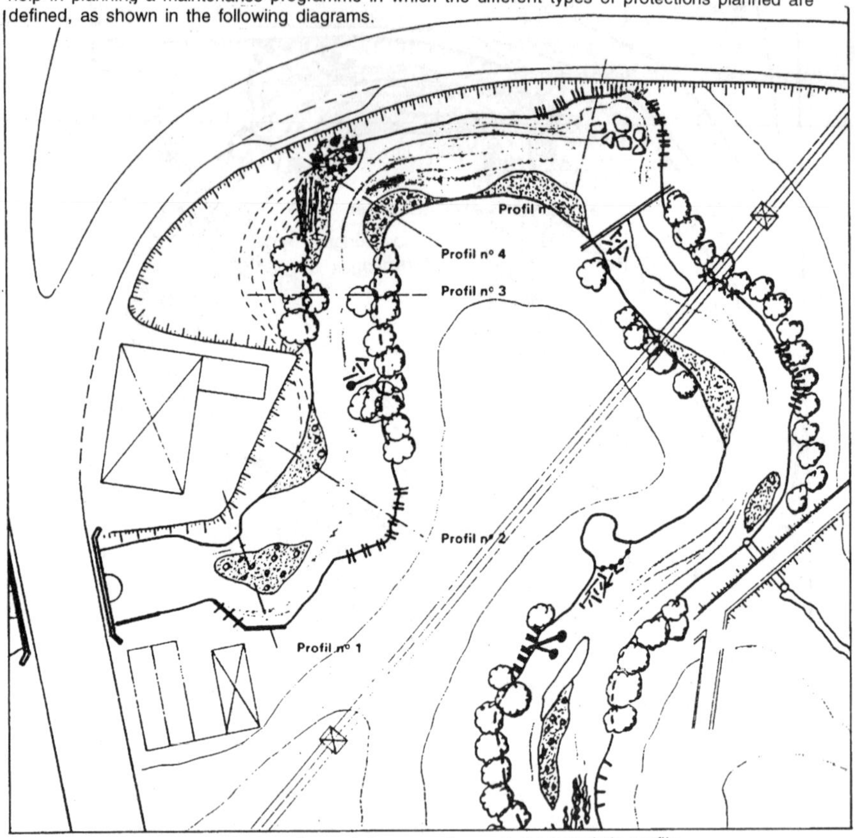

Example of a maintenance plan and characteristic profile

Profile no. 1

a) A 2/1 slope of the bank with turfing on polyester net
b) Blocking of the foot with rock quarry
c) Removal of sand-sludge deposits
d) Cleaning and reprofiling of the low water level channel
e) Remaking of walls in natural stone with natural foot protection in the rock quarry
f) Slope planted with bushes

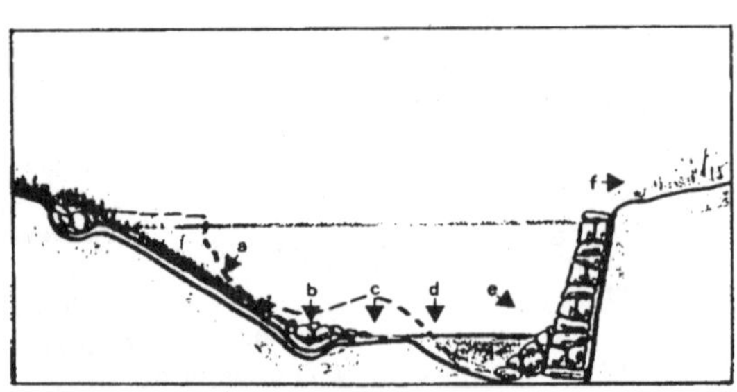

Fig. 304. Development: 2. Project (Anonymous, 1985). Generally, banks are maintained by a combination of protection techniques. The compiling of data will help in planning a maintenance programme in which the different types of protections planned are defined, as shown in the following diagrams.

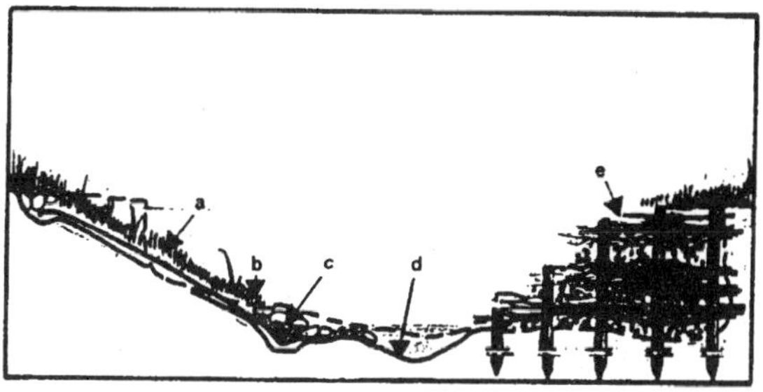

Profile no. 2

a) **Reprofiling of the embankment in 2/1 with turfing on the polyester net**

b) **Removal of deposits**

c) **Protection of the foot with rock quarry**

d) **Cleaning of the low water level channel**

e) **Fascines in live willow branches with covering of the surface vegetation layer**

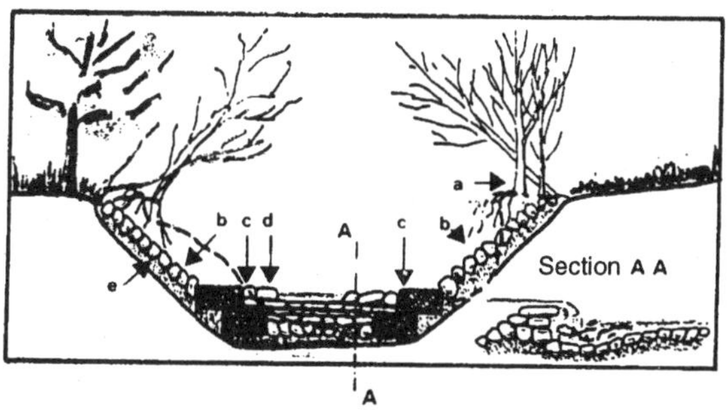

Profile no. 3

a) Removal of fragile trees or badly planted trees with rewiring of the others. Clearing of the high bank.

b) Stabilizing the banks with quarry rocks laced on the filter (geotextile or gravel)

c) Clay cylindered end wall

d) Creation of a small threshold in rocks with protection of the diversion canal (see section)

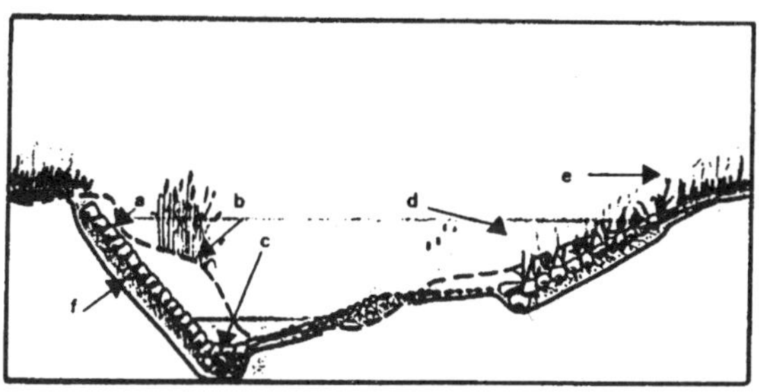

Profile no. 4

a) Additional protection in rock quarry

b) Extraction of accumulated gravel

c) Improvement of the low water channel

d) Protection rocks of the convex bank

e) Vegetation on the entire bank

f) Filtering layer

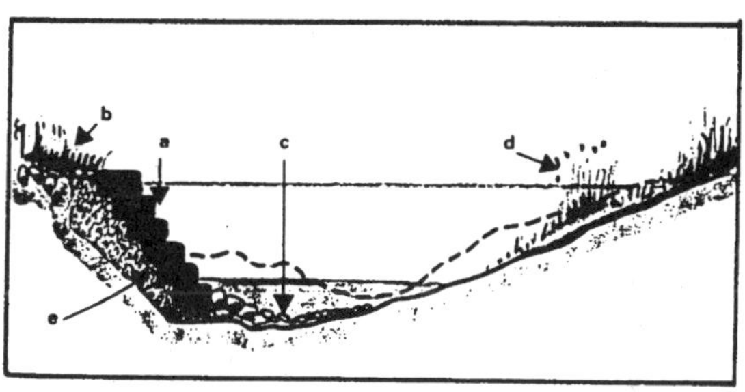

Profile no. 5

a) Bank protection with clay cylinder

b) Rocks of the high bank with planting

c) Low water channels with cover

d) Vegetation on the convex bank

e) Filtering bed

Fig. 305. Development: 3. Detail of interventions in the profiles (Anonymous, 1985)

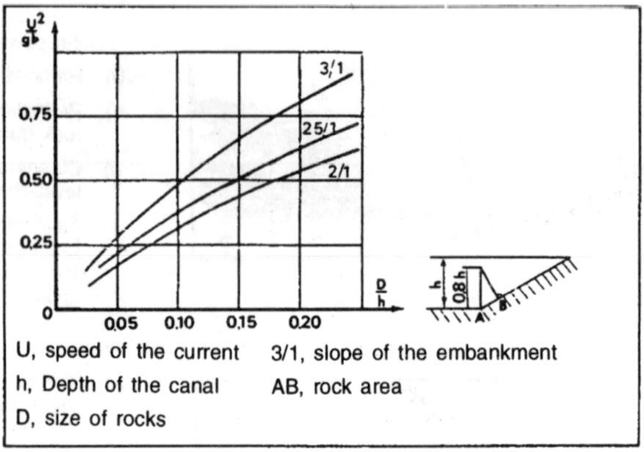

Fig. 306. Protection of the footing of banks: calculating the slope of the underwater foundation of rough masonry (Doc. LNH)

4. MANAGEMENT OF CONFLUENCES AND ESTUARIES

For the fish, it is important to keep open the possibilities of moving from a river to a tributary. Although salmonids, which are good jumpers, can easily cross landings not more than 70 cm, it is not so for cyprinids, pikes, and young eels. It is preferable to plan for planes inclined at 1% or 2% at most and equipped with inclined pipes placed diagonally to facilitate the flow.

Some urban passages and inlets are underground. At the downstream end of these sections, it is better to have a shock-absorbing basin and if the slope in the canal is steep, steps can be added. The bottom of the Armco pipes can have two lateral platforms that help in the flow of high waters and in the control and maintenance of lower waters. Groovers in the platforms allow thresholds to be inserted for breaking the current and for encouraging fishes to move up. Thresholds are generally placed 65 m apart for a 3‰ slope, 43 m apart for a 4‰ slope, 32 m apart for a 5‰ slope, and 25 m apart for a 6‰ slope.

E. MANAGEMENT OF WATER COURSE FOR MIGRATORY FISHES

All French water courses are frequented by migrating fish at the lower levels of their flow: shads, eels, smelts, sturgeons, lampreys, mullets, salmon, or sea trout. Some migrating species have limited their movement to this lower part, some have practically disappeared, and in some cases the surroundings have proved unfavourable for migration. For these reasons, the number of water courses frequented by large migrating varieties such as salmon, sea trout, and shads, but not eels, has been relatively restricted and may be further reduced by the consequences of developments such as river or coastal thermal stations.

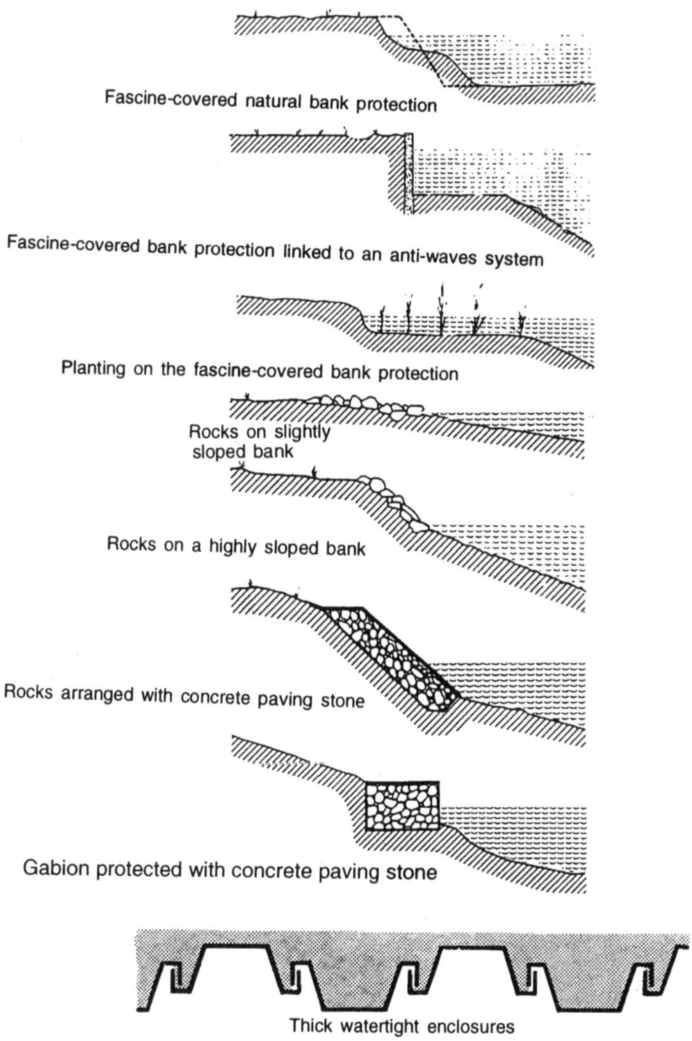

Fig. 307. Protection of banks (after Tersen, 1990)

A number of factors influence large migrants frequenting water courses. These factors can be external to the river surroundings or closely associated with it but at different levels. The main factors are: movement of adults, availability of suitable and sufficient spawning grounds, young life and catadromous movement of small salmons, and use of stock for commercial and sports purposes.

Development of water courses for migratory fishes should be focussed rather on creating devices for crossing (leaping over), which help the adults get to the spawning

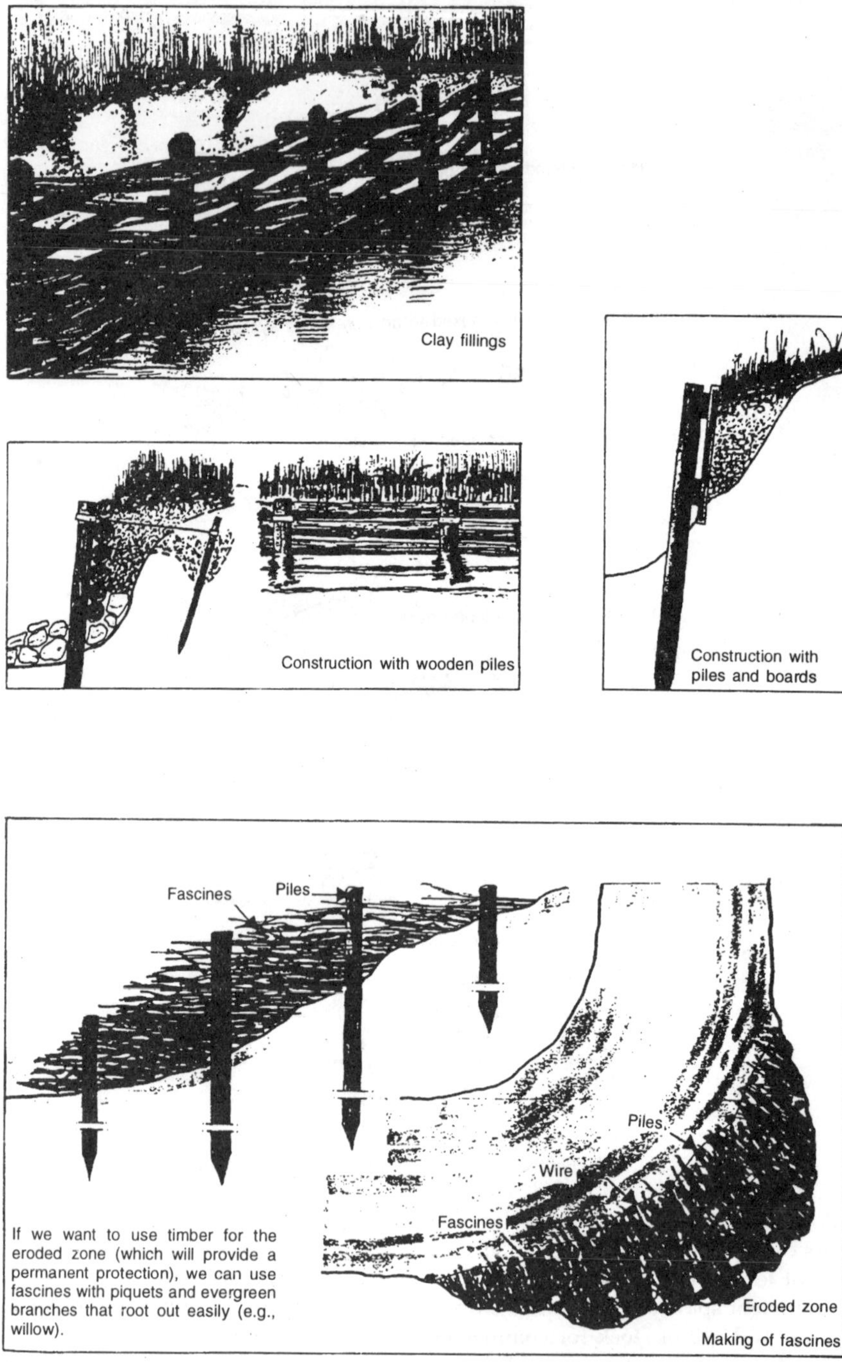

Fig. 308. Development: types of anti-erosion protection (Anonymous, 1985)

Fig. 309. Artificial underbank under construction (after J. Arrignon)

Fig. 310. Development of an artificial underbank (after J. Arrignon)

Fig. 311. Developed artificial underbank in a bank protection (after J. ARRIGNON)

grounds and the younger ones to descend to the sea, and also on setting up devices that help increase their dynamics and improving spawning conditions (see page 199).

1. CROSSING OVER OBSTACLES

Crossing of obstacles has been made easy by the extent to which hydraulic devices have been conceived keeping in mind the *functional behaviour* of migrants during crossings.

1.1 Behavioural Approach

Anadromous and catadromous periods sometimes condition the working and maintenance of hydraulic devices. Large salmons with two to four years of sea life move up the river during winter and sometimes continue to move even up to the end of the following autumn. Grilses and salmons having spent one year in the sea reach the coastal rivers of Brittany, Normandy, and Picardy in June and July and are on the spawning grounds in November. Trout follow the same pattern but move in both directions in summer. The smolt salmon comes down to the sea in April and May, when the shads move up. The adult eel migrates towards the ocean from September to December and the young eels reach the coast in the beginning of

Fig. 312. Bank protection with tetrapods, increasing the border fish habitat (after J. ARRIGNON)

spring like the lampreys. The control of works relating to crossing over should bear in mind the migrating species present in each water course and their division, movement, and reproduction.

Salmon and trout are sensitive and follow the call of the water current, which attracts them and guides them during anadromy. They follow the same itinerary and rest in the same places. They reach lateral zones when the current is very strong but follow the current as soon as possible.

At the maximum rise in water level, they stop their upward journey and remain stationed in the calm waters at the bottom along the banks. At the foot of a barrage, they always follow a strong, smooth, current with parallel veins rather than a swirling or weak current or cloudy waters. The entrance of a fish pass should be situated in such a way that the current passing out is preponderant and thus "attractive".

The salmon rejects a current that is faster than its swimming speed. It can get stuck in narrow passages. It continues to move according to its convenience, even if that leads to a dead end. However, if it happens to be in a dark channel for as long as 100 m, it gives up its attempt at crossing. Salmon and trout follow deep trenches (around 2 m deep) with hard bottom, crossed by a strong current, and in dark surroundings. When disturbed, they come back to the same place after a while. When faced with an obstacle, they are adamant, get tired and hurt, and often become a prey for poachers.

Fig. 313. Protection of the banks of a brook: turfing and aligning of the willow cuttings (*Salix* sp.), followed by a random laying of alveolar rock suitable to fish and aquatic invertebrates (after J. ARRIGNON).

Fig. 314. Reprofiled and recalibrated river

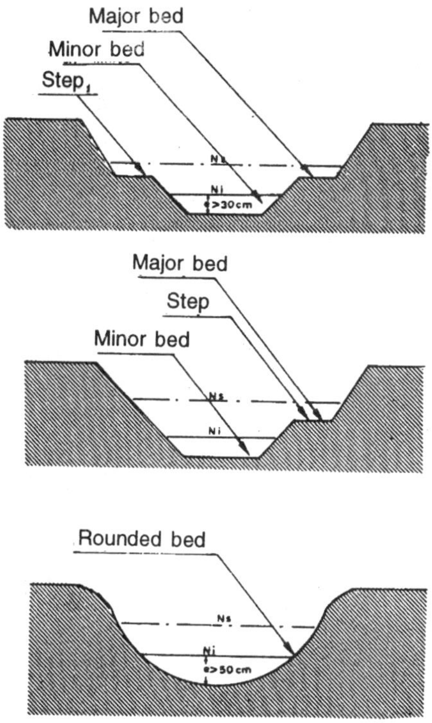

Fig. 315. Sections of water bed reconciling hydraulic requirements with the needs of fish and fishery

The means of crossing should satisfy certain requirements:

1.2 Inlet of the Pass

The fish should be rapidly able to identify and approach the inlet of a pass. The waiting salmonid, practically from the trench where it has halted, should be able to make itself feel from far away the pull of the approaching current. In case there is a threshold to leap over, even before crossing, they should have a sufficiently long and empty space in deep water where they can feel the pull and jump. For a flow of 5 cu m/sec passing by a fall 1 m wide, 0.70 m high, the length of the trench should be 6.5 m if the slopes of the upstream and downstream are 0.50%, 7.50 m for 1%, and 16 m if the upstream slope is 5% and downstream slope is 1%. The trench should be 1 m deep.

The inlet of the pass should be close to the foot of the barrier because the salmonids have the habit of looking for a passage by going along the obstacle. In an oblique rectilinear barrier, the inlet of the pass is conveniently located in an acute angle upstream. In a V-shaped barrier, it will be on the top coming from the angle

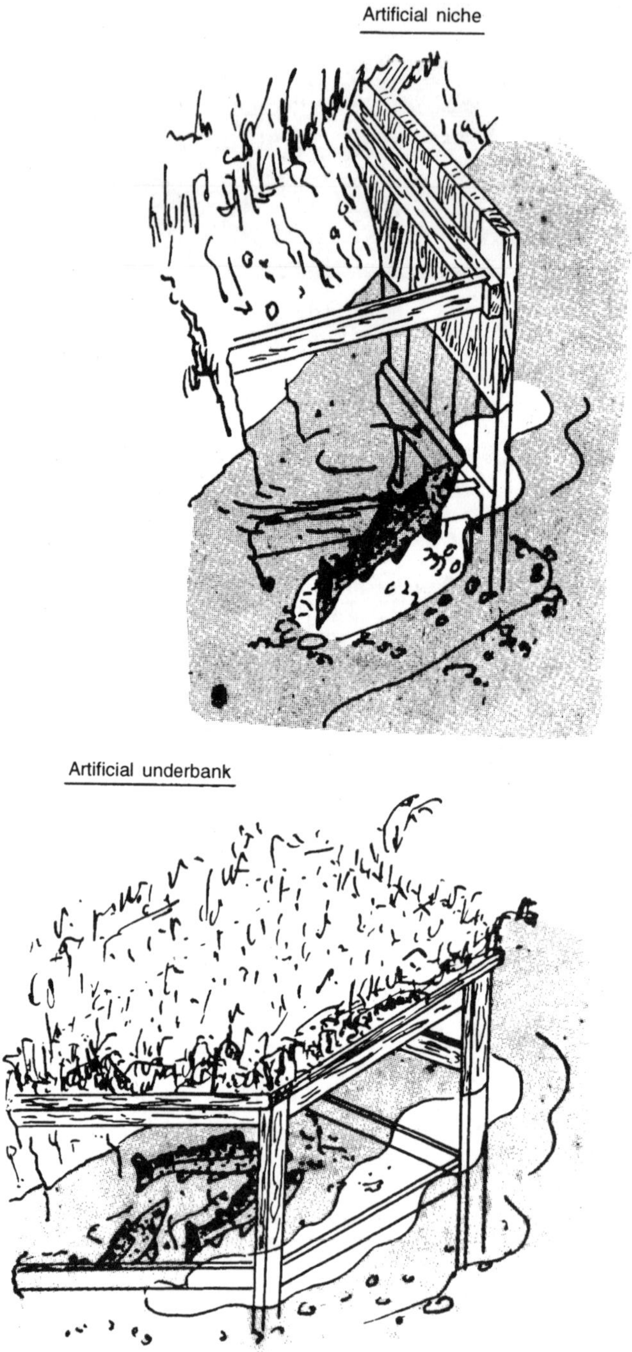

Fig. 316. Development of fish habitat

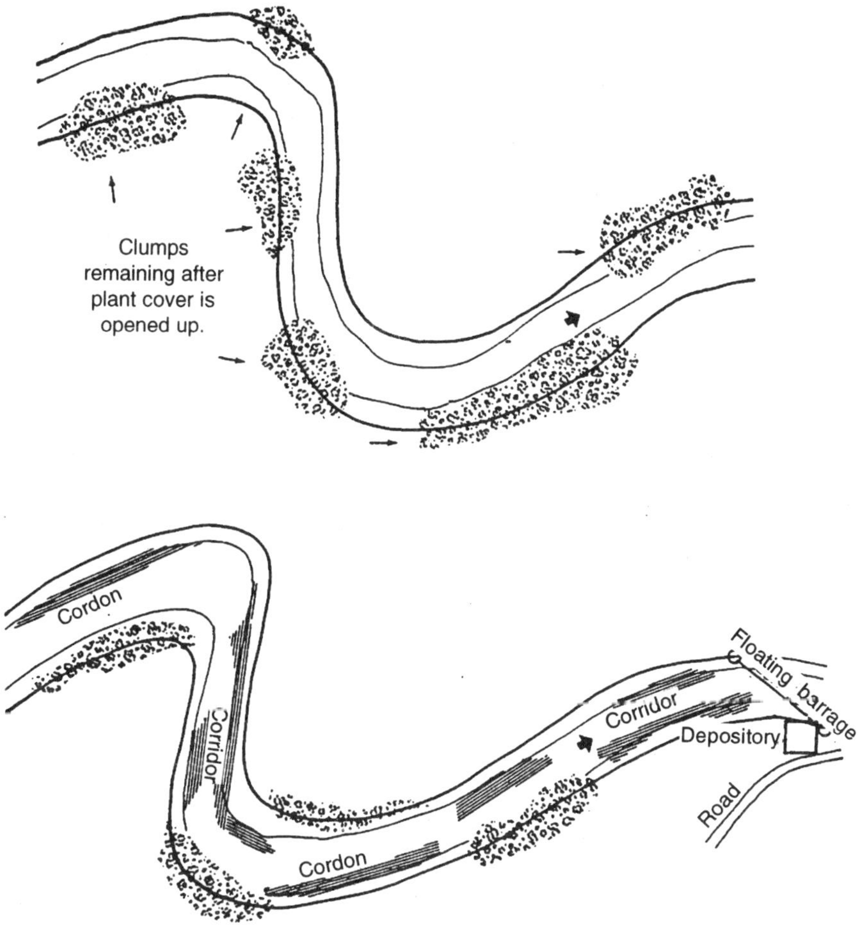

Fig. 317. Separation of plant cover after opening up the vegetation (top) and division of aquatic plants after scything (bottom). After J. ARRIGNON (1990a).

of the V-shape. Besides, it will be made known by a canal dug from the thalweg and 0.60 m to 1 m lower than the level of the lowest waters, according to COMPAIN (1968).

1.3 Speed of the Water Current

The speed of the water current in the pass depends on the maximum swimming speed of fish before crossing it and on the situation of the pass in the order of crossings found on a given water course. In the case of salmonids, this speed is approximately one-third the maximum speed of the species concerned and is around 1.50 and 2 m/sec. For other species, it is better to consult the table giving their maximum speed (Table 49).

In the passes found at the end of the water course, the speed of the current should be lower than the speed found at the beginning. The fish get weaker while moving upstream. The same will be the case if the passes have a supply of cold water (less than 8°C). The low temperature inhibits the fish and it does not jump. So it should be made to go up a weaker current.

1.4 Outlet of the Pass

The outlet from the pass should end in deep water (at least 1 m deep) in such a way that the subjects can reach a resting place without any effort before resuming their anadromy.

In the case of hydroelectric barrages, the turbine exits should be covered preferably with a fixed grill or, if not, with a flap that allows foreign bodies to pass through but stops the migrants from crossing over (ARRIGNON and JOSSART, 1973).

In order to prevent the passage of smolts coming downstream, mechanical devices such as louvers, or luminous or electric devices, rather than grills, should be used to orientate them. These devices should not be placed to end in a cul-de-sac, but at the upstream or downstream confluence of the river so that the fish will not be trapped.

1.5 Protection of Passes Against Siltation

Passes should be protected against siltation, sedimentation, or obstructions with the help of filtering blocks and a barrier made up of wooden posts lined up at every metre upstream of the upper opening.

The passes should also be protected from poaching by regulatory means and by putting up an enclosure that can be locked and placing a metal grating on the resting chambers.

2. DEVICES FOR CROSSING

Obstacles that hinder crossing during fish migration occur from the initial movement of migrating fish to their capture downstream, transport, or unloading upstream. Devices can be provided to help the migratory species cross the obstacles. These are passes, ladders, locks, lifts, screens, and escalators.

2.1 Passes

Passes are rough, low-cost interventions. The *water route* is made by fixing an inclined pipe diagonally on the downstream side of the spillway. The fish moves up the gutter thus formed, up to the indentation of the crest. The *pre-barriers* cause the fall to cascade from spillway to many planes so that it is possible to move from one passage to another and then to the upper part of the barrier. BACHELIER (1968) shows that the length of each intermediary basin should be three to four times the height to be crossed, which, on an average is 0.5 m. Pre-barriers made of mud fillings are widely used in North America. COMPAIN (1968) refers to the Pitlochry pass on the Tummel river in Scotland, which has 34 basins, of which 3 are resting basins and are bigger (16 m from the lower level). *Bedpasses* are indentations, often low in the centre and raised on the sides, used in the crest of barriers.

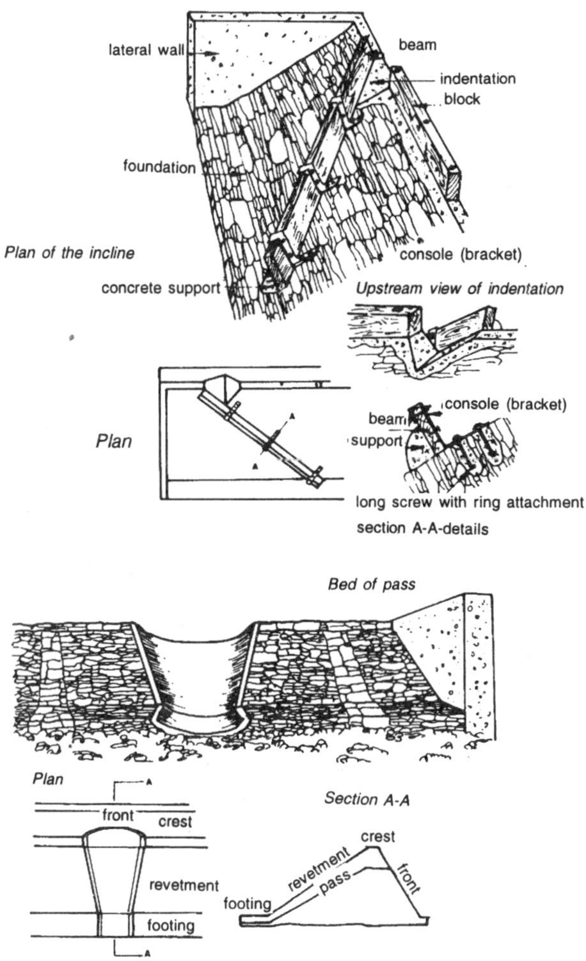

Fig. 318. Rustic passes

Fig. 319. Crossing of obstacle. Rustic pass. Narraguagus at Deblois, Maine (USA) (after J. ARRIGNON).

2.2 Sluice Gates

The sluice gates are sometimes equipped with a *mobile crest* that drains water not from the bottom but from the top. The salmonids thus cross from the lower level from 1 to 1.2 m because of the current created by the draining. The *automatic valve* is not an adjuster that can be lifted but an adjuster that disappears under the action of a counterpoise or a float that works by the vertical variations of the upstream stretch of water. The valves require some supervision, as do all mechanical systems operating in an aquatic surrounding.

2.3 Ladders

Fish ladders are very steep slopes that call for the use of artificial techniques. *Ladders with successive basins* have indented inclined partitions. The water current is stopped

Fig. 320. Crossing of obstacles. Ladder at Woodland on Sainte-Croix River (200 m length, inclined at 15.60 m, 7.30% slope), Maine, USA (after J. ARRIGNON).

by the indentations and the fishes thread through the water vein, passing through the indentations arranged in a zig-zag pattern. They are not forced to jump from one basin to another. The spillway of the indentation is sometimes prolonged by a mud flap to prevent water and air from getting emulsified. According to COMPAIN, the maximum speed of the current is 2.6 m/sec, the lower levels are 0.45 m per derivation canal, the length of each derivation canal is one-and-a-half times its width, the minimum width of an indentation is 0.6 m on the top and 0.45 m lower down, and the inclined vein should be at least 0.25 m thick. The *basins with sunken opening* should have a low level of 0.6 m. The openings at the base of the basins, with their bottom in the form of a ski jump, have a diameter of 0.6 m. These types of ladders are used for raised barriers. It is useful to insert resting basins measuring 3 × 3 m at every tenth basin. Their construction works out to be very expensive.

The *slowing ladders*, developed by DENIL and LACHADENEDE, have a canal, the bottom and lateral inner walls of which are grooved and can be equipped with deflectors of varying forms and arranged in varying numbers depending on the flow allowed by the ladder. These deflectors slow down the speed of the current and the indentations made between the projections allow the salmonids to pass through. Different models of this type, frequently used, are described by BACHELIER (1968).

2.4 Locks

The Borland lock comprises an entrance chamber downstream, a chimney placed at the side of the barrier establishing a link between this lower chamber and a higher

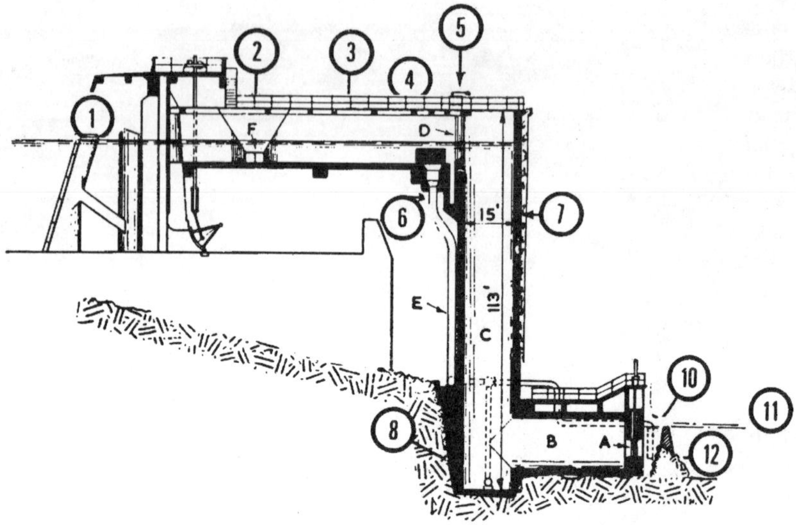

Fig. 321. Lock (sluice) for fish, Borland type. 1—upstream water; 2—electronic counter for migrating fish; 3—open canal (3 m wide); 4—upstream sluice gate; 5—electric hoist; 6—water supply pipe (70 m/m diameter); 7—vertical well; 8—supplier for attracting fish and filling wells; 9—horizontal chamber; 10—downstream sluice gate; 11—level of downstream water; 12—tubes for the flow of current before attracting fish in the chamber.

chamber situated upstream of the barrier. The two chambers have sluice gates with variable shutters and an automatic control. The system works as follows: Water is sent to the chimney. An approaching current sets in from the downstream chamber and the fish enter. The sluice gate being closed, water goes up the chimney. Fishes too go up and enter the lake when the water level reaches that of the lake. A study of the frequencies of this upward movement, depending on the concentration of fishes downstream, helps in defining a cycle that can control the automatic opening and closing of the sluice gates.

This lock is developed to ensure crossing of high barriers (Yla Tuloma, 62 m, USSR). It can be made to suit lakes of variable level by installation of sluice gates at different levels (Roznov and Czchow barriers on the Dunajec in Poland). It absorbs only a modest and cyclical flow. Moreover, it allows all species, including the shads, to move up, provided they do not create turbulence in the chamber downstream.

2.5 Lifts

The lift can be used in place of the chimney to transfer fish from a lower level to a higher level where they are free or captured. In the latter case, the cage touches a rolling bridge that takes it above the water tank of a truck. The lower opening of the cage is adapted to the opening of the tank into which the fishes pass. They are then transported either to the spawning grounds, eliminating all risks in intermediate crossings, or to the breeding grounds. Sometimes, the lift is replaced by an *escalator* with buckets or, to facilitate the upward movement of young eels, by a *doormat* placed on the floor of an inclined surface. Thus the young eels find traction, which is indispensable for their forward movement.

The inlet of some coastal water courses, frequented by migrants, is often equipped with a lock that blocks the dirty water and prevents it from submerging the low valley during high water. The water course crosses the *strand* in a long underground canal sometimes running to more than 100 m. This obstacle is crossed as follows: In the sea, at the downstream mouth of the canal, intermediate basins are set up to allow the low water to enter the canal. In the canal, the threshold meant to break the current should be sufficient so that the speed of the current is compatible with the physical capabilities of the migrant species concerned. The lock, which gives way only at low water, should be opened on the side by a hole measuring 50–60 cm. This allows the migrants to cross it at all times, without letting the sea water pass through it and thus destroy the riverside upstream. It is better to have the canal lighted up by chimneys measuring 1 m^2 placed at intervals of 10 m, or by windows paved with glass, or by artificial lighting as on the river Madeleine in Canada.

3. DEVICES FOR STUDY AND SAMPLING

Study and sample-taking devices are generally added on to the devices for crossing.

3.1 Orientation Screens (louvers)

Orientation screens are used to prevent fish from entering the escape channels of the hydroelectric stations during anadromy. In most cases, they consist of electric barriers. Above the danger zones (turbine entrance, straight down), they are also used to deflect the path of smolts and eels during catadromy. In the case of the latter, it involves luminous barriers or turbulence barriers rather than electric barriers. The *electric screens* are generally made up of an anodic grill placed across the canal or water course that has to be blocked, and 1 m behind a row of vertical cathodic bars are arranged in the same way. The current used is low frequency impulse current, according to LAMARQUE (1965). We can also use two rows of vertical electrodes between which a tension of 24–48 volts is established with direct current or alternating current. In both cases, the fishes make a half-turn as soon as they near the cathode. More often, *luminous screens* are used to direct lucifugous migrants near the points of forced passage in which a counting set or trap can be installed. They are generally made up of a ramp of luminous points, exposed or hidden, generally arranged diagonally, and the reflex angle ending in the point of forced passage. These screens are specially useful in the case of eels moving downstream. They are selective and do not obstruct the passage of non-lucifugous fish. The *louver* is a deflector made up of a screen of curved slats, separated by 20 cm, that can be oriented according to the speed of water current, which is between 1 and 1.6 m/sec on an average. The turbulence produced on each slat irritates the smolts and they go away. The louver

Fig. 322. Capture of young salmon smolts with the help of a sling (louvre) East River, Sheet Harbour Project (N.S. Canada) (after J. ARRIGNON).

Fig. 323. A pass for elvers on coil matting in a temporary dam; entrance to the Russ is supplied by an inlet (Vendée river—France) (after J. ARRIGNON).

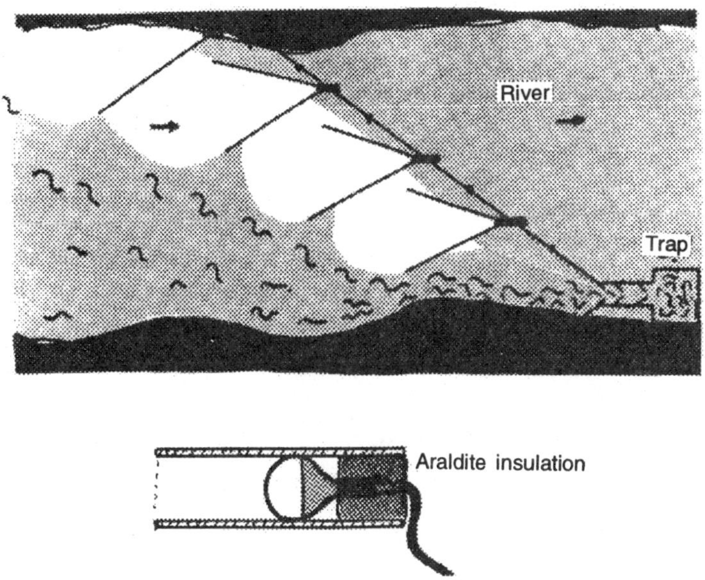

Fig. 324. Arrangement of a luminous barrage for fishing eels. Sealed ampullar piscina in a fibro-cement tube.

has an advantage. It allows very small debris to pass through and produces only a small loss of water force (1/5 of the height of fall). It is set up to direct the fish towards a canal in which a counting set can be installed.

3.2 Fences and Control Traps

Independent of biological and statistical reasons that dominate branding and control of adults and young ones, the least expensive and surest means of filling the spawning zones is to capture the fish in front of obstacles, transport the adults to the spawning grounds, and transport the young ones to the estuaries. This is also the best way of exploiting the reproductive potential of the males and increasing the rate of survival of smolts.

The fences for controlling and capturing fences set up in North America are primitive: simple V-shaped pattern in grills fixed on the posts, the reflex angle of the pattern opening into a mouthed cage forming a trap. The device helps to catch smolts. In order to capture the ones that reproduce, the trap is placed on the inside of the pattern and a V-shaped opening is made opposite the bottom, on the mouth of the trap. The water current going out serves to draw the fish. Greatly improved versions of this type of trap are used in Scotland and Ireland. In France, the density of floating bodies transported by the water currents is such that this type of barrier gets blocked and worn out quickly unless it is constantly supervised and cleaned.

Fig. 325. Capture of reproductive salmons. Rustic trap in the Polly River (Scotland) (after J. ARRIGNON)

Very efficient capturing traps are placed on fish passes as far as the reproductives are concerned. For the downstream migrants, modification of the eel grounds with openwork fences, laying of shutters with grating, and a recovery channel for smolts help in controlling a large part of the moving fish by a device that can also be installed below the louvers.

Fig. 326. Capture of reproductive salmons; they are held in a trap that is to be brought above from the tank truck and introduced there. Sheet Harbour barrage, N.S. (Canada) (after J. ARRIGNON).

Fig. 327. Salmons jumping in the Navarreux barrage (courtesy *La Peche Illustree*, review of the Fishing Club of France)

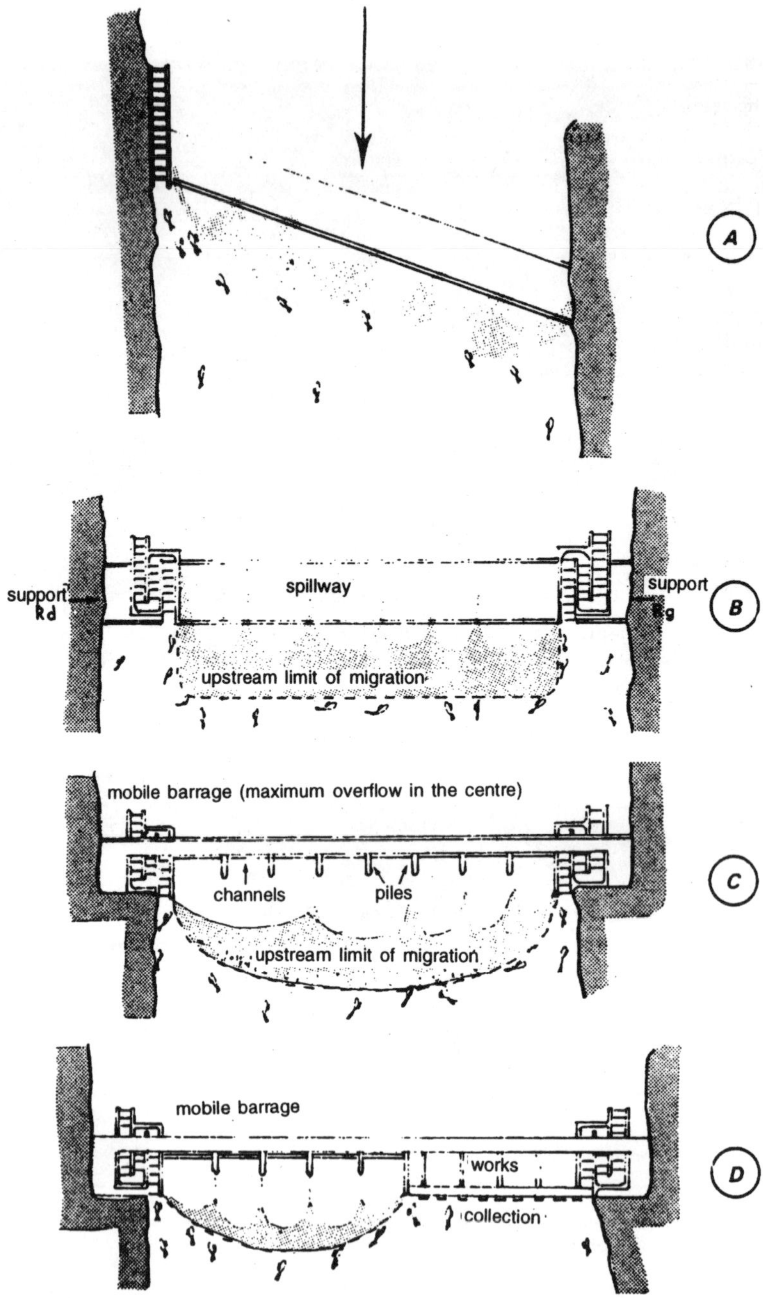

Fig. 328. Setting up fish passes (after CLAY, 1961): A, in an oblique spillway; B, in a frontal spillway; C, in a mobile barrage; D, in a barrage-works.

Table 49. Swimming speed of fish (after KREITMANN, 1932)

Species	Maximum speed (m/sec)	Corresponding height of fall (m)
Atlantic salmon	8.00	2.50
Trout	4.40	1.00
Nose carp	3.50	0.60
Chub	2.70	0.37
Barbel	2.40	0.29
Perch	0.60	0.02
Pike	0.45	0.01
Carp	0.40	0.01

We can distinguish three levels of swimming activity during the period when the fish can maintain speed (BELL, 1973; WEBB, 1975; LARINIER, 1978):

1) Cruising speed, which can be maintained for hours without causing any strong physiological modification of the organism.
2) Sustained speed, which can be maintained for several minutes but tires the fish.
3) Peak speed, resulting from a strong effort lasting from a few seconds to 10 seconds depending on species. For a jumping fish the peak speed can be estimated from the height covered, applying the following formula:

$$V = \frac{\sqrt{2gh}}{\sin\alpha}$$

where h is the jumping height and α is the angle of inclination of trajectory of the fish when it comes out of water.

The specific swimming speed is expressed by body lengths per second. Sustained speed and cruising speed depend not only on the size and species but also on abiotic features like dissolved oxygen content and water temperature. In optimal conditions the cruising speed of a majority of species is 2–3 lengths/sec. For the salmonids it is 3–4 lengths/sec.

The fish generally uses cruising speed for movement (like migrations), sustained speed in passages across the most difficult areas (rapids, passes), and peak speed to flee and to chase.

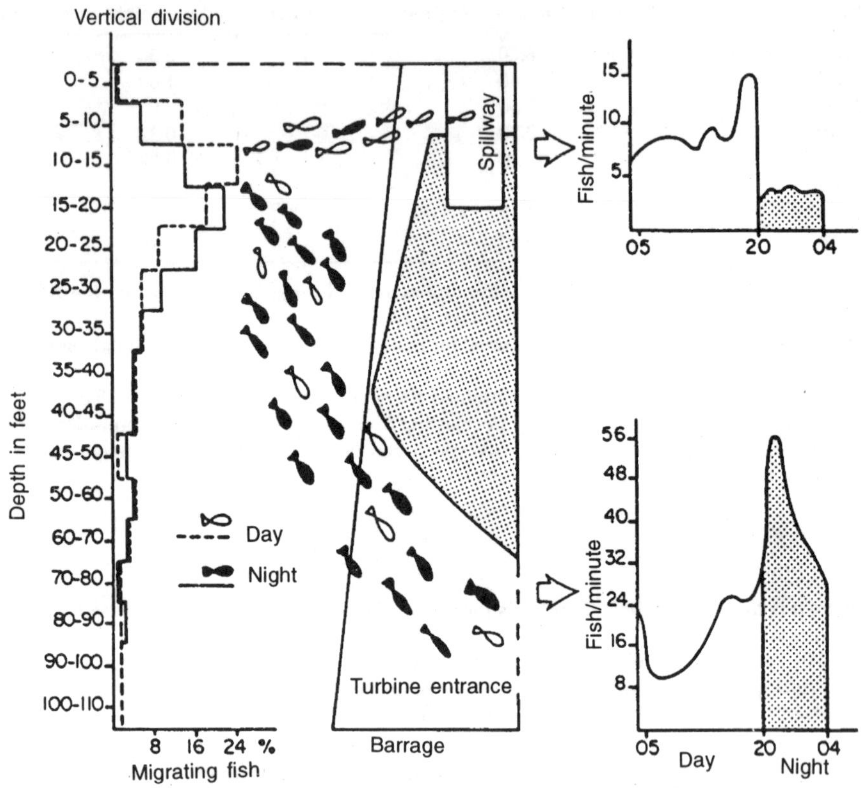

Fig. 329. Behaviour of salmons before a hydroelectric barrage. The fish are seen to move mostly towards the spillway during the day and towards the turbines at night. Ice Harbor barrage, USA (after *Soundings*, Biosonics publication).

2 INTERVENTION IN THE BIOLOGICAL MEDIUM

Except for transitory periods when the equilibrium in the aquatic medium is disturbed, and even then mostly provoked by humans, we can take it for granted that fish populations are always in a state of equilibrium. Some states of equilibrium are useful in fish culture economy or halieutic economy, or for water sports; others are less useful. In fact, fish populations are balanced not only among themselves but also according to human needs and human interventions.

A. AMELIORATION OF FISH CULTURE MEDIUMS

The kind of improvement to be brought about depends on whether the medium is in an excavated pond, where the fish population can very rarely be controlled, or a river, where populations are estimated only for the smallest of fishes, or a reservoir pond, where draining helps to precisely increase fish stock and overcome shortages. Some interventions can only be carried out in the last case.

1. INTERVENTIONS ON THE BED OF PONDS

Amelioration on the pond bottom requires drying in winter after the fishing is done. This exercise is seldom done every year. In fact, it is usually done once in two years. Modern methods of fertilization and improvement help prevent a long period of keeping the fish ponds empty. During the latter process, dikes and works can be repaired, alluvial deposits taken care of, and amendments implemented.

The deep ploughing should not completely uproot the reeds as this will bring to the surface the underlying sterile layers of soil, which in turn will reduce the productivity of the pond. Repeated cutting down of weeds is quite efficacious. Ploughing is useful when there is a thick layer of humus and when it can precede a long drying period. It can be followed by sowing of a mixture of cereals and clover. Livestock is then allowed to graze till the end of June, after which water is gradually released in order to raise year-old carp. This practice of *evolage*, however, has become obsolete because of the developments in cultural practices and fish culture and low productivity following a five-year cycle of rotation: [fish/empty pond (1 year) + fish/empty pond (1 year) + fish/empty pond (1 year) + cereal/clover (1 year) + grazing/fish (1 year)] or even a four-year cycle [fish/empty pond/ploughing (1 year) + leguminous plants/fish (1 year) + cereals (1 year) + fish/empty pond (1 year)].

Fig. 330. General site of a pond after clearing and ploughing (after J. Arrignon)

Fig. 331. Cereal seedlings seen on ploughing at the bottom of the pond (after J. Arrignon)

2. AMENDMENTS

Amendments are brought about with lime, calcium carbonate, and calcic cyanamide. They should not be improvised. The appropriate pH and hydrometric degree have to be scrutinized and sometimes more complex investigations undertaken.

2.1 Liming

Liming has many effects on the sanitary condition of fish and on the biological factors of production. Liming of the soil improves its condition by releasing bases and accelerates the decomposition of sludge. When the level of organic matter declines, the risk of propagation of certain bacterial and parasitic diseases also declines. Liming of acidic waters provides a pH that is more favourable to the health and growth of fish. It causes the suspended putrescible organic matter to precipitate. According to CHIMITS (1950), if the hydrometric degree of water (HD) is less than 15, it is better to do the liming using the following proportion:

57 (15 - HD) = K kg of quick lime/ha *or*

70 (15 - HD) = K, kg of slaked lime, in powder form, per ha.

Manure is spread at the end of winter on a dry surface, or three weeks before introduction of fish into the pond. If the water already has a population, then lime or milk of lime is introduced in several rounds (generally covering a quarter of the pond).

2.2 Other Amendments with Calcite

Use of pulverulent limestone improves the pH of water without adding the excessive amounts that are generally feared while using lime. According to SAWYER (1965) and M. LAURENT (1968), its use encourages growth of, and under certain conditions causes the reappearance of, a biological food having a base of chlorophyceae, diatoms, dinoflagellates, and rotifers. Moreover, it changes the texture and structure of the pond bottom and causes reappearance of aquatic plants. Marl, the pulverulent limestone present in certain marine algae, is used in the same way. Generally 5 t/ha is used so that an excess of it will not cause harm to the aquatic surroundings. It is applied either manually or mechanically, or directly from a tank by powder gun.

The calcic cyanamide acts as an important calcic amendment and nitrogenous manure causes the early and rich reappearance of phytoplankton. It is also a disinfectant and prophylactic agent. A mixture of slag and cyanamide or **scoramide** used at the rate of 350 kg/ha is one of the agents that improves closed aquatic surroundings and this brings about an annual fish yield of more than 1000 kg/ha.

However, its application is dangerous and the operators who do the manuring should not consume alcohol for a few hours before the spraying. They should also protect their hands and face and should work in calm weather conditions.

3. FERTILIZATION

Phosphoric, potassic, and nitrogenous fertilizers are used.

3.1 Mineral Fertilizers

Phosphoric manures are meant for dephosphoration of slag when the pH of water is acidic. The slag, which is hardly soluble in water, contains 40–50% of the lime necessary for the absorption of phosphates. If the pH is alkaline, superphosphates, which have an immediate action on the bottom, have to be used. CHIMITS (1950) recommends the spreading of 150–200 kg of slag when the HD is less than 15 and the same quantity of superphosphates when the HD is higher than 15. We can also use ammonium phosphate in the drop-by-drop distribution process or spreading of manure by using a diffusion ramp mounted on a stand.

With phosphorus as a nutritive agent the phytoplankton and zooplankton production increases. According to SCHAEPERCLAUS (1962), it also encourages nitrogen fixation by bacteria, in the presence of oxygen, lime, and colloidal sludge. Its role, however, depends on the increased treatments and is closely linked to the understanding of the evolution of plankton in the aquatic surroundings concerned. Manuring should be regulated in such a way that the average content of PO_4 is 0.4–0.6 mg/l so that the requirements of the phytoplankton are fulfilled. Manuring is frequent in May and June, sparse in July and August, and reduced to a single round in September; the interval between two operations is 10–14 days (ARRIGNON, 1965).

According to HUET (1970), it is advisable to use potassium during the earlier manurings. The dose should be 40–70 kg of potassium chloride/ha or 400 kg of kainite/ha. TERSEN (1990) is of a contrary opinion.

The use of nitrogenous mineral is useful only to encourage zooplankton in July, a period during which it becomes scarce while the fish tend to consume more. Moreover, we use liquid ammonium phosphate at the rate of 100 l/ha/year (14-48-0) two or three times. WURTZ-ARLET (1968) recommends the use of ammonium sulphate at the rate of 50 kg/ha/year or ammonium nitrate at 30 kg/ha or calcium nitrate at the same rate, in a single round in July.

3.2 Organic Manure

Fertilization by organic manure requires liquid manure used for the production of zooplankton, at the rate of 15 m^3/ha. It is used twice a week, in small quantities so that ammonium pollution can be prevented. The manure can be spread out on the dry ground at the rate of 30 t/ha or, after watering in spring, at the rate of 40 kg/ha every week. Sometimes, pig dung can be cured for at least 15 days and spread out. Poultry droppings mixed with water are sprayed during favourable weather conditions so that they will not ferment and cause a short supply of oxygen. Organic manuring in spring is very favourable for the young fish because it brings in a huge supply of the small invertebrates they feed on. Twenty quintals of manure contains a wide range of fertilizing material: 340 kg of organic matter, 11 kg of nitrogen, 5 kg of phosphoric acid, 14 kg of potassium, and 10 kg of lime (SCHAEPERCLAUS, 1962).

Table 50. Application of fertilizer (after RIEGGER)

Month	Treatment	Quantity (kg/ha)	
October	Application of quick lime	500	
March	Application of superphosphates	300	
May	"	100	
June	"	100	Total 600 kg/ha at 18% active
July or August	"	100	phosphorus
	Hardness of pond water: 18° TAC. Yield obtained: 1750 kg/ha/year		

Table 51. Summary of amendments and fertilization of ponds (after G. TERSEN, 1990)

Fertilizer	Form and quantity	Time	
Potassium	Never needed		
Calcium	Always useful, reserves must be present. Accelerates action of other amendments. Must be used before the other amendments.	100–1000 kg/ha	End of winter, on dry bed or 3 weeks after stocking fish
	Quick lime and lime water are most effective.	1000 kg/ha	
	One can use marl, pulverulent calcium from algae of geological origin or a form from Champagne called white chalk, sold under the name Nautex by MEAC.	5000 kg/ha	If there are fish, spread over 1/4 ha
Phosphorus	Indispensable because its absence prevents all other actions. In solid or liquid form, whichever is cheaper (by weight as P_2O_3).	30–60 kg/ha	At least 4–5 applications per year
Nitrogen	Reserved because of cost for alevin ponds. Naturally, mineralization of mud during drying out and rainstorms provide a little. One can choose from:		
	Liquid ammonium phosphate	100 l/ha/year	In 2 or 3 doses
	Ammonium sulphate	50 kg/ha/year	In 1 or 2 doses
	Ammonium nitrate	30 kg/ha/year	"
	Calcium nitrate	30–50 kg/ha/year	"
Organic manure	Spread well-decomposed manure along the banks (not in the water because fermentation consumes too much oxygen). One can also use a small quantity of sewage water, or poultry droppings. The effect varies widely according to the quality of each water body and each type of manure.		Before August

Table 52. Annual schedule of operations to be carried out on ponds (after B. MOLAIRE)

Operations	Jan.	Feb.	Mar.	Apr.	May	Jun.	Jul.	Aug.	Sept.	Oct.	Nov.	Dec.
Restocking			X								X	X
Draining											X	X
Amendments and fertilization				Limestone powder	Slag	superphosphates manure/liquid manure						lime
Scything						Rising plants (helophytes)		Floating plants (hydrophytes)				
Chemical clearing						X	X					
Feeding of carp fry	X	X							X		X	X
Maintenance of surroundings and minor works							X	X	X	X		
Storing (in the case of pond exploited by angling)	X	X	X	X	X	X	to be Reinforce in summer X	X	X	X	X	X

The debris left after scything is heaped up on the bank and sprayed with ammonium sulphate. This forms compost that can be used the following year in the same way as farm manure.

B. ARTIFICIAL EQUILIBRIUM

1. FISHING PRESSURE

Artificial equilibrium can be achieved by setting up means of restoration that correspond to the situations clearly explained by VIBERT and LAGLER (1961):

— The desired species are overexploited and the competitive species are underexploited.

— The desired species are overexploited and the competitive species proliferate.

— The desired species are underexploited and only the competitive species are present.

— The desired species are clearly underexploited and the competitive species are absent.

— The desired species are not captured.

— The desired species do not exist in the medium under consideration.

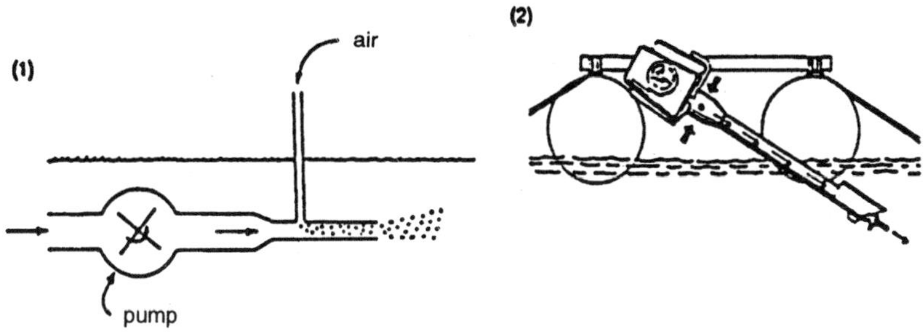

Sketch of the principle of a hydroejector (1) and air—O_2 (2)

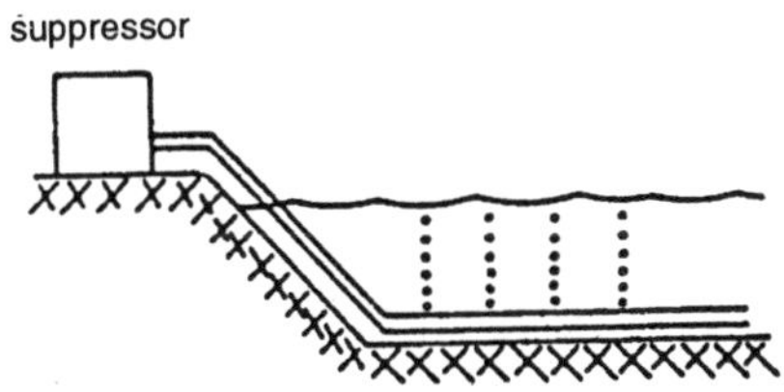

Sketch of the principle of a diffusion system

Type of aerator	Mean SAE	Range of variation
Paddle aerator (1)	2.7	2.2-3.0
Hydroejector	1.6	1.3-1.9
Paddle aerator (2)	1.4	1.1-1.8
Vertical aerator	1.4	0.7-1.8
Sprinkler	1.3	0.9-1.9
Diffuser	0.9	0.7-1.2

Standard of aeration efficiency (SAE) of different types of electric surface aerators, in kg of O_2/kWh (after BOYD, 1989)

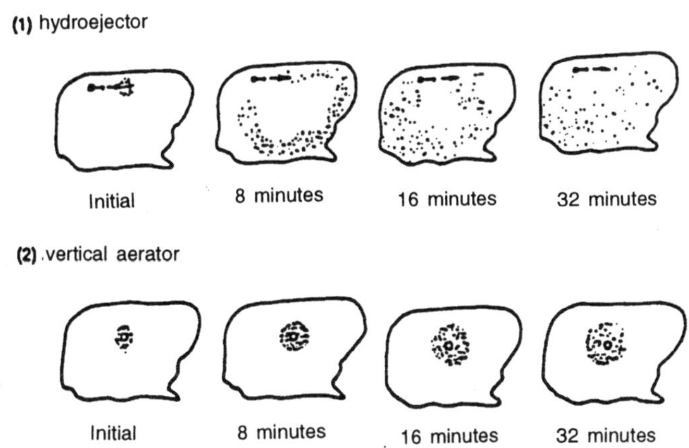

Fig. 332. Aerators and pond aeration (after V GOUBIER, 1990a)

Means of restoring or recreating a fish culture equilibrium require necessary information and eventually some action, such as liberalization of fishing in a particular place, application on a particular species, stocking with fish to fill severe deficits, strict poaching restrictions, and repairing the effects of pollution.

1.1 Notion of Fishing Effort

Knowledge of the fishing effort is useful in completing the hydrobiological information about the surroundings that have to be restored. The fishing effort is the density, frequency, and intensity of fishing in a fish population by professional fishermen and also by sportsmen. The density is expressed in number of fishermen per kilometre in a water course and per hectare in a water body. We can also calculate in rods/km or rods/ha when several fishing lines are permitted. As far as professional fishing is concerned, density is expressed in number of traps or nets per hectare. The periodicity is the number of fishermen who fish per day, per week, per month, or per season and, for professional fishing, the number of traps or nets used during the same periods. The intensity is given by the number of units or number of kilograms of fish caught per fisherman and per time period.

The fishing effort thus involves the quantity of fish procured from an aquatic surrounding with well-defined conditions of exploitation. It also involves the supply of different resources (licences, rights, contributions). Knowledge of fishing effort is the basis for the management of the fish culture medium because it provides:

— increase in fishing in the medium

— increase in the financial means necessary for the management or restoration of the medium.

Investigations that help increase the fishing effort generally give other information that helps in using the restocking formulae. BUTLER and BORGESON (1965) give the following formula, which has been adapted by CUINAT (1968):

$$D = \frac{0.7 \times C/J}{c}$$

where D is the number of fish to restock

C/J is the average success of fishermen:

$$\frac{\text{total number of catches}}{\text{number of fishing days}}$$

c is catchability:

$$\frac{\text{number of catches per fishing day}}{\text{previous catches}}$$

The time unit for accumulated catches can be a week, fortnight, or month. Our own observations, along with CUINAT'S, for the estimation of the increase in the catches give the following value:

$$0.0025 < c < 0.0275$$

Surveys conducted among 5000 fishermen fishing in ponds in the North of France and region around Paris over 133,000 fishing days have enabled us to set up a formula. This formula is drawn from the knowledge of the fishing effort and knowledge of theoretical productivity of the stretches of water concerned, and based on the formulae:

$$P = \frac{Na}{10} \times B \times K$$

$$D = 0.4\ J - P$$

where D is the quantity (in kg) of cyprinids to be stocked per hectare, J is the number of fishing days, and P is the theoretical productivity of the lake.

This formula is adjusted for ponds reserved for fishermen paying not a daily fee but an annual fee:

$$D' = 4S - P$$

where S is the number of fishermen, on a fixed basis of 10 fishing days per year per fisherman.

1.2 Under- and Overexploitation

Under- and overexploitation of the fish culture medium are caused by wrong understanding, which is serious, or a wrong interpretation of the ecological data, which is even more serious, and sometimes by complete ignorance of the elementary rules of exploitation and productivity of the medium.

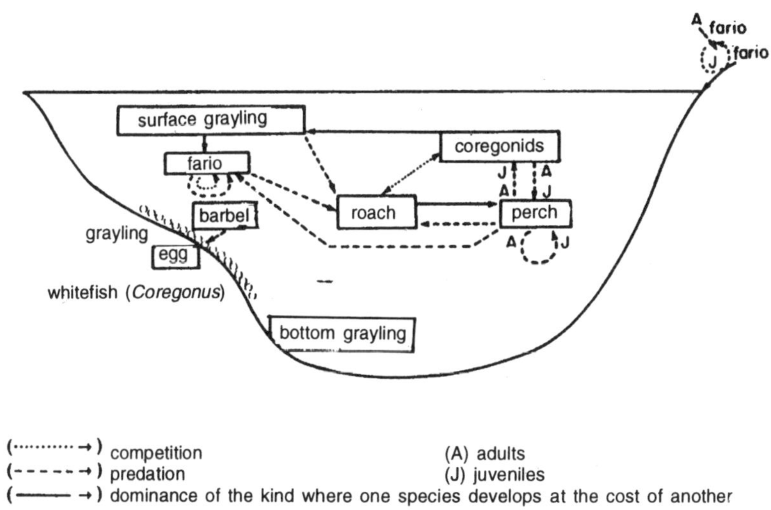

Fig. 333. Some inter- and intraspecific points of relation (after CHAMPIGNEULLE, 1985)

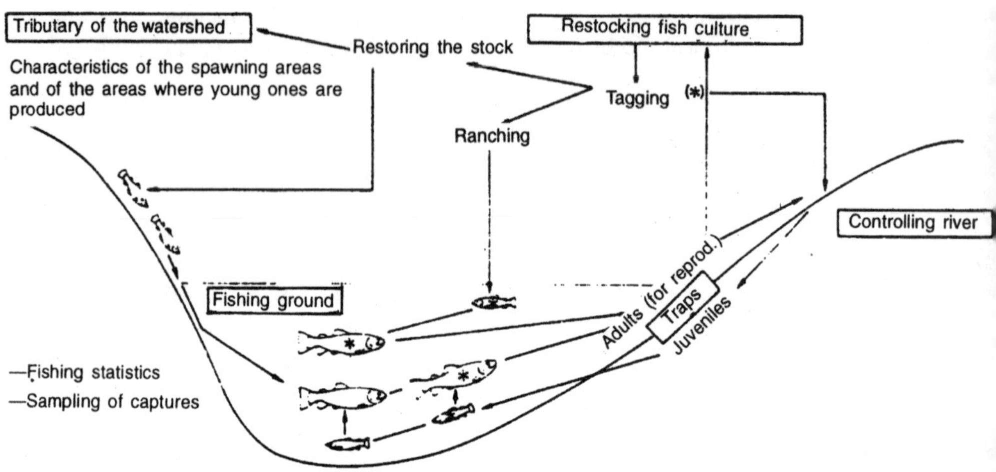

Fig. 334. Understanding and management of the production of fario trout in a lake ecosystem—associated tributaries (after CHAMPIGNEULLE, 1985)

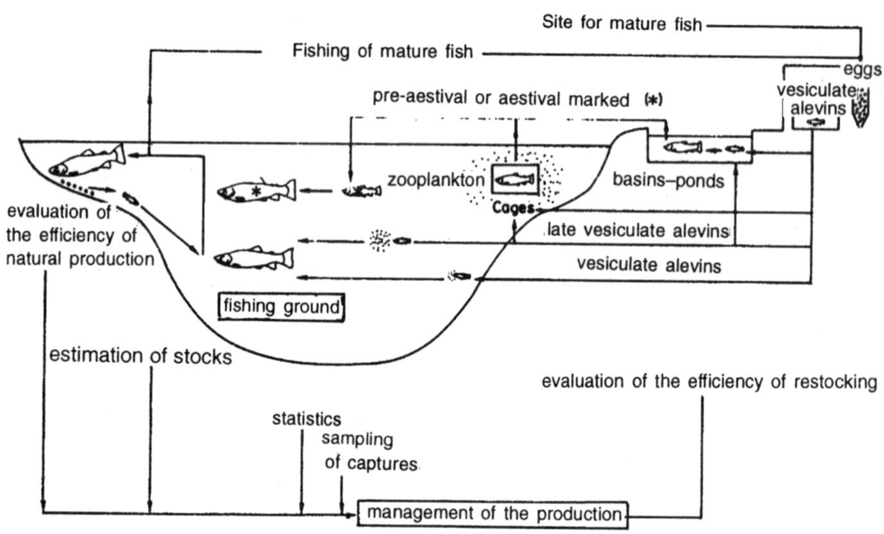

Fig. 335. Restocking and management of the production of whitefish (*Coregonus*) (after CHAMPIGNEULLE, 1985)

The following example demonstrates this fact:

— A salmonid river has a theoretical fish productivity of 290 kg/ha/year; an inventory of the population made during electrical fishing for eels shows that the actual population of adult salmonids that are old and unhealthy reaches 618 kg/ha. The owner of the riparian land, when consulted, says that he fishes 15 times and his guests fish 20 times in a year. *All the fish caught are put carefully back into the water.* Since the owner had read somewhere that a river needs to be regularly enriched, he gets an annual overflow of 50 kg of trout and introduces 10 Vibert's boxes, filled with embryonated eggs (9000–10,000 eggs) on a course of 700 m (area around 50,000 sq m). **There was a combination of reasons for the fish to become senile and degenerated. They were underexploited.** The Vibert's boxes were a total waste, the alevins being eaten by the adults as soon as they moved out. It is sheer chance that the cultured trout population was not decimated; density and poor sanitary conditions made it sensitive to all epizootic diseases.

This happens frequently during restocking of water courses and water bodies and in the latter case the fish may become completely degraded, since the enclosed surrounding makes it impossible for them to escape.

In zones with a high demographic density and in highly industrialized regions, the number of anglers outnumbers the quantity and quality of the available water body. Fishing in these areas results in rapid reduction of fish productivity and fish stocks.

Small-scale salmonid culture in rivers and in smaller water bodies are destroyed as soon as they are opened for fishing. The fishermen then can hope for only a very small catch in an *overexploited habitat.*

2. RESTOCKING

Production from springs, nurseries, growth streams and reserves is limited by ecological and biological as well as human and financial constraints.

A manager faced with a problem of over-fishing must make a serious analysis of the causes and solutions before making a decision, and restocking is often only a last resort. This kind of intervention should be ruled out except for considering systematic and annual restocking in water courses of a department as a justification enabling those responsible for protecting these water courses to complain against any harm done to the fish medium (e.g., pollutions, untimely hydraulic works and operations).

The pressure of fishing, however, justifies recourse to some artificial measures, of which the most important is **high-density restocking**. Such restocking is, in fact, only an input: the fish are intended to be caught again very soon. The water is only a support for them.

2.1 Salmonid Water Courses

In salmonid water courses, which are especially sensitive to overexploitation, overstocking includes mainly the rainbow trout, to a much lesser extent the fario trout, and rarely the brook trout. These are intensively cultured and introduced when they are large enough for capture.

Table 53. Plan and evaluation of the restocking operation

Objectives: recalling the diagnosis

Restocking techniques			
Duration of the programme		Type of restocking	
Species		Introduction: Yes No	
Source of stocks:	wild	Area of capture:	
	fish culture	Breeding conditions:	
Sanitary condition:			
Stage:		Age:	
Size of structure:		Average weight:	
Number released:		Number marked:	
Type of mark:			
Period of release:		Hour:	
Site:	Lake:		River:
–distance from bank		–name	
–depth		–habitat	
–loading		–loading	
–dispersion		–dispersion	
Accompanying measures:	regulation	fishing pressure	
	development	protection zone	

Technical and biological evaluation

Means used:	fishing statistics	Amateur	Professional
	return of marked fish		
	trapping		
	inventories		

Number captured (marked): from which calculate % of the number marked
Estimation of % restocked fish in the capture:
Total weight of capture: .... kg/1000 juveniles restocked
Distribution of recaptured fish in space and time:
Growth:
Time taken between the size at release and minimum permitted size:
Set up signals: presence on the spawning ground....
Expenses + economic assessment

Recalling cost:	price of 1000 restocked fish
	marking of 1000 fish
	estimation of recaptured fish

$$\frac{\text{kg of recaptured fish for 1000} \times \text{price of 1 kg}}{1000 \times \text{price of one restocked individual}}$$

Remarks:

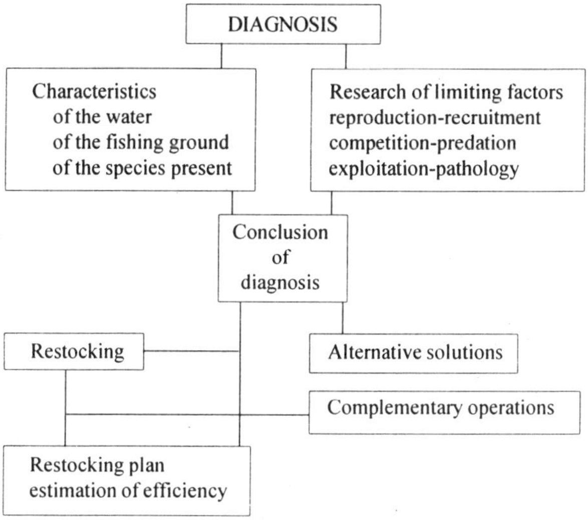

Fig. 336. Preliminary diagnosis for restocking and restocking plan

The fish should be put on fast for some days before the introduction as this makes their transportation less risky: their flesh is firmer and they are more aggressive. Compressed air is preferred to oxygen during transport. The fish should be introduced in the receiving containers in the early hours of the morning so that it has the time to make its reference points, choose a place, and fix itself in the zone into which it is introduced. If it is discharged in the evening, it may tumble down a long distance.

The overstocking operation should be done in a zone having alternately moderate and calm currents where, as according to CUINAT (1968), the amplitude of movements seems reduced. Depending on the fishing effort, the time of overdense discharges and their frequency can be varied. They are generally carried out some days before fishing is started and some days after so as to compensate the heavy fishing at the opening of the season. The overflows can be done in the season, a little before the peak periods (holidays). The frequency and size of the supply depends on fishing and these have to be rigorously examined. It is preferable to discharge smaller numbers of fish in more areas rather than larger numbers of fish in a few areas.

It is advisable to operate along the current, in a small boat containing or tugging a fish tank. The fish are divided and put in the most suitable places.

The supply can be done as soon as half the quantity introduced earlier has been captured.

The overstocking of trout can be done for temporary supply of the restricted fishing sections (during fishing competitions), for enrichment of sections preferentially frequented on the lots of a fishing club, and for enrichment of fishing sections of dense, constant, and generalized frequency.

Table 54. Opportunities and techniques for restocking trout (adapted from RICHARD, 1997)

Development priority	Fishing: Artificial support for fishing						Patrimonial: Improving the capacity of the medium to produce fish naturally				
Aim of restocking	Maintaining numbers if natural production does not meet expectations of anglers						Maintaining numbers if cause of population decline can be removed				Restoration of the population if cause of production decline is removed and where no natural recolonization is possible
Quality of the aquatic medium Nature of medium Altered functions	standard nil		peturbed or degraded repro./hatch.		growth		perturbed or degraded repro./hatch.		growth		degraded repro./hatch. growth
Type of fishing easy to be developed	easy	sport	easy	sport	easy	sport	easy	sport	easy	sport	natural fishing
Opportunity for restocking	YES	NO	WELL ADAPTED			NO	YES			NO	WELL ADAPTED
Restocking techniques to be implemented	Introduce catchable trout	/	Intro. catchable trout	Intro. juve-niles	Intro./ catchable trout		Intro. sterile catchable trout	Introduce sterile juveniles	Introduce sterile catchable	/	Transfer fish of similar hydrographic origin

2.2 Esocid-cyprinid Water Courses

In the esocid-cyprinid water courses, the overstocking of fish is done only for fishing competitions. The stocks are distinctly higher in canalized rivers and in canals to the extent that their capture rate is higher (TIMMERMANS, 1967). In ponds, the quantities introduced should strictly take into account the fishing carried out by anglers. The proportion of species to be introduced is linked to the preferences of anglers for one species over another. It is also linked to the selection of means and methods of fishing.

3. MANAGED FISHING STRETCHES

Frequently used tourist fishing courses are generally developed to enable social and sporting activities and the opportunity for relaxation in a pleasant site as well as a range of fishing opportunities that can satisfy a wide spectrum of anglers.

Fishing stretches in urban zones are meant for a small and permanent clientele who are keen on relaxation and sporting satisfaction. In rural zones the stretches of high tourist and fishing interest appeal to a flux of fishing tourists who sometimes stay there during summer vacations.

These stretches are organized on a somewhat large section of the river (5–20 km), on a vast pond, or on a string of smaller ponds.

In urban zones, restocking is regular and systematic. In extreme cases, water constitutes only a simple support for the transit of a fish population that is continuously fluctuating and renewed. In the rural zone, the restocking is aimed only to compensate the drain caused by sporadic use, which generally happens on water courses in good condition.

3.1 Fishing Stretches for Tourists

Stretches for tourists on rivers are chosen on such sections of water courses that are completely safe from any foreseeable variation that can break the biological equilibrium, such as pollution, breaches, sudden pumping, and uncontrolled overflow of encroaching or undesirable species. The servicing route, either on one bank or on both, should link the nearby tourist centres, which should be provided with a good hotel. The manager should be assured of a long-term land lease that gives him the right to fish on both banks of the stretch concerned. The seriousness of managerial problems is such that a frequently used tourist fishing stretch is administered like a techno-commercial enterprise. These are the conditions that have to be taken into consideration while preparing a fishing stretch of this sort.

More than anything else, a frequently used fishing stretch should be well explored, not only at the level of the river but also at its basin. The fish culture and halieutic possibilities should be assessed before a decision is taken to create a fishing stretch. A descriptive and preliminary estimate of the management of hydraulics, fish culture, and tourist development have to be precisely expressed in relation to various possible solutions for exploitation and their cost.

In case of a salmonid stretch, it is generally planned to reserve fishing stretches for anglers (using fly bait), one or several stretches open for all types of legally authorized fishing, a section set aside for tourists, and one or more sections meant for local fishermen (who pay their taxes in the riverside localities). Certain sectors are classified as reserved for convenience (enclosed private property) or by obligation (surroundings where work is in progress), or for biological reasons (downstream of fish culture site reserved for breeding). Parking lots are planned at the most logical points of concentration. So are footbridges and small drawbridges at certain passing points. Additional facilities are conveniently located areas meant for relaxation, which are provided with benches, tables, sand pits for young children, and waste bins.

The structure of the fish population has to be studied before the initial development and then re-evaluated after every fishing season. The inventories and exploration by electric fishing enable us to be aware of the surplus sectors. They also help in elimination of destructive species. Tagging of fish is sometimes useful in estimating their growth and migration.

A fishing stretch can be further developed by raising spare wild young trout that will reach the permissible size for fishing at the time of its opening. In the plain country rivers, it is even possible to introduce young trout in the entire stretch in autumn and these can be available for fishing the following spring. It is, however, important to guard against overstocking, which will keep fish from growing large enough for capture due to insufficient food. The quota should correspond to the gap existing between the relic population existing at the time of opening and the theoretical population, which corresponds to the production potential of the water course.

Fish culture and halieutic knowledge, particularly that pertaining to the weekly fishing effort, helps in defining the frequency and quantity of compensating overflow of fish required during the fishing season. For financial reasons, fish just exceeding the permissible size for capture should be used, particularly if the anglers are subjected to a daily catch limit. If large fish, which anglers get excited about, are rare, it will be a good idea to introduce some here and there, limiting them to 1% of the total population. This initiative should not, however, become a rule for enrichment; there are always a larger number of large fish than expected because of the fish carried forward from the previous years.

The same knowledge and the annual survey made with the help of fishermen enable developers to rearticulate the sectors opened to various modes of fishing, and also the reserves, scything periods, mowing time of the surroundings, and general maintenance.

The future of keeping a fishing stretch in frequent use is determined by the sale of licences, which forms the main source of income for the enterprise. The sale of licences also affects its future because overuse brings about overcrowding and then withdrawal. The general estimate for optimal simultaneous use is 5 fly anglers and 20 fishermen using other means for fishing per kilometre of the river. This data takes into account the seasonal variations and is applicable to the duration of the fishing season and not to the whole calendar year.

3.2 Reservoirs

Fishing stretches for tourists in ponds are chosen in good tourist sites, generally in forests, well connected and beyond the reach of pollution and floods.

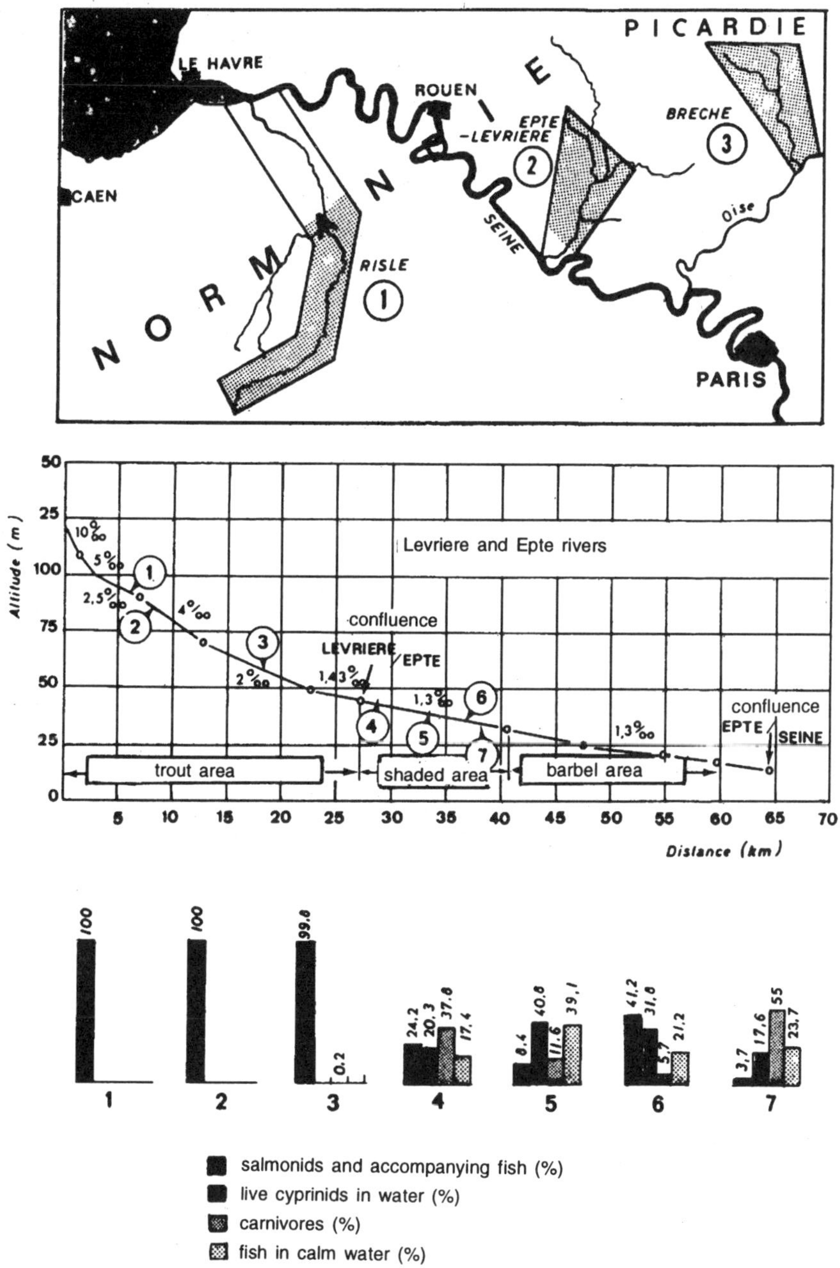

Fig. 337. Evolution of fish stocking of a salmonid water course

Ponds that can be drained are easy to regulate but expensive. However, they can be easily managed because the fish can be controlled. Besides, daily fishing as a leisure activity and the annual or biannual commercial fishing also come together here. The latter helps in eliminating undesirable fish and in releasing a new lot that meets the taste of fishermen and the requirements of the habitat.

The fishing directives are the result of investigations in which fishermen, people controlling future fishing, and the results of the autumn draining are all involved. Competitive fishing is indeed selective. It overexploits certain species and even certain sizes of fish and underexploits certain others that sometimes live as predators or competitors in vital space.

The necessity and size of the compensational overflows as well as their periodicity form part of the exploitation directives. They are specially important in case of trout ponds for they directly depend on exploitation by fishermen.

The quest for widely different species for fishing by various means demands different treatment of the pond periphery for different occupations, depending on the configuration, nature of the aquatic medium, and access. Sectors can be reserved for traditional fishing by casting and spinning nets and zones kept open for fishing in small boats. In case of a fishing stretch comprising a string of ponds, it is desirable to allot a specific function to each one, taking into account its characteristics, or otherwise the occupations along the bank can be rotated so that the mediums for fish culture are suitably exploited.

This arrangement is worthwhile in case of dug-out ponds that cannot be drained and in which the population cannot be easily controlled. The exploitation of these ponds is necessarily reduced to just recreational fishing. However, it is advisable to change over to commercial fishing (nets, traps) in order to be able to eliminate fish that are too big and too old. Here exploitation by occupation (along bank) and by rotation is often possible, given their number and proximity at the same site (in ballast holes, sand pits, peat bogs).

The approaches should be only slightly developed: steps made for fishing footpaths located away from the latter, relaxation zones, and parking lots.

Reservoirs are more frequented than the stretches on rivers: the general estimate is that optimal use should not cross 100 rods per day and per kilometre of the bank, but that depends very much on the mode of fishing and the occupation along the bank.

C. FISH PRODUCTION

Fish production depends on the morphodynamic, physicochemical, and hydrobiological characteristics of the aquatic medium. It also depends on the selection of the species to be produced and the fish culture practices that condition their growth and production.

1. SELECTION OF SPECIES

It is often difficult to select species that are to be introduced in the pond. The selection itself has to take into consideration many factors, which, on study, lead to

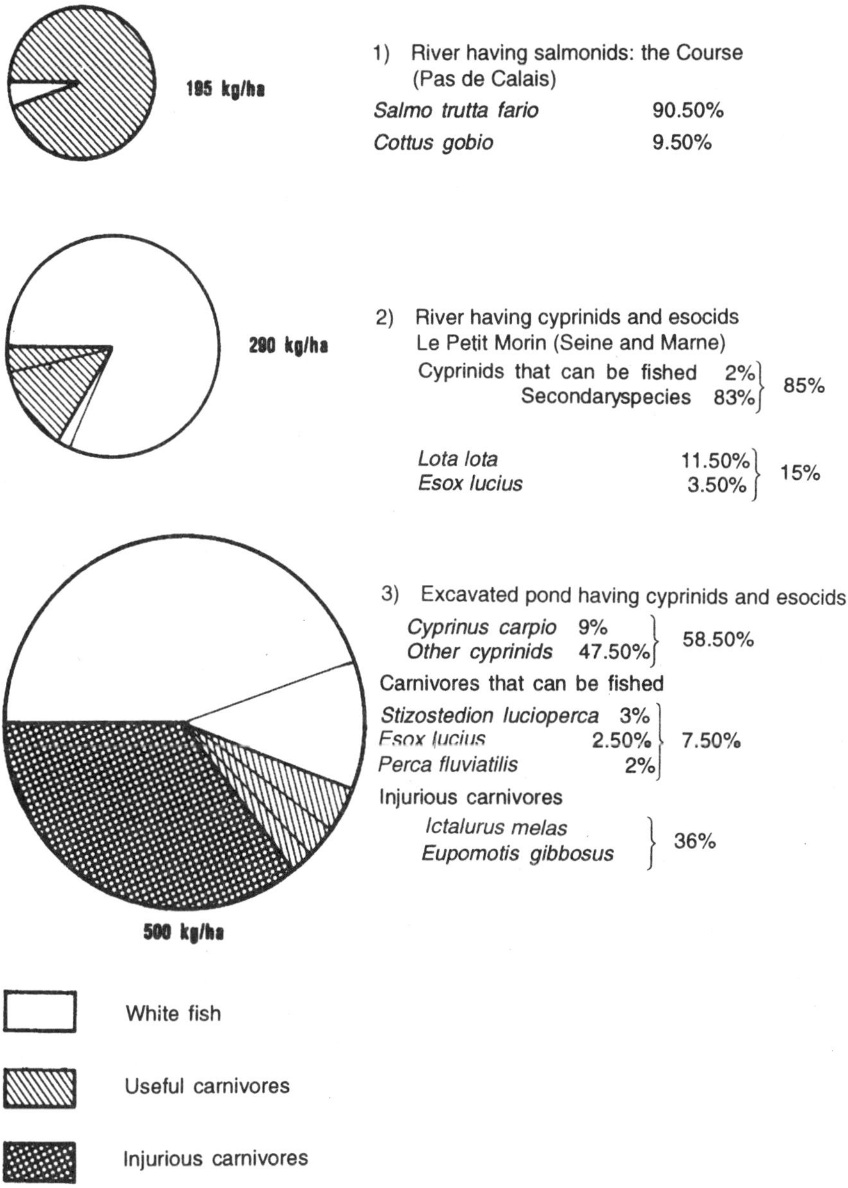

Fig. 338. Distribution of fish populations

many equally valuable proposals. So the decision lies with the manager and very often depends on his own wishes. The following example demonstrates the fact.

— A water body is fed by an aquiferous sheet of water. The deep water, fresh during all seasons, is well oxygenated by aquatic plants growing in the shallow parts and on the banks. The banks are not overcrowded with vegetation. The surroundings are shaded and pleasant with easy access. Such conditions bring forth many combinations.

Rainbow trout + gudgeon + rudd + dace (Rhone toxostome)

Pike + rudd + dace + bleak

Pike-perch + tench + gudgeon + roach

Perch + gudgeon + roach + bleak

Pike-perch + *rainbow trout* + gudgeon + roach + tench

Pike-perch + *pike* + gudgeon + tench + roach + dace

This list of combinations is not exhaustive, and no combination can be rejected *a priori*. However, a phytozoological study will restrict the range of choices by revealing the nature and extent of the phytoplankton and zooplankton, as well as the food habits of the species of each association.

In a virgin pond, the constitution of the fish population will depend on the objectives of the manager. If it is already populated, it is better to study the structure and dynamics of the indigenous population before adding to it.

For example, if the sampling indicates the presence of *perch* + *pike* + *pike-perch* + *gudgeon* + *roach* + *tench*, the existence of a superfluous carnivorous species prevents the introduction of a fourth predaceous species, the *rainbow trout*. The question arises whether it is better to favour the perch over the pike and what the utility of the pike-perch is in such an association. The answer can be found from the study of growth rate of each of the three carnivores, their degree of dominance, and the structure of their population as well as that of "forage fish". We can thus state that the pikes are very old and do not reproduce because of an inconvenient spawning ground or that the pike-perches do not have enough prey to achieve a harmonious growth.

Even if it is not possible to achieve an ideal association, in general, one should take into consideration the following series of recommendations, which can be constantly verified:

— It is necessary to have carnivorous species in a fish population.

— Having two of them is a delicate association.

— Having three of them is often harmful. Experiments carried out in France in the past fifty years have yielded some feasible associations (before taking into account the characteristics of the aquatic mediums):

Carnivorous fish	Accompanying fish
Rainbow trout	+ gudgeon + rudd + minnow + dace
Pike	+ chub + roach + carp + rudd + bleak + tench + bream + carp

Perch	+ roach + carp
	+ rudd + tench
Pike-perch	+ gudgeon + tench
	+ bream
Pike + pike-perch	+ roach + carp
	+ gudgeon + tench
Black bass	+ roach + carp
	+ dace + bream

2. QUANTITATIVE ESTIMATION

Quantitative estimation takes into account the biogenic capacity of the plain water body and the ratio of the carnivorous fish to the entire fish population. This ratio should be between 10 and 20%. In other words, if the total stock per hectare is 200 kg, the carnivores should comprise 20–40 kg and the accompanying fish 180–160 kg. Fish productivity in ponds is expressed by HUET (1970) on the basis of the quality and vocation along the banks.

The productivity brought about by manuring results from the application to P of a coefficient F, which varies from 0.1 to 2 in proportion to the manure used and the fish species raised. Productivity that comes from nutrients is obtained from coefficient A, which increases from 0.1 to 3, depending on the nutrient, its distribution, and the species raised. These coefficients are determined empirically for F and from nutrition tables for A; such tables are usually supplied by the nutrient manufacturers.

The calculation of the total productivity is simple. For example:

P = 250 kg/ha · year, F = 0.5, A = 0.2

Total productivity = 250 + 125 + 50 = 425 kg

3. INTRODUCING A NEW LOAD OF FISH

The introduced fish load in the pond consists of a particular quantity of a fish species of a certain size that constitutes the main base of production.

Table 55. Formula of natural annual productivity of intensive-culture ponds (after HUET, 1970)

	Grow-out ponds (K varies from 1 to 3)		Alevin ponds (K varies from 1.5 to 4.5)	
Types	Acid waters	Alkaline waters	Acid waters	Alkaline waters
Trout ponds	$P = \frac{Na}{10} \times B \times 1.0$	$P = \frac{Na}{10} \times B \times 1.5$	$P = \frac{Na}{10} \times B \times 1.5$	$P = \frac{Na}{10} \times B \times 2.25$
Cyprinid ponds	$P = \frac{Na}{10} \times B \times 2.0$	$P = \frac{Na}{10} \times B \times 3.0$	$P = \frac{Na}{10} \times B \times 3.0$	$P = \frac{Na}{10} \times B \times 4.5$

Na is the numer of units of 100 sq m. B = the biogenic capacity.

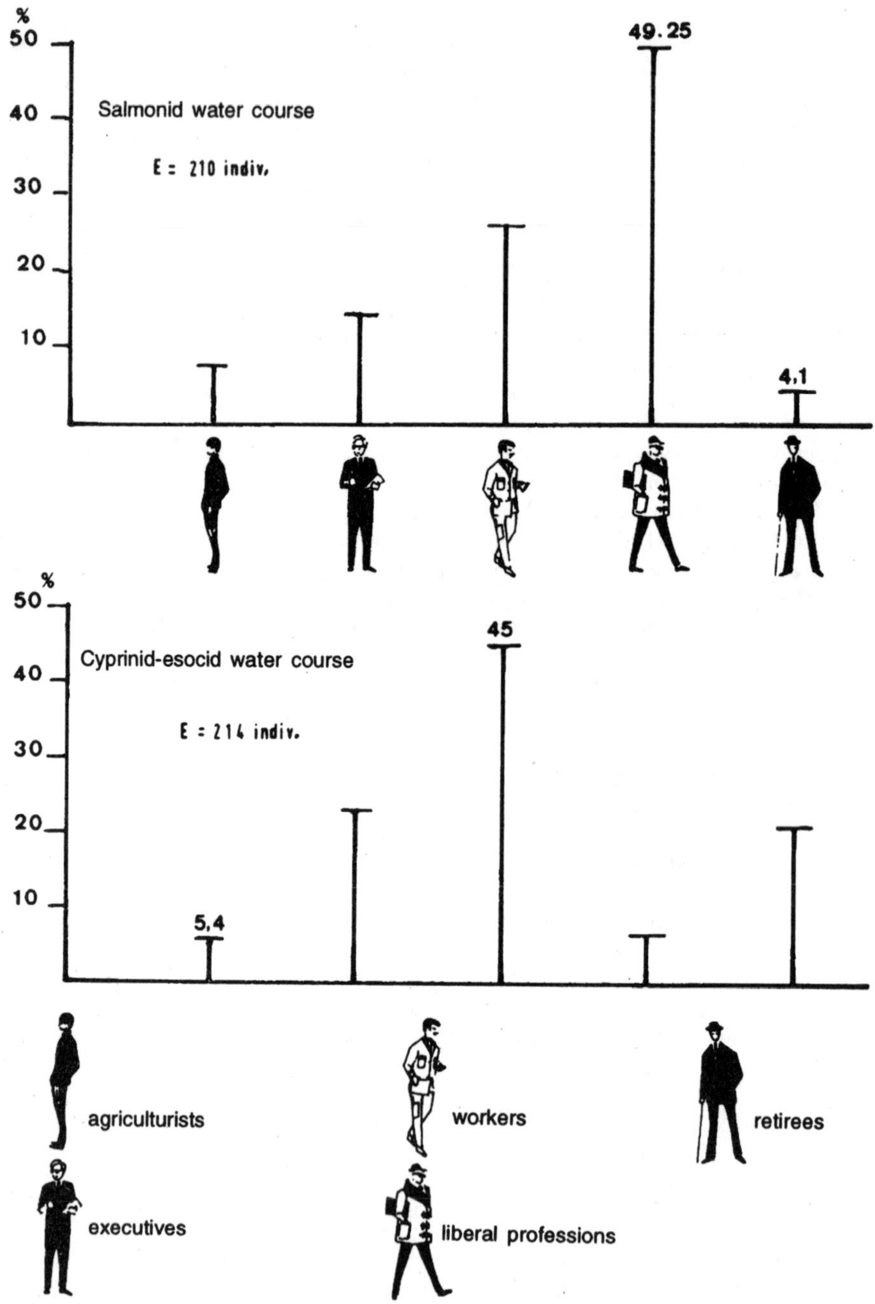

Fig. 339. Breakdown of frequentation by profession of two types of fishing sectors

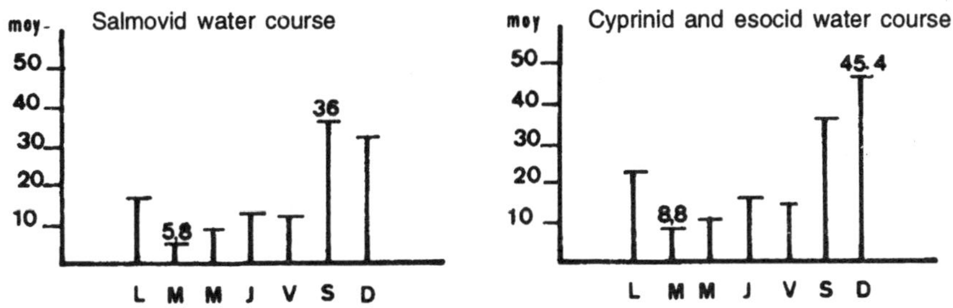

Fig. 340. Weekly frequentation of two types of fishing sectors

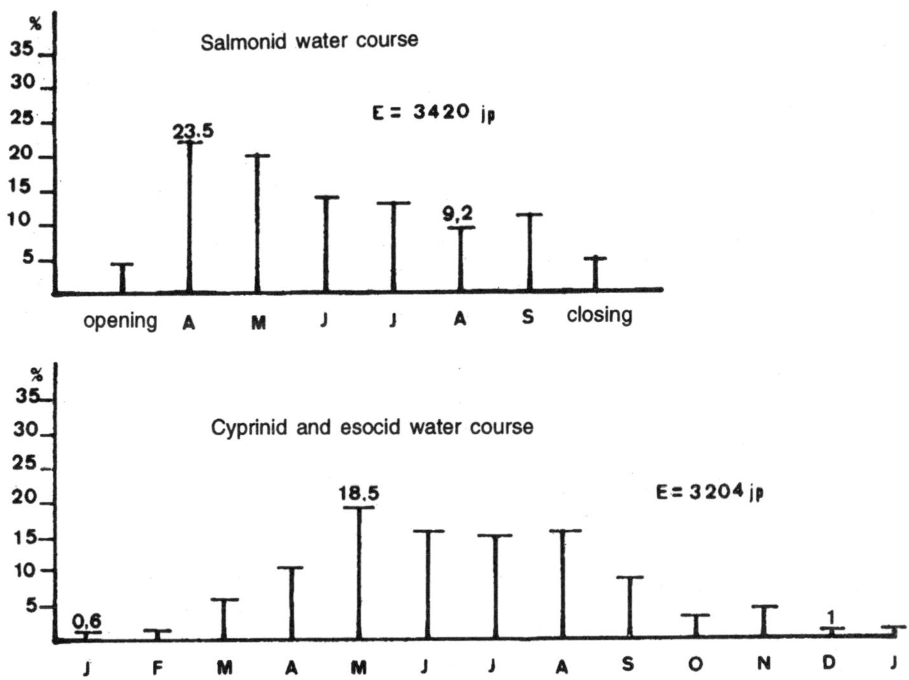

Fig. 341. Annual frequentation of two types of fishing sectors

The quantity of the introduced fish at natural productivity has to be carefully judged by the following criteria:

– New ponds are more productive than the old ones, at least in the first five years after they are filled with water.

Table 56. Total productivity of ponds

Total productivity	=	Natural productivity	+	Productivity due to manure	+	Productivity due to artificial feeding
		↘ ↓ ↙				↓
		Natural nutrients				Artificial nutrients

Table 57. Weight and growth (after SCHAEPERCLAUS, 1962, modified by ARRIGNON)

Species and age	Av. individual wt at introduction (g)	Av. individual growth (g)	Av. wt during drainage (g)	Normal wastes
Carp (1 yr)	35	315	350	10
Carp (2 yr)	350	900	1250	2–5
Tench (1 yr)	6	44–64	50–70	20
Tench (2 yr)	50–70	150–200	200–270	2–5
Rainbow trout (1 yr)	30	170	200	2–10
Rainbow trout (2 yr)	200	150–300	350–550	20
Fario trout (1 yr)	20	140	160	2–10
Fario trout (2 yr)	160	80–140	240–300	20

– Productivity depends on the race, size, and number of fish to be raised; it depends on certain associations of which each species (and in each of them, each group of sizes) best uses different links of a food chain.

– The greater the number of fish introduced, the greater the consumption of the natural food, and the greater the number of prospectors.

– The ratio of growth rate to food intake being high for young fish, the introduced load will be higher, as will be the utilization of natural nourishment, as indicated by increase in their weight.

– So, generally, it is recommended that a greater number of young fish be introduced rather than a limited number of larger individuals. However, there is danger that fish density could increase too much, causing a poor individual growth rate and, in extreme cases, a fall in population.

The general formula for the introduction of the fish load, by HUET (1970), is as follows:

$$\text{Introduction of load } (u) = \frac{\text{Growth or total productivity (kg)}}{\text{Individual growth (kg)}} + \text{losses } (u)$$

SCHAEPERCLAUS (1962) gives a table of average individual weight, average individual growth, and average weight during draining and losses, which have been modified here for salmonids raised in ponds.

The period for introduction should take into account the quality of the medium if the pond has been filled up recently. Therefore, it is better for the fish to be introduced in a plain water body rich in phytoplankton and zooplankton. It also has to take into account the physical and physiological condition of the fish.

The annual releases in the pond are in two well-defined periods: in autumn, during fishing in ponds, the introduction comprises recently caught fish, chosen

Table 58. Size and weight range of the main species of pond fish

	Carp		Tench		Roach (or rudd)	
Age	size (cm)	wt (g)	size (cm)	wt (g)	size (cm)	wt (g)
1 summer	6–12	15–80	3–8	2–10	6–8	3–5
2 summers	12–20	200–800	8–15	40–100	8–12	25–60
3 summers	20–40	1200–1800	18–25	150–350	15–20	100–150
	Pike		**Pike-perch**		**Perch**	
Age	size (cm)	wt (g)	size (cm)	wt (g)	size (cm)	wt (g)
1 summer	9–20	100–300	6–10	50–80	4–6	10–25
2 summers	30–45	600–1000	12–20	120–350	8–12	30–150
3 summers	40–50	1000–2500	25–35	400–800	12–20	75–250

from the harvest of the pond that has to be restocked or from neighbouring productions. In spring, the introduction is from fish stored in winter.

It is not advisable to introduce anything but trout at the end of spring, the season in which the cyprinid species reproduce. In summer, the high temperature affects the transport conditions and causes the fish to catch parasitic and infectious diseases.

Fish must be transported under cool conditions and, if possible, at night, so that they can be released early in the morning. During the overflow, the fish are gradually acclimated to the temperature of the medium of their destination. In case the fish appear fatigued, they are left to rest in a tank of canvas (of flax or jute). As soon as they assume the normal swimming position, they are released. It is advisable to be aware of the source and time of transport so that all steps can be taken to receive and divide the fish. It is even desirable to do a sanitary check on fish chosen randomly from the transported group.

4. EXPLOITATION

Exploitation includes various phases depending on the type of breeding. Exploitation at the end of the cycle is done in three phases: introducing fish, breeding cycle, and harvest (or entire fishing).

Exploitation in a clear interval is done in more than three phases: introduction of a new lot, one or many clear intervals of the breeding cycle, and harvesting at the end of the cycle of whatever is left. Samples taken during the course of the cycle help in determining the nutritive yield and growth rate, and the feeding can be adjusted accordingly. If possible, this is followed by a clear interval for fish that have already attained the market size and have nothing more to get from the pond. These fishes can be replaced by an additional introduction of young ones.

This practice generally calls for well-planned ponds and fishing means that are well adapted and manipulated. It brings in a good yield and optimal exploitation of the plain water body if additional introductions have been well calculated.

Exploitation during clear intervals is the rule followed in plain water bodies that cannot be drained (e.g., lakes, dug-out ponds, backwaters).

Fig. 342. Ponds. Depressed and controlled fishing. Sassa fish culture (Israel) (after J. ARRIGNON).

Fig. 343. Ponds. Partial fishing. The captured fish are drained in a small wagon, which is hoisted by an electrical winch up to the sorting tower. Sassa fish culture (Israel) (after J. ARRIGNON).

5. HARVESTING

Harvesting begins with draining the pond or with directly catching the fish as in the following case. The fish are sorted, then transported or stocked.

– A barrier pond has to be gradually drained by stages in autumn or in the beginning of winter so that fish that are in a state of slow growth can be harvested. The draining in stages helps the fish to move to deeper water and prevents sludging after water reaches the lowest level. This operation takes one month in a 50–200 ha pond, 15 days in a 10–50 ha pond, one week in a 5–10 ha pond, and one night to one week in much smaller ponds. The pond is then "in fishing" and at the end of this period the fish are concentrated in the pan and captured, either in this pan or down the barrier in a fishing ground fed by successive drainage.

Fig. 344. Ponds. Sorting tower for fish hoisted by small wagons. Sassa fish culture (Israel) (after J. ARRIGNON).

Fig. 345. Ponds. The sorted fish (carps here) follow the inclined pipe and fall on the transport ferry. Sassa fish culture (Israel) (after J. ARRIGNON).

In dug-out ponds, the favourable breaks are got with the use of a casting net or with a net from the bank, sometimes from a turfed area, which is slightly inclined.

In industrial exploitations, the fish caught are put in small wagons pulled towards a tower meant for sorting, grading, and loading. In smaller exploitations, fish are brought to sorting tables installed on the dike or bank. The tables are made in such a way that the fish are handled and sorted quickly without being hurt or traumatized by a very long drying period.

If the harvest is not sold immediately, it is stored in stocking basins by species. For a 15-day-old stock, the weight loss is 2–3%.

– The *fishing yard* is controlled by a chief who coordinates the work of the fishing team, transport team, and sorting team. The fishing team, the size of which depends on the size of the pond, is in charge of catching the fish in the pan or in fishing or saving those remaining in the pool. The transport team uses various containers, wheelbarrows, small wagons, dumpers, and vehicles, all of which operate on land. The sorting team has two or three workers per table, a weighing point, and an office that records the species, age, size, quantities weighed, and destination of the fish.

Table 59. Techno-economic chart for traditional pond culture (after J. MARCEL, 1988b)

	Case 1	Case 2
BREEDING		
Species (%)		
Carp	60	20
Roach	20	60
Tench	15	15
Pike	5	5
Loading 33 kg/ha (kg)		
Carp (15 francs/kg)	20	6
Roach (15 francs/kg)	6	20
Tench (15 francs/kg)	6	6
Small pike (60 francs/kg)	1	1
Gross output 200 kg/ha (kg)		
Carp	120	40
Roach	40	120
Tench	30	30
Pike	10	10
PROFITABILITY (francs/ha)		
Cost of loading fish	540	540
Income from exploitation		
Retail sales	3800	4100
Wholesale	2010	2410
Earnings from exploitation		
Retail sales	3260	3560
Wholesale	1470	1870
Fixed expenses and cost of fish		
Retail	1000	1000
Wholesale	750	750
Gross profit (before taxes)		
Retail	2260	2560
Wholesale	720	1120

Table 60. Regulation of introduction and transport of fish in France

Species		Introduction in waters covered under the articles of the Rural Code: Waters of 1st category	Waters of 2nd category	Transport of live (all costs included)	Transport of dead fish
Species found in waters covered by the article L231-3 of Rural Code	Pike, perch, san, black-bass	Prohibitted	Permited*	Permitted only at opening of season[a]	Permitted only at opening of season[a]
	Other species	Permitted*		Permitted only at opening of season[b]	Permitted only at opening of season[b]
	Catfish, Chinese Crab, Pacific cray fish, American cray fish, Sun perch	Prohibited		Prohibited without authorization	Permitted
Species liable to cause biological imbalances	Other species	Prohibited		Prohibited without authorization	Permitted
Other species		Prohibited without authorization***		Permitted	Permitted

Notes
*On condition that the fish come from registered fish culture or aquaculture establishments.
**1. On condition that their source is approved. However, transport at the closing of the season is permitted for: (a) fish coming from waters covered or not covered under article L231-3 of the Rural Code; (b) fish species found in waters covered under maritime regulations, during the time at which fishing is authorized there; (c) fish coming from foreign countries from which import is permitted.
**2. Transport at the closing of the season can be subject to administrative authorization in the case of fish meant for reproduction or restocking (art., 1st paragraph).
[a]Permission for introduction in waters covered under article L231-3 of the Rural Code can be given only for scientific or other purposes.
[b]Transport at any time can be subject to administrative operations for sanitary or scientific purposes or in case of biological imbalances.

3 ECONOMY OF AQUATIC RESOURCES

The economy of aquatic resources is based on the evolution of two main elements: market value of the products (fish, crustaceans, plants) and the suitability value of the surroundings for fishing, hunting, water sports, and other water-related activities.

The evolution of these two elements follows a different pace depending on the modes or methods. They sometimes contradict one another in time or even in the protection, development, space management and resource strategies that apply to them.

Consequently, the conditions under which these modes or methods arise and influence the economy of aquatic resources should be examined. Similarly, the conditions explaining the "strategies" that organize and in fact condition this economy should also be examined.

A. DEVELOPMENT AND MANAGEMENT STRATEGIES OF FISH STOCKS

It is disturbing to refer to the word and concept "strategy" in the context of the development and management of renewable resources, since many examples show that apparently the most optimum development strategies are miscalculations.

J.C. PIERRE (1979) says in an editorial: "...the agriculturalists learn that the mathematical model of the EEC is no more adapted to France. So much the better if this statement leads to an agriculture that is more economical and better respects the laws of nature. The script, which is only the name of the preceding logic, has been adapted ... for farmland and rural economy at the demand of an agricultural mechanization developed for the great plains of Northern Europe or the American Midwest. Though humans get adapted, it is not the same with nature...."

The consequences of the application of principles of maximum yield for renewable resources are thus manifested in the degradation of aquatic resources—an integral part of basic terrestrial resources that one would wish to develop. To date the best specialists have not presented a coherent ecological-economic redevelopment programme since there are uncertainties looming large in the future.

Absence of strategies also leads to sudden ecological and socio-economical developments that are not in any way related to the initial initiative, whatever it may have been.

From 1950 onwards, the obsession with the empty ecological niche led to the introduction of aquatic animals with the most extraordinary qualities, if their promotors were to be believed.

Introduction of pike-perch, for which there was a craze at that time, increased in Central Europe, then in Morocco, before coming to France with the know-how of the specialists on the species. CORCHUS, the inventor of the incubator box, was one such specialist. The policy of the fishing officials, which was conservative at first but paradoxically encouraged later fishing, led to an always ambiguous situation for fish culture. This led to protection of a species in one spot while it was considered practically harmful in another.

The pike-perch acts as intermediary host in the development cycle of a parasite, *Bucephalus polymorphus*. With the pike-perch, the bucephalus larva develops and, year after year, from the end of June, affects the cyprinid population of canals, small rivers, and navigable rivers.

The pike-perch was added to the pike and the perch in the range of carnivores that are normally seen in the water courses. They disturb the fish stocks here and there, but more than that, they disturb the fishing practices of the fishermen and lead them to conclude that the pike-perch eliminates the pike.

The species favours only deep, large water bodies and apparently causes neither sickness nor trouble as those deeper areas are less frequented by perches or pikes.

We can add to this the fact that pike-perches are not well exploited by amateur fishermen alone because those fishermen are incapable of covering the areas visited by the species in big rivers. The complementary action of professional fishing, using other means, can ensure an equilibrium in the fish population and also produce highly valued fish for the market.

This is a single authentication, but we have other observations as well for other species: catfish, black-bass, silurid and other species show the fragility of the smallest of water courses—their fragility increases with the decrease in their size, as also the apparent incoherence of the evolution of ecological and socio-economic situations.

Elaborate precautions have to be taken in decision-making. These are technocratic in nature and highly esoteric, depending in a very general way on the systematization prevalent in the late twentieth century.

It is advisable to draw attention to the risks involved in such development and to explain the dangers brought about by aquatic development centred on a concept that is apparently reassuring in that it aims for maximum production that can be obtained from a water body without compromising the productive future and without seriously affecting the distribution of species.

1. CONCEPT OF MAXIMUM SUSTAINABLE YIELD

In the following section, it is clear that a development strategy for aquatic resources based only on the concept of maximum sustainable yield (MSY) involves many difficulties. These are both theoretical and practical and are normally not thought of while planning and pursuing a fish culture policy.

In a classical example of a logistical model, the net growth rate of a population is considered dependent on diversity. The growth rate leans towards zero when the population reaches saturation point of the productive environment: the population reaches an equilibrium point where recruitment (replacement) is equivalent to mortality. If we exploit this population in a given way, we reach a hypothetical point X_0 where the net growth rate is maximum. By definition, this is the MSY for the population in question.

For the definition of an optimal strategy or policy, various optimization models are introduced by which parameters other than biological parameters (particularly economical) are involved.

Thus, the definition of MSY seems to have a high degree of precision, at least in theory, but in practice, the system cannot function at all. Indeed, one should presuppose a number of hidden hypotheses that are not as precise and can bring down the MSY increase to a simple, particular case.

2. PITFALLS IN A STRATEGY BASED ON MSY

2.1 Absence of Spatio-temporal Dimensions

The MSY is an equilibrium concept that lacks both spatial and temporal dimensions.

When we affirm that MSY is that production which cannot endanger future productions, we can hardly wait for the future to unfold and follow the evolution of future productions. If the yield of an accomplished future is what we had waited for earlier, then we can say that the initial yield was the MSY but we cannot give it an absolute value. Our concepts cannot show us what the world will be but will only help us to make some prospective trials. The MSY in case of fish culture management thus has a highly relative value so that it can be generalized to the mosaic of biotopes under study.

2.2 Fallibility of the Notion of Adaptation

The MSY takes into account the hypothesis of the capacity of species to adapt. This capacity is not absolute but relative. The organisms are never perfectly adapted to their special environment; they can disappear from this environment without putting into question their adaptation capacity. The relationship between the organism and its environment is not a simple cause-effect relationship. The environment is not a unidimensional entity but the component of very different parameters. The impact of some of these parameters is almost completely unknown (e.g., the effects of magnetic fields on some species).

The production capacity of a particular surrounding also depends on the genetic organization of the species. This means that these species are capable of using different surroundings at different times in a way that we cannot predict or give a satisfactory explanation for.

2.3 Contradictions in Optimization

While calculating the optimization it is difficult to select the parameters that have to be optimized: it could be an irrational procedure by which a certain number of hidden hypotheses that have yet to be proved are taken into consideration by a planner in preference to other hypotheses. We can thus try to find (or think that we have actually found) the biological optimum of a fishing ground while the socio-economic optimum should be looked for elsewhere. It is impossible to maximize more than two variables at the same time.

The MSY presupposes that only one stable point exists. That means, paradoxically, that no parameter other than the biological one is indispensable in the calculation. This would signify that the optimization of a fishing ground should be strictly of a biological nature, which contradicts the intuitive experience that has been gained in the management of many fishing grounds.

In addition, in optimization calculations, we normally take into account well-known parameters, whereas in actual life perhaps rare events (for example, local calamities) mould and regulate the fate of a particular ecosystem and, in this ecosystem, "the fishing ground" function (VIBERT and LAGLER, 1961). By definition, rare events direct the ecosystem towards an unpredictable route. An optimum system based on everyday events can be very unreliable.

2.4 Difficulties in Assessment

Difficulties in using the concept of MSY by a renewable natural resource are also reflected by what is called "balance effect".

Certain authors talk of a state of "balance" related to the size of a population (EHRLICH and BIRCH, 1967). In fact, populations have a size that changes constantly and there is no ideal or normal population for which the MSY can be calculated. MSY ignores the fact that all parameters of the environment are constantly changing with time. A water course that is known to be thoroughly polluted, with all the aquatic population missing since time *t*, can, within a few years' time, become biogenic after the pollutions are eliminated. An obsolete legislative decision based on MSY calculated at time *t* can lead to giving up the water course on the assumption that it does not support life.

While calculating the MSY at time *t*, one can find out the time period for which the information will be valid. Between the measuring and calculating moment and the moment of using the MSY, a certain time will pass and during this time the population condition under consideration will change. What, therefore, is the predictability of the system? While setting up the hunting plan, one can take a head-, sex-, and age-count of the animals in order to fix a reasonable cutting-down quota. In case of fish living in a less accessible environment, each time period between the estimation of information and its use will be long. *A management body for aquatic mediums should thus have means of assessment that are highly credible, repeatedly used procedures, and the capacity for flexible and decentralized intervention.*

3. STRATEGY

Incomplete understanding of parameters that regulate the exploitation of renewable aquatic resources, whatever be its degree of finesse, is likely to confuse decision-makers.

The advantage of specialized scientific meetings is that they impart to the decision-maker the knowledge that has been initiated, developed, and acquired by the researcher. Besides the fact that the decision-maker rarely has the capacity to assess intellectually, objectively, and impartially the validity of a particular scientific proposal, the abundance and diversity of the facts related to an ecosystem as complex as the aquatic mediums demand an organization of their assessment, selection, and hierarchy so that it is practical to exploit them.

Moreover, the mediums and the living creatures in them are not the only ones involved. An understanding of them, however complex it may be, seems insufficient in the presence of heavy human activity. This activity is not only the multifarious "indirect" activity that has an impact on the watershed basins, but also the "direct" activity of the predator, the fisherman.

Consequently, the strategy of scientific knowledge based on hydrobiology and even limnology, which covers in a very large way the phenomena present in inland waters, will not at all suffice to fund the requirements of protection, management, and administration of fish culture mediums if it ignores the perspectives of sociology, micro- and macro-economy, and geography.

It would be wrong to take this matter lightly. The analogical reasoning resulting from it, based on foreign fishery structures and fish management and aggravated by a habit of discounting the incompatibilities and highlighting the positive aspects, will probably lead fishing activity into more regrettable situations than we are in now.

In this matter, the strategy of management and administration of aquatic resources is linked to the strategy of understanding—all types of understanding—required to define and propose scenarios that not only answer immediate needs but also set up long-term perspectives.

For more than a century, the fishing policy in France has been resolutely based on a democratic, recreational activity basically organized in an associative structure of pyramidal type. Except for the fact that such an activity could suddenly be called upon to change course and become conservative and elitist due to the pressure of events external to the French context, the management and administration strategy of fish culture in this country still has a certain originality, a very clear definition, and a real difficulty in execution.

4. FISHING POLICY IN FRANCE

In the nineteenth century, professional fishing in France was not as important as it was in other countries. At first, professional fishing in fresh water competed with maritime fishing because maritime products with a higher value could immediately take advantage of transport and conservation facilities. Apart from fishing in lakes and rivers, the profession decreased and naturally drifted to an unfavourable position vis-a-vis its other competitors in the same surroundings, the amateur anglers.

Leisure fishing also got the benefit of transport facilities. Its recruitment, which was rural earlier, is general these days for the whole population, except for categorical variations applicable primarily to the socio-professionals (Fig. 339).

Thus, in France, fishing as a hobby rather than professional fishing exploits more of the aquatic resources of the country along with the salmonid culture industry, the details of which are beyond the scope of this work.

The fishing policy is historical. Since the 1789 revolution, it was established that the practice of this hobby was generally democratic, i.e., popular, open to whoever paid very modest taxes and subscriptions, compared to the cost of various other hobbies that are also supposed to be popular.

This policy is in contrast to fishing carried out in other countries where, in general cases, it is seen as a privileged activity (in the etymological sense of the word), reserved for people possessing riparian land or for private clubs made up of coopted or sponsored members whose number is strictly limited.

In this case, the exploitation of resources in these countries gives great freedom to a riverside resident to dispose at will of his aquatic property, flowing or stagnant, which includes the bottom, the water, and the fish, with, however, some recent restrictions on the quantitative and qualitative hydraulic management.

Not only in the salmonid waters but in all situations, the exploitation is elite in nature. It combines the existence of knowledge and hydro-ecological and halieutic know-how of the selected practitioners and the extent of their investment in the sport, in such a way that the quality expected or even demanded of the exploited fish culture property is perennial and forms a sort of durable and sought-after label. This exploitation generally leads to simple management forms and a certain consistency in the fish culture and halieutic quality of the passage.

The French policy, owing to its democratic nature, absolutely forces the political, scientific, administrative, and technical protagonists and the users to resort to a diversified, complex, and sometimes expensive management. The aquatic property is itself extremely diversified because of the **orography** and hydrography of the country. Management is complicated by the large number of prospective fishermen and their multifarious requirements. Everything else, such as pollution and other strains on the aquatic mediums, is the same as in other countries.

No doubt, ecology presently creates a train of thought that tends to subordinate human leisure activity in order to safeguard the natural mediums in which it is conducted. This concept is basically sound but it must not be adopted dogmatically so as to lead to situations that are absurd, paradoxical and, eventually, harmful to the mediums it is supposed to protect.

This applies to fishing as a leisure activity. The manager of a fishery who is a "generalist" must ensure that scientific arguments are not based on the dogma of specialists seeking public recognition of their science. What, for example, can we say about an argument on genetics being given precedence over other parameters—including the social argument—on the sole pretext, often simplistic, even naive, that restockings could genetically pollute the existing fish fauna?

Economics is no less dangerous in the application of today's very aggressive principles, which greatly favour profitability and are scornful of human values. Decision makers must, for example, be wary of the temptation to extend the fishing tax net, thereby favouring indirectly certain profitable groups such as youth and vacationers, to the detriment of weaker and less profitable groups such as the poor, the retired, the handicapped and unemployed.

In France, fishing has been the object of a pluralistic policy. Barring the possibility that genuine popular will, based on mature consideration, could opt for a concept of fishing practice that is resolutely elitist and even essentially contemplative, the French manager is compelled to organize the conduct of this leisure activity within very narrow limits. These limits are actually between the satisfaction of a very large number of interested parties, with many varied tastes and pretentions, and respect for the mosaic of French aquatic mediums. Development is even more difficult to implement now when it is subjected, more than earlier, to pressure from the media, which is not concerned with long-term evaluation.

B. ANIMAL RESOURCE

1. ECONOMIC IMPORTANCE

With regard to fish alone, the annual world production has risen to 21 million tonnes (FAO, 1993), of which 82% is produced in the Indo-Pacific region and 12% in Europe. A project (UNO, 1996) has forecast that the total volume of fish required for human consumption will be, inclusive of fishing and aquaculture, 84.5 million tonnes in the year 2000, 97.2 in 2010, and 114.8 in 2020.

France itself produces between 58,000 and 64,000 tonnes of fish including what is provided by industrial fisheries (1995).

Taking into account only fish, the world production is annually 21 million tonnes, of which 82% is produced in the Indo-Pacific region and 12% in Europe (FAO, 1993).

France produces 50,000 tonnes of fish, including the commercial production of inland fisheries (1995).

In the case of sea fish, only half of world production is directly consumed. The rest is used for making by-products or is lost. It is interesting to note that a Chinese consumes 48 kg of fish per year, whereas a French person consumes only 22 kg, of which only 1 kg comes from fresh water (out of which 0.800 is salmonids). A French person fishes more for pleasure than for food.

The largest part of freshwater food is produced in regions where necessity along with food habits pushes the local population to fully consume fish as either fresh or preserved products. Freshwater fish make up 30–40% of aquatic products for human consumption. In overpopulated regions where the population is underfed, species with a high lipid index (the sinyonia carp, for example), having a high energy value (160–240 cal/100 g), are raised. On the other hand, in countries where fish has become a back-up product it is more of a gastronomic delicacy than a necessity. Here, the selection is based more on obtaining muscular fish with thin flesh, rich in albuminoids, with lower energy value (65–75 cal/100 g).

In France, the economic importance of water resources is controlled by the impact of promotional efforts. These efforts can be applied more for commercially prepared and conditioned products that can please the consumer and do not demand too much time and effort.

Certain private activities of social life (e.g., receptions, cocktails) having been restored, elaborately prepared products, which were earlier relatively expensive, have become common and fashionable: eel, trout, smoked salmon sometimes cut into slices, and caviar of sturgeon and lumpfish. The import of salmon, which was a luxury item ealier, increased from 350 tonnes in 1974 to 68,255 tonnes in 1990 (51,594 tonnes in 1989) and the cost of imports decreased from 42.44 francs/kg in 1988 to 30 francs/kg in 1990 (source: INSEE).

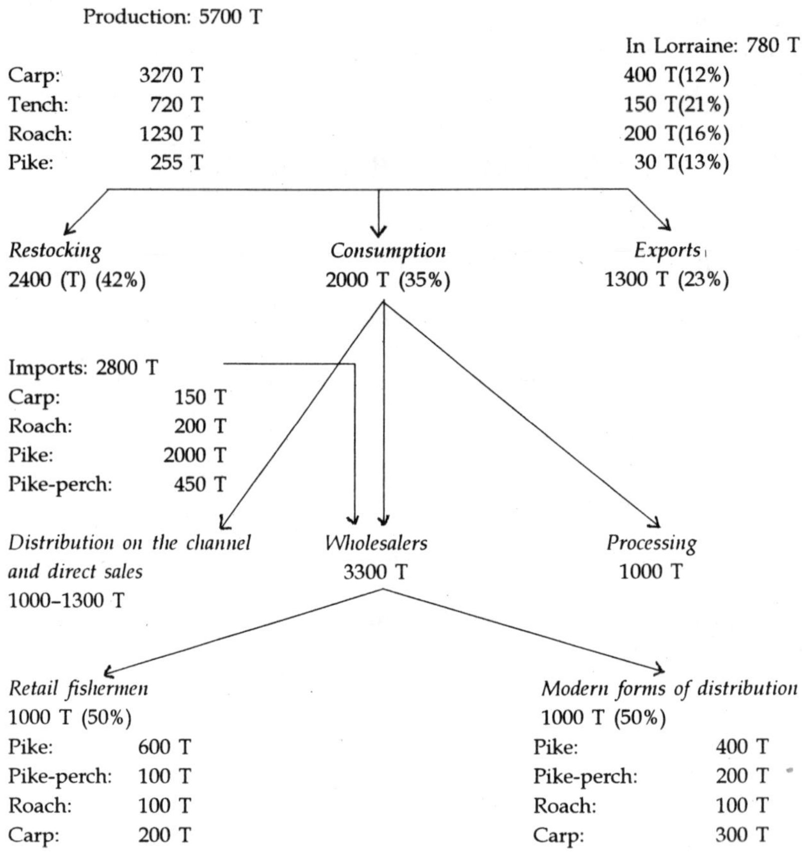

Fig. 346. Distribution of fish in ponds in France (source: GEM/SIGMA)

Table 61. Regions with major production and tonnage

Region	Area (ha)	Prod. (t)	Yield (kg/ha)
Brenne	7500	900	120
Sologne	11,000	1000	90
Val de Loire	1200	180	150
Limousin	8700	480	55
Dombes	10,000	1600	160
Est	7000	1000	142
Camargue	600	310	516
Forez	1500	450	300
Poitou-Vendee	3000	450	150
Bourbonnais	2500	290	116
Sundgau	1320	320	242
Franche-Comte	3000	300	100
Champagne	3000	300	100
Miscellaneous	500	35	70
TOTAL	59,500	7615	

Table 62. Distribution of various species produced in some regions (t) (after J. MARCEL, 1988b)

	Carps	Tench	Roach	Pike	Total
Dombes	1000	200	400	50	1650
Brenne	900	220	270	30	1420
Sologne	300	200	430	50	980
Lorraine	500	250	220	40	1010
Camargue	245	20	40	5	310
Poitou	250	40	90	20	400
Limousin	250	50	80	20	400
Forez	200	100	100	20	420
TOTAL	3645	1080	1630	235	6590

Table 63. Productivity of different ecosystems (g of M.S./sq m/year) in R. BILLARD (1980)

Cultivated land	650
Rivers and lakes	400
Eutrophic lakes	1000
Marsh	2000

Crayfish and frogs show the same trend. More than 2000 tonnes of freshwater crustaceans were imported in France every year till the Turkish supplies were exhausted. The red and green frogs are purchased from foreign countries (India and Czechoslovakia) so that the restaurants have sufficient supplies.

Like chicken, the trout is no longer a luxury item in France, where trout production was a cottage industry in 1945 (1500 tonnes) and became industrial with the introduction of dry, granular nutrients. It went up to 35,000 tonnes in 1989 (source: INSEE).

Whitefish, cyprinids, pike, perch, and pike-perch became less popular with the increase in standard of living, because of the local and artisanal nature of their production and commercialization (apart from a few exceptions), and finally because of the basically protectionist and restrictive conditions regulating the exploitation of public water bodies. Annual imports are of the order of 1500 tonnes, about half of which consists of pike-perches and eels. Commercial production is not known, but the productivity of French waters very much exceeds the demand.

2. ECONOMIC DEVELOPMENT

Improvement in living conditions has already brought about development in animal production, including that of fish, though a little delayed. The number and equipments of the prospectors have no doubt brought about the progressive disappearance of the most sought-after sea fish. The difficulties and cost of a prospection increases the scope in such a way that marine aquaculture, a relatively recent field, becomes more and more competitive in certain countries where the coastline is especially favourable to installing a fish-breeding ground. Aquaculture will probably have the same protective effect on the natural marine surroundings as pisciculture has on the river systems. It will produce the most sought-after fish and crustaceans for consumption. The natural stock is presently in danger, if not in deficit.

It will certainly play this role vis-à-vis certain migratory species that are disappearing, for example, the salmon (*Salmo salar*) and the sturgeon (*Acipenser sturio*), found on the Atlantic coast. The salmon, particularly, is valuable game fish since the time its production in industrial breeding reduced its market value below profit point for commercial capture in natural surroundings.

The efforts at selecting and promoting cyprinids in Central Europe for the past twenty years have resulted in production of improved races, particularly with regard to the organoleptic qualities of the meat and less dense bones, as in the case of carps. Fishing technology and methods lead to production of quality fish according to the demand of the consumers. Processing and preservation techniques used and experimented with by the maritime fishing industry make available to the public preparations based on freshwater fish that are elaborate, well presented, and of a standard quality. These are frozen quenelles, pastes, and fish sausages. Smoked carp fillets open up new perspectives for this fish. The same is true for the American crayfish (*Orconectes limosus*), which is not much appreciated in Europe but is sold in the form of bisques in sachets, in the manner of soups.

If such a wave, seen in Central Europe, reaches France, we may consider the river systems, often overcrowded with low-value cyprinids, American crayfish, and adult eels, capable of supplying sought-after products. Commercial fishing regulated on the basis of the fish productivity of a property, rather than on the blind protection of the species that constitute it, is likely to increase productivity. For example, if the regulation on fish in France facilitated a rational organization of eel fishing grounds in salmonid waters (first fish culture category), this fish would not be overcrowded here. The management service charges mobilize every year considerable means for removing the excess eels that can destroy the trout, the normally dominant species, specially sought after by anglers fishing for sport. The national economy suffers a double loss, since, paradoxically, eels have to be imported for certain requirements. Moreover, the fishermen carry on with restocking trout to counteract predation by the overpopulated eels.

The paradox, developed by both ecological and economic means, becomes even more absurd as far as eels are concerned. It is a species that, for reasons mentioned above and also because of the absolute disorder in overfishing of young eels, is in a critical situation in a certain number of basins. The mode has been to *restock* and facilitate anadromy by setting up *passes for young eel* in barrages. Eel has not been rationally and reasonably exploited because the domination of traditions and profit rendered the technical solutions ineffective. The regulation has also been inefficient, let alone the fact that it has been unsuitable.

C. SUITABILITY OF THE AQUATIC MEDIUM

Suitability value of aquatic mediums depends on the interest in certain relaxation and leisure activities.

1. RECREATIONAL FISHING

Angling is a recreational activity. In countries facing nutrition problems, it occupies an important part of the agricultural economy sector, whereas in other countries it is a recreation not only for riverside or lakeside inhabitants but also for city dwellers.

For a long time, only horsehair and hook were used for fishing. Then came the fishing rod and fishing float, the spool, and finally the reel. The fishing methods that we presently know were thus born: stroke fishing, cast fishing, fishing with whipped fly, spoonbait fishing, fishing with many baits, and baits and artifices. The manufacture of all these constitutes a flourishing industry.

More than *4 million fishermen* in France are involved in fish culture, spread over resources including even artificial water bodies. Though their operation was quite disordered in the past, it has now become organized in such a way that each angler, wherever he comes from, can find the pleasure and relaxation that he is seeking.

Angling has been freely practised for over 2000 years in sparsely populated and industrial countries. In France, it is a socio-economic phenomenon because of the constraints and developments involved. These are needed because of the large number of anglers (1/13 of the total population), spread over all social classes and age groups, and also because of the saturation of the aquatic surroundings that attract a weekly influx of anglers from the city.

Management of fisheries should meet a *social need* by offering water courses that satisfy a large section of the population. That demand is itself highly diversified and regionally differentiated. Objectives also include development of fishing tourism and reorientation of people practising this sport abroad by bringing them towards French zones that are known for fishing stretches. This is an economic action aimed at preventing a massive outflow of foreign exchange. Development should also bring about a certain natural harmony necessary in practising fishing and in respecting the environment. It should also refuse to entertain the continuously growing demand of fishermen, whose numbers have been increasing, to convert pleasant sites into fishing ghettoes.

It is true that fishermen today are more curious, more critical, more demanding, more informed, and more flexible in their behaviour than in the past. The majority include seasoned anglers and also neophytes. Some have a sense of water that reflects an intelligent observation of the aquatic surroundings. Their objective is shifted from the fish towards putting into practice their halieutic knowledge and their talent. Others, while seeking a contact with elements of the natural surroundings, do not have this sense of water. Above all, they desire a physical contact with the animal and are animated by a possessive instinct: they want fish and lots of them.

Management of fishing as a hobby should also take into account different behavioural patterns. For some, rivers and especially natural ponds with fish populations maintained by bottom enrichment are suitable as they enable a real confrontation of talent between the fisherman and the wild fish or fish rendered wild and placed in a medium suitable to their ecology. Others are better satisfied with prepared water bodies and water courses regularly stocked with fish that are immediately caught (the American "put and take"), having both access and reception facilities as well as ancillary entertainment facilities.

The suitability value of the aquatic mediums is thus variable, depending on the behaviour and aspirations of the fisherman. But it is expressed differently according to the fish species sought or the fishing method adapted, if we consider taxes and subscriptions. In fact, the physical development of the medium is a very small portion of the subscription cost, whereas the cost of fish restocking as well as the security constitutes the main part.

If we agree that fish culture resources are, for the most part, managed by the Fisheries Board (CSP), we can consider that the suitability value is expressed by the revenue of that body, since it looks after their full reuse in development and management of fish culture. This value was 185 million francs in 1991. To this should be added the revenue collected by the Departmental Federations of Fishing and Fish Culture Associations and also their revenue from subscriptions, which touches approximately 400 million francs.

The turnover of leisure-time fishing, which is much larger, touches 12 billion francs because it applies to various sectors of activity; over and above the taxes and subscriptions, it should also take into account charges of transport, lodging, and restaurants, material and fishing equipments, camping caravans, preparation of reviews, and other works.

2. DEVELOPMENTAL TRENDS

The aspirations and satisfaction of the angler while practising his sport will increase faster because of the pace of present-day life. The rural exodus and the concomitant growth of the urban population, which has almost completely broken down all permanent contact with nature, has shaken the means and methods of fishing and also brought about an imbalance in human needs.

Angling is no longer static and easy-going. It has become rather active and sportive, owing to either the natural physical efforts required in the searching and hunting of carnivores, which are remarkably sly, or the skill required in using equipments that have been perfected relatively recently.

This process of development, a progressive change, has come about because of the rise in living conditions, which allows many people to participate in a relaxation activity that had earlier been reserved for people living close to fishing grounds or for those privileged people enjoying money, power and sufficient spare time for such a sport.

It is also facilitated by the rapid and personal means of transport, which brings anybody to sites that were earlier considered far away. A persuasive media promotes the attractions of the big fishing regions, which were earlier frequented only by fishermen living nearby and rarely by people who took the initiative to come from afar.

Information also encourages people to practise angling. Urban people and those from age groups that earlier kept away from angling now join in the sport. Moreover, it develops the use of fishing methods that are continuously being perfected and made more attractive.

French regulation and fishing organizations, by corporate concepts and very democratic structures, give the best facilities to make this relaxing activity accessible

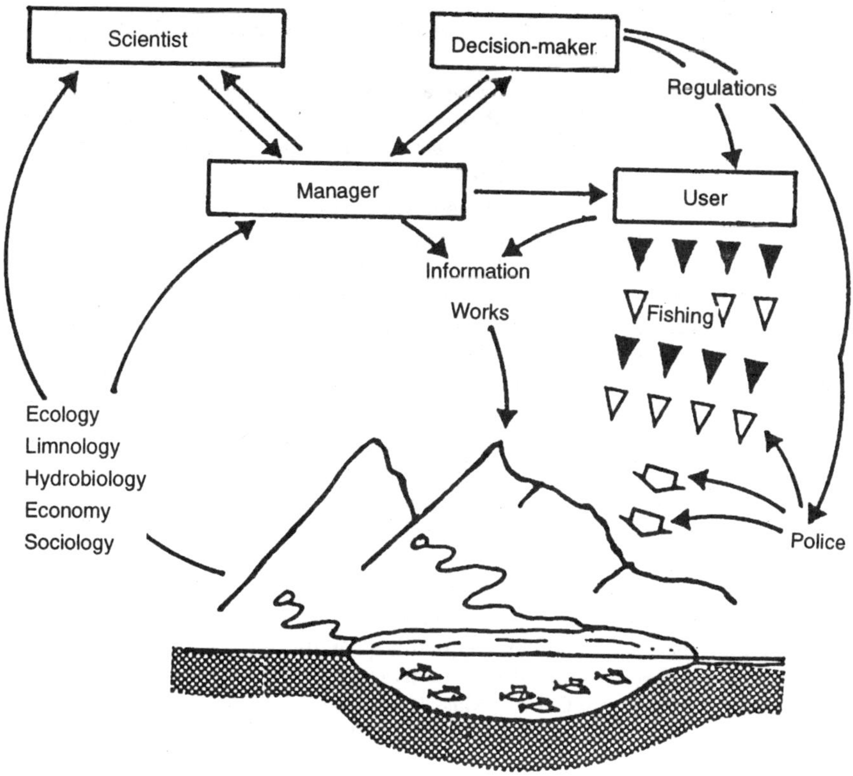

Fig. 347. Interventions in the management of French fish resources

at less cost over the entire national territory. The tax called fishing tax does not account even for 1/20 of the tax charged annually for possessing a television set.

A look at the revenue from this fishing tax shows the process of development as shown earlier:

– The number of fishermen increased in 30 years by nearly 250%, the number of fishermen catching carnivores by nearly 650%.

– In 30 years, the number of the latter, in relation to the total number, increased from 17% to 82.5%.

This means that the need for fish that can be immediately caught follows the same trend, and although trout culture can provide for these needs, pike culture is presently incapable of doing so. Fish culture policy should thus plan for two main aims that are well coordinated and linked: educating the fisherman and settling him more closely in the natural surrounding. Since he is the preferential user of the surroundings, he should agree to a catch corresponding to the capacity of the surrounding and see fish more as a suitable objective than as a consumable item. The second aim, which belongs more to the biologist, the manager, and the decision-maker, deals with the devolution of aquatic systems that are well known and well developed, according to the ecological characteristics and pressure from the users, fishermen and non-fishermen.

But the drop recorded in 1972 in the payment of basic taxes and also the supplements for catching carnivores should be analysed. It is probably due less to the effects of water pollution and the hazards of angling, than to a combination of other effects. It is not certain if this drop is entirely due to the settling of active and potential fishermen in private fishing areas. One possible cause is new or renewed leisure, which is more related to lifestyle changes, exemplified by many activities in the life of twentieth century Frenchmen, such as accession to property, sailing, motorboat racing, other water-related leisure activities, concern with ecology, secondary residence, private fishing water courses, vehicles, charters, interior renovations, and various gadgets. Whatever we may think at first sight, this standing favours an individual, consumer-oriented life at the cost of constructive associative activities. Fishing policy should analyse and integrate this phenomenon.

The French case, though unique on several accounts, requires several measures in the following order of priority:

1) Create and develop highly used fishing water courses close to big towns. Some of them are meant to supplement the large degraded waterways and others developed and managed to attract the general fishing public, who, in the escape area of their city (100–150 km range), exhaust the rivers that are constantly overexploited.

2) Organize big fishing water courses in the seasonal corridors frequented by the French and foreigners on vacation with the objective of creating high quality fishing for tourists in regions they frequently pass through without stopping.

3) Develop salmonid regions that are active or that can be retrieved, for example in Normandy, Brittany, the Central Massif, and the Pyrenees.

4) Remanage the exploitation of trout resources by several regulations and techniques.

It is to be feared that trout regions that are safe because of their present distance from urban centres will one day suffer from vast industrialization and exploitation surpassing the danger mark mentioned earlier.

D. MANAGEMENT OF FISHERIES RESOURCES

Management of fisheries resources consists of the administrative organization of fishing and users.

1. ACTION OF PUBLIC AUTHORITIES

The public authorities study fishing problems relating to legislation, regulation, and litigation. They ensure direct management of certain fish culture establishments belonging to private estates. They control the fishing policy, supervision, and exploitation of fish in lakes and water courses that are not canalized and belong to private estates and also reservoir lakes formed by barriers set up on water courses. They also control the policy and supervision of water courses and lakes that do not belong to private estates. They study the fish culture clauses framed in the terms and conditions of electricity concessions. These assignments are given to the department of fisheries and hydrobiology of the Environment Protection Directorate falling under the Ministry of Fisheries with regional and departmental services provided by the Ministry of Agriculture.

Some problems of water come under the Equipment Administration, which manages one part of the national hydrographic network, particularly the navigable ways. Some others come under the Maritime Affairs Administration. All questions pertaining to river fishing are submitted to an interministerial commission that is responsible for ensuring coordination and continuity of regulations in the field of fishing.

The technical aspects of these problems are taken up at the national level by specialized sections of the Centre for Studies in Agricultural Mechanization, Rural Engineering, Waters and Forests (CEMAGREF), coming under the Ministry of Agriculture. The methods and solutions are popularized by regional centres of the Fisheries Board, which advises public powers and fishing groups.

2. COLLECTIVE ACTION OF THE ANGLERS

Amateur anglers practising in free waters are organized according to the requirements of the rural code. They form part of a fishing and water protection association (AAPPMA) accepted by the Prefect of the Department and pay an annual parafiscal tax. This sum is entirely used for the supervision and development charges of national fish culture resources.

Professional fishermen are required to follow similar rules.

The fishing and water protection associations constitute a federation in each department. The federation's duty is to develop and protect the departmental fish resources from poaching and pollution. It has fishing guards provided by the Fisheries Board and its own financial means, and sometimes it is given concessions for raising of fish for restocking, construction of ponds, and stocking of rivers with alevins.

The anglers fishing for sport and professionals are represented in the Fisheries Board. Administrations that deal with fishing problems under different heads also have an equal representation. Representatives of riverside property holders, manufacturers and salesmen of fishing articles, national associations of specialized fishermen, fish culture professionals, and finally the consumers are also consulted.

The body is a national public organization, administrative in nature, provided with a civil character and financial autonomy under the guidance of the Ministry of Freshwater Fisheries. It can go to court, can acquire property, and has two main responsibilities:

— To centralize and use the products that are to come from fishing tax. In this direction, the establishment has to play the role of a national cooperative.

— To provide all opinion and advice that it considers appropriate to public powers in matters of river fishing legislation and regulation. It can also be asked by the ministries concerned to give its opinion on any issue.

These structures, which we basically owe to CHARPY, have according to DARLEY (1975) "the mark of decentralization, the possibility of adapting to local situations that are infinitely varied."

3. INTERACTIONS

Basically, management hierarchy operates at four levels.

3.1 Researcher

The researcher's job is to provide facts and ideas of fundamental and applied research. In France, the National Centre for Scientific Research (CNRS), National Institute of Agronomical Research (INRA), Centre for Studies in Agricultural Mechanization, Rural Engineering, Waters and Forests (CEMAGREF), some university laboratories, institutes, and academic societies pursue hydrobiological and fish culture researches.

3.2 Manager

The manager experiments and exploits on a given hydrogeographic territory the fruits of researches done according to local situations. CEMAGREF is mainly concerned with the inventory and study of waters so as to improve and develop fish production and the fight against pollution.

The regional scientific and technical units of the Fisheries Board help elaborate methods for the study and improvement of waters and implement study programmes related to halieutic and fish culture development. It plays an advisory role vis-a-vis regional, departmental, and local public powers in fishing and fish culture. The technicians of these units are also the advisors of fishing federations and companies concerned with restocking, fish culture, civil engineering, and, in general, concerted and organized development of the regional hydrographical resources.

3.3 Decision-maker

The decision-maker at the level of public powers implements the regulation and developments that have been stalled, according to the knowledge imparted by the scientist and manager, and also the needs expressed by the users. The power of decision making rests with different levels of the French administrative hierarchy, vertical and horizontal, depending on the ministries concerned, with the national, regional, and departmental executives having a say in the matter.

3.4 User

The user is the nerve centre of the fisheries body, from which the various stages of representation take over: fishing associations, departmental federation, national unions sand federations.

Once they are organized, their observations, needs, and complaints are presented by the Fisheries Board to the authorities concerned, to the decision maker, who approaches the researcher and the manager in trying to find solutions. The management and development of fish are well carried out if each party fulfills its responsibilities. This means that each participant has information of the whole that is as exact, complete, and comprehensible as possible. In the case of leisure fishing in France, which is a unique and important recreational activity, as is shown by the number of enthusiasts, public participation plays a vital role.

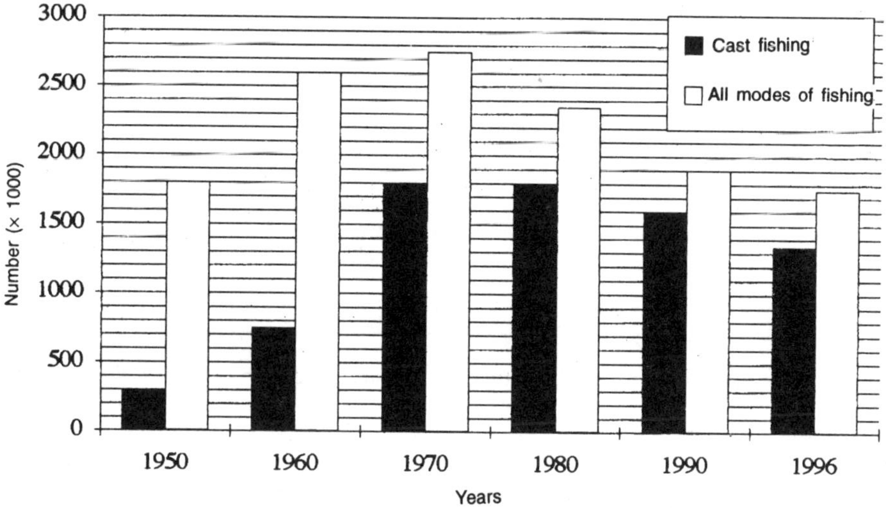

Fig. 348. Progressive change in the numbers of fishermen paying fish culture tax

Table 64. Exigencies of different types of water hobbies (after G. TERSEN, 1990)

1. *Parking*
   No. of people per car: 3.7
   No. of cars that can be parked simultaneously per ha: 400

2. *Swimming areas, beach and lawn*

Beach needed for 1000 people:	3000 m^2, on a 40 m wide stretch
Lawn needed (for play and rest):	9000 m^2
Planting (stacks or 10 m for every 50 m):	2000 m^2
TOTAL:	14,000 m^2

   700 persons/ha need:
   - 1 toilet for 100 people
   - 1 changing room for 100 people

3. *Water sports (sailing, boating)*
   4 boats/ha
   8 boats/ha with mooring pontoons

4. *Fishing*
   1 fishing post for every 10 m
   1 fishing post for every 5 m (shape of banks studied for this purpose)

area reserved for fishing:	30 m from the water's edge
reception:	40 fishermen/ha on 20 m depth
playing area for children:	50 m^2/person
picnic lawns:	25 m^2/person
picnic woods:	50 m^2/person
pedestrian path on the banks:	15 persons/ha

Table 65. Open air activities practised (after RIQUOIS and BERTHERY, 1990)

Activity	Frequenting population out of the total population
Swimming	20%
Sailing	4%
Fishing	15%
Horse riding	1%
Tennis	2%
Volleyball	2% of swimmers
Walking	10% with a renewal coefficient of 0.2
Table tennis	2%
Restaurant-picnic	20%
Ball games	1%

Table 66. Potential use of a tourist site (see Fig. 353, after RIQUOIS and BERTHERY, 1990)

Example of application		Towns or districts		
		A	B	C
a) Population within the zone of influence		50,000	5000	
b) Highest rate of visits		45	35	
Number of people visiting		20,000	1750	
c) Radius of distance in relation to	S1	80–100	40–70	
% of peoplė visiting in the radius		8%	16%	
Number of people visiting in the radius		1600	280	
d) % going to dense areas		70	70	
Potential clientele per zone		1120	200	
Attraction rate:				
Increase of competing activities	S1	40	60	
	S2	25	–	
	S3	35	10	
	S4		30	
e) Daily peak visiting for S1		450	120	
f) Sudden peak visiting (0.6)		270	72	
TOTAL		342 = 340		
g) Seasonal visiting (x40)			13,600	
Annual visiting (x50)			17,000	

4. COEXISTENCE

The coexistence of various water-related activities has been a source of recent attention. The chief activities are angling, waterfowl hunting, bathing, boating, sailing, motorboat racing, water skiing, deep sea diving, and exploration in paludal, aquatic and subaquatic waters.

These activities can be regulated either in time or space or by a division, sometimes holding forth both options when a wide range of activities occur in the same place.

Some regulations provide immediate solutions: hunting and fishing periods generally do not coincide, but if fishing is done within an enclosed water body, it can be permanent.

Except for boating, very few leisure activities compete with angling in private water courses and also in small water bodies covering an area of less than a hectare. The joint activities exist primarily in public water courses, particularly in big ponds and lakes.

In the latter, the division of areas and periods of activity is fixed according to the rules, generally in accordance with the requirements of navigation, hydraulic equilibrium, or hydroelectric exploitation.

Problems with coexistence occur in large ponds, lakes, and large water courses, during the setting up of organized recreational bases. Imaginative solutions can be found during the study of sketches and pilot studies by specialists in various activities working in full unanimity. This is followed up by an organizational effort and management of these activities by local groups that are in charge and organized, in the best cases, as a managing committee in which regulations and decisions are discussed and laid down.

The bases for **study and observation of the aquatic surroundings** are generally planned in pond corners that are often sludgy, difficult to reach, and frequented by birds, amphibians, and aquatic mammals.

If a chain of plain water bodies is under consideration, the wildest of them, far removed from the penetration channels, is the best choice. Here, one can set up aerial and subaquatic observation posts. Wildlife photography does not disturb the fish fauna, which have excellent spawning grounds in these places. As a consequence, fishing is prohibited here.

The largest water body in the chain, a pond that is wide and extensive, very deep and well swept by wind, is suitable for **sailing**. A series of buoys mark the development area beyond which **angling** can be done without disturbing any other sport.

Boating, swimming, occasional motorboat racing, and **water skiing** can coexist and develop from the same base if, out of a chain of water bodies, one having a large area (at least 10 ha) is reserved for these activities. In a single stretch of water, except for lakes, experience shows that motorboat racing and water skiing pose real threats to other users.

For **swimming** and **underwater diving**, the clearest of waters is recommended. Such is the case of ballast ponds, some of which are very deep. Angling can coexist

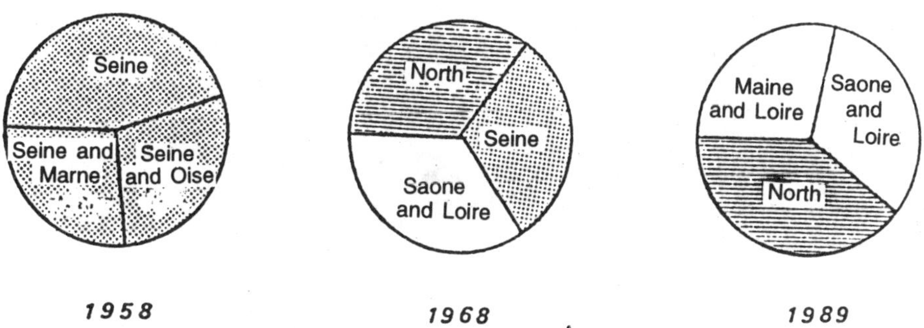

Fig. 349. Decentralization of sport fishing. The three departments having the greatest numbers of fishermen in 1958, 1968, and 1989.

Fig. 350. Progressive change in the modes of fishing, anglers—cast fishing

Fig. 351. High-yielding commercial fishery (after J. ARRIGNON)

with swimming and boating confined to areas indicated by buoys, but not with underwater diving. This sport is generally practised in deep areas (5–15 m, indicated by marker buoys or floats).

Fig. 352. Leisure fishing in a highly frequented pond (after J. ARRIGNON)

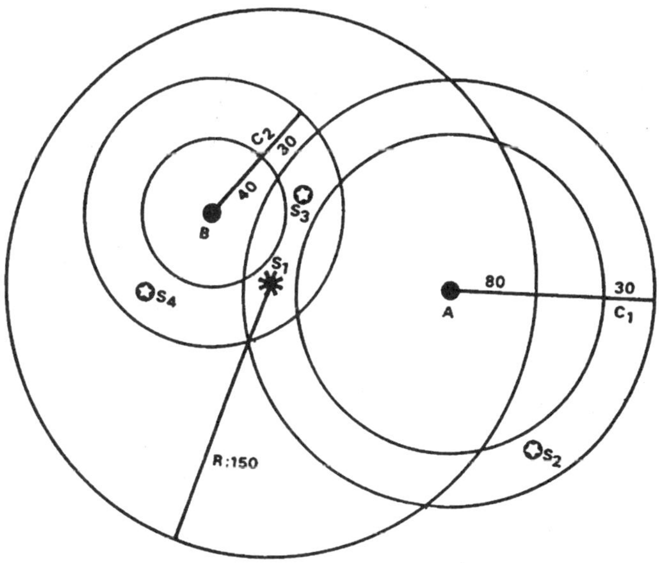

S1—site to be developed
S2—site outside the zone of concurrent influence of S1 for A
S3—concurrent site of S1 for A and B
S4—concurrent site of S1 for B
R—radius of influence
A and B—areas meant for development
C1—area centred on A
C—area centred on B

Fig. 353. Evaluation of concurrent uses (after RIQUOIS and BERTHERY, 1990)

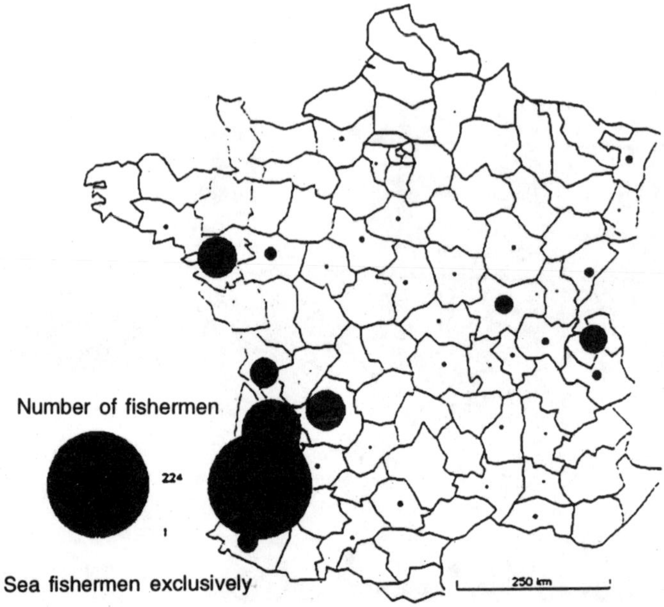

Fig. 354. Distribution of professional fishermen on French territory in fresh waters in 1990 (910 fishermen) (source: CEMAGREF)

For economic reasons, exploitation of a recreational base calls for collective common set-ups: access, parking, bathrooms, lodgings, camping caravans, sometimes with special installations for certain sports like sailing clubs, bungalows, hunting huts, sites for fishing caravans, anchorages, wharfs, springboards for skiing.

A recreational base provides fishermen general leisure and relaxation space, thus limiting a tendency to segregation that should not be encouraged. Introducing angling along with other water activities within a quality aesthetic space brings together families to relax in natural surroundings, which is desirable. Arranging a range of recreational activities in the same site gives young children a choice of activities, depending on whether they are of an active or contemplative nature.

Given the fact that sizeable investments are necessary for setting up and developing large water bodies, an organized recreational base is probably the best solution to financing and managing them, by planning a peaceful coexistence of various activities.

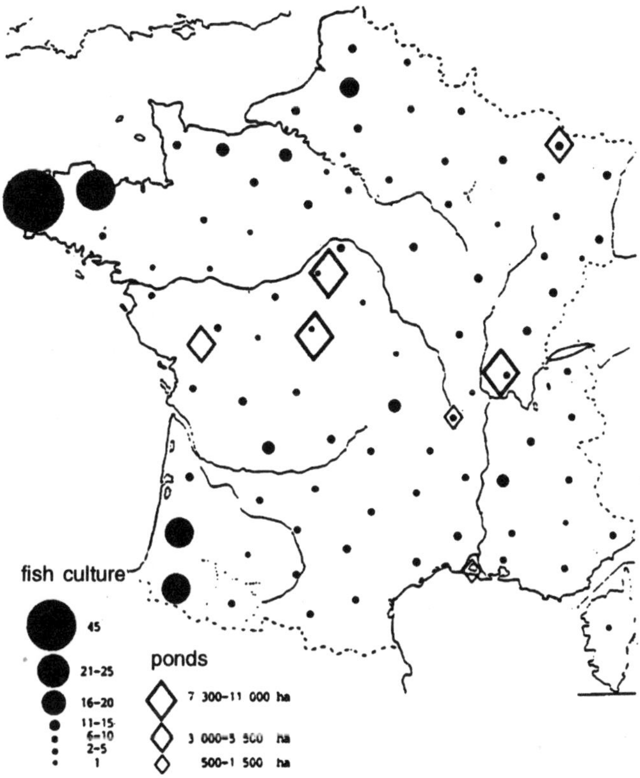

Fig. 355. Distribution of intensive fish culture and pond fish culture on French territory in 1989.

PART FOUR

Appendices

1 FORMULAE AND PROGRAMS

A. ON THE KNOWLEDGE OF THE AQUATIC MEDIUM

1. INDEX OF BIOTIC INTEGRITY (IBI)

Criteria for evaluation of the IBI parameters. The scores vary from 1 to 5 depending upon the higher quality (after T. Oberdorff, R.M. Hughes and R. Billard, 1989).

Category	Parameters	Criteria		
		5	3	1
a) Richness and composition of species	1. Total no. of spp. (% MSRL)	≥ 67	33–67	≤ 33
	2. No. of pelagic spp.			
	3. No. of benthic spp.			
	4. No. of intolerant spp.			
	5. % of roaches (*Rutilus rutilus*)	≤ 30	30–60	≥ 60
	6. Age classes of trout and brochets	0–2	0–2	0
b) Trophic composition	7. % of omnivorous individuals (1)	≤ 1	1–5	≥ 5
	8. % of insectivorous individuals	≥ 35	20–35	≤ 20
	9. % of carnivorous individuals	≥ 5	1–5	≤ 1
c) Condition and abundance of fish	10. % of individuals spawning on gravel	≥ 10	5–10	≤ 5
	11. % of individuals with anomalies			
	12. No. caught/min. while fishing (% of maximum legally permitted catch)	33–67	≥ 67	≤ 33

(1) with the exception of *Rutilus rutilus* (roach)

2. DETERMINATION OF THE DIATOMIC INDEX (DI)

Enabling evaluation of the extent of global pollution in waters with reference to the natural type of the station under consideration, the diatomic index is calculated on the basis of a list of more than a hundred diatoms of which the pollution sensitivity is expressed by an index (i_j) that varies from 1 to 5. Further, an estimation of the indicative value of the diatoms is integrated in the calculation. This is a function of their ecological variation vis-à-vis the pollution. Depending on the degree of their wide range of tolerance, indicative value (V_j) varies from 1 to 3 (see Table 1). The formula for calculation is:

$$Id = \frac{\sum_{i=1}^{p} A_j \times i_j \times V_j}{\sum_{i=1}^{p} A_j \times V_j}$$

where A_j is the relative abundance of the species j.

a) On the species

List of diatoms used in calculation for the diatomic index with their index of pollution sensitivity (*i*) and their indicative value (*v*) (after Descy, 1980).

	i	*v*
Achnanthes conspicua A. Mayer	5	3
lanceolata (Bréb.) Grun. [and var.]	3	1
linearis (W. Smith) Grun.	5	3
microcephala (Kütz.) Grun	5	3
minutissima Kütz. [and var. *cryptocephala* Grun.]	4	1
Amphora ovalis Kütz.	4	2
ovalis Kütz. var. *pediculus* Kütz	5	2
Anomoeoneis serians (Bréb.) Cleve var. *brachysira* (Bréb.) Cleve	5	3
Caloneis bacillum (Grun.) Cleve [and var. *lancettula* (Schulz) Hust.]	5	3
silicula (Ehr.) Cleve [and var. *truncatula* Grun.]	5	3
Ceratoneis arcus (Ehr.) Kütz. [and var.]	4	3
Cocconeis pediculus Ehr.	4	2
placentula Ehr. [and var.]	4	2
Cyclotella meneghiniana Kütz.	3	1
Cymatopleura elliptica (Bréb.) W. Smith	5	3
solea (Bréb.) W. Smith [and var.]	4	2
Cymbella cistula (Hemprich) Grun. [and var. *maculata* (Kütz) v. Heurck]	4	3
gracilis (Rabenh.) Cleve	5	3
lanceolata (Ehr.) v. Heurck	5	3
naviculiformis Auerswald	5	3
prostrata (Berkeley) Cleve	5	2
sinuata Gregory	5	2
tumida (Bréb.) v. Heurck	4	3
ventricosa Kütz.	4	2
Denticula tenuis Kütz. var. *crassula* (Näg.) Hust.	5	3
Diatoma hiemale (Lyngb.) Heib. var. *mesodon* (Ehr.) Grun.	5	3
vulgare Bory	5	2
vulgare Bory var. *productum* Grun.	4	2
Diploneis ovalis (Hilse) Cleve	5	3
Eunotia diodon Ehr.	5	3
exigua (Bréb.) Rabenh.	5	3
flexuosa (Bréb.) Kütz.	5	3
lunaris (Ehr.) Grun.	5	3

pectinalis (Dillw.) Rabenh. [and var.]	5	3
pectinalis (Dillw.) Rabenh. var. *minor* (Kütz) Rabenh.	5	2
polydentula Brun	5	3
tenella (Grun.) Hust.	5	3
veneris (Kütz.) O. Müll.	5	3
Fragilaria capucina Desm. [and var.]	5	2
construens (Ehr.) Grun.	4	2
pinnata Ehr.	5	3
rumpens (Kütz) Carlson	4	2
vaucheriae (Kütz) Peters.	4	1
virescens Ralfs	5	3
Frustulia rhomboides (Ehr.) De T. var. *amphipleuroides* (Grun.) Cleve	5	3
rhomboides (Ehr.) De T. var. *saxonica* (Rabenh.) De T.	5	3
vulgaris (Thwaites) De T.	4	2
Gomphonema abbreviatum (Ag.) Kütz.	3	2
acuminatum Ehr. [and var.]	4	2
angustatum (Kütz) Rabenh. [and var.]	4	2
constrictum Ehr. [and var.]	4	2
gracile Ehr.	5	3
longiceps Ehr. [and var.]	5	3
olivaceoides Hust.	5	3
olivaceum (Lyngb.) Kütz.	4	2
parvulum Kütz. [and var.]	2	1
Gyrosigma attenuatum (Kütz.) Rabenh.	5	3
spenceri (W. Smith) Cleve var. *nodiferum* Grun.	5	3
Hantzschia amphioxys (Ehr.) Grun.	3	2
Melosira italica (Ehr.) Kütz. [and var.]	3	2
varians Ag.	3	1
Meridion circulare Ag.	5	2
Navicula accomoda Hust.	1	3
contenta Grun.	5	3
cryptocephala Kütz.	3	1
cryptocephala Kütz. var. *intermedia* Grun.	5	2
cuspidata Kütz.	3	2
cuspidata Kütz. var. *ambigua* (Ehr.) Cleve	3	2
cocconeiformis Gregory	5	3
gothlandica Grun.	3	2
gracilis Ehr.	5	3
hungarica Grun. var. *capitata* (Ehr.) Cleve	4	2
menisculus Schum.	5	2
minuscula Grun.	3	2
mutica Kütz. [and var.]	1	3
placentula (Ehr.) Grun. [and var.]	5	3
pupula Kütz.	3	2
radiosa Kütz.	4	3
rhynchocephala Kütz.	4	2
rotaeana (Rabenh.) Grun.	5	3

subhamulata Grun. [and var.]	5	3
viridula Kütz.	4	1
Nitzschia acicularis W. Smith	3	2
amphibia Grun.	2	3
dissipata (Kütz.) Grun.	5	2
filiformis (W. Smith) Hust.	3	3
fonticola Grun.	4	2
inconspicua Grun.	4	2
linearis W. Smith	4	2
palea (Kütz.) W. Smith	1	2
paleacea Grun.	3	2
recta Hantzsch	5	2
romana Grun.	4	2
sigmoidea (Ehr.) W. Smith	5	3
tryblionella Hantzsch [and var.]	5	3
Peronia heribaudii Brun and Per.	5	3
Pinnularia brebissonii (Kütz.) Cleve [and var. *hybrida* (Grun.) Cleve]	1	3
subcapitala Gregory [and var.]	5	2
Rhoicosphenia curvata (Kütz.) Grun.	4	2
Surirella angustata Kütz.	3	2
biseriata Bréb.	5	3
linearis W. Smith	5	3
ovata Kütz.	2	1
Synedra pulchella Kütz. var. *lanceolata* O'Meara	3	2
ulna (Nitzsch.) Ehr. [and var.]	2	1
Tabellaria flocculosa (Roth) Kütz.	5	3

b) On the genera (DIG) (after Rumeau and Coste, 1988)

Method of calculation:

Table B gives the list of taxa likely to be encountered or used with their three-letter codes facilitating data acquisition. For each taxon there is a value of global sensitivity *S* that varies from 1 to 5 and a value *V* that varies from 1 to 3 representing the extent of the narrow range of tolerance, which is higher when the distribution is restricted.

It is enough to total up the products of abundance *A* for each taxon (expressed in a percentage) by the two values ($\Sigma\, SVA$) and to divide the obtained total by the $\Sigma\, VA$ to obtain a global generic index varying from 1 to 5.

The resulting index, the DIG (diatomic index based on the genera), may then be written as:

$$\text{DIG} = \frac{\sum_{i=1}^{n} S_i V_i A_i}{\sum_{i=1}^{n} V_i A_i}$$

This value may be transformed easily as a figure based on 20 using the following formulae:

—change of a figure N varying from 1 to 5, to a figure Q varying from 1 to 10: $Q = N \times 2.25 - 1.25$

—change of a figure N varying from 1 to 5, to a figure Q varying from 1 to 10: $N \times 4.75 - 3.75$

EXAMPLE of calculation of the DIG based on the result of an inventory obtained by crushing of plants

Taxa	Sensitivity S		Range of tolerance V		Numbers A		$\Sigma\ SVA$		$\Sigma\ VA$
CENTRICS									
Stephanodiscus	2	×	1	×	7	=	14	=	7
ARAPHIDAE									
Asterionella	4	×	1	×	3	=	12	=	3
Diatoma	4	×	1	×	117	=	468	=	117
Fragilaria	4	×	1	×	7	=	28	=	7
Meridion	5	×	2	×	2	=	20	=	4
Synedra	3	×	1	×	25	=	75	=	25
MONORAPHIDAE									
Achnanthes	5	×	1	×	29	=	145	=	29
Cocconeis	4	×	1	×	3	=	12	=	3
BIRAPHIDAE									
Amphora	3	×	2	×	6	=	36	=	12
Cymbella	5	×	1	×	17	=	85	=	17
Gomphonema	3	×	2	×	4	=	24	=	8
Gomphoneis	4	×	2	×	40	=	320	=	80
Navicula (Orthostichae)	2	×	2	×	2	=	8	=	4
Navicula (Punctatae mutica)	1	×	2	×	1	=	2	=	2
Navicula (others)	3	×	1	×	129	=	387	=	129
Nizschia (Dissipatae)	4	×	2	×	13	=	104	=	26
Nizschia (others)	1	×	1	×	20	=	20	=	20
Surirella	3	×	3	×	8	=	72	=	24
TOTAL							1832		517
Total of *SVA* = 1832 = 3.54	3.54	×	2.25	-	1.25	=	DIG		6.7/10
Total of *VA* = 515	3.54	×	4.75	-	3.75	=	DIG		13/20

Table B. Genera used for calculation of the DI

Alphabetic classification				Classification by sensitivity group			
TAXONS	Code	*S*	*V*	TAXONS	Code	*S*	*V*
Achnanthes	ACH	5	1	*Amphipleura*	AMH	5	3
Amphipleura	AMH	5	3	*Denticula*	DEN	5	3
Amphora	ARA	3	2	*Rhopalodia*	RHA	5	3
Anomoeoneis	ANO	5	2	*Stenopterobia*	SLA	5	3
Asterionella	AST	4	1	*Tetracyclus*	TET	5	3
Attheya	ATT	2	3	*Anomoeoneis*	ANO	5	2
Caloneis	CAL	4	2	*Campylodiscus*	CAM	5	2
Campylodiscus	CAM	5	2	*Ceratoneis (Hannaea)*	CER	5	2
Ceratoneis (Hannaea)	CER	5	2	*Epithemia*	EPI	5	2
Cocconeis	COC	4	1	*Frustulia*	FRU	5	2
Cyclotella	CYC	3	1	*Meridion*	MER	5	2
Cymatopleura	CMA	4	2	*Stauroneis*	STA	5	2
Cymbella	CMB	5	1	*Achnanthes*	ACH	5	1
Denticula	DEN	5	3	*Cymbella*	CMB	5	1
Diatoma	DIA	4	1	*Diploneis*	DIP	5	1
Diploneis	DIP	5	1	*Eunotia*	EUN	5	1
Epithemia	EPI	5	2	*Tabellaria*	TAB	5	1
Eunotia	EUN	5	1	*Gyrosigma*	GYA	4	3
Fragilaria	FRA	4	1	*Neidium*	NEI	4	3
Frustulia	FRU	5	2	*Pinnularia*	PIN	4	3
Gomphoneis	GIS	4	2	*Caloneis*	CAL	4	2
Gomphonema	GMA	3	2	*Cymatopleura*	CMA	4	2
Gyrosigma	GYA	4	3	*Nitzschia dissipatae*	NDI	4	2
Hantzschia	HAN	1	3	*Asterionella*	AST	4	1
Melosira	MEL	3	1	*Cocconeis*	COC	4	1
Meridion	MER	5	2	*Diatoma*	DIA	4	1
Navicula orthostichae	NOR	2	2	*Fragilaria*	FRA	4	1
Navicula punctatae mutica	NPM	1	2	*Gomphoneis*	GIS	4	2
Navicula (others)	NAV	3	1	*Rhoicosphenia*	RHO	4	1
Neidium	NEI	4	3	*Surirella*	SUR	3	3
Nitzschia dissipatae	NDI	4	2	*Amphora*	ARA	3	2
Nitzschia (others)	NIT	1	1	*Gomphonema*	GMA	3	2
Pinnularia	PIN	4	3	*Cyclotella*	CYC	3	1
Rhizosolenia	RHI	2	3	*Melosira*	MEL	3	1
Rhoicosphenia	RHO	4	1	*Navicula* (others)	NAV	3	1
Rhopalodia	RHA	5	3	*Synedra*	SYN	3	1
Stauroneis	STA	5	2	*Attheya*	ATT	2	3
Stenopterobia	SIA	5	3	*Rhizosolenia*	RHI	2	3
Stephanodiscus	STE	2	1	*Thalassiosira*	THA	2	3
Surirella	SUR	3	3	*Navicula orthostichae*	NOR	2	2
Synedra	SYN	3	1	*Stephanodiscus*	STE	2	1
Tabellaria	TAB	5	1	*Hantzschia*	HAN	1	3
Tetracyclus	TET	5	3	*Navicula punctatae mutica*	NPM	1	2
Thalassiosira	THA	2	3	*Nitzschia* (others)	NIT	1	1

CODE = Abbreviation suggested for data processing.
S = Sensitivity class varying from 1 for the more resistant to 5 for the most sensitive.
V = Ecological amplitude of the genus: 1 = high, 2 = average, 3 = low.
Comment: Strictly halophilous genera (*Amphiprora, Bacillaria, Biddulphia,* etc.) are not included in this table.

B. ON THE FISH POPULATIONS

1. THEORETICAL PRODUCTIVITY (Leger, Huet and Arrignon, 1970)

a) Parameters

(1) $P = 10 \times B \times K$ in kg/yr/ha

(2) $P = B \times K \times L$ in kg/yr/km of a water course with a width of L metres

where B = points awarded from 1 (very poor waters) to 10 (very rich waters) for the *biogenetic capacity*, which is an expression of the nutritive value for fish, and K = the product of productivity factors ($K1$)($K2$)($K3$)($K4$)($K5$).

Value of the productivity factors (K) (J. Arrignon, 1976)

$K1$	$K2$	$K3$	$K4$	$K5$
Physical characteristics (a)	Chemical characteristics (b)	Types of fish	Age of fish (c)	Characteristics of the impluvium (d)
temperate region (10°C) = 1 warm temperate region (16°C) = 2 intertropical region (22°C) = 3 equatorial region (24°C) = 4	acid water = 1 alkaline water = 1.5	salmonids = 1 cyprinids in streams = 1.5 cyprinids in stagnant waters = 2 cichlids = 3	> 6 months = 1 < 6 months = 1.5	continuous urban 0.2–0.5 diffused urban 0.5–1 pastureland valley 1b = 1.1 valley 1c = 1.2 valley 2 = 1.3 pasture valley 1c = 1.4 valley 2 = 1.5 valley 3 = 1.6–1.8

(a) Average annual temperature.
(b) Acidity or alkalinity of the water.
(c) The coefficient with fish less than 6 months old applies to nursery streams and ponds for growth of fry.
(d) Continuous urban type: main bed completely urbanized, canalized, steep banks, banks impermeable (concrete or bitumen), direct evacuation of rain water.

b) Example

Situation: A salmonid water course has suffered accidental pollution, at the bottom of a pastureland valley in a silted U shape and in a chalky region. A report on the incident provided the following data:

—origin of the occurrence: discharge of potassium cyanide

—mortality: fish and aquatic invertebrates, total over 2000 m and partial over the next 5000 m

—width of the water course: 7 m

The record based on its use for fish farming provides the following information:

—water temperature, average for the 6 warm months: 15°C

—water temperature, average for the 6 cold months: 7°C

– pH = 7.2
IB = 7, IBG = 14, quality class 1B

During samplings two records have indicated the biogenetic capacity (*B*) at the level of 7.

Application of the formula $P = K \times B \times L$, where $B = 7$, $L = 7$ and $K = (K1)\ (K2)\ (K3)\ (K4)\ (K5)$ where:

*K*1, the thermal factor, is between 10 and 16°C, nearer 10 and, therefore, 1.1;
*K*2, chemical factor, alkaline = 2;
*K*3, relative to the fish, in this case salmonids = 1;
*K*4, relative to the age, in this case more than 6 months = 1
*K*5, factor relative to the impluvium, pastureland in a valley of type 2 = 1.3

or: $K = 1.1 \times 2 \times 1 \times 1 \times 1.3 = 2.86$

$$P = 7 \times 7 \times 2.86 \text{ or } \pm 140 \text{ kg over } 1000 \text{ m}$$

The annual productivity is equal to half of the existing stock of fish. The stock before the pollution was, therefore, 280 kg over 1000 m or 560 kg over 2 km. Over these 2 km the damage is, therefore:

complete destruction of stock	560 kg
loss in productivity of the year	280 kg
loss in productivity during the next 2 years, the time needed for rebuilding the stock if the trout reproduce at the age of 3 years (280/2) + (280/3)	233 kg
Total	1073 kg

Over the next 5000 m, calculations will be made in the same conditions with a coefficient that takes the degressive effect of the pollution into account.

1/2 over the first 2000 m	536 kg
1/3 over the next 2000 m	357 kg
1/4 over the last 1000 m	134 kg
That is, a total of	1027 kg
Total damage = 1073 + 1027 =	**2100 kg**

Comments: This simplistic application of the formula does not take into account the duration for the restoration of invertebrates, effecting the restoration of a stock of trout as a replacement for the one destroyed, or the possible escape of fish because of pollution or other biological phenomena which, by synergy, aggravate the damage.

2. DE LURY FORMULA (in the regression methods)

After an initial catch, $No\ q$ fish remain in the water course: after the *K*2 catch there remain $No\ q^k$, in other words:

$$No = t\,(1 - q^k) \qquad (1)$$

Before the *i*th catch, the number present (1) was $No\ q^{(i-1)}$ or $No\ q^i/q$
At the *i*th catch, the number caught was $C\,i = pNo\ q^i/q$ or, by using logarithms,

$$\log Ci = i \log q + \log \frac{p \cdot No}{q} \qquad (2)$$

The relationship (2) between log Ci and i is, therefore, a curve log q. Adjustment of the points to the curve enables an estimation of log q and, then, $p \cdot No$ is calculated by Equation (1).

3. SCHNABEL METHOD

From the practical aspect, after first two catches we verify the Seber and Le Cren condition on all the fish:

$$\frac{m^2(m-n)^2}{n^2(m+n)^2} > 16$$

If it is verified we do not go beyond two catches.

Otherwise, we carry out a third catch and calculate the correlation coefficient r with the help of the formula:

$$r = \frac{\sum_{i=1}^{i=n} (x_1 + x)(y_1 + y)}{\sqrt{\sum_{i=1}^{i=n} (x_1 + x)^2 \sum_{i=1}^{i=n} (y_1 + y)^2}}$$

If $r > 0.997$ we do not continue.
Otherwise we carry out a fourth catch.
If $r < 0.95$ we do not continue.
Otherwise we carry out a fifth catch, and so on, till we have a correlation coefficient higher than the limiting value.

Number of catches	3	4	5	6	7	8	9	10
Limiting value of r	0.997	0.957	0.88	0.8	0.75	0.71	0.67	0.63

(after Lamotte, 1957, in Laurent and Lamarque, 1975)

Because of the difficulty in calculating r on the spot during fishing operations we may also apply a rule that is simple and sufficient for three catches.

If we catch less than 10 fish in the first fishing operation m, we cannot evaluate anything with certainty.

If $11 < m < 50$, it must be that $n \leq 2/3\ m$ and $0 \leq 2/3\ n$

If $50 < m < 100$, it must be that $n \leq 3/4\ m$ and $0 \leq 3/4\ n$

If $m > 100$, the second fishing expedition should not reach 90% of the first and third 90% of the second.

It is possible to design programmes in order to avoid manually working out all the very long and cumbersome calculations (Laurent and Lamarque, 1975).

4. LIST OF SYMBOLS USED IN A STUDY OF FISH POPULATIONS (in Vibert and Lagler, 1961)

Note: Standard symbols are those preceded by an asterisk (*). Those without an asterisk are employed, usually, by VIBERT and LAGLER (1961), since they do not exist in the standard list. The other symbols used in the work and not given in the list are those used in practical studies and their significance is given immediately in the text (NDA).

Subject	Symbols
Natality	A
Instantaneous coefficient of natality	$A_{(0-t)}$
Percentage of natality from 0 to t	
Mortality	
Instantaneous coefficient of mortality	$*Z$
Total annual percentage of mortality	Z_a
Percentage of total mortality from 0 to t	$Z_{(0-t)}$
Instantaneous coefficient of natural mortality	$*M$
Percentage of natural annual mortality	M_a
Percentage of natural mortality from 0 to t	$M_{(0-t)}$
Instantaneous coefficient of mortality due to fishing	$*F$
Annual percentage of mortality due to fishing	F_a
Percentage of mortality due to fishing from 0 to t	$F_{(0-t)}$
Survival	
Actual percentage of annual survival	$*S$
Observed or calculated percentage of annual survival	$*S$
Abundance	
Density (no.)	$*D$
No. of young fish arriving at the catchable phase (instant t_r)	$*R$
Total no. of fish in the catchable phase (starting from t_r)	$*N$
Total no. of fish in the catchable phase (starting from t_c)	$*P$
Total wt of fish in the caught phase (starting from t_c)	$*P'$
Growth	
Length	$*L, l$
Height	$*W, w$
Condition factor W/L 3	$*k$
Age at entry in the catchable phase	$*t_r$
Age at entry in the caught phase	$*t_c$
Length at entry in the catchable phase	$*l_r$
Length at entry in the caught phase	l_c
Parameters in the Bertalanfly equation	$*L_\infty, W_\infty, K_\infty$
Instantaneous coefficient of individual growth	I
Rate of individual annual growth	I_a
Rate of individual growth from 0 to t	$I_{(0-t)}$
Instantaneous coefficient of growth of a population	G
Rate of annual growth of a population	G_a
Rate of growth from 0 to t of a population	$G_{(0-t)}$
Fishing	
Fishing effort (rough figure based on fishing statistics)	$*g^{(1)}$
Effective intensity of fishing (fishing effort worked out on a unit of surface of the fishery)	$*f$
No. of fish caught	$*C$
Wt of fish caught	$*Y$
Relationship between the highest index in the intensity of effective fishing (f) and the instantaneous coefficient of mortality per corresponding fishing expedition (F)	$*q$
Constant in the formula linking the density to the catches per unit of effort ($c/f = q'D$)	q'
Miscellaneous	
Base of Neperian logarithms (2.718...)	$*e$
Factor corresponding to 50% of the escape of a category of length of fish for a given net mesh	$*b$
Conventionally used term for the record in the equation of weight yield	U_n

Code names for fish (French)

1. Verkhovka, *Leucaspius delineatus*	ABH
2. Bleak, *Alburnus alburnus*	ABL
3. Twaite shad, *Alosa fallax*	ALF
4. Alis shad, *Alosa alosa*	ALA
5. Eel, *Anguilla anguilla*	ANG
6. Spanish aphanius, *Aphanius iberus*	APH
7. Danube perch, *Zingel asper*	APR
8. Sand smelt, *Atherina boyeri*	ATH
9. Bass, *Dicentrarchus labrax*	LOU
10. Common barbel, *Barbus barbus*	BAF
11. Southern barbel, *Barbus meriodionalis*	BAM
12. Large mouth black bass, *Micropterus salmoides*	BBG
13. Small mouth black bass, *Micropterus dolomieu*	BBP
14. Beaked carp, *Leuciscus soufia*	BLN
15. River blenny, *Blennius fluviatilis*	BLE
16. Bitterling, *Rhodeus sericeus*	BOU
17. Common bream, *Abramis brama*	BRE
18. Silver bream, *Blicca bjoerkna*	BRB
19. Northern pike, *Esox lucius*	BRO
20. Crucian carp, *Carassius carassius*	CAS
21. Common carp, *Cyprinus carpio*	CCO
22. Leather carp	CCU
23. Mirror carp	CMI
24. Sculpin, *Cottus gobio*	CHA
25. Chub, *Leuciscus cephalus*	CHE
26. Whitefish, *Coregonus* sp.	COR
27. Rock bass, *Ambloplites rupestris*	CDR
28. Lake trout, *Salvelinus namaycush*	CRI
29. Cypriniids (juvenile poorly identified form)	CYP
30. Killifish, *Valencia hispanica*	CPV
31. Three-spined stickleback, *Gasterosteus aculeatus*	EPI
32. Nine-spined stickleback, *Pungitius pungitius*	EPT
33. Sturgeon, *Acipenser sturio*	EST
34. Flounder, *Platichthys flesus*	FLE
35. Mosquito fish, *Gambusia affinis*	GAM
36. Roach, *Rutilus rutilus*	GAR
37. Gudgeon, *Gobio gobio*	GOU
38. Pope, *Gymnocephalus cernua*	GRE
39. Nose carp, *Chondrostoma nasus*	HOT
40. Danube salmon, *Hucho hucho*	HUC
41. Cyprinid hybrid	HYB
42. Ide, *Leuciscus idus*	IDE
43. Sea lamprey, *Petromyzon marinus*	LPM
44. Brook lamprey, *Lampetra planeri*	LPP
45. Lampern (river lamprey), *Lampetra fluviatilis*	LPR
46. Pond loach, *Misgurnus fossilis*	LOE
47. Common loach, *Nemacheilus barbatulus*	LOF
48. Spined loach, *Cobitis tenia*	LOR
49. Burbot, *Lota lota*	LOT
50. Thick-lipped grey mullet, *Chelon labrosus*	MGL
51. Common grey mullet, *Mugil cephalus*	MUC
52. Long-finned grey mullet, *Liza aurata*	MUD
53. Thin-lipped grey mullet, *Liza ramada*	MUP
54. Arctic char, *Salvelinus alpinus*	OBL
54. Common grayling, *Thymallus thymallus*	OBR
55. Perch, *Perca fluviatilis*	PER
56. Sunfish, *Lepomis gibbosus*	PES
57. Plaice, *Pleuronectes platessa*	PLI
58. Freshwater catfish, *Ictalurus melas*	PCH
59. Mudminnow, *Umbra pygmea*	UMP
60. Goldfish, *Carassius auratus*	CAA
61. Rudd, *Scardinius erythrophthalmus*	ROT
62. Pike-perch, *Stizostedion lucioperca*	SAN
63. Atlantic salmon, *Salmo salar*	SAT
64. Coho salmon (silver salmon), *Oncorhynchus kisutch*	SCO
65. Brook trout, *Salvelinus fontinalis*	SDF
66. Sheatfish (European catfish), *Silurus glanis*	SIL
67. Bleak, *Alburnus bipunctatus*	SPI
68. Tench, *Tinca tinca*	TAN
69. Rhone chondrostome, *Chondrostoma toxostoma*	TOX
70. Rainbow trout, *Salmo gairdneri*	TAC
71. Lake trout, *Salmo trutta lacustris*	TRL
72. Sea trout, *Salmo trutta trutta*	TRM
73. River trout (fario trout), *Salmo trutta fario*	TRF
74. Common minnow, *Phoxinus phoxinus*	VAI
75. Dace, *Leuciscus leuciscus*	VAN

Shrimp name code (International)

Astacus astacus	ASA
Astacus leptodactylus	ASL
Austropotamobius pallipes	APP
Orconectes limosus	OCL
Pacifastacus leniusculus	PFL
Procambatus clarkii	PCC

5. LESLIE FORMULA (in regression methods)

The number in the *i*th catch is equal to the probability of the catch multiplied by the number in the population present before the *i*th catch.

$$Ci = (No - Ni)\, p$$

$$Ci = pNi - pNo \tag{1}$$

Equation (1) indicates the relationship between the catch at an instant *i*, and the cumulative catch *Ni* before this attempt at fishing is a curve. For $Ci = 0$ we obtain $pNi = pNo$, in other words, the curve cuts the axis of the abscissae at a point *No* and the slope of the curve is an estimation of *p*. The point of intersection on the Y axis is the product of the initial population *No* and the probability of a catch.

We may determine, graphically, the value of *No* or even carry out a simple linear regression calculation to obtain the equation of the curve and the abscissa *No*. Most statistical calculation software can be used for these operations.

The interval of confidence is given by the extreme values that are solutions of the Ricker equation (GERDEAUX, 1987).

6. THE ZIPPIN METHOD (estimation by the maximum of probability)

In estimation of numbers in a population based on catches without returning the fish to the water, ZIPPIN (1956 and 1958) established a graphical procedure to calculate and determine the asymptotic precision of the estimator (GERDEAUX, 1987).

Based on the hypotheses (1) of DE LURY, the method uses the principle of maximum probability by considering the probability of extracting successive samples C_1, C_2, C_3 ... C_k from a population of size *No*. The probability of obtaining a single sample of C 1 individuals in the *i*th catch is:

$$P\,(Ci/ni) = C\, p^{ci}\, q^{No\,-\,ni\,-\,Ci} \tag{1}$$

This is the number of ways for selecting *Ci* individuals among $No - ni$.

The probability or verisimilitude to obtain the catches observed in the successive *k* attempts is the product of *k* probabilities *P*(*Ci*) noted as *P*(*s*). We then look for the value *p* that maximizes this probability, *O*(*s*) to have the observed samples.

The equations resulting from these calculations are:

$$R = \frac{\sum_{i=1}^{k} (i-1)Ci}{\sum_{i=1}^{k} Ci} \tag{2}$$

$$R = \frac{q}{p} - \frac{kq^k}{(1-q^k)} \tag{3}$$

R, indicated by the relationship of Eq (2), is used by the graphic Zippin method. With a computer it is easy to obtain the value of R and then find p by iteration with a precision selected by the programme.

Estimation of the number in the population is obtained by

$$N = \frac{\sum_{i=1}^{k} Ci}{1 - q^k}$$

The value of the standard error is

$$SE^2 = \frac{N(N-T)T}{T^2 - N(N-T)(kp)^2 / (1-p)} \tag{5}$$

7. RICKER EQUATION, WHICH PROVIDES THE INTERVAL OF CONFIDENCE (Ricker, 1975)

This is a second-degree equation.

$$N^2(q^2 - t^2 S_{yx} C_{22}) - 2(q^2 No - t^2 S^2{}_{yx} C_{12})N + (q^2 No^2 - t^2 S^2{}_{yx} C_{11}) = 0$$

with

$$C_{11} = k(\Sigma_i Ni^2) / (k(\Sigma(Ni^2) - (\Sigma Ni)^2)$$

$$C_{12} = k(\Sigma_i Ni) / (k(\Sigma(Ni^2) - (\Sigma Ni)^2)$$

$$C_{22} = k / (\Sigma(Ni^2) - (\Sigma Ni)^2)$$

T = the Student value of t corresponding to a given level for n - 2 degrees of freedom

$$S_{yx}{}^2 = (\Sigma Ci^2 - (\Sigma(CiNi))^2 / \Sigma Ni^2)) / k - 2$$

8. CARLE AND STRUB METHOD (after Gerdeaux, 1987)

The method evaluates the probability of a catch p by the two parameters of a distribution function B. It is useful whenever the probability of a catch has not been constant during the course of fishing. The number in the ith catch may even be more than in the $(i - 1)$th catch. The bias in the estimation is less than the bias in the Zippin method. It is always negative and always low as long as p is greater than 0.3.

a) *Software*

This leads us to the concept of a software for calculation in Basic for an estimation of numbers of fish (GERDEAUX, 1987).

```
10   DIM Y (50)
20   PRINT
30   PRINT    "ESTIMATION OF A POPULATION BY THE CARLE AND STRUB
              METHOD"
40            CALCULATION OF TOTAL CATCH T
50   PRINT
60   PRINT
70   PRINT    "NAME OF FISHING SITE"
80   INPUT    S$
90   PRINT
100  PRINT    "GIVE DATE OF FISHING"
110  PRINT    D$
120  PRINT
130  PRINT    "GIVE THE SAMPLE SURFACE AREA IN SQ M"
140  INPUT
150  PRINT
160  PRINT    "STUDIED SPECIES"
170  INPUT    F$
180  PRINT
190  PRINT    "HOW MANY SUCCESSIVE CATCHES"
200  INPUT    K
210           T = 0
220           S = 0
230           U = 1
240           N = 0
250  PRINT
260  PRINT    "TYPE OUT THE NUMBER OF FISH CAUGHT IN EACH CATCH"
270  FOR      I = 1 TO K
280  INPUT    Y(1)
290           T = T + Y(1)
300           S = S + (K - 1)*Y(1)
310  NEXT     I
320  SOLUTION OF THE CARLE AND STRUB EQUATION
330           M$ = "CARLE AND STRUB"
340  FOR      N = T TO 10,000
350           U = 1
360  FOR      I = 1 TO K
370           U = U*(((KK*N) - S - T + 1 + (K - I)/((K*N) - S + 2 + (K - I)))
380  NEXT     I
390           U = (N + 1)* U/(N - T + 1)
400  IF       U ≤ 1 THEN 420
410  NEXT     N
420  PRINT    "U ≤1 TO THE ITERATION NUMBER", N
430           D = T/(K*N - S)
440           Q1 = 1 - D
```

```
450  E = 2*SQR(N*(N - T)*T/((T*T) - N*(N - T)*((K*D)^2)Q1))
460  PRINT
470  PRINT
480  PRINT    RESULTS
490  PRINT    "__"
500  PRINT
510  PRINT    S$, D$
520  PRINT
530  PRINT    "SPECIES OF FISH STUDIED":";F$
540  PRINT    "__"
550  PRINT
560  PRINT    "NUMBER OF FISH CAUGHT IN EACH CATCH"
570  PRINT    "__"
580  FOR      I = 1 TO K
590  PRINT    " ",Y(1)
600  NEXT     I
610  PRINT
620  PRINT    "TOTAL SAMPLED ARE IN SQ M";A
630  PRINT    "NUMBER OF SUCCESSIVE CATCHES";K
640  PRINT    "TOTAL FISH CATCH" - T
650  PRINT    "MINIMUM DENSITY PER SQ M =";T/A
660  PRINT    "ESTIMATION BY THE CARLE AND STRUB METHOD N =";N
670  PRINT    "INTERVAL OF CONFIDENCE AT 5% =+,-";E
680  PRINT    "ESTIMATED DENSITY PER SQ M =";N/A
690  PRINT    "INTERVAL OF CONFIDENCE AT 5% =+,-";E
700  PRINT    "__"
710  PRINT
720  PRINT    "WHAT IS REQUIRED NOW?"
730  PRINT    "A – ANOTHER CALCULATION AT THE SAME SITE, SAME
              DATE"
740  PRINT    "B – AN OUTPUT OF THESE RESULTS ON A PRINTER"
750  PRINT    "C – END OF CALCLATIONS"
760  INPUT    Q$
770  IFQ$ = "A" THEN 160
780  IFQ$ = "B" THEN 810
790  IFQ$ = "C" THEN 1050
800  GOTO     730
810  LPRINT
820  LPRINT   S$, S$
830  LPRINT
840  LPRINT   "FISH SPECIES STUDIED;";F$
850  LPRINT   "__"
860  LPRINT
870  LPRINT   "NUMBER OF FISH CAUGHT ON EACH OCCASION"
880  LPRINT   "__"
890  FOR      I = 1 TO K
900  LPRINT   "__", Y(1)
910  NEXT     I
```

```
920  LPRINT
940  LPRINT  "TOTAL SAMPLED AREA IN SQ M =";A
950  LPRINT  "NUMBER OF SUCCESSIVE CATCHES";K
960  LPRINT  "TOTAL NUMBER OF FISH CAUGHT";T
970  LPRINT  "MINIMUM DENSITY PER SQ M =";T/A
980  LPRINT  "ESTIMATION BY THE METHOD OF";M$;"=";N
990  LPRINT  "INTERVAL OF CONFIDENCE AT 5% = +,-";E
1000 LPRINT  "ESTIMATED DENSITY PER SQ M =";N/A
1010 LPRINT  "INTERVAL OF CONFIDENCE AT 5% = +,-";E/A
1020 LPRINT  "__"
1030 LPRINT
1040 GOTO    710
1050 END
```

b) Example

```
RUN

ESTIMATION OF A POPULATION BY THE CARLE AND STRUB METHOD

NAME OF FISHING SITE
? MARGNY

GIVE THE DATE OF CATCH
? 18/11/1988

GIVE THE SAMPLED SURFACE IN SQ M
? 728

STUDIED SPECIES
? FARIO TROUT ≥ 10 CM

HOW MANY SUCCESSIVE CATCHES
? 3

TYPE THE NUMBER OF FISH CAUGHT EACH TIME
? 40
? 18
? 7

U ≤ 1 WITH REITERATION NUMBER 69

RESULTS

MARGNY 18/11/1988

STUDIED SPECIES: FARIO TROUT ≥ 10 CM

NUMBER OF FISH CAUGHT IN EACH ATTEMPT
40
18
7
```

SAMPLED AREA SQ M = 728
NUMBER OF SUCCESSIVE CATCHES 3
TOTAL FISH CAUGHT 65
MINIMUM DENSITY PER SQ M = 8.9287572 E - 02
ESTIMATION BY THE CARLE AND STRUB METHOD N = 69
INTERVAL OF CONFIDENCE AT 5% = +, - 5?935722
ESTIMATED DENSITY PER SQ M = 9.4798022 E - 02
INTERVAL OF CONFIDENCE OF THE DENSITY AT 5% = 8.153464 E - 03

WHAT IS NEEDED NOW?
A – ANOTHER CALCULATION FROM THE SAME SITE, SAME DATE
B – AN OUTPUT OF THESE RESULTS ON A PRINTER
D – END OF CALCULATIONS
? D
OK

SITUATION

DATE	______	LOCALITY	....
DEPARTMENT	______	RIVER	....
DIRECTION	______	WATER BODY	....
DISTANCES FROM			
SPRINGS	....	SECTOR	
LENGTH STUDIED (m)	....	WATER SURFACE (sq m)	

FLOW	____
HYDRAULIC REGIME	____
1. dry weather 2. normal 3. flood period	
GRADIENT ‰	____
GEOLOGICAL FORMATIONS	
CURRENT VELOCITY (cm/s)	
SURFACE normal	____
maximum	____
BED normal	____
maximum	____
DEPTH OF THE WATER	
normal	____
maximum	____
FLOOD LEVEL (m)	____
AVERAGE SURFACE WIDTH (m)	____
AVERAGE WIDTH OF THE BED (m)	____
% OF SILLS	____
REINFORCEMENT ON THE BANK	
0 = nil 1 = yes	____
% right bank	____
% left bank	____

CONDITION OF BANKS

STABLE	____	EROSION considerable	– – –
		EROSION slight	– –
ROCKY	____	CLAY or MARL	____
STONE BLOCKS	____	STONE FACING	____
PEBBLES	____	CONCRETE	____
GRAVEL	____	FOUNDATION	____
SAND	____	(under water)	
DYKE	____		

UTILIZATION

	B.V.	MAJOR BED
URBAN ZONE	____	____
INDUSTRY	____	____
CONIFEROUS FOREST	____	____
DECIDUOUS FOREST	____	____
GRASSLANDS	____	____
FALLOW LAND	____	____
LIVESTOCK FARMING	____	____
HUMID ZONE	____	____
CROPS	____	____
type	____	____

VEGETATION ON THE BANKS

	L. BANK	R. BANK
GRASSLAND	____	____
SCRUB	____	____
SHRUBS	____	____
SCATTERED TREES	____	____
DENSE TREES	____	____
INCLINED TREES	____	____
FALLEN TREES	____	____
STUMPS OF TREES	____	____
NO VEGETATION	____	____
WIDTH OF THE SCREEN OF VEGETATION		
1 : I < 2 m - 2 : 2 m < I , 5 m - 3 : I > 5 m		
DOMINANT SPECIES		

DESCRIPTION OF BANKS

	R. BANK	L. BANK
HEIGHT (m)	____	____
VERTICAL BANKS	____	____
BEACHES	____	____
UNDER CAVES	____	____
% ABOVE THE WATER LINE DURING DRY PERIODS	____	____
HOLLOWS OR HOLES	____	____
of which $P < 10$ cm	____	____
$10 \times P < 20$ cm	____	____
$P > 30$ cm	____	____
% ABOVE THE WATER LINE DURING DRY PERIODS	____	____
TREE STUMPS	____	____
STONE BLOCKS	____	____
ROCK FACINGS	____	____
ROOTS	____	____
incl. HAIR ROOTS	____	____
FINE < 2 cm diameter	____	____
LARGE	____	____

Transverse section

Dominant faunal groups

Invertebrates	Fish

Description of the bed

EMERGED VEGETATION		STONE BLOCKS	____	UNDER THE FLOW	
incl. SINGLE PLANTS	--------	PEBBLES	____	1 yes 2 no	____
PLANT GROUPS	--------	GRAVEL	____	BLOCKING OF	
SUBMERGED VEGETATION		LEAVES	____	SUBSTRATE	____
incl. LEAVES IN WATER	--------	ROOTS	____	STONE PAVING	____
FLOATING LEAVES	--------	incl. HAIR ROOTS	____	CLAY	____
FILAMENTOUS ALGAE	--------	> 2 cm	____	SILT	____
incl. TUFTS/WISPS	--------	< 2 cm	____	BRANCHES	____
BACTERIA or FUNGI	--------			STUMPS	____
BRYOPHYTES	--------			TUFT	____

ILLUMINATION

BRIGHT SUNLIGHT	____
LIMITED SHADE	____
SEMI-DARKNESS	____

WATER

TEMP (°C)	____	ALKALINITY	____
OXYGEN (mg/l)	____	CALCIUM	____
pH	____		
CONDUCTIVITY	____		

Description sheet of the fish habitat (CEMAGREF)

General characteristics of the station
Service responsible for the information □

Water course .... □
Tributary of ....

Basin: | | | .... □

Precise location of the station
....
....
....
....

Hydrological code .... □□□□□□
Average pK .... □□□□□
Number of personnel in the station .... □□□

Fish culture category | 1 | 2 | ....

Flow: interannual modules .... cu m/s □□□□
average monthly flow with a frequency of 1/5 .... cu m □□□
*Distance from the source .... km □□□□
*Gradient of bed of the stream in the sector .... ‰ □□□□□
Altitude .... m □□□□
*Total average hardness (Ca + Mg) .... mg/l □□□

*Average maximum water temp. during the hottest month .... °C □□□

*Average width of the water surface in the dry period (limits in m) □□

2-3	3-5	5-7	7-10	10-16	16-24	24-35	35-50	50-80	80-120	120-180	180-270	>270
1	2	3	4	5	6	7	8	9	10	11	12	13

*Average covered section in dry weather (limits in sq m)

2-4	4-8	8-15	15-30	30-60	60-130	130-250	250-500	>500
1	2	3	4	5	6	7	8	9

□

Changes in morphodynamic conditions

	in process	recent	earlier	date		
Dredging	1	2	3	□□	□□	□ □□ □□
Clearing/weeding	1	2	3	□□	□□	□ □□ □□
Recalibration works	1	2	3	□□	□□	
				month	year	

Canalized water	1	□
Navigated water	1	□

Sector subjected to the effects of a dam or dams located

Upstream of the station	1	□□□

At a distance of .... km □

Downstream of the station	2	□

Changes in chemical quality

Sector located downstream of pollution source(s)	1	□

At a distance from the main source of .... km □□□
Describe clearly the nature of the pollution(s)
....
....
....

Information marked with an asterisk is essential for calculating the theoretical typological level.

Characteristics of fishing activity

Water course ....

Precise location of the station

....

....

....

Number of personnel in the station ....

Date .... □□□□□□

Mesological conditions

Water temp. .... °C □□□

Conductivity .... μS/cm □□□□

Hydrological regime

Dry period	1		Normal	2		Flood	3

□

Average width of the minor bed .... m □□□

Average width of the water surface .... m □□□

Length of the station .... m □□□□

Fishing equipment

Number of nets used .... □

Number of anodes .... □

Group - box

Heron II	1		EPMC	2		Others	3

□

Specify: ....

In case 2 groups are used

Assembly

in parallel	1		in series	2

□

Voltage .... volts □□□

Current .... amps □□

Survey of the station

on foot	1		in a boat	2

□

complete	1		partial	2

□

If complete, go to the paragraph on effective fishing period.

Partial	Over the entire width of the water course?	Yes	1
		No	2

□

If yes, the effectively surveyed length .... m □□

If no,

Left bank	G

Effectively surveyed width .... m □□

Effectively surveyed length .... m □□□□

Right bank	D

Effectively surveyed width .... m □□

Effectively surveyed length .... m □□□□

Effective fishing period

Recorded on a stopwatch (in 1/100 h) fishing time □□□

Recorded on a chronometer (in minutes) fishing time □□□

	Point number	1	2	3	4	5	6	7	8	9	10	11	12	13	14	15
	Water level (cm)															
Granulometry	Stone blocks															
	Large stones (pebbles)															
	Small pebbles															
	Gravel															
	Sand															
	Clay-silt															
	Clogged substrate*															
Dominant plant formations	Macrophytes with no roots															
	Heliophytes															
	Phanerogams with floating leaves															
	Submerged phanerogams															
	Bryophytes															
	Filamentous algae															
	Proliferation of bacteria and fungi															
	Branches															
	Litter															

	Point number	16	17	18	19	20	21	22	23	24	25	26	27	28	29	30
	Water level (cm)															
Granulometry	Stone blocks															
	Large stones (pebbles)															
	Small pebbles															
	Gravel															
	Sand															
	Clay-silt															
	Clogged substrate*															
Dominant plant formations	Macrophytes with no roots															
	Heliophytes															
	Phanerogams with floating leaves															
	Submerged phanerogams															
	Bryophytes															
	Filamentous algae															
	Proliferation of bacteria and fungi															
	Branches															

Fish culture study	Date
	Place

Sample taken

	Sp.	Length F	Length T	Wt	Lot	No.	Sex/Mat	Health	Mark/No.	No. in catch
1										
2										
3										
4										
5										
6										
7										
8										
9										
10										
11										
12										
13										
14										
15										
16										
17										
18										
19										
20										
21										
22										
23										
24										
25										
26										
27										
28										
29										
30										

9. FISH INVENTORY

Working Documents

Habitats

The granulometry of beds and plant formations is, if possible, observed over a surface of about 0.1 sq m corresponding to the "mesh" for extracting benthic invertebrates around each point.

The existing granulometric classes are noted by the figure 2 if they occupy more than 50% of the observed surface and the figure 3 if they cover 20–50% of the observed surface.

Existing plant formations are recorded by the figure 1 in the corresponding columns.

Characteristics of the granulometric classes and examples of plant formations are given in the following tables.

Table 1. Granulometric classes

Nomenclature	Characteristics
Clays, silt	< 50 μ
Sands	50 μ to 2 mm
Gravel	2 mm to 2 cm
Small pebbles	2–10 cm
Large pebbles	10–20 cm
Rock blocks	> 20 cm

Table 2. Examples of plant formations

Nomenclature	Examples
Macrophytes without roots	*Salvinia, Lemna*
Heliophytes	*Apium, Veronica, Typha, Phragmites, Sparganium, Equisetum*
Phanerogams with floating leaves	*Nuphar luteum, Nymphea alba, Potamogeton natans*
Submerged phanerogams	*Isoetes, Potamogeton* in calm sectors of water, *Myriophyllum, Elodea, Ranunculus fluitans, Callitriche*
Bryophytes	*Fontinalis, Cinclidotus, Brachytecium*
Filamentous algae	*Vaucheria, Cladophora, Lemanera*
Proliferation of bacteria	*Sphaerotilus, Leptomitus, Fusarium* and fungi

10. PRODUCTIVITY OF TROPICAL RIVERS AND LAKES (RYDER, HENDERSON and WELCOME)

Morpho-edaphic index = MEI

$$\frac{\text{Conductivity K20 } (\mu\text{mhos / cm})}{\text{Average depth (m)}} = \text{MEI}$$

a) For Lakes

As a measure of potential richness of water for primary production we consider the *conductivity* as well as an assessment of the configuration of the morphology of the lake, the *average depth.*

The index automatically gives what, in each case, is qualitatively well known: lakes that are shallow or rich in nutrients are more productive than deep lakes or those that are poor in nutrients.

The production from reservoir lakes, at least in their early period, is somewhat higher than that from natural lakes.

*Reservoir lakes: fish catch = 17.8813 $MEI^{0.4999}$ ($r^2 = 0.7516$; $n = 7$)

*Natural lakes: fish catch = 5.4250 $MEI^{0.7282}$ ($r^2 = 0.5825$; $n = 11$)

b) For Rivers (Welcome)

We consider two cases:

*Rivers with a normal flood plain (less than 1.5% of the total area of the basin)

(1) fish catch (t) = 0.1326 $A^{0.8533}$

*Rivers with an extensive flood plain (between 2.5 and 3.8% of the total area of the basin)

(2) fish catch (t) = 0.2961 $A^{0.9024}$

where t = weight in tonnes, A = total surface area of the basin in sq km with a correlation per km of the major bed for (1).

Fish catch (t) = 0.0033 $L^{1.95}$, where L = length in km of the main bed.

C. ABOUT WATER

1. KINETIC ENERGY OF RAINS (Wischmeier and Smith)

KE (kgm/sq m) = $A + \log I$

Rain index (Wischmeier)

$RI = KE \times I$ max x 1/100 where

I max = maximum intensity of rain in 30 min.

2. UNIVERSAL EQUATION FOR SOIL LOSSES (Wischmeier)

$A = RI \times K \times LS \times C \times P$ where

A = soil loss,
RI = rain index in US tons/acre,
K = soil index, that is the extent of susceptibility of a soil to erode, depending on its nature,
LS = index of slope (taking into account the gradient and the length of the slope),
C = extent of soil protection by the natural vegetation or the crop,
P = index of effectiveness of anti-erosion measures by their effect on the relief of the ground.
(Multiply A by 2.24 to obtain the results in metric units.)

Calculation of indices

RI or rain index

$$RI = R = \frac{Eg \times Im}{1000} \text{ where}$$

Eg = the energy produced by a fall of 1 mm of rain, calculated on the basis of the unit energy (Eu),

$$Eu = a + b \log Ih$$

a and b being variable paremeters with the selected unit, if we express Eu in ft/ton/acre/inch of rainfall and Ih in inches/h, the equation is written as follows:
$Eu = 916 + 331 \log Ih$

K = soil index

The K factor is calculated using the Wischmeier equation by giving all other factors the value 1 and measuring the soil loss per unit of the erosion index.

K varies, generally, from 0.1 for the most stable soils (alluvial soils) to the following values:

$\leq$ 0.05, soils that do not erode easily
0.05–0.1, soils that erode only very slightly
0.1–0.2, soils that erode moderately
0.2–0.4, soils that erode quickly
0.4–0.6, soils that erode very quickly

LS = slope index

$$LS = \sqrt{l(0.76 + 0.53s + 0.076s)^2}\,/100, \text{ where}$$

l = length of slope (in feet)
s = coefficient of slope (%)
LS = 1 for a slope of 9% and a length of 72.6 feet (22.12 m)

C = culture index

Calculation of C is complex. It varies for different cultivations with different phases of the agricultural cycle, as under:

– forest, grassland, 0.01
– rotation of crop with fodder, 0.2
– rotation of crop with cereal, 0.4

—rotation of crop with cereal, 0.4
—wheat (continuous cultivation), 0.7
—fruit-bearing arboriculture, 0.9
—ploughed fallow land, 1

We may estimate the danger in a particular crop rotation with regard to soil erosion and suggest a changeover to another less harmful one for the catchment area and the water course vector.

P = treatment index

Wischmeier has given *P* the maximum value (1) for a crop planted in the direction of the slope, with intermediate values for treatments and slopes, as under:

Slope %	Contour farming	Plantation in alternate fields
1–2	0.6	0.3
2–7	0.5	0.25
7–12	0.6	0.3
12–18	0.8	0.4
18–24	0.9	0.45

In the system of alternate fields, the width to be given to these fields depends on the slope:

Slope %	Width of fields (m)
2–7	30–35
7–12	25–30
12–18	20–25
18–24	15–20

3. THE BLACKMORE FORMULA

Calculation of the lamination is based on characteristics of the flood waters to be laminated, those of the retaining basin (height/area curve) and the law governing the flow at the outlet of the flood waters. There are two types of evacuators (outlets):

—overflow or surface evacuators where the flow law is $q = f(h3/2)$
—buried pipes or bottom evacuators where the flow law is $q = f(h1/2)$

The downstream flood waters, $Q2 = f(t)$, starting from the upstream flood waters $Q1 = F(t)$ and the curve of the evacuator $q = f(h)$, h being the load in metres on the evacuator.

Lamination will be more effective when the relationship Ve/Vc is greater, where:

Ve is the volume stored in the reservoir, i.e.:
$Ve = V2 + V1$ where
$V2$ = retentive volume
$V1$ = volume above the normal retention (on the side of the evacuator), which is greater when the area of the basin of a dam is greater and the load h on the outlet is greater.
Ve = total volume of the flood waters.

It is quite clear that during short periods of flooding lamination is easier.

4. STUDY OF EVACUATION OF FLOOD WATERS

Calculation of the flow of flood waters (*tc* = concentration period) is based on the characteristics of the catchment area, on pluviometric relationships, the spatial dispersal of the rainfall, the maximum outflow of the flood waters and the lamination effect. It involves the coefficient of total flow and calculation of the characteristics of the outlet and the evacuation channel of the particular storage dam.

The following examples provide a useful idea:

a) Characteristics of the Catchment Area

S:	extent of the catchment area	= 7.5 km^2
L:	the longest flow path of the water	= 4 km
I:	average gradient of the flow	= 0.033 mm
h:	difference in level between the average slope of the catchment area and its outlet	= 67 m

According to the Giadotti formula:

$$tc = \frac{4\sqrt{S} + 1.5L}{0.8\sqrt{h}}$$

$tc = 2.59$

Verifying this with the Passini formula:

$$tc = \frac{0.108^3\sqrt{SL}}{\sqrt{I}}$$

$tc = 1.85$

The Passini formula, fairly approximate for catchment areas of more than 4000 ha, is acceptable for basins with an area of 4000–2000 ha but should not be adopted for smaller basins. In such cases we use:

$tc = 2.59$ or about 2 h 30 min.

bearing in mind that this value can only be very approximate since it is possible to know only one order of magnitude of the duration of flow.

b) Pluviometric Relationships

We apply the Montana law.

Classification of the highest levels of precipitation recorded in a region, adjusted by a law of probability, leads approximately to the following formulae, which give the level of rainfall, based on duration, for the probability of a 500-year return.

—Frechet adjustment

$h = 40.5\ tc^{0.46}$

—Gumbel adjustment

$h = 28\ tc^{\ 0.37}$

The results after the Frechet adjustment are clearly better than those after the Gumbel adjustment because, for a duration of rainfall equal to the time of concentration, i.e., 2 h 30 minutes, we obtain:

$h = 63$ mm

$h = 40$ mm

These variations are obviously quite considerable and lead us to state that a 500-year rainfall according to Frechet would be repeated only after 1000 years according to Gumbel. However, the aforementioned formulae are only approximations in view of the extremely short period for which records of rainfall are available and, as a matter of caution, we assume a water level of

$h = 65$ mm.

c) Total Flow Coefficient

According to Richard, the coefficient is from 0.1 to 0.2 for wooded areas with an average slope. The same coefficient, according to Poirier and Ollier, is from 0.005 to 0.10.

We will adopt 0.10.

d) Spatial Dispersion of Rainfall

For all catchment areas, Richard forecasts a reduction in the intensity of rainfall.

For a small basin it is prudent to maintain the selected water level as there is practically no dispersion.

e) Maximum Outflow of Flood Waters

This outflow is given by the Turraza formula

$$Qm = \frac{e \times h \times S}{3.6tc}$$

where e is the total flow coefficient = 0.10
h is the level of rainfall, in mm = 65
s is the catchment area in sq km = 7.5
tc is the concentration period in hours = 2.59

$Qm = 5.23\ \text{m}^3/\text{s}$

f) Lamination Effect

Since the function $Q = f(t)$, defining the hydrograph of a flood, is not sufficiently known to be able to apply strictly the graphic method of Blackmore, we have selected the simplified method given by Bratanek.

Thus, for a water level of 0.65 m,
volume of the reserve at the PEN side Vo = 27,000 m^3
volume of the reserve at the PHE side Vi = 41,700 m^3
regulation volume = 14,700 m^3
Maximum flow volume

$$\Sigma Q = 3600 \times Qm \times tc$$

$$\Sigma Q = 3600 \times 5.23 \times 2.59 = 49{,}000 \text{ m}^3$$

Effect of lamination: (14,700 × 100)/49,000 = 30%, whence the flow to be evacuated = 3.66 m^3/s.

g) Calculation of the Outlet of a Storage Dam

1) *Sill*

The dimensions are: width, 2 × 1.20 m = 2.40 m
water draught = 0.65 m
(wet) water section = 1.56 m^2

The maximum velocity of water for an outlet of 3.66 m^3/s to be evacuated will be 2.35 m/s.

The load on the sill of the outlet will be:

$$H = \frac{0.65 \text{ m} \times 2.35^2}{2g} = 0.93 \text{ m}$$

The flow from the outlet with a width of 2.40 m, a load of 0.93 m, and a flow coefficient of 0.385 is:

$$Q = 0.38lH^{3/2}\sqrt{2g} = 3.67 \text{ m}^3/\text{s}$$

This sill is, therefore, large enough (as a safety measure the water draught may reach 1 m) and the water level above the sill will reach a maximum of $h = 2/3\ H$ = 0.62.

2) *Downstream facing*

We usually extend the outlet by a facing that channels the flow of flood waters and it is important to determine the characteristics:

- width of the top = 2.60 m
- gradient = 1.5/1

with 70 being the Manning Strickler coefficient of roughness or $1/n$ and n = 0.015.

V = velocity in m/s

R = hydraulic radius
I = slope in mm

The velocity will be 3.20 m/s, which results in a water draught at the foot of the weir (contracted section) of about 0.05 m.

The energy due to the velocity of the water on the downstream face will be dissipated by a horizontal extension of this face. The changeover from a torrential to a calm regime determines the jump. The height of this jump is essentially based on the formula:

$$h_2 = 1/2\left[-1+\sqrt{1+8F}\right] \times h_1$$

F (the Froude number) = $(Q/l)^2/gh_1$

$h_2 = 0.12$

and the length of the jump will be: $0.12 \times 5 = 0.60$ m

h) Evacuation Channel

We may, in this way, calculate the rate of evacuation of flood waters:

$S = 2\ \text{m}^2$ $\qquad$ $p = 3.74$ m

$R = 0.53$ m $\qquad$ $U/\sqrt{RI} = 31.2$

$$U = 31.2\sqrt{0.53 \times 0.0075} = 1.97 \text{ m/s}$$

$$Q = 1.97 \times 2 = 3.94 \text{m}^3/\text{s}$$

$$3.94 \text{ m}^3/\text{s} > 3.66 \text{ m}^3/\text{s}$$

D. HARMFUL EFFECTS

1. ESTIMATE OF CONSECUTIVE DAMAGES CAUSED BY POLLUTIONS

The damages are, generally:

– *Direct damages* to:

- the aquatic medium: degradation of banks, disappearance of spawning areas, shelters, and plants.
- the fish living in water: mortality, escape, diseases.
- the individual or legal entities having the use: the inability to catch fish.

– *Indirect damages affecting:*

• the medium: restoration works.

• the fish: recovery of dead fish, handling, transport, logistical costs relative to restocking.

• the user: costs incurred on the study, expertise and procedure.

– *Damages suffered by the fish,* involving:

• partial or total disappearance of the fish population:

■ over a distance or a surface area of a course or a water body to be determined by estimating the degressive effect of the adverse event until its effects are over.

■ regarding the diversity of species that normally populate the particular site: carnivores and their accompanying fishes.

■ in each intraspecific structure: fry, summerlings, young adults, breeders.

We are considering the **stock in place** before the adverse event, which is equal to twice the productivity (TIMMERMANUS).

• Loss in productivity of all or part of this stock, calculation based on the Leger, Huet and Arrignon formula.

This damage is degressive in relation to restocking of the population after the event. It is accepted that, in the bioclimatic zone of Western Europe, restocking of all associated species is achieved at the end of three years.

Restocking, if done with fry, will therefore need three years before the restored population is demographically balanced and may autonomously ensure its future, provided that the ambient medium has fully recovered the qualities it had before the event.

The lack of productivity will therefore be totally compensated during year 0, to the extent of one-half during year 1, and one-third during year 2.

– *Estimate of damages suffered by the fish*

Let P be the productivity. We have:

stock in place = $2P$
productivity, year 0 = P
productivity, year 1 = $P/2$
productivity, year 2 = $P/3$

or, in all, $23P/6$

– *Estimate of other damages*

• on actual costs of works and outlays.

• by identifying the share of loss of each user of the affected resource: amateur anglers, professional fishermen (with equipment) who do not fish in the same zones or even catch the same fish.

• with regard to private fishing: on the loss of fishing days due to the event, in relation to the average number of days during the three years preceding it, and taking into consideration the duration of the open fishing season.

• with regard to fishing clubs, on the loss of subscription of members due to the event, in relation to the average during the previous three years.

• with regard to professional fishing, on the loss of income based on examination of records of catches during the previous three years and subsequent expenses (disbanding of personnel . . .).

• to the result, we apply the daily wages and/or the subscriptions that were prevalent at the time of the adverse event.

2. DAMAGE TO FISH CAUSED BY TURBINES (according to Larinier and Dartiguelongue, 1989)

The movement of fish across turbines results in death rates and injuries depending on the families. Various salmonid species do not appear to be affected differently but cupeids (*Alosa*), for example, appear to be more fragile as the death rate observed among them is higher by a factor of 2 or 3.

The damages are classified, generally, in three categories depending on their probable origin. Those of a mechanical type, those due to cutting, and those due to exposure of the fish to very rapid changes in pressure or cavitation.

Fish appear to safely tolerate higher pressures upstream of the turbines. The subsequent effect of a sudden change in pressure when passing through the wheel, especially on the air bladder, depends on the relative extent of this reduction in pressure to which the body structure of the fish is adapted and the rate at which this reduction occurs.

When water is drawn from the bottom level, the sudden drop in pressure during its passage through the wheel, or even a simple return to atmospheric pressure in the outlet channel, may result in considerable damage.

For fish that swim on the surface, the maximal pressure drop acceptable in a turbine without risk of damage is 5–6 m of water (0.5–0.6 atm).

The death rate due to cuts when fish are in or near the periphery of high speed jets is high when the velocity is around 20 m/s.

There do not appear to be any noticeable differences between the effects of various types of turbine jets—whether Francis or Kaplan. Although the death rates observed with Francis turbines (37%) is more than that observed with Kaplan turbines (9%), this is because the former are used on falls at higher levels.

Whatever the type and characteristics of the turbine, the minimum death rate is 3–5%. The size of a fish, relative to the size of the turbine or the spacing between the blades of the wheel, appears to be an important parameter. We need only to compare, in a given installation, the death rates among fish of very different sizes.

The best predictive regression in the death rate—or more specifically its transformed variable (AMO)—on Francis turbines, is as follows:

$$AMO = -4.21 + 1.25\,V1^{0.821} + 2.28N^{0.19}\,(TL/sp)^{0.84}\,W1^{0.71}$$

In Kaplan turbines, the effect of hydraulic variables is less clear: the relationship between the size of a fish and the inter-blade spacing, calculated at the middle of the blade, appears to be the best indicator of potential damages:

$$AMO = 10.7 + 68.8\,(TL/sp)$$ where

V1 = absolute velocity of the water at the entrance of the wheel (correlated with the height of the fall)

W1 = relative velocity

TL = size of the fish

sp = inter-blade spacing calculated at the middle of the blade
N = rotation speed of the wheel

These models may be used to obtain the mortality rate among salmonids and eels. They are not adapted for other species, especially for young alosa, on which the damages are much more severe.

3. SAMPLING AND DESPATCH OF WATER OR MUD FOR CHEMICAL ANALYSIS

Material and Quantity of Water to Be Taken

A litre of water is necessary to carry out a complete analysis. The bottles used for this purpose are carefully washed and rinsed several times with the same water that is to be analysed. They must be tightly closed. Glass is always preferable if we wish to identify a toxin. Otherwise, a plastic bottle is suitable for the purpose. Packing and protection against shock and deformation should be carefully monitored. Note: the oxygen content can only be checked immediately at the site of the pond.

Label

Each bottle should have a label indicating legibly the name of the pond or the locality, the water temperature, the date and time the sample was taken, and a serial number, if there are several samples.

Sampling Technique for Ponds

To obtain a representative sample from a body of water we can prepare an average sample using several litres of water taken from several points in the pond.

For a pond that is less than 5 ha in area we can take one litre of water from the area upstream of the monk, if possible using a boat and at a depth of about 0.50 m.

If a water current passes through the pond we must always take a sample at its inlet and another at its outlet.

Despatch

The packaged sample is despatched, preferably early in the week, by parcel post or by an express delivery agency. If there is a delay in sending it, the bottle should be kept in a refrigerator.

A letter is sent with the package indicating the characteristics of the pond (see below, "Information that should be provided in the covering letter").

Choice of an Analytical Laboratory

Analysis of pond or river water does not aim to determine its potability but to determine certain elements in order to indicate its suitability for fish culture. Medical or pharmacological laboratories are not generally equipped to conduct this type of analysis. Comments on the results are often given after providing the chemical data. Interpretation of data from the piscicultural aspect is not always within the capabilities of an analytical laboratory and the owner of the pond will often have to draw his own conclusions in this respect.

Analysis of Need

Mud samples should be taken at the surface, within the top 10 cm, in a central zone considered to be most representative of the water body (except in special cases we avoid areas near the bank).

The samples should be obtained preferably with the use of a shovel or a large spade so that they can be lifted carefully without being mixed with the pond water.

The sample, from which the pond water is removed immediately, is collected in a hermetically sealed glass jar (at least the equivalent of one litre) and then despatched.

Information that should be provided in the covering letter

Name and address
- of the applicant
- of the person to whom the bill and results should be sent

Reason for analysis and despatch of sample
- to improve production
- to check probability of pollution (presumed type)

Summary of samples with their serial numbers, the date and place of sampling

Description of the water body
- name of water body
- location (community)
- area
- depth
- water source (e.g., spring, stream, run-off)
- fish populations, weights and species, date, origin
- fertilization, date, type, weight of fertilizer per ha

Table. List of 135 taxa used for calculation of the GBI (the 38 indicator taxa are in bold type)

INSECTA	Curculionidae	CRUSTACEA
	Donaciidae	
PLECOPTERA	Dryopidae	BRANCHIPODA
Capniidae	Dytiscidae	AMPHIPODA
Chloroperlidae	Eubriidae	**Gammaridae**
Leuctridae	**Elmidae**	ISOPODES
Nemouridae	Gyrinidae	**Asellidae**
Perlidae	Haliplidae	DECAPODA
Perlodidae	Helodidae	Astacidae
Taeniopterygidae	Helophoridae	Atyidae
TRICHOPTERA	Hydraenidae	Grapsidae
Beraeidae	Hydrochidae	Cambaridae
Brachycentridae	Hydrophilidae	
Ecnomidae	Hydroscaphidae	**MOLLUSCA**
Glossosomatidae	Hygrobiidae	
Goeridae	Limnebiidae	BIVALVES
Helicopsychidae	Spercheidae	Dreissenidae
Hydropsychidae	DIPTERA	Sphaeriidae
Hydroptilidae	Anthomyidae	Unionidae
Lepidostomatidae	Athericidae	GASTEROPODES
Leptoceridae	Blephariceridae	Ancylidae
Limnephilidae	Ceratopogonidae	Bithynidae
Molannidae	Chaoboridae	Bythinellidae
Odontoceridae	**Chironomidae**	Hydrobiidae
Philopotamidae	Culicidae	Limnaeidae
Phryganeidae	Dixidae	Neritidae
Polycentropodidae	Dolichopodidae	Physidae
Psychomyidae	Empididae	Planorbidae
Rhyacophilidae	Ephydridae	Valvatidae
Sericostomatidae	Limoniidae	Viviparidae
Thremmatidae	Psychodidae	
EPHEMEROPTERA	Ptychopteridae	VERMES
Baetidae	Scatophagidae	
Caenidae	Sciomyzidae	**ACHETA**
Ephemerellidae	Simuliidae	Erpobdellidae
Ephemeridae	Stratiomyidae	Glossiphoniidae
Heptageniidae	Syrphidae	Hirudidae
Leptophlebiidae	Tabanidae	Piscicolidae
Oligoneuriidae	Thaumaleidae	**TRICLADIDA**
Polymitarcidae	Tipulidae	Dendrocoelidae
Potamanthidae	**ODONATA**	Dugesiidae
Prosopistomatidae	Aeschnidae	Planariidae
Siphlonuridae	Calopterygidae	**OLIGOCHAETA**
HETEROPTERA	Coenagrionidae	NEMATHELMINTHES
Aphelocheiridae	Cordulegasteridae	HYDRACARINA
Corixidae	Corduliidae	
Gerridae	Gomphidae	
Hebridae	Lestidae	
Hydrometridae	Libellulidae	HYDROZOA
Naucoridae	Platycnemididae	
Nepidae	MEGALOPTERA	SPONGIA
Notonectidae	Sialidae	
Mesoveliidae	PLANIPENNIA	BRYOZOA
Pleidae	Osmylidae	
Veliidae	HYMENOPTERA	NEMERTINI
COLEOPTERA	LEPIDOPTERA	

2 GLOSSARY

Aberrant: indicative of an organism with rare and somewhat considerable variations from the typical members of the species.
Abiotic: refers to a medium in which life is impossible.
Ablation: removal of an organ. *By extension,* ablation of a fin—marking by ablation of a fin.
Acclimation: adaptation to a changed environment of an organism (e.g., a fish) that must live in a new medium, generally under human surveillance and protection. Genuine acclimation is observed when the organism reproduces without human intervention.
Adaptability: all natural and acquired features that enable an organism, at different phases of its existence, to establish balanced relationships with a new medium or a new situation.
Adjutage: a device fixed to the outlet of a system of canals, in order to alter the flow of the fluid passing through it.
Aerobic: an aerobic organism takes the oxygen it needs from atmospheric air or from air dissolved in water. *Ant.* anaerobic
Alevin: a young fish or fry, morphologically different from the adult.
Alevin stocking: stocking of young fish in a water course (or a tank or reservoir) (*by extension*).
Algivorous: feeding on algae. *Alt.* algicolous.
Alkalinity: content of carbonates and bicarbonates of alkali or alkaline-earth metals. The predominant element is usually calcium bicarbonate.
Alluvium: deposit of solid material carried and deposited by streams (such as pebbles, gravel, sand, silt). Depending on the places where it is deposited it may be called river, lake, or sea alluvium.
Ambience (or environment): all organic or inorganic factors surrounding an individual or a group. It comprises all individuals of the same species and other species that surround them as well as the physical factors of the habitat. As a result, we often differentiate between the organic or biotic environment and the inorganic or physical environment.
Amendment: all measures adopted in fish farming, as in agriculture, designed to increase productivity by soil maintenance and good management.
Amphibious: capable of living in air and in water (e.g., amphibians).
Amplitude: the greatest difference between the highest and lowest values of an element that is subject to variations (temperature, electric current).
Anadromous: refers to migratory fish that grow in sea water and migrate to fresh water for spawning. *Cf.* potamodromous, *ant.* catadromous (thalassic).
Anthropic: refers to factors linked with human activity that have considerable influence on the distribution of living creatures.
Assessment: in fish biology, an estimate made by the manager of the location of a fishery and, especially, its over- or underutilization.
Association: association of fish normally found in piscicultural zones along with the characteristic species of that zone.
Astaciculture: crayfish breeding (*Astacus:* crayfish, a freshwater crustacean).
Atavism: reappearance of some characteristics of a distant ancestor that were not manifest in intermediate generations. *Alt.* reversion.

Backwater: stagnant water, shallow and limited in extent, in periodic communication (during floods) or permanent communication with a water course.
Bacteriophage: that which destroys bacteria.
Bait: a lure that is attached to the hook.
Bank: the side of a reservoir or water course that is generally above the water level but may be submerged temporarily during high-water periods.
Basin: a reservoir of variable dimensions with banks of masonry or concrete.
Bed: part of a valley submerged by a running stream, which runs in it without overflowing.
Beine: a French term for a low-gradient extension of a sandy bank under the surface of a lake, also called a "white bed". It may be formed by erosion or by deposits of alluvium. In the latter case it is of finer material.
Berm: a path along an embankment or at the side of a canal or a ditch.
Biocoenosis: all living creatures that, in specified ecological conditions, constitute by the selection of species and the number of individuals a community of organisms that tolerate each other, are complementary, and perpetuate themselves.

The term always refers to a living population of an ecologically homogeneous and fairly extensive biotype (pond or marsh) that is self-sufficient and not to the population of a restricted and dependant medium.
Biocoenotics (or synecology): analysis of the relationships between individuals belonging to different species in a group and their medium.
Biogenic capacity: expression of the nutritive value of water for fish. It is indicated by the symbol B, of which the value extends from I (very poor water) to X (extremely rich water). It is estimated by determining the positive factors (e.g., piscicultural fauna, nutritive fauna, flora, nature of the bed, the banks, temperature, chemical characteristics) and the negative factors (e.g., clearing, pollution, dams) on which the eventual productivity of the particular water depends. This provides quantitative data and should not be mistaken for the *biotic index,* which is exclusively qualitative.
Biological cover: all animal and plant organisms, dead or alive, covering the substratum. It is observed in the form of a coloured scum or soft coating on submerged stones and debris.
Biomass: quantitative estimate of living material existing in an aquatic ecosystem per unit of volume or area and expressed in units of mass (living material of benthos or plankton).
Biotope: habitat of a biomass (e.g., a spring, a large rock in a torrent, a submerged tree stump).
Bluff: a bank that descends steeply into a river.
BOD (biochemical oxygen demand): expression of the amount of oxygen needed for the destruction or degradation of organic matter in a body of water with the help of microorganisms developing in the medium in given conditions.
Borehole: a deep borewell of small diameter for a hydrological reconnaissance or for looking for water or piping it from a water table.
Bolting (cloth): cloth with a fine, regular, standardized mesh used for sifting flour to a given degree of fineness.
Brackishwater farming: fish breeding in brackish water.
Breakers: violent return of waves when they break against an obstacle.
Brook: a small stream with a fairly high gradient and a width of less than 1 m (channel).
Bypass: a conduit providing a detour.
Carcinology: study of crustaceans.
Cast: to put or throw into water. We cast a line or an anchor.
Catadromous: refers to a migratory species that grows in fresh water and migrates to reproduce in the sea (e.g., eel).
Catharobic (water): very clean water.
Clearing of weeds: removal of plants in water.
Climax: in water, as happens generally in nature, all normal, complete, successive changes in species occur in three stages: a period of colonization of a habitat by "pioneers", a period

of development of the ecosystem and the community within it, where there is a successive predomination of species, and finally a period of relative equilibrium or climax, characterized by the existence of species capable of reproduction and able to thrive indefinitely in the same ecosystem as long as it is not subjected to considerable transformations.

COD (chemical oxygen demand): expression of the amount of oxygen necessary for the oxidation of industrial waters containing reducing elements (e.g., sulphides, ferrous salts, cyanides, higher phenols).

Cofferdam: a temporary structure forming a drained site protected against any inflow of water. It may be a simple dyke of earth or rows of piles or sheeting piles with a filling of earth between two walls to prevent the entry of water.

Cold branding: marking with a cold burn.

Community: all the various animal and plant populations of a particular habitat.

Competition: in ecology, the interaction between two or several organisms (e.g., fish) whose requirements for space, food, shelter, etc. are identical and which, as a result, have to compete for most of their requirements.

Competition in fishing: various line fishing competitions for prizes or otherwise where there is a classification based on weight, or occasionally the number, of fish caught in a given time.

Confluence: a junction point of two water courses.

Convection current: in water, a current caused by differences in density, temperature, etc.

Cosmopolitan: a species adapted to certain conditions of a medium (biotope) that exist over an entire continent or even everywhere on earth (*ant.* endemic, *syn.* ubiquitous).

Creno-: prefix relating to a spring.

Crenophilous: thriving in or near a spring.

Dam berm: a space filled with fascines or gabions filled with stones to protect the foundations of a hydraulic structure.

Dangling: manner of fishing in which a bait or lure at the end of a line with a fairly heavy weight is constantly moved or dangled to attract fish.

Deficiency: insufficiency or lack of some factors essential for nutrition of the tissues, in food, e.g., vitamins, nitrogen.

Degenerate: organism that has degenerated because of a hybridization of an undesirable type.

Dejection cone: alluvium deposited, generally in the shape of a wide cone, in a main valley by the current of a stream (generally a torrent).

Delta: a region of alluvial deposits at the mouth of a water course that divides into two or more branches.

Demineralization: elimination of dissolved mineral matter mainly by consumption in exchanges.

Detergents (or detergent products): a cleansing material in which there are surface-active chemical preparations that like soap are capable of emulsifying dirt, a visible manifestation of pollution by detergents.

Detritivorous: feeding on fragmented particulate decomposed organic debris or detritus.

Devon: a rotary metallic lure with an ovoid body and two propellor-shaped blades.

Discharge: volume of water flowing in a river or a water channel in a unit of time (expressed in l/s, m 3 /s, l/min., m 3 /min.).

Downstream: along with the current.

Downstream migration: movement of river fish to the sea (migrating eels: eels caught while moving to the sea, where they intend to reproduce).

Dragnet: a triangular fishing net that is drawn along regular and shallow bottoms.

Drained: refers to a pond when it has been emptied.

Draining: in fish breeding all operations to empty out a body of water. In hydraulics, the action to completely drain hydraulic equipment or a work. All the equipment required to ensure this draining.

Dwarfism: occasional when it is due to an excessive number of fish with regard to the possibilities of the medium in terms of vital space and food (for example in the perch family); racial when due to an inability to grow as a result of a genetic mutation.

Dyke: a raised earth structure designed to contain a water course or a body of water within specific limits.

Dystrophic (water): fresh water rich in humic substances (e.g., dystrophic lake).

Ecological assessment (of a water course or a water body): a rapid investigation by fishing (electric or otherwise) with a view to identifying its physiological state, finding out the possibilities of improving its piscicultural or halieutic potential, and determining the studies to be carried out to achieve this objective.

Ecotone: a transition zone where conditions in a medium are intermediate between those of two adjacent communities or biocoenoses.

Ecotype: a variety associated with particular conditions of a medium but not of a given region. An ecotype is the result in a heterogeneous population of a selection based on predominant ecological factors.

Edaphic: refers to factors associated with the nature of soil that have considerable effect on the distribution of living creatures.

Eel pot: a trap of cane or willow used to catch eels. The diameter of the opening should not be more than 4 cm and the space between the bars should be less than 10 mm. Where the mesh is hexagonal, a quarter of the perimeter of each mesh should not be less than 10 mm.

Effluent: generally, liquid flowing out from an installation that treats waste water; also discharge of industrial or urban waste material into environment; outflow from a lake or river.

Egg-bearing: refers to an egg-bearing female. Mainly used to describe crustaceans (egg-bearing shrimp).

Elver: young eel at a stage when it has reached a cylindrical form at the time it enters fresh water.

Embryonated: in fish farming, refers to an egg in which the eyes of the embryo are visible.

Endemic: refers to an organism or species particular to a specific region.

Endobenthic: refers to animals that live buried in the substratum.

Endogenous: descriptive of an element produced in a particular medium (e.g., endogenous food). Also, arising or originating from within the organism or system. *Ant.* exogenous.

Epi-, meta-, hypolimnion: the aquatic layers located, respectively, during the summer stagnation of lakes, above, at the level, and below the layer of the thermocline.

Epiphytes: plant or animal organisms living on other plants without extracting nutritive substances from them, which distinguishes them from parasites.

Epizootic: a contagious disease affecting a large number of animals, such as fish.

Esociculture: pike breeding (*Esox:* pike).

Estuary: region at the mouth of a water course in a lake or of a river in the sea; in the latter case the water is brackish.

Ethology: the science dealing with behaviour and habits of an individual, community, or population; study of animal behaviour.

Etiology: the branch of medicine that investigates the causes of diseases.

Euryhaline: that which exists equally well in both salt and fresh water.

Eutrophic: refers to water rich in nutritive substances.

Exogenous: refers to an element produced outside a particular medium (e.g., exogenous food). *Ant.* endogenous.

Exuviae: rejected, cast-off cuticles after ecdysis in crustaceans (e.g., crayfish, shrimp); cast-off skins, shells, etc. of animals.

Factor analysis: statistical method designed to determine the common factors in a group of variables that have strong correlations between them.

Fertilization: an operation carried out to enrich an aquatic medium with fertilizer.

Fingerling: a small fish about the length of a finger; a young fish up to the end of the first year.

Fish ladder (or leap): an arrangement that helps migratory fish to cross natural or artificial obstacles.

Fish lift: an arrangement formed of a tank or cage raised mechanically from a lower to a higher level enabling fish to cross over a dam.

Fish preserve: a water body in which live fish are kept. *By extension,* a case submerged in water enabling fish to be kept alive.

Fish tank: a tank or small pond in which fish caught from a major pond are kept alive before despatch.

Fissure: an abnormally created outlet or one formed by water in a dyke or dam.

Flocculation: formation of aggregates by a combination of fine particles, due to a mechanical, chemical, or mechano-chemical process

Flushing: an operation in which a release valve is opened in a dam or reservoir in order to flush out sand, gravel, and silt deposits at the bottom by the rush of water.

Gametogenesis: formation of gametes, from spermatocytes in males (spermatogenesis), from oocytes in females (oogenesis). An egg is the result of the union of gametes – an ovum and a sperm. Gametogenesis includes an important phenomenon, meiosis.

Geotextile: a synthetic, soft industrial textile used in earthworks to prevent looseness in soil, used in foundation and sealing techniques.

Gravel bed: a place where a water course flows on a bed of gravel, and where it is shallow.

Gravel pit: an artificial water body formed as a result of extraction of gravel, pebbles, etc., to be used as ballast on railway lines. *By extension,* any quarry filled with water.

Gregarious: living in colonies.

Grilse: a two- to three-year-old salmon on its first return from the sea to fresh water.

Habitat: a place in which, or on which, a community, species, or individual lives. This normally includes all its physical components, such as geographical location, temperature, winds, or water currents, but not biological components that are based on either communities or the organic environment. This definition is, obviously, not applicable to parasitic organisms, which have practically only one organic environment that forms their habitat, in the absence of any inorganic support.

Halieutic: relative to line fishing.

Halo-: prefix indicating a relationship with salt water.

Halocrene: refers to a source from which water flows out in thin streams from many places, located in humid or marshy terrain.

Hardness: indicates the content of calcium or magnesium salts. Measurement of hardness is based on the fact that water will not produce a lather with a soap unless calcium or magnesium suds have been precipitated. Hardness is expressed in hydrotimetric degrees.

Herringbone work: an arrangement constructed at a particular angle against a bank of a water course to fix the form of its bed.

Heterotrophic: refers to organisms that obtain nourishment from external organic substances only. *Ant.* autotrophic.

Homing: in ecology, the regular return of migratory species to the same places.

Homothermal: refers to living creatures whose average temperature is constant and independent of that in the surrounding medium (e.g., mammals). *Ant.* poikilothermal (heterothermal).

Hybridization: a crossing of two varieties, subspecies, or species (true hybridization). Crossings between two different species are generally sterile except, for example, among cyprinids.

Hydrobiology: etymologically, a knowledge of life in aquatic habitats.

Hydrographic: relative to all running or static waters in a region.

Hydrographic basin: an area in which inflows empty into the same water course, following the natural gradient, through streams, torrents, etc., till the main river or the outlet.

Hydrology: the science dealing with waters, their distribution on the surface and underground, their characteristics, and their properties.

Ichthyology: the branch of zoology dealing with fish.
Impluvium: a catchment basin that receives the rainfall (catchment area of a water course).
In vitro: in an artificial medium, in a laboratory.
In vivo: on or in a living organism.
Incubation: period of development of a fish egg, from fertilization till it is hatched.
Incubator: an apparatus used in fisheries in which eggs and fry are able to develop from fertilization till resorption of the yolk sac.
Interspecific: between two or more distinct species.
Intertidal (or intercotidal): descriptive of the fauna and flora that develop in a zone between the extreme limits of the tides.
Intraspecific: between individuals or populations of the same species.
Jahrling: A German term that refers to a one-year-old alevin (yearling).
Kainite: a double salt of natural hydrated magnesium sulphate and potassium chloride.
Kelt: a salmon that has spawned but has not yet lost its display coloration and is returning to the sea.
Lagoon: a small lake in a coral reef connected with the sea. Also, a coastal pond that is in communication with the sea.
Lake: natural or artificial large water surface with an average depth of more than 5 m and a particular hydrological entity. (The Balaton lake is called such only because of its size and its hydrobiological entity.)
Lateral wall: in a hydraulic system, a wall that blocks the side of a channel or a lock. A wall strengthening a bank, a dyke on all sides of a drainage system.
Lentic (or lenitic): characteristic of waters that are still, stagnant, or slow-flowing. *Ant.* lotic.
Leptocephalus: a flat larva of the eel that lives in the sea before its metamorphosis to an elver.
Lethal: in the toxicology of fish, synonymous with mortal.
Limnimetric scale: graduated levels enabling direct estimation of the level of water in a reservoir or a water course. It is generally fixed to the wall of a structure (pier of a bridge, for example).
Limnology: the science that deals with all matters concerning lakes, ponds and other standing waters (physical or biological). *By extension*, relative to running and stagnant inland waters.
Line: a fishing implement formed of a rod, a butt, and a hook. It may or may not have a float and a weight. *Mistakenly*, a line for a fishing rod. Line fishing generally implies modes of fishing with a line other than casting. There is, nevertheless, a difference between line fishing from a selected spot with or without a bait, called *sedentary* fishing, and ground bait fishing with a line where the hook and the weight rest at the bottom of the water as opposed to using a line and float.
Live fish bait: small fish intended as food for carnivorous fish.
Lotic: pertaining to running, troubled water habitats. *Ant.* lentic.
Low-water level: the lowest flow rate of a water course. *By extension*, the average low-water level over several years and *mistakenly* the period of low-water level.
Lucifugous: that which shuns and avoids light (lucifugous fish). *Alt.* photophobic.
Macro-: prefix indicating relative size, large or at least visible to the naked eye.
Major river: a large water course that ends in the sea. If it ends in an inland sea it is said to be *continental*. If it is a small river it is called *coastal* (e.g., coastal rivers of the English Channel).
Malacology: branch of zoology that deals with the study of molluscs.
Malacophagous: feeding on molluscs.
Management: all steps adopted to regulate the use of a water course or reservoir so as to obtain the best yield for the particular method adopted and implemented.
Marking: making marks on fish to study their growth and movements.
Marshland: a stagnant area of water with very little depth and no flow where it is impossible to move either on foot or in a boat because of the large amount of silt and vertical aquatic vegetation.

Meanders: sinuosities in a water course.

Meso-: prefix indicating the average extent of a characteristic or property.

Mesology: the branch of biology that deals with the study of interrelationships between organisms and their surroundings.

Mesosaprobic (water): aquatic habitat with an average amount of pollution, with a small amount of oxygen and substantial organic decomposition. Beta-mesosaprobic is less polluted than alpha-mesosaprobic.

Metabolism: all transformations a living organism is subjected to by substances of which it is formed: synthetic reactions (anabolism) and degradative biochemical reactions that release energy (catabolism).

Micro-: prefix indicative of small size, generally invisible to the naked eye.

Microclimate: all conditions of temperature, humidity, and wind in a homogeneous space of limited area (immediate surroundings or habitat) on a soil surface.

Migration: a long and periodic or seasonal movement.

Milt: fish sperm. *By extension*, testes of fish.

Monk: a hydraulic work located at the deepest part of a pond that enables regulation of the water level, evacuating the excess from the bottom or the surface, preventing an escape of fish, and thereby emptying the pond when it is to be drained.

Moving downstream: refers to a fish when it moves down a water course.

MS 222: a logotype of a tranquilizer for cold-blooded animals.

Nekton: refers to aquatic fauna of which the elements swim actively and may migrate over long distances. Nekton is often compared to plankton and, with tripton and neuston together, is called seston.

Neuston: all organisms that live on the surface film of waters.

Niche: function of a species or a population in the medium to which it belongs especially in relation to its food as well as to predators of which it is afraid. While a habitat is for all purposes the "address" of a group of individuals, their niche, or *nesting area*, indicates the "profession" of these individuals in their area of residence (VIBERT).

Nursery: an establishment where larvae or fry with vesicles are looked after, ensuring their "weaning" in conditions of survival better than the usual ones due to the progressive distribution of elaborated foods.

Nutritional quotient: the number of kilograms of food needed to produce 1 kg of fish.

Ohm: unit of electrical resistance. An ohm-centimetre (Ω-cm) is the resistance of a cylinder 1 cm in length and with a section of 1 sq cm.

Oligo-: prefix indicating a low value.

Oligosaprobic (water): aquatic habitat with a relative abundance of oxygen, low levels of dissolved organic matter, and a low level of organic decomposition.

Orography: layout of terrestrial relief.

Outlet: exit point of a water body, canal, or drain.

Outlet channel: a water course or a canal through which the overflow of a lake or a pond is evacuated.

Palustrine: palustrine plants form the vertical aquatic vegetation (marshy habitats).

Parameter: a variable factor.

Parr (or smolt): a small salmon before it goes for the first time to the sea.

Peat bog: bog in which there is a partial decomposition of plant material leading to the formation of peat. The water in it is extremely acid and poor in nutritive elements (low and high peat bogs). The development of stagnant waters progresses from lake to pond to marsh to peat bog.

Pedology: study of the structure, formation, changes, and properties of soil.

Pelagic: living in deep waters at middle or surface levels (pelagic fish).

Perennial: constant, permanent.

Periphyton: all organisms living on submerged objects, mainly higher aquatic plants.

Pesticides: synthetic chemical products used in agriculture especially against animals, insects, harmful lower fungi, and mildew.

Photoperiod: light phase of a light-dark cycle.

Photosynthesis: production by green plants (higher or lower, for example, algae) of organic substances (carbohydrates) from carbon dioxide and water with the help of chlorophyll pigments using light energy.

Phreatic table: underground table of well water. *By extension*, the somewhat superficial water table that feeds springs.

Phyto-: prefix indicating a relationship with plants.

Piezometer: a piezometric pipe introduced into the soil to the level of the water table and open at both ends, used to measure the water pressure in an aquifer.

Pile plank: an element of a caisson made of sheet metal with grooves on both sides and a device enabling it to be joined with another so as to form a continuous space.

Piscicultural inventory: investigation in an aquatic medium having recourse to methods of calculation.

Plankton: all microscopic organisms living and floating in water, passively or otherwise, without, however, being able to effectively resist the current. We refer to plant plankton as phytoplankton and animal plankton as zooplankton.

Poikilothermal: pertains to a living organism whose temperature varies with that of the surrounding medium (e.g., fish). *Ant.* homothermal.

Poly-: prefix indicating a large quantity.

Polysaprobic (water): putrid water with no oxygen.

Pond: an enclosed body of water, smaller than a lake and less than 5 m deep, which can be colonized all over by littoral flora (FOREL).

Pool: stagnant water of shallow depth (less than 80 cm) and limited surface likely to dry up periodically, especially in summer. In a river, the deep portion of a water course (as opposed to a sill).

Population: a collection of individuals of one or several species forming a whole in a given environment.

Potamo-: prefix indicating a relationship with rivers and streams.

Predator: an organism (e.g., fish) that feeds on generally smaller individuals of another species.

Present stock: the number of organisms existing on a particular surface or in a volume calculated at the time of investigation.

Profile (of a river): a graph showing the height of the bed on the ordinate and the distance from the source on the abscissa.

Rafting: a sport in which rafts are used to move downstream in a fast-flowing water course.

Reach: a diversion canal that leads water to the wheel of a mill. An area between two locks. *By extension*, a term used in fish farming: portion of a stream, minor river, or major river with a characteristic feature. *Syn.* section.

Recruit: in fish biology, a young fish that has passed the early stage, where there is a very high rate of mortality, and reached a stage where the mortality is relatively stable.

Regime (of a water course): this is based on the characteristics of the flow, the variations in discharge in relation to time, and the periodicity of high- and low-water conditions (e.g., the *nival regime* of a fast-flowing stream).

Reinforcement: protection of a bank using piles that support planks or timber behind which material is packed.

Release: a controlled or forced evacuation of water in a reservoir dam. The volume of water that is "released".

Relic: a species (formerly widespread) whose existence can be explained only by the prevalence of natural conditions different from existing ones in the area under consideration; *Alt.* relict.

Resilience: reproductive capacity of an animal species, independent of the environment (hostile or favourable).

Restocking: in fish biology, the action of replacing the fish population in an ecosystem that should naturally contain it and from which it has been lost (ordinary, maintenance, extraordinary, or over-restocking).

Resurgence: a surface outlet of an underground stream in widely fissured terrain.

Rheo-: prefix meaning flowing current (*rheophilous* species: a species living in a stream, *rheocrene*: a spring in which the water runs out as soon it emerges from the ground).

River: a water course that is a tributary of a larger river with a width of 5–100 m.

Riverine: covers what is located in the humid zone on the banks of a river.

Rock fauna: fauna that lives in water that seeps on the surface of vertical or steep rocks.

Run: a clear path between two areas of water plants.

Salinity: indicates the weight of all salts in solution in water.

Salmon breeding: breeding of salmonids. *By restriction*, breeding of salmon.

Saltiness: the quantity of salt (mainly sodium chloride) contained in sea water or brackish water. Should not be confused with salinity.

Saprobics (system of —): method of biological analysis of waters polluted by decaying organic matter, enabling an assessment of its purity or pollution.

SBV: abbreviation of the German term *Sauer Bindungs Vermogen* with reference to the content of alkaline reserves or the alkalinity of waters. Multiplying this by 5 we obtain the hardness, expressed in French degrees.

Scalimetry: study of scales to determine the age and growth of fish.

Sealing: (1) preventing the leak of a liquid flow, (2) sealing, (3) causing to dry.

Seiche: a variation in level recorded at certain points in a lake due to local variations of atmospheric pressure.

Selenitic: refers to water with a content of calcium sulphate.

Self-purification (water): a biochemical or chemical process in which water polluted by organic substances recovers its original state of purity without any external intervention.

Shellfish breeding: breeding of shellfish, especially mussels.

Shutdown: a period in which a channelized water course or a canal is partly emptied.

Sill: a portion of a water course over which the water flows rapidly and where there is no depth.

Silt: deposit formed by very fine particles (diameter 0.02–2 mm) on riverine areas exposed by a fall in water level. The sediment is rich in water and organic matter.

Silting: invasion of a water body and uplift of the bed by deposits. These may be of mineral or plant origin. In the latter case the plants may be directly involved in the silting because of their litter or indirectly by acting as a strainer under which mineral particles are deposited.

Sink hole: a cavern or funnel-shaped opening in soil that is normally calcareous through which surface water enters the underground circulation network.

Spawn: action of spawning. Period of reproduction in fish and amphibians. Eggs laid by fish. *By extension*, fry emerging from eggs.

Spawner: a mature fish or even a fish intended for spawning purposes.

Spawning area: place where fish lay their eggs.

Species: a collection of individuals with similar characteristics transmissible by heredity.

Sperm-bearing: capable of ejaculating or emitting sperm.

Spermatogenesis: *See* gametogenesis.

Square dipping net: a square net held in place by four arms in an X shape. It is submerged at the bottom and raised suddenly to trap fish moving above it. To be effective the net should not be slack. In water courses the authorized dimensions should not be more than 5 m on each side and that of the mesh should not be less than 50 mm.

Steno-: prefix meaning narrow, indicative of a lack of resistance of certain organisms to a particular change, however small, in their surroundings (*stenothermal*, that which cannot accept a notable temperature variation).
Stocking quantum: in fish farming, a value indicating the quantity of fish (per hectare) to be introduced in a pond.
Stone-living: living on stones.
Storage (storage tanks): tanks in which breeder fish are kept before they are made to spawn.
Strand (or foreshore): part of a shore between the highest and lowest levels of the sea.
Stream: a small water course 1–5 m wide.
Stress: all non-specific reactions of an organism that are triggered by a harmful agent called an "agent of stress".
Subspecies (race): a subdivision of an animal species with hereditary characteristics, represented by a certain number of individuals. In the case of plants we use the term "variety"
Summerlings: young fish, one summer old.
Supplementing: in zootechnology, providing an additional balanced food ration with a supplementary element such as vitamins or medicine.
Surfacing: said of a fish that rises to the surface because of some discomfort.
Swallowing the hook: swallowing the bait, as applied to fish.
Swamp: stagnant, shallow water covered with vertical aquatic plants.
Swarm: a dense flight during some spring evenings of adult ephemeropterans (mayflies).
Symbiosis: the living together of two or more organisms to their mutual advantage.
Syndrome: all symptoms that characterize an illness.
Tactism: a directional reaction due to the effect of various factors (e.g., light, current).
Taxis: directed locomotor reactions of moving animals induced by external physiochemical agents (e.g., light, weight, heat).
Taxonomy: science of the laws of describing, naming, and classifying organized living creatures.
Temperature regulation: automatic regulation of the internal temperature of organisms that have a constant temperature, or are homeothermal. Fish have no temperature regulation system.
Territoriality: the somewhat sedentary nature of a species.
Thalweg: all the lowest points in a valley.
Thermocline: during the summer warming of water in lakes, the upper layers are heated more than the lower ones, which remain cold. The temperature variation is not regular and changes abruptly at the level of a thinner intermediate layer (of a few metres) known as the layer where there is a sudden increase or the thermocline. Here, there is a reduction in temperature of about 1°C per metre.
Thiosaprobic (water): polluted aquatic habitat containing sulphides and releasing H_2S.
Tide level: variation in the level of a barrier lake.
Tip: the terminal portion of a fishing rod.
Tolerance: applies to an organism that can without much inconvenience tolerate new conditions or a new lifestyle (tolerance of some fish to a certain amount of pollution in water); also refers to a reduction in specific reaction to a stimulus or a toxic substance ("mithridatization").
Torrent: a fast-flowing stream with a flow that is often irregular.
Torrent-living: living in a torrent.
Tracer element: a substance, material, or product that when introduced into water or an organism in movement enables us to study its movement or development. We use dyes (fluorescent) or radioactive elements with a somewhat long half-life.
Tributary: a water course that enters another larger water course.
Tripton: all wastes of endogenous or exogenous origin suspended in water or floating on its surface.
Trophic levels: the various stages in the food chain within an aquatic ecosystem.

Trophogenic layer: upper aquatic illuminated layer (epilimnion) where, because of the energy of light, the photosynthesis of phytoplankton, and the littoral flora, there is an elaboration of organic substances. *Ant.* tropholytic layer.

Tropism: a directional reaction of growing plant organs due to the influence of various factors such as light or current.

Ubiquitous: describes an animal or plant species that is found everywhere. *Syn.* cosmopolitan, *ant.* stenotopic.

Upstream: upper region of a water course with respect to a given point. *Ant.* downstream. *Used as adjective*, against the current (to fish upstream).

Very young pike: a pike fry that has just absorbed its vitellin vesicle (swimming fry).

Vitellogenesis: formation of a yolk, a collection of nutritive material in a fertilized egg. Its assimilation ensures the build-up of young embryonic structures.

Wader: a waterproof trouser worn for fishing.

Wading: fishing after entering the water.

Wake: a succession of waves against the banks of a water course produced by the movement of a boat.

Water flowers: a proliferation of unicellular algae in the upper layer of stagnant water that gives it a particular colour.

Water meadow: a natural or artificial arm of a river remaining mainly in communication with it in a downstream direction. These arms of still water are often spawning zones for fish.

Water-meadow farming: emptying of a pond followed by agriculture.

Whitefish: all fish of the cyprinid family (e.g., carp, roach, chub).

Yield: in fish breeding, a percentage indicating the number or weight of fish harvested as compared with the number or weight introduced (net yield).

Yolk sac (vitellin vesicle): a nutritive reserve vesicle under the abdomen of a fry when it is hatched and from which it draws its food during the first few days of its life.

Young pike: a pike that is 4–6 weeks old (fingerling).

Zonation: a theory (LEGER-HUET) that, in fish breeding, divides running water courses into trout, char, barbel, bream, and smelt zones, depending on the gradient; stagnant waters are divided into coastal, deep, abyssal, and pelagic zones, with a certain number of subdivisions in each of these.

Zoug bottles: glass containers used for incubating eggs of pike or freshwater herrings.

3 REFERENCES

ABSI, CABRIDENC AND LUNDAHL	1975	"Evaluation des nuisances résultant des polluants au moyen d'un test Daphnie." *Trib. C.E.B.E.D.O.C.* 28, 381–382.
ALIKUNHI (K.H.)	1966	"Synopsis of biological data on common carp *Cyprinus carpio* (Linnaeus) 1758." *Asia and the Far East F.A.O. Fisheries synopsis* 31.1.
ALLEE W.C.	1931	*Animal Aggregations*, Chicago University Press.
ALZINGRE M.	1975	"Etude de l'aménagement piscicole et halieutique du lac du Val Joly." *Mém. E.N.I.T.E.F., C.S.P.*, Compiègne.
AMBUHL H.	1959	"Die Bedeutung der Strömung als ökologischer Faktor." *Schweiz Z. Hydrol.* 21, 133–264.
AMBUHL H.	1962	"Die Besonderkeiten der Wasserströmung in physikalischer, chemischer und biologischer Hinsicht." *Schweiz Z. Hydrol.* 24, 367–381.
AMOROS C.	1988	"Les concepts d'hydrosystème et de secteur fonctionnel dans l'analyse des systèmes fluviaux à l'échelle des écocomplexes." *Bull. Ecol.*, 19–4: 531–546.
ARRIGNON J.	1966	"Action d'une population de brochets sur le cheptel trutticole hébergé par les eaux de 1re catégorie." *Bull. E.N.S.A.N.* VIII, I, Nancy.
ARRIGNON J.	1968	"Comportement de l'espèce *Salmo trutta fario* dans le bassin de la Seine." *Bull. Franç. Pisc.* No. 227–228–229. Paris.
ARRIGNON J.	1968	"Application de l'électricité aux barrages et écrans orienteurs." *Bull. franç. Pisc.* No. 72. II. Paris.
ARRIGNON J.	1970	"Les écrans et les barrières électriques." *Bull. franç. Pisc.* No. 239. Paris.
ARRIGNON J.	1971	"Introduction à l'étude écologique d'un cours d'eau." *R.F.F. XXIII.* 5. Nancy.
ARRIGNON J.	1972 (a)	"Station expérimentale d'élevage du brochet du Vivier du Grès-Oise." *Bull. franç. Pisc.* No. 246. Paris.
ARRIGNON J.	1972 (b)	"Zonation piscicole de quelques cours d'eau normands." *Verh. Internat. Verein. Limnol.* 18, 1135–1146. Stuttgart.
ARRIGNON J.	1978	"Calcul pratique de la section d'un moine de vidange." *Bull. Liais. C.S.P.* No. 1–2/78, 12–14.
ARRIGNON J.	1986	"L'aquaculture en Afrique," *in* Barnabé (TEC. & DOC.) *Aquaculture*, 11–6, 1018–1058.
ARRIGNON J.	1987	"Agro-écologie des zones arides et sub-humides." Maisonneuve et Larose, Paris, 283 p.

ARRIGNON J.	1990 (a)	"Aménagement d'un parcours de pêche." *Plaisirs de la pêche*, Paris, 6, 11–15.
ARRIGNON J.	1990 (b)	*L'écrevisse et son élevage.*—Lavoisier Tec. & Doc., Paris, 208 p.
ARRIGNON J.	1993	"Les revenus reliés à la pêche sportive en France," *in Le développement du saumon atlantique au Québec – Salmo salar*, Ed. Shoner and Asselin, 181-188.
ARRIGNON J. AND DEBRUILLE M.	1970	"Commentaires sur la valeur piscicole du canal de Roubaix." *Bull. franç. Pisc.* No. 239. Paris.
ARRIGNON J. AND JOANNIS G.	1972	*Carte piscicole de l'Oise.* Edit. C.S.P. Paris.
ARRIGNON J. AND JOSSART S.	1973	"Un modèle de grille défeuilleuse battante." *Bull. franç. Pisc.* No. 251. Boves.
ARRIGNON J. *et al.*	1975	*"La sauvegarde des intérêts piscicoles au cours des travaux d'aménagement des cours d'eau." La Houille Blanche.* No. 2/3. Grenoble.
ARRIGNON AND JUSTINE	1975	"Le rateau faucardeur relevable." *Bull. franç. Pisc.* Boves.
ARRIGNON J. *et al.*	1990 (a)	"Freshwater fish species recently adopted for cultivation in Europe"—*in Aquaculture Europe 89-Business Joins Science*, N. De Pauw and R. Billard (Eds). E.A.S. B-Bredene, Special publication No. 12, 199–208.
ARRIGNON J. *et al.*	1990 (b)	*L'écrevisse Rouge des Marais.* Maisonneuve et Larose, Paris, 87 p.
ASHWORTH S.T. AND BLANC G.	1997	"*Anguillicola crassus*, un colonisateur agressif récemment introduit dans les stocks européens d'anguilles." *Bull. Fr. Pêche Piscic.* (1997), 344/345, 335–342.
BACHELIER R.	1968	"Aménagements pour les poissons migrateurs." *B.T.I.*—*Minagri*, No. 228, 3/4. Paris.
BAGLINIERE J.-L. AND LE LOUARN H.	1987	"Caractéristiques scalimétriques des principales espèces de poissons d'eau douce de France." *Bull. Fr. Pêche Piscic.*, Paris, 306, 1–39.
BAMS A.B.	1973	"Evaluation of gravels incubators on first 'hatchery' generation Tsolum River Pink Salmon." 1970/72, Part 1—Evaluation at the fry stage. Part 2—Evaluation at the adult stage. Fish. Res. Bd. Can. Tech. Rep.
BARBE J.	1984	"Les végétaux aquatiques; données biologiques et écologiques; clés de détermination des macrophytes de France." *Bull. Fr. Pêche Piscic.* No. sp. 42 p.
BARBIER B.	1973	"Ètude d'un détecteur de pollutions utilisant les poissons dulçaquicoles." Thèse Biol. anim. Hydrobiol, Univ. Toulouse.
BARDACH J.E. *et al.*	1972	*Aquaculture.* Wiley Interscience, John Wiley & Sons, New York, p. 105.
BARIL D. AND GUENEAU P.	1986	"Radio-pistage de saumons adultes *(Salmo salar)* en Loire." *Bull. Fr. Pêche Piscic*, Paris, 302, 86–105.
BERNHARD C. AND LECLERCQ B.	1990	"Pour les fonds et les berges: les géotextiles." *Forêt, loisirs, équipements de plein air*, IDF, Paris 46–53.
BEUKEMA, *in* HUET 1970	1967	*Traité de pisciculture.* De Wingaert. Bruxelles.
BILLARD R.	1991	"Elevage des anguilles au Japon." *Aquarevue*, Bordeaux, 34, 19–22.

BILLARD R.	1975	"L'insémination artificielle de la truite." *Bull. franç. Pisc.* No. 256–257. Boves.
BILLARD R.	1996	*"Les systèmes de productions aquacoles."* *C.R. Acad. Agri. Fr,* 1996, 82(9), 7–16.
BILLARD R. AND MARCEL J.	1980	"Quelques techniques de production de poissons d'étangs." *La Pisc. Franç.,* Paris, 59, 9-16-41.
BILLARD R. *et al.*	1976	"L'insémination artificielle du brochet." *Bull. Fr. Piscic.,* Paris, 262, 30–34.
BLANC G.	1997	"L'introduction des agents pathogènes dans les écosystèmes aquatiques: aspects théoriques et réalités." *Bull. Fr. Pêche Piscic.* (1997), 344/345, 489–513.
BOET P. AND LE LOUARN H.	1985	"La croissance du poisson; techniques d'étude" *in Gestion Piscicole des Lacs et Retenues Artificielles.* Ed. D. Gerdeaux and R. Billard. INRA, Paris, pp. 125–142.
BOISNEAU P. *et al.*	1990	"Description d'une frayère et comportement de reproduction de la grande alose (*Alosa alosa*) dans le cours supérieur de la Loire." *Bull. Fr. Pêche Piscic.,* 316, 15–23.
BOURREAU P.	1975	"La pisciculture—salmoniculture." *La Pisc. Franç.,* No. 43. Paris.
BOVEE K.D.	1982	"A guide to stream habitat analysis using Instream Flow Incremental Methodology." Instream Flow Information Paper No. 12, FWS/OBS 82/86. Western Energy and Land Use Team, U.S. Fish and Wildlife Service, Fort Collins, Colorado, 248 p.
BREMOND R. AND VUICHARD R.	1973	"Paramètres de la qualité des eaux." S.P.E.P.E. *Doc. Franç.* Paris.
BRUNET R.	1971	"Problèmes sur la pisciculture du goujon." Coll. I.N.R.A., Biarritz.
BRY C.	1984	"Recherches sur la reproduction et l'élevage du brochet en petits étangs." *Bull. Liais. CSP,* Paris, 32, 7–15.
BURDIN G.	1967	"Propos sur les rigoles d'alevinage." *Bull. Off. C.S.P.* No. 67, Paris.
CARLE F.L. AND STRUB M.R.	1978	"A new method for estimating population size from removal data." *Biometrics,* 34, 621–630.
CHAMPIGNEULLE A.	1985	"Analyse bibliographique des problèmes de repeuplement en omble chevalier (*Salvelinus alpinus*), truite fario (*Salmo trutta*) et corégones (*Corgonus* sp.) dans les grands plans d'eau," *in Gestion Piscicole des Lacs et Retenues Artificielles* Ed. D. Gerdeaux and R. Billard—INRA, Paris, pp. 187–217.
CHAMPIGNEULLE A.	1990	"Pacage lacustre de salmonidés - 2: production de juvéniles en bassins avec alimentation sèche." *Aqua-Revue,* Bordeaux, 33, 35–41.
CHIMITS P.	1950	"Epandage d'engrais." *Bull. franç. Pisc.* No. 1, III. Paris.
CLOPPER AND PEARSON *in* VIBERT AND LAGLER 1961	1934	*Pêches Continentales.* Dunod, Paris.
COMPAIN L.	1968	"Les aménagements des rivières à saumons." *Penn Ar Bed,* No. 6. S.E.P.N.B. Brest.

CUINAT R. 1965 "Utilisation des formulaires condensés pour la présentation des diagnoses démographiques." *I.N.R.A. Hydrobio.*, Paris.

CUINAT R. 1968 "Repeuplements surdensitaires." *La Pisc. Franç.* No. 13. 1, Paris.

CUINAT R. 1971 "Ecologie et repeuplement des cours d'eau à truites." *Bull. franç. Pisc.*, No. 240-242-243, Paris.

CUINAT R. 1974 "*Les exigences des poissons dans nos eaux courantes.*" Conf. E.N.G.R.E.F., Paris.

CUINAT R. AND VIBERT R. 1963 "Diagnoses démographiques sur les populations de poissons dans les cours d'eau à truites." *C.G.P.M.-F.A.O.*, No. 21, Rome.

CURY PH. 1985 "Note sur la production biologique et l'exploitation d'une population de poissons," *in Gestion Piscicole des Lacs et Retenues Artificielles*" Ed. D. Gerdeaux and R. Billard, INRA, Paris, pp. 147–155.

DAJOZ R. 1971 *Précis d'écologie*, Dunod, Paris.

DARLEY R. 1975 "Interventions du Secrétaire général du C.S.P. au cours des Congrès régionaux." *Bull. Inf. C.S.P.*, No. 100, Paris.

DENIEL J. 1990 "La toxicité chronique des pesticides—Le test sur *Daphnia pulex* à 21 jours."—*5e Coll. int. relat. entre trait. phytosan. et reproduc. animaux.* Paris, 5 p.

DESCAMPS H. 1971 "La vie dans les cours d'eau." P.U.F. Paris.

DESCY J.-P 1980 "Utilisation des algues benthiques comme indicateurs biologiques de la qualité des eaux courantes" *in La Pollution des Eaux Continentales*, Gauthier-Villars, Paris, pp. 168–194.

DESSART H. 1990 "Utilisation de carbonate de soude sous forme de briquettes pour la neutralisation des lacs acides par traitement du sédiment." *SOLVAY*, Bruxelles, 12 p.

DOWNING R.A. 1973 "The effects of pumping groundwater for river regulation." Comm. Sémin. Reading on the chalkstreams, Reading.

DULAC B. *et al.* 1989 "Esociculture d'Assay (Indre-et-Loire): production à grande échelle de brochetons suivant la méthode dite de reproduction naturelle aménagée." *Bull. Liais. CSP*, Paris, 58, 13–15.

DUSSART B. 1954 "Température et mouvements des eaux dans les lacs." *Ann. Stat. centr. Hydrob.* Appl. V, Paris.

DUSSART B. 1966 *L'étude des Eaux Continentales.* Gauthier-Villars, Paris.

ECHAUBARD M. AND NEVEU A. 1975 "Perturbations qualitatives et quantitatives de la faune benthique d'un ruisseau à truites, la Couze Pavin-Puy-de-Dôme dues aux pollutions agricoles et urbaines." *Ann. Stat. Biol.* Besse-en-Chandesse, No. 9.

EHRLICH P.R. AND BIRCH C.C. 1967 "The balance of nature and population control." *Am. Nat.*, 101, 99–107.

EMPAIN A. *et al.* 1980 "Utilisation des bryophytes aquatiques et subaquatiques comme indicateurs biologiques de la qualité des eaux courantes." *in La Pollution des Eaux Continentales.* Gauthier-Villars, Paris, pp. 195–223.

FERLIN AND LEDOUX 1974 "L'élevage des salmonidés au Danemark et en Norvège." Rapp. Miss. C.T.G.R.E.F. Bordeaux.

FRAISSE L.	1990	"Essai de discrimination de deux populations de vandoise (*Leuciscus leuciscus*, L., 1758) par étude de la forme de leurs écailles: aspects méthodologiques." *Hydroécol. Appl.* Paris, 1/2, 135–149.
FRETEY	1975	*Guide des Reptiles et Batraciens de France.* Hatier, Paris.
GAGNIARD A.	1965	"Premiers résultats des déversements de craie." *T.O.S.*, No. 7, Paris.
GAUDIN P.	1989	" Méthodologie de repeuplement en ombre commun." *Rapport CSP* Paris, 4 p.
GERARD J.-P.	1974	"Notes techniques No. 1-2-3-4-5-6"., *Bull. franç. Pisc.* No. 254.
GERDEAUX D.	1987	"Revue des méthodes d'estimation de l'effectif d'une population par pêches successives avec retrait; programme d'estimation d'effectif par la méthode Carle et Strub." *Bull. Fr. Pêche Piscic.* (1987), 304, 13–21.
GIBAN J.	1960	"La lutte contre le rat musqué." *Bull. Inf. Off. C.S.P.*, No. 41, III, Paris.
GILLET C.	1989	"Réalisation de frayères artificielles flottantes pour les poissons lacustres." *Hydroécol. Appl.* 1/2, 145–193.
GOUBIER V.	1990 (a)	"Le phytoplancton et les problèmes de désoxygénation en étang de pisciculture." *ADA*, 21, 45 p.
GOUBIER V.	1990 (b)	"Reproduction et élevage larvaire de la perche (*Perca fluviatilis*)." *Aqua Revue*, Bordeaux, 31, 13–18.
GOUBIER V.	1994	Relation d'une table ronde dans *Aqua Revue*, 51, 1994, p. 9.
GUYARD R.	1966	"Eléments de génétique et d'embryologie piscicoles." Pers. comm.
GUYOMARD R.	1989	"Diversité génétique de la truite commune." *Bull. Fr. Pêche Piscic.* Paris, 314, 118–135.
HAFFNER P.	1997	"Bilan des introductions récentes d'amphibiens et de reptiles dans les milieux aquatiques continentaux de France métropolitaine." *Bull. Fr. Pêche Piscic.* (1997), 344/345, 155–163.
HELAND M. *et al.*	1995	"Mise en place des premiers comportements et utilisation de l'habitat après l'émergence chez les salmonidés d'eau courante. *Bull. Fr. Pêche Piscic.* (1995), 337/338/339, 191–197.
HOESTLANDT H.	1955	"L'extension de l'*Eriocheir sinensis* H.M.EDW (crustacé décapode) en France depuis 1937." 80th Congr. Soc. Sav. Paris.
HOESTLANDT H. AND BRUNET R.	1974	"Recherches sur la biologie et la pisciculture du goujon, *Gobio gobio* L. en France." *Ichtyologia*, 6(1), 59–67, Belgrade.
HOESTLANDT H. AND RUDELLE J.	1979	"Examen électronique densitométrique d'opercules de perches (*Perca fluviatilis* L.), en vue de la détermination de l'âge des Poissons." C.R. Acad. Sc. Paris, 288 (8/01/79) série D. 117.
HOESTLANDT H. AND DEVIENNE A.	1980	"Précision sur la relation entre la durée d'incubation et la température chez le Poisson téléostéen, *Perca fluviatilis* L." C.R. Acad. Sc. Paris, 290, série D. 1123–1125.
HOLLEBECQ M.G. *et al.*	1988	"Etudes expérimentales sur la reproduction artificielle du silure glane." *Aqua Revue*, Bordeaux, 17, 22–24.

HUBERT M.	1990	"Comment construire un plan d'eau." *Forêt, loisirs, équipements de plein air,* IDF, Paris, 7–38.
HUET M.	1949	"Aperçu des relations entre la pente et les populations piscicoles dans les eaux courantes." *Rev. suisse Hydrol.,* XI, 3/4.
HUET M.	1949	"Appréciation de la valeur piscicole des eaux douces." *Tx. Stat. Rech. Groenendaal* Tx. D, No. 10.
HUET M.	1962	"Influence du courant sur la distribution des poissons dans les eaux courantes." *Rev. suisse Hydrol.,* 24(2), 411–432.
HUET M.	1970	*Traité de Pisciculture.* De Wingaert, Bruxelles.
HUET M. *et al.*	1969	"Contribution à l'identification des zones piscicoles de quelques cours d'eau de Moravie (Tchécoslovaquie)." *Verh. Internat. Verein. Limnol.,* 17, 1103–1111, Stuttgart.
JATTEAU P.	1990	"Elevage du saumon du Danube." *Aqua Revue,* Bordeaux, 30, 15–18.
KAUSHIK SA. AND CHEVASSUS B.	1988	"Aquaculture continentale: état de nos connaissances et perspectives." *Aqua Revue,* Bordeaux, 20, 5–22.
KHALANSKI M.	1997	"Conséquences industrielles et écologiques de l'introduction de nouvelles espèces dans les hydrosystèmes continentaux: la moule zébrée et autres espèces invasives." *Bull. Fr. Pêche Piscic.* (1997), 344/345, 385–404.
DE KINKELIN P. *et al.*	1968	"Etude épizootiologique de la bucéphalose larvaire à *Bucephalus polymorphus* dans le peuplement piscicole du bassin de la Seine." *Rech. vétér.,* I, 77–98. I.N.R.A. Paris.
DE KINKELIN P. *et al.*	1973	"Pathologie des poissons d'eau douce." *Inform. tech. Serv. Vétér.,* No. 43–44. Paris.
DE KINKELIN P. *et al.*	1985	"Précis de pathologie des poissons." INRA-OIE. Paris, 348 p.
KRIEG Fr.	1989	"La génétique des caractères quantitatifs: méthodes d'analyse et possibilités d'utilisation." *Bull. Fr. Pêche Piscic.* Paris, 314, 109–114.
LACHAVANNE J.-B.	1985	"The influence of accelerated eutrophication on the macrophytes of Swiss lakes: abondance and distribution." *Verh. Internat. Verein. Limnol.* 22, 2950–2955.
LADLE M. AND WESTLAKE D.F.	1975	"Rivières crayeuses de l'Angleterre et activités humaines." *Comm. Sémin. Eaux continent. N.O. Europe.* I.E.B.S. Amiens.
LAMARE *et al.*	1985	"Elevage en cage flottante de truites fario juvéniles et lâcher *in situ* aux fins de repeuplement dans une retenue artificielle du Verdon " *in Gestion Piscicole des Lacs et Retenues Artificielles.* Ed. D. Gerdeaux and R. Billard, INRA, Paris, pp. 261–268.
LAMARQUE P.	1965	"Application de l'électricité à l'aménagement des eaux douces." I.N.R.A. Biarritz.

LAMARQUE P.	1968	"Electrophysiologie des poissons soumis à l'action d'un champ électrique." F.A.O.-C.E.C.P.I.-Sympos. Belgrade. I.N.R.A. Paris.
LAMBERT A.	1997	"Introduction de poissons dans les milieux aquatiques: quid de leurs parasites?" *Bull. Fr. Pêche Piscic.* (1997), 344/345, 323–333.
LARINIER M.	1978	"Les passes à poissons." La pêche illustrée - I/78-H.S. No. 550 bis p. 7–32.
LARINIER M. AND DARTIGUELONGUE J.	1989	"La circulation des poissons migrateurs: le transit à travers les turbines des installations hydroélectriques." *Bull. Fr. Pêche Piscis.*, 212–213, Paris.
LAURENT M. AND LAMARQUE P.	1975	"Utilisation de la méthode des captures successives (De Lury) pour l'évaluation des peuplements piscicoles." B.F.P. No. 259 IV - 1975, 66–77.
LAURENT P.	1973	"Astacus and Cambarus in France." *Freshwater crayfish. Lund.*, Suède.
LAURENT P.	1982	"Quelques données sur l'élevage de l'omble chevalier (*Salvelinus alpinus* L.)." *Bull. Liais. CSP.* Paris, 21, 10–13.
LEBRETON J.-C.	1974	*Dynamique Fluviale.* Eyrolles, Paris.
LEFEVRE M. *in* VIVIER P., 1972	1943	"La vie dans les eaux douces." Que sais-je? No. 243. P.U.F. Paris.
LEGER L.	1932	"La pratique des déversements d'alevins dans les cours d'eau." Conf. Lab. Pisc. Univ. Grenoble.
LEGER L.	1949	"Pratique rationnelle de la petite salmoniculture." Imp. Allier. Grenoble.
LELEK A.	1980	"Les poissons d'eau douce menacés d'Europe." *Sauvegarde de la nature* No. 18, 276 p. Cons. Europe.
LEYNAUD G. AND COSTES M.	1974	*"Etudes de la mise au point d'une méthode biologique de détermination de la qualité des eaux en milieu fluvial."* C.T.G.R.E.F.-D.Q.E.P.P. Paris.
LIM PUY *et al.*	1990	"Inventaire piscicole de la retenue des Saints-Peyres (Tarn) à l'occasion d'une vidange décennale." *Hydroécol. Appl.* Paris. 1/2, 5–19.
LITTLE (E.C.S.)	1979	"Handbook of utilization of aquatic plants." *F.A.O. Rome FIRI/T 187*, 176 p.
LUCCHETTA J.-C.	1985	"Etude de l'influence de gypse micronisé sur l'eau, fonds d'étangs et rivière." *Bull. Liais. CSP*, Paris, 40, 11–18.
LUCCHETTA J.-C. AND DEHEEGER J.-C.	1982	"Une nouvelle forme de grossissement d'alevins de brochet issus de pisciculture; le milieu naturel." *Bull. Liais. CSP.* Paris, 25, 14–17.
MAILLY M.	1967	"Orientation de la politique des réempoissonnements en brochets". *Bull. Union nat. Féd.* A.P.P. 4, Paris.
MAISSE G.	1986	"La reproduction artificielle de l'ombre commun." *La Pisc. Franç.* Paris, 83, 53–55.
MALAVOI J.R.	1989	"Typologie des faciès d'écoulement en unité morphodynamiques des cours d'eau à haute énergie." *Bull. Fr. Pêche Piscic.* Paris, 315, 189–210.
MANELPHE J. AND BRY C.	1989	"La production de brochetons par la méthode de reproduction naturelle aménagée: évaluation de la rentabilité actuelle." *Aqua Revue.* Bordeaux, 22, 25–30.

MARCEL J. 1988 (a) "Le brochet: réalités sur son élevage." *Aqua Revue*. Bordeaux, 21, 15-17.

MARCEL J. 1988 (b) "Exploitation et valorisation des étangs et retenues." *Aqua Revue*, Bordeaux, 20, 24-34.

MARCEL J. 1989 "Exploitation et valorisation des étangs et retenues." *ADA*, Bordeaux, 20, 24-34.

MARCHAL E. 1985 "La détection acoustique dans l'étude des peuplements pisciaires." *in Gestion Piscicole des Lacs et Retenues Artificielles*, Ed. D. Gerdeaux and R. Billard, INRA, Paris, 107-124.

MARION L. 1990 "Les oiseaux piscivores et les activités piscicoles: impact et protection." Secr. Envir. et Min. Agric., Paris, 28 p.

MARION L. 1997 *Recensement national des grands cormorans hivernant en France durant l'hiver 1996-1997*, Min. Environ. LC 95/147, SESLG, 17 p.

MAURIN H. 1997 "L'homme et les mammifères de France métropolitaine: évolution historique et introductions d'espèces dans les milieux humides et aquatiques." *Bull. Fr. Pêche Piscic.* (1997), 344/345, 117-132.

MICHAUD Chr. 1996 "Le rôle économique de la salmoniculture dans le développement rural." *C.R. Acad. Agri. Fr*, 1996, 82(9), 33-43.

MILLS D. 1971 *Salmon and Trout*. Oliver & Boyd, Edinburgh.

MEROT, CARNET AND MONTEIX 1975 "Premières données sur le rôle du bocage dans la circulation de l'eau." *Comm. Sémin. Eaux continent. N.O. Europe*. I.E.B.S. Amiens.

MOREAU J. 1980 "Influence des divers paramètres sur l'estimation du rendement par recruê: application aux pêches continentales tropicales." CYBIUM - 3e sér. 1980, No. 8, Paris, p. 67-76.

MUSTIN M. *et al.* 1989 "L'aquaculture continentale dans les grands lacs artificiels: premières installations et perspectives." *Aqua Revue*, Bordeaux, 24, 18-23.

NAULLEAU G. 1973 "Les serpents de France." *Rev. Franç. Aquariologie*. Paris.

NISBET M. 1968 "L'eau critère de qualité pour la vie piscicole—L'évolution de cette qualité." *Minagri. B.T.I.*, No. 228, 3/4. Paris.

NISBET M. AND VERNEAUX J. 1970 "Composantes chimiques des eaux courantes." *Ann. Limnol.*, T6, fasc. 2. Paris.

OBERDORFF T. *et al.* 1989 "Modification et utilisation d'un Indice d'Intégrité Biotique basé sur la communauté piscicole afin d'évaluer la qualité des rivières du Bassin de la Seine, France."

PAPERNA II. 1980 "Parasites, infections and diseases of fish in Africa." *FAO Rome, CIFA*-T7, pp. 181-182.

PELLETIER J.-L. 1990 "Les petits barrages d'oxygénation." Rapp. T.O.S. Paris, 12 p.

PERENNOU C. 1987 "L'impact du héron cendré *Ardea cinerea* en bassin d'alevinage." *L'Oiseau et RFO*, V57, No. 3, 262-265.

PESSON P. *et al.* 1976 *La Pollution des Eaux Continentales*. Gauthier-Villars, Paris.

PIONNIER E. AND HEYMANN A.	1987	"Quelques aspects de la reproduction du silure glane à Fénétrange." *Aqua Revue*, Bordeaux, 11, 32–33.
PORCHER-DECHAR C.	1975	"Situation hydrobiologique de l'Aisne dans son cours inférieur Oct. 1975". *Doc. C.S.P.* Compiègne.
POURCHER A.-M. AND SALENCON M.-J.	1990	"Modélisation du plancton: Sainte-Croix sur le Verdon." *Hydroécol. Appl.*, Paris, 1/2, 91–134.
PROTEAU J.-P. AND THOLLOT T.	1988	"Elevage intensif du silure glane en eau chaude—premiers résultats de croissance obtenus sur pilote expérimental." *Aqua Revue*, Bordeaux, 21, 23–26.
QUESNEL	1964	*Traité d'Hydraulique Fluviale Appliquée.* Eyrolles, Paris.
QUINCY D.	1986	"Aquaculture et retenues collinaires." *Aqua Revue*, Bordeaux, 6, 35–37.
RENARD E.	1971	"Essai d'incubation d'oeufs de truites fario en gravières Guyard et en incubateurs flottants." *Doc. C.S.P.* Compiègne.
RICKER W.E.	1975	"Computation and interpretation of biological statistics of fish population." *Bull. Fish. Res. Board Can.* 191, 383 p.
RIEDEL D.	1974	*Fisch und Fischerei.* Ulmer, Stuttgart.
RIQUOIS M. AND BERTHERY M.	1990	"Evaluation prévisionnelle de la fréquentation et normalisation des sites de loisirs aquatiques." *Plan d'eau, exploitation pour les loisirs,* 3e éd., IDF, Paris, p. 2-1.
ROBBINS W. AND Mac CRIMMON H.	1974	"The black bass in America and overseas." Div. Biomanagement and Research Enterprises. Sault Ste Marie, Canada.
ROFES G.	1974	"Influence de la craie en poudre sur les londs envasés en eau courante." *Bull. franç. Pisc.*, No. 258. Boves.
ROLLAND J.-C.	1987	"La pêche au coup et les personnes handicapées." *Bull. liais. CSP*, Paris, 49–50, 3–6.
RUMEAU A. AND COSTE M.	1988	"Initiation à la systématique des diatomées d'eau douce pour l'utilisation d'un indice diatomique générique." *Bull. Fr. Pêche Piscis.* Paric, 309, 1–69.
RUTTNER, *in* VIVIER P., 1972	1940	"La vie dans les eaux douces." Que sais-je? P.U.F. No. 233, Paris.
SAWYER F.	1965	"La craie joue-t-elle un rôle essentiel dans la croissance de la truite?" No. 98-99, S.E.D.E.T.E.C., Paris.
SCHAEPERCLAUS W.	1962	*Traité de Pisciculture en Étang*, Vigot Fr., Paris.
SCHEIDT A. VON.	1983	"Où en est la sandre dans le Nord-Est?" *Bull. Liais. CSP,* Paris, 29, 13–20.
SEABURG	1957	"A stomach sampler for life fish". *Progr. Fish. Cult.*, 19(3), Canada.
SEBER G.A.F. AND LE CREN	1967	"Estimating population parameters from catches large relative to the population." *J. Anim. Ecol.* 36, 631–643.
SERVAN J. AND ARVY C.	1997	"Introduction de la tortue de Floride *Trachemys scripta en* France. Un nouveau compétiteur pour les espèces de tortues d'eau douce européennes." *Bull. Fr. Pêche Piscic* (1997), 344/345, 173–177.
SIMONET J.-P.	1973	"Création et gestion d'un ruisseau pépinière." *Plais. Pêche*, No. 149, S.E.D.E.T.E.C., Paris.
SOUCHON Y. *et al.*	1989	"Les modèles numériques des microhabitats des poissons: applications et nouveaux développements."

		Ed. Lavoisier Paris, Rev. Sciences de l'eau, 2-4, 807-830.
TACHET *et al.*	1984	"Introduction à l'étude des macroinvertébrés des eaux douces." Ass. Française de Limnol., Paris.
TERSEN G.	1990	"Quelques aménagements de détail destinés aux plans d'eau." *Plans d'eau, exploitation pour les loisirs,* IDF, Paris, p. 16-21.
THIRAPHAN BHUKASWAN	1980	"Management of asian reservoir fisheries." *FAO, Rome FIRI/T.* 207, 69 p.
TIMMERMANS J.-A.	1961	"Estimation des dommages piscicoles causés par les pollutions". *Stat. Rech. Groenendaal,* Tx. D No. 34, Bruxelles.
TIMMERMANS J.-A.	1967	"Repeuplement des eaux de pêche en gardons pêchables." *Stat. Rech. Groenendaal,* Tx. D No. 39, Bruxelles.
TUFFERY G. AND VERNEAUX J.	1967	"Méthode de détermination de la qualité biologique des eaux courantes." *C.E.R.A.F.E.R.* 4, Paris.
TUFFERY G.	1980	"Incidences écologiques de la pollution des eaux courantes - révélateurs biologiques de la pollution." *in La Pollution des Eaux Continentales.* Gauthier-Villars, Paris, pp. 243-280.
VAN HOOREN G.	1975	"Etude de la microflore et de la microfaune de l'Yser et leurs relations avec la pollution des eaux." *Comm. Sémin. Eaux continent. N.O. Europe,* I.E.B.S., Amiens.
VERNEAUX J.	1973 (a)	"Cours d'eau de Franche-Comté. Recherches écologiques sur le réseau hydrographique du Doubs. Essai de biotypologie." Thèse, Besançon.
VERNEAUX J.	1973 (b)	"Les principales méthodes biologiques de détermination du degré de pollution des eaux courantes." *Econom. Médec. anim.,* 14(1), Paris.
VERNEAUX J. AND LEYNAUD G.	1974	"Note sommaire sur la définition d'objectifs et de critères de la qualité des eaux courantes." C.T.G.R.E.F.-D.Q.E.P., Paris.
VIBERT R.	1975	"Repeuplement des eaux à truites." *Pisc. Franç.,* No. 42, Paris.
VIBERT R. AND LAGLER K.	1961	*Pêche Continentales.* Dunod, Paris.
VIVIER P.	1972	"La vie dans les eaux douces." Que sais-je? P.U.F., No. 233, Paris.
WALKER Jearl	1984	"Expériences d'amateur." *Pour la Science.* Paris, May 1984, 104-108.
WEBB P.	1984	"Les formes et les nages des poissons." *Pour la Science.* Paris, Sept. 1984, 44-54.
WILLIOT P.	1987	"L'élevage des esturgeons en eau douce, un espoir? peut-être." *La Pisc. Franç.* Paris. 87: 18-19.
WILLIOT P. *et al.*	1988	"Grossissement intensif de l'esturgeon sibérien (*Acipenser baerr*) en bassin." *Aqua Revue,* Bordeaux, 17, 29-32.
WURTZ A.	1961	"Cours élémentaire d'hydrobiologie animale." *Stat. Hydrobiol. appl.,* Paris.
WURTZ-ARLET J.	1952	"Le black-bass en France," *Ann. Stat. Centr. Hydrobiol.,* Appl. IV, Paris.
WURTZ-ARLET J.	1968	"Gestion des étangs." *Minagri-B.T.I.,* No. 128, III, Paris.
ZAHNER, JUNKE	1972	"Contrôle automatique et continu de l'eau de surface

AND BESCH, *in* POELS, 1975		par des poissons." *Trib. C.E.B.E.D.O.C.* Vol. 28, No. 381-382, Bruxelles.
Anonymous	1976	"Abaques de calcul d'hydraulique à surface libre." C.T.G.R.E.F. Antony. Div. Hydrol. 33-39.
Anonymous	1985	"L'entretien des cours d'eau." *Cahiers techniques*, DPP, Min. Env. Paris, 100 p.
Anonymous	1987	"Comment augmenter la productivité piscicole." *Forêt, loisirs, équipements de plein air*, IDF, Paris, 22, 4-32.
Anonymous	1988 (a)	"Pièges et techniques de piégeage." *Bull. Cons. Sup. Chasse, No. 122* in *Forêt, loisirs, équipements de plein air*, Paris, 23, 7-19.
Anonymous	1988 (b)	"Comment pêcher et vendre son poisson. *Forêt, loisirs, équipments de plein air*, IDF, Paris, 23, 20-55.
Anonymous	1988 (c)	"Les vidanges des barrages d'altitude." C.G.G.R.E.F. *Bull. Liais. CSP*, Paris, 52-53, 15-18.
Anonymous	1988 (d)	"Spécial poissons grands migrateurs." Collectif. *Bull. Liais. CSP*, 54, 56 p.
Anonymous	1989	"Pacage lacustre: présentation sommaire des recherches menées à la station INRA de Thonon." *Aqua Revue*, Bordeaux, 25, 2.

4 INDEX

A

C

R

S

Y

Z